STUDENT SOLUTIONS MANUAL

CALCULUS

FOR BUSINESS, ECONOMICS, LIFE SCIENCES, AND SOCIAL SCIENCES

TENTH EDITION

RAYMOND A. BARNETT
MICHAEL R. ZIEGLER
KARL E. BYLEEN

PEARSON

Prentice
Hall

Upper Saddle River, NJ 07458

Editor-in-Chief: Sally Yagan
Acquisitions Editor: Petra Recter
Supplement Editor: Joanne Wendelken
Assistant Managing Editor: Nicole Jackson
Production Editor: Allyson Kloss
Supplement Cover Manager: Paul Gourhan
Supplement Cover Designer: Joanne Alexandris
Manufacturing Buyer: Ilene Kahn

© 2005 Pearson Education, Inc.
Pearson Prentice Hall
Pearson Education, Inc.
Upper Saddle River, NJ 07458

Printed in the United States of America

10   9   8   7   6   5   4   3

ISBN 0-13-143646-5

Pearson Education Ltd., *London*
Pearson Education Australia Pty. Ltd., *Sydney*
Pearson Education Singapore, Pte. Ltd.
Pearson Education North Asia Ltd., *Hong Kong*
Pearson Education Canada, Inc., *Toronto*
Pearson Educación de Mexico, S.A. de C.V.
Pearson Education—Japan, *Tokyo*
Pearson Education Malaysia, Pte. Ltd.

CONTENTS

| CHAPTER 1 | A BEGINNING LIBRARY OF ELEMENTARY FUNCTIONS | 1 |

EXERCISE 1-1 1

EXERCISE 1-2 7

EXERCISE 1-3 13

EXERCISE 1-4 20

CHAPTER REVIEW 28

| CHAPTER 2 | ADDITIONAL ELEMENTARY FUNCTIONS | 39 |

EXERCISE 2-1 39

EXERCISE 2-2 48

EXERCISE 2-3 55

CHAPTER REVIEW 62

| CHAPTER 3 | THE DERIVATIVE | 72 |

EXERCISE 3-1 72

EXERCISE 3-2 80

EXERCISE 3-3 89

EXERCISE 3-4 103

EXERCISE 3-5 110

EXERCISE 3-6 118

EXERCISE 3-7 125

CHAPTER REVIEW 130

| CHAPTER 4 | GRAPHING AND OPTIMIZATION | 148 |

EXERCISE 4-1 148

EXERCISE 4-2 162

EXERCISE 4-3 178

EXERCISE 4-4 215

EXERCISE 4-5 222

CHAPTER REVIEW 229

CHAPTER 5	ADDITIONAL DERIVATIVE TOPICS	250

EXERCISE 5-1 250

EXERCISE 5-2 254

EXERCISE 5-3 266

EXERCISE 5-4 277

EXERCISE 5-5 286

EXERCISE 5-6 292

CHAPTER REVIEW 299

CHAPTER 6	INTEGRATION	314

EXERCISE 6-1 314

EXERCISE 6-2 323

EXERCISE 6-3 334

EXERCISE 6-4 343

EXERCISE 6-5 349

CHAPTER REVIEW 358

CHAPTER 7	ADDITIONAL INTEGRATION TOPICS	370

EXERCISE 7-1 370

EXERCISE 7-2 378

EXERCISE 7-3 388

EXERCISE 7-4 398

CHAPTER REVIEW 406

CHAPTER 8	MULTIVARIABLE CALCULUS	419

EXERCISE 8-1 419

EXERCISE 8-2 422

EXERCISE 8-3 430

EXERCISE 8-4 438

EXERCISE 8-5 446

EXERCISE 8-6 453

CHAPTER REVIEW 459

CHAPTER 9   TRIGONOMETRIC FUNCTIONS   471

EXERCISE 9-1 471

EXERCISE 9-2 474

EXERCISE 9-3 478

CHAPTER REVIEW 481

CHAPTER A   BASIC ALGEBRA REVIEW   488

SELF TEST 488

EXERCISE A-1 493

EXERCISE A-2 496

EXERCISE A-3 500

EXERCISE A-4 503

EXERCISE A-5 507

EXERCISE A-6 511

EXERCISE A-7 515

EXERICSE A-8 520

APPENDIX B   SPECIAL TOPICS   526

EXERCISE B-1 526

EXERCISE B-2 530

EXERCISE B-3 535

1 A BEGINNING LIBRARY OF ELEMENTARY FUNCTIONS

Things to remember:

<u>1</u>. A FUNCTION is a rule (process or method) that produces a correspondence between one set of elements, called a DOMAIN, and a second set of elements, called the RANGE, such that to each element in the domain there corresponds one and only one element in the range.

<u>2</u>. EQUATIONS AND FUNCTIONS

Given an equation in two variables, if there corresponds exactly one value of the dependent variable (output) to each value of the independent variable (input), then the equation defines a function. If there is more than one output for at least one input, then the equation does not define a function.

<u>3</u>. VERTICAL LINE TEST FOR A FUNCTION

An equation defines a function if each vertical line in the coordinate system passes through at most one point on the graph of the equation. If any vertical line passes through two or more points on the graph of an equation, then the equation does not define a function.

<u>4</u>. AGREEMENT ON DOMAINS AND RANGES

If a function is specified by an equation and the domain is not given explicitly, then assume that the domain is the set of all real number replacements of the independent variable (inputs) that produce real values for the dependent variable (outputs). The range is the set of all outputs corresponding to input values.

In many applied problems, the domain is determined by practical considerations within the problem.

<u>5</u>. FUNCTION NOTATION — THE SYMBOL $f(x)$

For any element x in the domain of the function f, the symbol $f(x)$ represents the element in the range of f corresponding to x in the domain of f. If x is an input value, then $f(x)$ is the corresponding output value. If x is an element which is not in the domain of f, then f is NOT DEFINED at x and $f(x)$ DOES NOT EXIST.

1. The table specifies a function, since for each domain value there corresponds one and only one range value.

3. The table does not specify a function, since more than one range value corresponds to a given domain value. (Range values 5, 6 correspond to domain value 3; range values 6, 7 correspond to domain value 4.)

5. This is a function.

7. The graph specifies a function; each vertical line in the plane intersects the graph in at most one point.

9. The graph does not specify a function. There are vertical lines which intersect the graph in more than one point. For example, the y-axis intersects the graph in three points.

11. The graph specifies a function.

13. (A) This correspondence is a function; there is exactly one representative for each congressional district.

(B) This correspondence is not a function; there are two senators representing Pennsylvania.

15. The graph of f is:

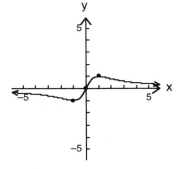

17. $f(x) = 100x - 5x^2$; $g(x) = 150 + 20x$, $0 \leq x \leq 20$

(A) $f(0) = 100(0) - 5(0)^2 = 0$, $g(0) = 150 + 20(0) = 150$;

$f(5) = 100(5) - 5(5)^2 = 500 - 125 = 375$, $g(5) = 150 + 20(5) = 250$;

$f(10) = 100(10) - 5(10)^2 = 1000 - 500 = 500$, $g(10) = 150 + 20(10) = 350$;

$f(15) = 100(15) - 5(15)^2 = 1500 - 1125 = 375$, $g(15) = 150 + 20(15) = 450$;

$f(20) = 100(20) - 5(20)^2 = 2000 - 2000 = 0$, $g(20) = 150 + 20(20) = 550$;

$f(0) - g(0) = 0 - 150 = -150$; $f(5) - g(5) = 375 - 250 = 125$;

$f(10) - g(10) = 500 - 350 = 150$; $f(15) - g(15) = 375 - 450 = -75$;

$f(20) - g(20) = 0 - 550 = -550$

(B)

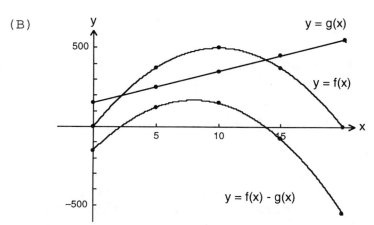

19. $y = f(-5) = 0$

21. $y = f(5) = 4$

23. $f(x) = 0$ at $x = -5, 0, 4$

25. $f(x) = -4$ at $x = 6$

27. $f(2) = 2 \cdot 2 - 3 = 4 - 3 = 1$

29. $f(-1) = 2(-1) - 3 = -2 - 3 = -5$

31. $g(-3) = (-3)^2 + 2(-3) = 9 - 6 = 3$

33. $f(1) + g(2) = [2 \cdot 1 - 3] + [2^2 + 2 \cdot 2] = -1 + 8 = 7$

35. $g(3) \cdot f(0) = [3^2 + 2 \cdot 3] \cdot (2 \cdot 0 - 3) = 15(-3) = -45$

37. $\dfrac{g(-2)}{f(-2)} = \dfrac{(-2)^2 + 2(-2)}{2(-2) - 3} = \dfrac{4 - 4}{-7} = \dfrac{0}{-7} = 0$

39. domain: all real numbers or $(-\infty, \infty)$

41. domain: all real numbers except -4

45. f is not defined at the values of x where $x^2 - 9 = 0$, that is, at 3 and -3; f is defined at $x = 2$, $f(2) = \dfrac{0}{-5} = 0$.

47. $g(x) = 2x^3 - 5$

49. $G(x) = 2\sqrt{x} - x^2$

51. Function f multiplies the domain element by 2 and subtracts 3 from the result.

53. Function F multiplies the cube of the domain element by 3 and subtracts twice the square root of the domain element from the result.

55. Given $4x - 5y = 20$. Solving for y, we have:
$$-5y = -4x + 20$$
$$y = \frac{4}{5}x - 4$$

Since each input value x determines a unique output value y, the equation specifies a function. The domain is R, the set of real numbers.

57. Given $x^2 - y = 1$. Solving for y, we have:

$-y = -x^2 + 1$ or $y = x^2 - 1$

This equation specifies a function. The domain is R, the set of real numbers.

59. Given $x + y^2 = 10$. Solving for y, we have:

$y^2 = 10 - x$

$y = \pm\sqrt{10 - x}$

This equation does not specify a function since each value of x, $x < 10$, determines two values of y. For example, corresponding to $x = 1$, we have $y = 3$ and $y = -3$; corresponding to $x = 6$, we have $y = 2$ and $y = -2$.

61. Given $xy - 4y = 1$. Solving for y, we have:

$(x - 4)y = 1$ or $y = \dfrac{1}{x - 4}$

This equation specifies a function. The domain is all real numbers except $x = 4$.

63. Given $x^2 + y^2 = 25$. Solving for y, we have:

$y^2 = 25 - x^2$ or $y = \pm\sqrt{25 - x^2}$

Thus, the equation does not specify a function since, for $x = 0$, we have $y = \pm 5$, when $x = 4$, $y = \pm 3$, and so on.

65. Given $F(t) = 4t + 7$. Then:

$$\frac{F(3 + h) - F(3)}{h} = \frac{4(3 + h) + 7 - (4 \cdot 3 + 7)}{h}$$

$$= \frac{12 + 4h + 7 - 19}{h} = \frac{4h}{h} = 4$$

67. Given $Q(x) = x^2 - 5x + 1$. Then:

$$\frac{Q(2 + h) - Q(2)}{h} = \frac{(2 + h)^2 - 5(2 + h) + 1 - (2^2 - 5 \cdot 2 + 1)}{h}$$

$$= \frac{4 + 4h + h^2 - 10 - 5h + 1 - (-5)}{h} = \frac{h^2 - h - 5 + 5}{h}$$

$$= \frac{h(h - 1)}{h} = h - 1$$

69. $f(x) = 4x - 3$

(A) $f(x + h) = 4(x + h) - 3 = 4x + 4h - 3$

(B) $f(x + h) - f(x) = 4x + 4h - 3 - (4x - 3) = 4h$

(C) $\dfrac{f(x + h) - f(x)}{h} = \dfrac{4h}{h} = 4$

71. $f(x) = 4x^2 - 7x + 6$

(A) $f(x + h) = 4(x + h)^2 - 7(x + h) + 6$
$$= 4(x^2 + 2xh + h^2) - 7x - 7h + 6$$
$$= 4x^2 + 8xh + 4h^2 - 7x - 7h + 6$$

(B) $f(x + h) - f(x) = 4x^2 + 8xh + 4h^2 - 7x - 7h + 6 - (4x^2 - 7x + 6)$
$$= 8xh + 4h^2 - 7h$$

(C) $\dfrac{f(x + h) - f(x)}{h} = \dfrac{8xh + 4h^2 - 7h}{h} = \dfrac{h(8x + 4h - 7)}{h} = 8x + 4h - 7$

73. $f(x) = x(20 - x) = 20x - x^2$

(A) $f(x + h) = 20(x + h) - (x + h)^2 = 20x + 20h - x^2 - 2xh - h^2$

(B) $f(x + h) - f(x) = 20x + 20h - x^2 - 2xh - h^2 - (20x - x^2)$
$$= 20h - 2xh - h^2$$

(C) $\dfrac{f(x + h) - f(x)}{h} = \dfrac{20h - 2xh - h^2}{h} = \dfrac{h(20 - 2x - h)}{h} = 20 - 2x - h$

75. Given $A = \ell w = 25$.

Thus, $\ell = \dfrac{25}{w}$. Now $P = 2\ell + 2w$
$$= 2\left(\dfrac{25}{w}\right) + 2w = \dfrac{50}{w} + 2w.$$

The domain is $w > 0$.

77. Given $P = 2\ell + 2w = 100$ or $\ell + w = 50$ and $w = 50 - \ell$.

Now $A = \ell w = \ell(50 - \ell)$ and $A = 50\ell - \ell^2$.

The domain is $0 \le \ell \le 50$. [Note: $\ell \le 50$ since $\ell > 50$ implies $w < 0$.]

79.

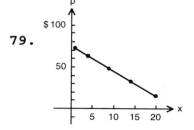

$p(x) = 75 - 3x$
$p(7) = 75 - 3(7) = 75 - 21 = 54;$
$p(11) = 75 - 3(11) = 75 - 33 = 42$
Estimated price per chip for a demand
of 7 million chips: $54; for a demand
of 11 million chips: $42

81. (A) $R(x) = x \cdot p(x) = x(75 - 3x) = 75x - 3x^2,\ 1 \le x \le 20$

(B)

x	$R(x)$
1	72
4	252
8	408
12	468
16	432
20	300

(C)

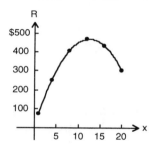

83. (A) Profit: $P(x) = R(x) - C(x) = 75x - 3x^2 - [125 + 16x]$
$$= 59x - 3x^2 - 125, \quad 1 \le x \le 20$$

(B)

x	$P(x)$
1	−69
4	63
8	155
12	151
16	51
20	−145

(C)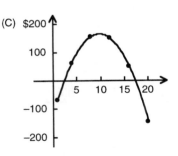

85.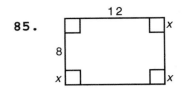

(A) $V = $ (length)(width)(height)
$V(x) = (12 - 2x)(8 - 2x)x$
$\quad\quad = x(8 - 2x)(12 - 2x)$

(B) Domain: $0 \le x \le 4$

(C) $V(1) = (12 - 2)(8 - 2)(1)$
$\quad\quad\quad = (10)(6)(1) = 60$
$\quad V(2) = (12 - 4)(8 - 4)(2)$
$\quad\quad\quad = (8)(4)(2) = 64$
$\quad V(3) = (12 - 6)(8 - 6)(3)$
$\quad\quad\quad = (6)(2)(3) = 36$

Thus,

Volume

x	$V(x)$
1	60
2	64
3	36

(D)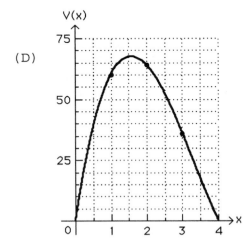

87. (A) The graph indicates that there is a value of x near 2, and slightly less than 2, such that $V(x) = 65$. The table is shown at the right.

Thus, $x = 1.9$ to one decimal place.

x	y_1
1.7	67.252
1.8	66.528
1.9	65.436
2.0	64.000

x	y_1
1.90	65.436
1.91	65.307
1.92	65.176
1.93	65.040
1.94	64.902
1.95	64.760
1.96	64.614

(B)

Thus, $x = 1.93$ to two decimal places.

89. Given $(w + a)(v + b) = c$. Let $a = 15$, $b = 1$, and $c = 90$.
Then: $(w + 15)(v + 1) = 90$

Solving for v, we have

$$v + 1 = \frac{90}{w + 15} \quad \text{and} \quad v = \frac{90}{w + 15} - 1 = \frac{90 - (w + 15)}{w + 15},$$

so that $v = \dfrac{75 - w}{w + 15}$.

If $w = 16$, then $v = \dfrac{75 - 16}{16 + 15} = \dfrac{59}{31} \approx 1.9032$ cm/sec.

EXERCISE 1-2

Things to remember:

<u>1</u>. LIBRARY OF ELEMENTARY FUNCTIONS

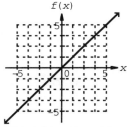

Identity Function
$f(x) = x$
Domain: All real numbers
Range: All real numbers
(a)

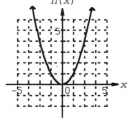

Square Function
$h(x) = x^2$
Domain: All real numbers
Range: $[0, \infty)$
(b)

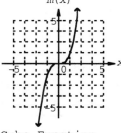

Cube Function
$m(x) = x^3$
Domain: All real numbers
Range: All real numbers
(c)

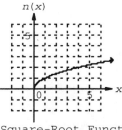

Square-Root Function
$n(x) = \sqrt{x}$
Domain: $[0, \infty)$
Range: $[0, \infty)$
(d)

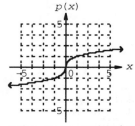

Cube-Root Function
$p(x) = \sqrt[3]{x}$
Domain: All real numbers
Range: All real numbers
(e)

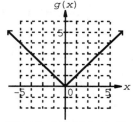

Absolute Value Function
$g(x) = |x|$
Domain: All real numbers
Range: $[0, \infty)$
(f)

NOTE: Letters used to designate the above functions may vary from context to context.

2. GRAPH TRANSFORMATIONS SUMMARY

Vertical Translation:

$$y = f(x) + k \begin{cases} k > 0 & \text{Shift graph of } y = f(x) \text{ up } k \text{ units} \\ k < 0 & \text{Shift graph of } y = f(x) \text{ down } |k| \text{ units} \end{cases}$$

Horizontal Translation:

$$y = f(x + h) \begin{cases} h > 0 & \text{Shift graph of } y = f(x) \text{ left } h \text{ units} \\ h < 0 & \text{Shift graph of } y = f(x) \text{ right } |h| \text{ units} \end{cases}$$

Reflection:

$y = -f(x)$ Reflect the graph of $y = f(x)$ in the x axis

Vertical Expansion and Contraction:

$$y = Af(x) \begin{cases} A > 1 & \text{Vertically expand graph of } y = f(x) \text{ by} \\ & \text{multiplying each ordinate value by } A \\ 0 < A < 1 & \text{Vertically contract graph of } y = f(x) \text{ by} \\ & \text{multiplying each ordinate value by } A \end{cases}$$

3. PIECEWISE-DEFINED FUNCTIONS

Functions whose definitions involve more than one rule are called PIECEWISE-DEFINED FUNCTIONS.

For example,

$$f(x) = |x| = \begin{cases} -x & \text{if } x < 0 \\ x & \text{if } x \geq 0 \end{cases}$$

is a piecewise-defined function.

To graph a piecewise-defined function, graph each rule over the appropriate portion of the domain.

---

1. $f(x) = 2x$; domain: all real numbers; range: all real numbers

3. $h(x) = -0.6\sqrt{x}$; domain: $[0, \infty)$; range: $(-\infty, 0]$

5. $m(x) = 3|x|$; domain: all real numbers; range: $[0, \infty)$

7. $r(x) = -x^3$; domain: all real numbers; range: all real numbers

9.

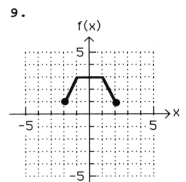

11.

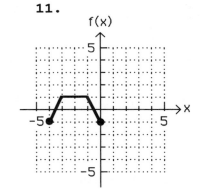

13.

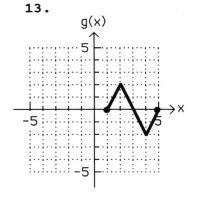

15.

17.

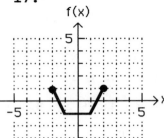

19.

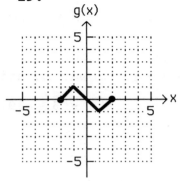

21. The graph of $g(x) = -|x + 3|$ is the graph of $y = |x|$ reflected in the x axis and shifted 3 units to the left.

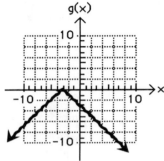

23. The graph of $f(x) = (x - 4)^2 - 3$ is the graph of $y = x^2$ shifted 4 units to the right and 3 units down.

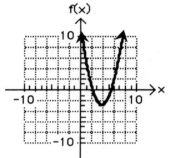

25. The graph of $f(x) = 7 - \sqrt{x}$ is the graph of $y = \sqrt{x}$ reflected in the x axis and shifted 7 units up.

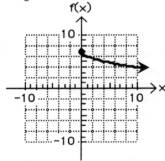

27. The graph of $h(x) = -3|x|$ is the graph of $y = |x|$ reflected in the x axis and vertically expanded by a factor of 3.

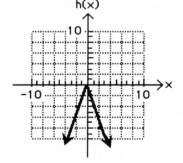

29. The graph of the basic function $y = x^2$ is shifted 2 units to the left and 3 units down. Equation: $y = (x + 2)^2 - 3$.

31. The graph of the basic function $y = x^2$ is reflected in the x axis, shifted 3 units to the right and 2 units up.
Equation: $y = 2 - (x - 3)^2$.

33. The graph of the basic function $y = \sqrt{x}$ is reflected in the x axis and shifted 4 units up. Equation: $y = 4 - \sqrt{x}$.

35. The graph of the basic function $y = x^3$ is shifted 2 units to the left and 1 unit down. Equation: $y = (x + 2)^3 - 1$.

37. $g(x) = \sqrt{x - 2} - 3$

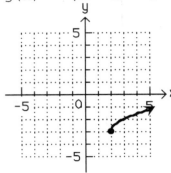

39. $g(x) = -|x + 3|$

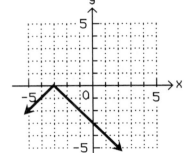

41. $g(x) = -(x - 2)^3 - 1$

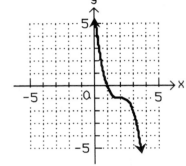

43.

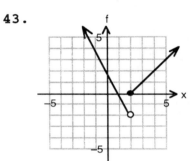

45.

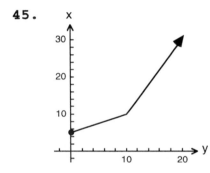

47.

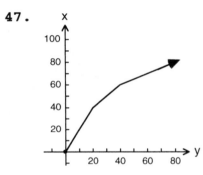

49. The graph of the basic function: $y = |x|$ is reflected in the x axis and has a vertical contraction by the factor 0.5.
Equation: $y = -0.5|x|$.

51. The graph of the basic function $y = x^2$ is reflected in the x axis and is vertically expanded by the factor 2. Equation: $y = -2x^2$.

53. The graph of the basic function $y = \sqrt[3]{x}$ is reflected in the x axis and is vertically expanded by the factor 3. Equation: $y = -3\sqrt[3]{x}$.

55. Vertical shift, horizontal shift.
Reversing the order does not change the result. Consider a point (a, b) in the plane. A vertical shift of k units followed by a horizontal shift of h units moves (a, b) to $(a, b + k)$ and then to $(a + h, b + k)$.

In the reverse order, a horizontal shift of h units followed by a vertical shift of k units moves (a, b) to $(a + h, b)$ and then to $(a + h, b + k)$. The results are the same.

57. Vertical shift, reflection in the *x* axis.
Reversing the order can change the result. For example, let (*a*, *b*) be a point in the plane with *b* > 0. A vertical shift of *k* units, *k* ≠ 0, followed by a reflection in the *x* axis moves (*a*, *b*) to (*a*, *b* + *k*) and then to (*a*, -[*b* + *k*]) = (*a*, -*b* - *k*).
In the reverse order, a reflection in the *x* axis followed by the vertical shift of *k* units moves (*a*, *b*) to (*a*, -*b*) and then to (*a*, -*b* + *k*); (*a*, -*b* - *k*) ≠ (*a*, -*b* + *k*) when *k* ≠ 0.

59. Horizontal shift, reflection in *y* axis.
Reversing the order can change the result. For example, let (*a*, *b*) be a point in the plane with *a* > 0. A horizontal shift of *h* units followed by a reflection in the *y* axis moves (*a*, *b*) to the point (*a* + *h*, *b*) and then to (-[*a* + *h*], *b*) = (-*a* - *h*, *b*).
In the reverse order, a reflection in the *y* axis followed by the horizontal sift of *h* units moves (*a*, *b*) to (-*a*, *b*) and then the (-*a* + *h*, *b*), (-*a* - *h*, *b*) ≠ (-*a* + *h*, *b*) when *h* ≠ 0.

61. (A) The graph of the basic function $y = \sqrt{x}$ is reflected in the *x* axis, vertically expanded by a factor of 4, and shifted up 115 units.

(B)

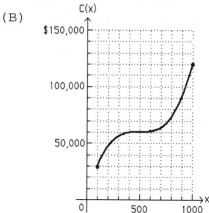

63. (A) The graph of the basic function $y = x^3$ is vertically contracted by a factor of 0.00048 and shifted right 500 units and up 60,000 units.

(B)

65. (A) $S(x) = \begin{cases} 8.50 + 0.0650x & if \quad 0 \le x \le 700 \\ 8.50 + 0.0650(700) + 0.09(x - 700) & if \quad x > 700 \end{cases}$

$= \begin{cases} 8.50 + 0.0650x & if \quad 0 \le x \le 700 \\ -9 + 0.09x & if \quad x > 700 \end{cases}$

(B)

67. (A) If $0 \leq x \leq 30,000$, $T(x) = 0.035x$, and $T(30,000) = 1,050$.
If $30,000 < x \leq 60,000$, $T(x) = 1,050 + 0.0625(x - 30,000)$
$$= 0.0625x - 825, \text{ and}$$
$$T(60,000) = 2,925.$$
If $x > 60,000$, $T(x) = 2,925 + 0.0645(x - 60,000)$
$$= 0.0645x - 945.$$
Thus, $T(x) = \begin{cases} 0.035x & if \quad 0 \leq x \leq 30,000 \\ 0.0625x - 825 & if \quad 30,000 < x \leq 60,000 \\ 0.0645x - 945 & if \quad x > 60,000 \end{cases}$

(B)

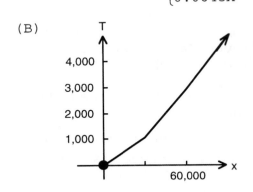

(C) $T(40,000) = 0.0625(40,000) - 825$
$$= 1,675;$$
$1,675

$T(70,000) = 0.0645(70,000) - 945$
$$= 3,570;$$
$3,570

69. (A) The graph of the basic function $y = x$ is vertically expanded by a factor of 5.5 and shifted down 220 units.

(B)

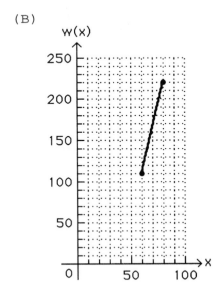

71. (A) The graph of the basic function $y = \sqrt{x}$ is vertically expanded by a factor of 7.08.

(B)

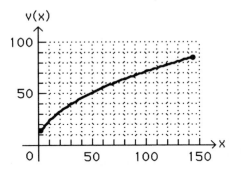

Things to remember:

1. INTERCEPTS

   If the graph of a function f crosses the x axis at a point with x coordinate a, then a is called an **x intercept** of f. If the graph of f crosses the y axis at a point with y coordinate b, then b is called the **y intercept**. The x intercepts are the real solutions or roots of $f(x) = 0$; if f is defined at 0, then $f(0)$ is the y intercept.

2. LINEAR AND CONSTANT FUNCTIONS

   A function f is a LINEAR FUNCTION if

   $$f(x) = mx + b \qquad m \neq 0$$

   where m and b are real numbers. The DOMAIN is the set of all real numbers and the RANGE is the set of all real numbers. If $m = 0$, then f is called a CONSTANT FUNCTION
   $$f(x) = b$$
   which has the set of all real numbers as its DOMAIN and the constant b as its RANGE.

   THE GRAPH OF A LINEAR FUNCTION IS A STRAIGHT LINE THAT IS NEITHER HORIZONTAL NOR VERTICAL. THE GRAPH OF A CONSTANT FUNCTION IS A HORIZONTAL STRAIGHT LINE.

3. GRAPH OF A LINEAR EQUATION IN TWO VARIABLES

   The graph of any equation of the form

   $$AX + By = C \qquad \text{Standard Form}$$

   where A, B, and C are real constants (A and B not both 0) is a straight line. Every straight line in a Cartesian coordinate system is the graph of an equation of this type. Vertical and horizontal lines have particularly simple equations, which are special cases of the standard form equation:
   Horizontal line with y intercept b: $y = b$
   Vertical line with x intercept a: $\quad x = a$

4. SLOPE OF A LINE

   If a line passes through two distinct points $P_1(x_1, y_1)$ and $P_2(x_2, y_2)$, then its slope is given by the formula

   $$m = \frac{y_2 - y_1}{x_2 - x_1} \qquad x_1 \neq x_2$$

   $$= \frac{\text{Vertical change (rise)}}{\text{Horizontal change (run)}}$$

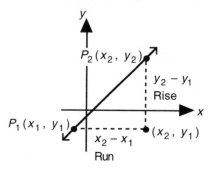

GEOMETRIC INTERPRETATION OF SLOPE

Line	Slope	Example
Rising as x moves from left to right	Positive	
Falling as x moves from left to right	Negative	
Horizontal	0	
Vertical	Not defined	

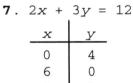

<u>5</u>. EQUATIONS OF A LINE

Standard form	$Ax + By = C$	A and B not both 0
Slope-intercept form	$y = mx + b$	Slope: m; y intercept: b
Point-slope form	$y - y_1 = m(x - x_1)$	Slope: m; Point: (x_1, y_1)
Horizontal line	$y = b$	Slope: 0
Vertical line	$x = a$	Slope: Undefined

1. (d)

3. (c); The slope is 0.

5. $y = 2x - 3$

x	y
0	-3
1	-1
4	5

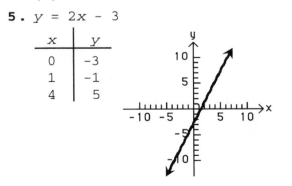

7. $2x + 3y = 12$

x	y
0	4
6	0
9	-2

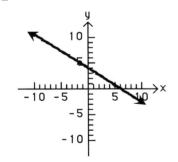

9. $y = 3x + 1$; slope: $m = 3$; y intercept: $b = 1$

11. $y = -\dfrac{3}{7}x - 6$; slope: $m = -\dfrac{3}{7}$; y intercept: $b = -6$

13. $m = -2$, $b = 3$; Using <u>5</u>, equation: $y = -2x + 3$

15. $m = \dfrac{4}{3}$, $b = -4$; using $\underline{5}$, equation: $y = \dfrac{4}{3}x - 4$

17. $y = -\dfrac{2}{3}x - 2$

$m = -\dfrac{2}{3}$, $b = -2$

x	y
0	-2
3	-4
-3	0

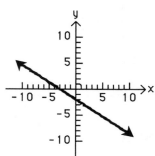

19. $3x - 2y = 10$

x	y
0	-5
10	10
-4	-11

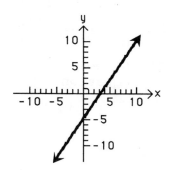

21.

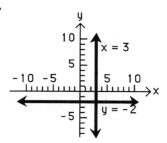

23. $4x + y = 3$
$y = -4x + 3$; slope: $m = -4$

25. $3x + 5y = 15$
$5y = -3x + 15$
$y = -\dfrac{3}{5}x + 3$; slope: $m = -\dfrac{3}{5}$

27.

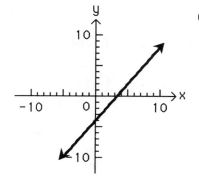

29.

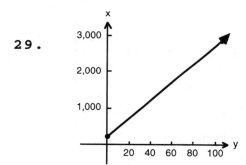

31. (A)

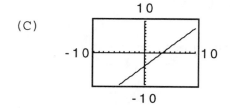

(B) x intercept--set
$f(x) = 0$:
$1.2x - 4.2 = 0$
$x = 3.5$
y intercept--set
$x = 0$:
$y = -4.2$

(D) x intercept: 3.5; y intercept: -4.2

(E) $x > 3.5$ or $(3.5, \infty)$

(C)

33. Vertical line through $(4, -3)$: $x = 4$;
horizontal line through $(4, -3)$: $y = -3$.

35. Vertical line through $(-1.5, -3.5)$: $x = -1.5$;
horizontal line through $(-1.5, -3.5)$: $y = -3.5$.

37. Slope: $m = -4$; point: $(2, -3)$. Using $\underline{5}$,
equation: $y - (-3) = -4(x - 2)$
$$y + 3 = -4x + 8$$
$$y = -4x + 5$$

39. Slope: $m = \dfrac{3}{2}$; point: $(-4, -5)$. Using $\underline{5}$,

equation: $y - (-5) = \dfrac{3}{2}(x - [4])$

$$y + 5 = \dfrac{3}{2}x + 6$$

$$y = \dfrac{3}{2}x + 1$$

41. Slope: $m = 0$; point: $(-1.5, 4.6)$. Using $\underline{5}$,
equation: $y - 4.6 = 0(x - [-1.5])$
$$y - 4.6 = 0$$
$$y = 4.6 \qquad \text{(horizontal line)}$$

43. Points $(2, 5)$, $(5, 7)$

(A) Using $\underline{4}$, slope: $m = \dfrac{7 - 5}{5 - 2} = \dfrac{2}{3}$

(B) Using the point-slope form: $y - 5 = \dfrac{2}{3}(x - 2)$;

simplifying: $3y - 15 = 2x - 4$
$$-2x + 3y = 11$$

(C) Linear function

45. Points $(-2, -1)$, $(2, -6)$

(A) Using $\underline{4}$, slope: $m = \dfrac{-6 - (-1)}{2 - (-2)} = -\dfrac{5}{4}$

(B) Using the point-slope form: $y - (-1) = -\dfrac{5}{4}[x - (-2)]$

$$y + 1 = -\dfrac{5}{4}(x + 2)$$

Simplifying: $4y + 4 = -5x - 10$
$$5x + 4y = -14$$

(C) Linear function

47. Points $(5, 3)$, $(5, -3)$

(A) Using $\underline{4}$, slope: $m = \dfrac{-3 - 3}{5 - 5} = \dfrac{-6}{0}$, not defined

(B) The line is vertical; equation $x = 5$.

(C) Neither a linear function nor a constant function.

49. Points $(-2, 5)$, $(3, 5)$

(A) Using 4, slope: $m = \dfrac{5 - 5}{3 - (-2)} = \dfrac{0}{5} = 0$

(B) The line is horizontal; equation $y = 5$.

(C) Constant function.

51. The graphs of $y = mx + 2$, m any real number, all have the same y intercept $(0, 2)$; for each real number m, $y = mx + 2$ is a non-vertical line that passes through the point $(0, 2)$.

53. (A)

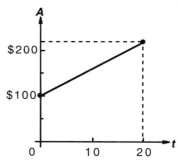

(B) Varying C produces a family of parallel lines; varying C does not change the slope $\left(m = -\dfrac{A}{B} \right)$ but does the intercepts.

55. The graph of $g(x) = |mx + b|$ coincides with the graph of $f(x) = mx + b$ for all x satisfying $mx + b \geq 0$. The graph of g is the reflection of the graph of f in the x axis for all x satisfying $mx + b < 0$. The function g is **never** a linear function.

57. We are given $A = 100(0.06)t + 100 = 6t + 100$

(A) At $t = 5$, we have $A = 6(5) + 100 = \$130$ (B)
At $t = 20$, we have $A = 6(20) + 100 = \$220$

(C) The equation $A = 6t + 100$ is in slope-intercept form. Thus, the slope is 6. Interpretation: The amount in the account is growing at the rate of \$6 per year.

59. (A) We find an equation $C(x) = mx + b$ for the line passing through $(0, 200)$ and $(20, 3800)$.

$$m = \frac{3800 - 200}{20 - 0} = \frac{3600}{20} = 180$$

Also, since $C(x) = 200$ when $x = 0$, it follows that $b = 200$.
Thus, $C(x) = 180x + 200$.

(B) The total costs at 12 boards per day are:
$$C(12) = 180(12) + 200 = 2{,}360 \text{ or } \$2{,}360$$

(C)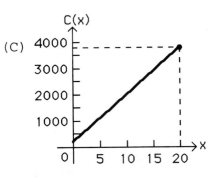

61. (A)

p(x)

(B) slope: $m = \dfrac{160 - 200}{2{,}400 - 0} = \dfrac{-40}{2400} = -\dfrac{1}{60}$

y intercept: 200

equation: $p(x) = -\dfrac{1}{60}x + 200$

(C) $p(3000) = -\dfrac{1}{60}(3000) + 200 = -50 + 200 = \$150$

(D) The equation $p(x) = -\dfrac{1}{60}x + 200$ is in slope-intercept form.

Thus the slope is $-\dfrac{1}{60} = -0.01666 \approx -0.02$. The price decreases $\$0.02$ (2 cents) for each unit increase in demand.

63. Let p = price per bushel

(A) Price-supply equation: $p(x) = mx + b$

at $p = 2.50$, supply: $x = 8.5$

at $p = 3.30$, supply: $x = 10.5$

slope: $m = \dfrac{3.30 - 2.50}{10.5 - 8.5} = \dfrac{0.8}{2} = 0.4$

$p - 2.50 = 0.4(x - 8.5)$

$p = 0.4x - 0.9$

Price-demand equation: $p(x) = mx + b$

at $p = 2.50$, demand: $x = 9.8$

at $p = 3.30$, demand: $x = 7.8$

Slope: $m = \dfrac{3.30 - 2.50}{7.8 - 9.8} = \dfrac{0.8}{-2} = -0.4$

$p - 2.50 = -0.4(x - 9.8)$

$p = -0.4x + 6.42$

(B) Equilibrium point: supply = demand

$$0.4x - 0.9 = -0.4x + 6.42$$
$$0.8x = 7.32$$
$$x = 9.15$$
$$p = 0.4(9.15) - 0.9 = 2.76$$

The equilibrium point is: 9.15 million bushels at $\$2.76$ per bushel.

65. (A)

x	0	1	2	3	4
Sales	16.7	19.8	23.6	26.9	32.7
$f(x)$	16.1	20.0	23.9	27.9	31.8

(B)

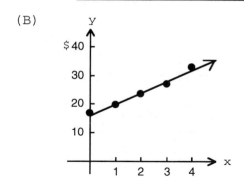

(C) At 2005, $x = 10$

$$f(10) = 16.12 + 3.91(10)$$
$$= 16.12 + 39.1 \approx 55.22$$

Sales in 2005, $55.22 billion

At 2010, $x = 15$

$$f(15) = 16.12 + 3.91(15) = 74.77$$

Sales in 2010, $74.77 billion

(D) Sales doubled in the five year period.

67. (A) Slope: $m = \dfrac{22 - 72}{60 - 20} = \dfrac{-50}{40} = -1.25$

equation: $y - 72 = -1.25(x - 20)$
$$y = -1.25x + 97$$

Therefore, $f(x) = -1.25x + 97$

(B) $f(27) = -1.25(27) + 97 = 63.25$
Coal consumption in 1927: 63.25%
$f(53) = -1.25(53) + 97 = 30.75$
Coal consumption in 1953: 30.75%

(C) Solve $f(x) = 0$

$$-1.25x + 97 = 0$$
$$x = \dfrac{-97}{-1.25} = 77.6$$

According to the model, the percentage of coal consumption will be 0 in mid 1977.

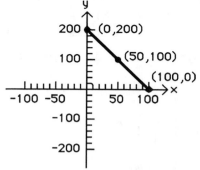

f is a good model.

69. Mix A contains 20% protein. Mix B contains 10% protein. Let x be the amount of A used, and let y be the amount of B used. Then $0.2x$ is the amount of protein from mix A and $0.1y$ is the amount of protein from mix B. Thus, the linear equation is:
$$0.2x + 0.1y = 20$$

The table shows different combinations for mix A and mix B to provide 20 grams of protein.

[<u>Note</u>: We can get many more combinations. In fact, each point on the graph indicates a combination of mix A and mix B.]

Mix A x	Mix B y
100	0
0	200
50	100
10	180

71. $p = -\frac{1}{5}d + 70$, $30 \le d \le 175$, where d = distance in centimeters

and p = pull in grams

(A) $d = 30$

$p = -\frac{1}{5}(30) + 70 = 64$ grams

$d = 175$

$p = -\frac{1}{5}(175) + 70 = 35$ grams

(B)

d	p
30	64
50	60
175	35

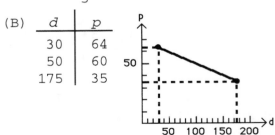

(C) Select two points (30, 64) and (50, 60) as (x_1, y_1) and (x_2, y_2), respectively, from part (B).

Using 2:

$$\text{Slope } m = \frac{y_2 - y_1}{x_2 - x_1} = \frac{60 - 64}{50 - 30}$$

$$= -\frac{4}{20} = -\frac{1}{5}$$

EXERCISE 1-4

Things to remember:

1. QUADRATIC FUNCTION

   If a, b, and c are real numbers with $a \ne 0$, then the function

   $$f(x) = ax^2 + bx + c \qquad \text{STANDARD FORM}$$

   is a QUADRATIC FUNCTION and its graph is a PARABOLA. The domain of a quadratic function is the set of all real numbers.

2. PROPERTIES OF A QUADRATIC FUNCTION AND ITS GRAPH

   Given a quadratic function

   $$f(x) = ax^2 + bx + c, \qquad a \ne 0,$$

   and the VERTEX FORM obtained by completing the square

   $$f(x) = a(x - h)^2 + k.$$

   The general properties of f are as follows:

   a. The graph of f is a parabola:

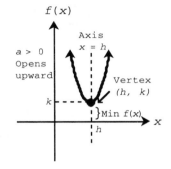

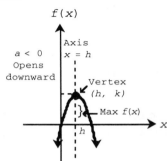

b. Vertex: (h, k) [parabola increases on one side of the vertex and decreases on the other]

c. Axis (of symmetry): $x = h$ (parallel to y axis)

d. $f(h) = k$ is the minimum if $a > 0$ and the maximum if $a < 0$

e. Domain: All real numbers
   Range: $(-\infty, k]$ if $a < 0$ or $[k, \infty)$ if $a > 0$

f. The graph of f is the graph of $g(x) = ax^2$ translated horizontally h units and vertically k units.

---

1. $f(x) = x^2 - 4x + 3$
$$= (x^2 - 4x) + 3$$
$$= (x^2 - 4x + 4) + 3 - 4 \quad \text{(completing the square)}$$
$$= (x - 2)^2 - 1 \quad \quad \text{(standard form)}$$

3. $f(x) = -x^2 + 6x - 4$
$$= -(x^2 - 6x) - 4$$
$$= -(x^2 - 6x + 9) - 4 + 9 \quad \text{(completing the square)}$$
$$= -(x - 3)^2 + 5 \quad \quad \text{(standard form)}$$

5. From Problem 1, the graph of $f(x)$ is the graph of $y = x^2$ shifted right 2 units and down 1 unit.

7. From Problem 3, the graph of $m(x)$ is the graph of $y = x^2$ reflected in the x axis, then shifted right 3 units and up 5 units.

9. (A) m   (B) g   (C) f   (D) n

11. (A) x intercepts: 1, 3; y intercept: -3 (B) Vertex: $(2, 1)$
(C) Maximum: 1   (D) Range: $y \leq 1$ or $(-\infty, 1]$
(E) Increasing interval: $x \leq 2$ or $(-\infty, 2]$
(F) Decreasing interval: $x \geq 2$ or $[2, \infty)$

13. (A) x intercepts: -3, -1; y intercept: 3   (B) Vertex: $(-2, -1)$
(C) Minimum: -1 (D) Range: $y \geq -1$ or $[-1, \infty)$
(E) Increasing interval: $x \geq -2$ or $[-2, \infty)$
(F) Decreasing interval: $x \leq -2$ or $(-\infty, -2]$

15. $f(x) = -(x - 3)^2 + 2$
(A) y intercept: $f(0) = -(0 - 3)^2 + 2 = -7$
x intercepts: $f(x) = 0$
$$-(x - 3)^2 + 2 = 0$$
$$(x - 3)^2 = 2$$
$$x - 3 = \pm\sqrt{2}$$
$$x = 3 \pm \sqrt{2}$$

(B) Vertex: $(3, 2)$ (C) Maximum: 2

(D) Range: $y \leq 2$ or $(-\infty, 2]$

17. $m(x) = (x + 1)^2 - 2$

(A) y intercept: $m(0) = (0 + 1)^2 - 2 = 1 - 2 = -1$

x intercepts: $m(x) = 0$

$$(x + 1)^2 - 2 = 0$$
$$(x + 1)^2 = 2$$
$$x + 1 = \pm\sqrt{2}$$
$$x = -1 \pm \sqrt{2}$$

(B) Vertex: $(-1, -2)$ (C) Minimum: -2

(D) Range: $y \geq -2$ or $[-2, \infty)$

19. $y = -[x - (-2)]^2 + 5 = -(x + 2)^2 + 5$

21. $y = (x - 1)^2 - 3$

23. $f(x) = x^2 - 8x + 12 = (x^2 - 8x) + 12$
$$= (x^2 - 8x + 16) + 12 - 16$$
$$= (x - 4)^2 - 4 \quad \text{(standard form)}$$

(A) y intercept: $f(0) = 0^2 - 8(0) + 12 = 12$

x intercepts: $f(x) = 0$

$$(x - 4)^2 - 4 = 0$$
$$(x - 4)^2 = 4$$
$$x - 4 = \pm 2$$
$$x = 2, 6$$

(B) Vertex: $(4, -4)$ (C) Minimum: -4

(D) Range: $y \geq -4$ or $[-4, \infty)$

25. $r(x) = -4x^2 + 16x - 15 = -4(x^2 - 4x) - 15$
$$= -4(x^2 - 4x + 4) - 15 + 16$$
$$= -4(x - 2)^2 + 1 \quad \text{(standard form)}$$

(A) y intercept: $r(0) = -4(0)^2 + 16(0) - 15 = -15$

x intercepts: $r(x) = 0$

$$-4(x - 2)^2 + 1 = 0$$
$$(x - 2)^2 = \frac{1}{4}$$
$$x - 2 = \pm\frac{1}{2}$$
$$x = \frac{3}{2}, \frac{5}{2}$$

(B) Vertex: $(2, 1)$ (C) Maximum: 1

(D) Range: $y \leq 1$ or $(-\infty, 1]$

27. $u(x) = 0.5x^2 - 2x + 5 = 0.5(x^2 - 4x) + 5$
$$= 0.5(x^2 - 4x + 4) + 3$$
$$= 0.5(x - 2)^2 + 3 \quad \text{(standard form)}$$

(A) y intercept: $u(0) = 0.5(0)^2 - 2(0) + 5 = 5$
   x intercepts: $u(x) = 0$
   $0.5(x - 2)^2 + 3 = 0$
   $(x - 2)^2 = -6$; no solutions.
   There are no x intercepts.

(B) Vertex: $(2, 3)$ (C) Minimum: 3   (D) Range: $y \geq 3$ or $[3, \infty)$

29. $f(x) = 0.3x^2 - x - 8$

(A) $f(x) = 4$: $0.3x^2 - x - 8 = 4$
   $0.3x^2 - x - 12 = 0$

(B) $f(x) = -1$: $0.3x^2 - x - 8 = -1$
   $0.3x^2 - x - 7 = 0$

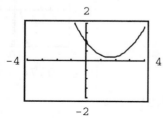

$x = -4.87, 8.21$

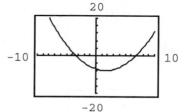

$x = -3.44, 6.78$

(C) $f(x) = -9$: $0.3x^2 - x - 8 = -9$
   $0.3x^2 - x + 1 = 0$

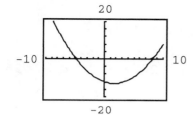

No solutions.

31.

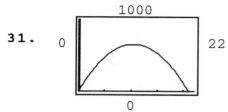

maximum value $f(10.41667) = 651.0417$

33. The vertex of the parabola is on the x axis.

35. $g(x) = 0.25x^2 - 1.5x - 7 = 0.25(x^2 - 6x + 9) - 2.25 - 7$
$$= 0.25(x - 3)^2 - 9.25$$

(A) x intercepts: $0.25(x - 3)^2 - 9.25 = 0$
$$(x - 3)^2 = 37$$
$$x - 3 = \pm\sqrt{37}$$
$$x = 3 + \sqrt{37} \approx 9.1, \ 3 - \sqrt{37} \approx -3.1$$

y intercept: -7
(B) Vertex: $(3, -9.25)$ (C) Minimum: -9.25
(D) Range: $y \geq -9.25$ or $[-9.25, \infty)$

37. $f(x) = -0.12x^2 + 0.96x + 1.2$
$$= -0.12(x^2 - 8x + 16) + 1.92 + 1.2$$
$$= -0.12(x - 4)^2 + 3.12$$

(A) x intercepts: $-0.12(x - 4)^2 + 3.12 = 0$
$$(x - 4)^2 = 26$$
$$x - 4 = \pm\sqrt{26}$$
$$x = 4 + \sqrt{26} \approx 9.1, \ 4 - \sqrt{26} \approx -1.1$$

y intercept: 1.2

(B) Vertex: $(4, 3.12)$ (C) Maximum: 3.12
(D) Range: $y \leq 3.12$ or $(-\infty, 3.12]$

39.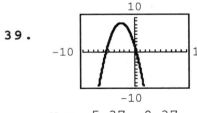
$x = -5.37, 0.37$

41.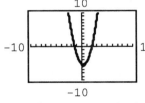
$-1.37 < x < 2.16$

43.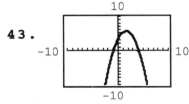
$x \leq -0.74$ or $x \geq 4.19$

45. f is a quadratic function and min $f(x) = f(2) = 4$
Axis: $x = 2$
Vertex: $(2, 4)$
Range: $y \geq 4$ or $[4, \infty)$
x intercepts: None

47. (A)
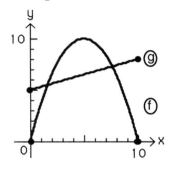

(B) $f(x) = g(x)$

$$-0.4x(x - 10) = 0.3x + 5$$
$$-0.4x^2 + 4x = 0.3x + 5$$
$$-0.4x^2 + 3.7x = 5$$
$$-0.4x^2 + 3.7x - 5 = 0$$
$$x = \frac{-3.7 \pm \sqrt{3.7^2 - 4(-0.4)(-5)}}{2(-0.4)}$$
$$x = \frac{-3.7 \pm \sqrt{5.69}}{-0.8} \approx 1.64, \ 7.61$$

(C) $f(x) > g(x)$ for $1.64 < x < 7.61$

(D) $f(x) < g(x)$ for $0 \le x < 1.64$ or $7.61 < x \le 10$

49. (A)

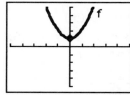

(B) $f(x) = g(x)$

$$-0.9x^2 + 7.2x = 1.2x + 5.5$$
$$-0.9x^2 + 6x = 5.5$$
$$-0.9x^2 + 6x - 5.5 = 0$$
$$x = \frac{-6 \pm \sqrt{36 - 4(-0.9)(-5.5)}}{2(-0.9)}$$
$$x = \frac{-6 \pm \sqrt{16.2}}{-1.8} \approx 1.1, \ 5.57$$

(C) $f(x) > g(x)$ for $1.10 < x < 5.57$

(D) $f(x) < g(x)$ for $0 \le x < 1.10$ or $5.57 < x \le 8$

51. $f(x) = x^2 + 1$ and $g(x) = -(x - 4)^2 - 1$ are two examples. Their graphs
are:

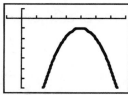

Their graphs do not intersect the x axis.

53. Mathematical model: $f(x) = -0.518x^2 + 33.3x - 481$

(A)

x	28	30	32	34	36
Mileage	45	52	55	51	47
$f(x)$	45.3	51.8	54.2	52.4	46.5

(B)

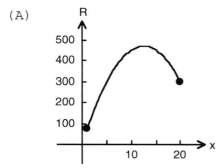

(C) $x = 31$: $f(31) = -0.518(31)^2 + 33.3(31) - 481 = 53.502$
$\qquad\qquad f(31) \approx 53.50$ thousand miles

$\quad x = 35$: $f(35) = -0.518(35)^2 + 33(35) - 481 \approx 49.95$ thousand miles

(D) The maximum mileage is achieved at 32 lb/in^2 pressure. Increasing the pressure or decreasing the pressure reduces the mileage.

55. $p(x) = 75 - 3x$; $R(x) = xp(x)$; $1 \le x \le 20$

$$R(x) = x(75 - 3x) = 75x - 3x^2$$
$$= -3(x^2 - 25x)$$
$$= -3\left(x^2 - 25x + \frac{625}{4}\right) + \frac{1875}{4}$$
$$= -3\left(x - \frac{25}{2}\right)^2 + \frac{1875}{4}$$
$$= -3(x - 12.5)^2 + 468.75$$

(A)

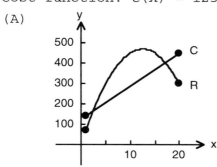

(B) Output for maximum revenue:
$x = 12,500,000$ chips;
Maximum revenue: $468,750,000

(C) Wholesale price per chip at maximum revenue: $p(12.5) = 75 - 3(12.5)$
$\qquad\qquad\qquad\qquad\qquad = 37.5$ or $37.50

57. Revenue function: $R(x) = x(75 - 3x) = 75 - 3x^2$
Cost function: $C(x) = 125 + 16x$

(A)

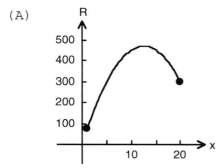

(B) Break-even points: $R(x) = C(x)$
$$75x - 3x^2 = 125 + 16x$$
$$-3x^2 + 59x - 125 = 0$$
or $3x^2 - 59x + 125 = 0$
$$x = \frac{59 \pm \sqrt{(59)^2 - 4(3)(125)}}{2(3)}$$
$$= \frac{59 \pm \sqrt{1981}}{6} = \frac{59 \pm 44.508}{6}$$
$x = 2.415$ or 17.251
The company breaks even at $x = 2,451,000$ chips and $17,251,000$ chips.

(C) Using the results from (A) and (B):
   Loss: $1 \leq x < 2.415$ or $17.251 < x \leq 20$
   Profit: $2.415 < x < 17.251$

59. Revenue function: $R(x) = x(75 - 3x)$
Cost function: $C(x) = 125 + 16x$
(A) Profit function: $P(x) = x(75 - 3x) - (125 + 16x)$
$$= 75x - 3x^2 - 125 - 16x;$$
$$P(x) = 59x - 3x^2 - 125$$

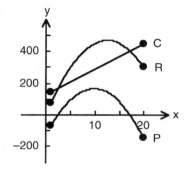

(B) The x coordinates of the intersection points of R and C are the same as the x intercepts of P.

(C) x intercepts of P: $-3x^2 + 59x - 125$
$$x = \frac{-59 \pm \sqrt{(59)^2 - 4(-3)(-125)}}{-6}$$
$x = 2.415$ or 17.251 (See Problem 55)
The break-even points are: 2,415,000 chips and 17,251,000 chips.

(D) The maximum profit and the maximum revenue do not occur at the same output level and they are not equal. The profit function involves both revenue and cost; the revenue function does not involve the production costs.

(E) $P(x) = -3x^2 + 59x - 125$
$$= -3\left(x^2 - \frac{59}{3}x\right) - 125$$
$$= -3\left[x - \left(\frac{59}{6}\right)\right]^2 - 125 + 3\left(\frac{59}{6}\right)^2$$
$$= -3(x - 9.833)^2 + 165.083$$
The maximum profit is \$165,083,000; it occurs at an output level of 9,833,000 chips. From Problem 55(B), the maximum revenue is \$468,750,000. The maximum profit is much smaller than the maximum revenue.

61. Solve: $f(x) = 1,000(0.04 - x^2) = 20$
$$40 - 1000x^2 = 20$$
$$1000x^2 = 20$$
$$x^2 = 0.02$$
$$x = 0.14 \text{ or } -0.14$$
Since we are measuring distance, we take the positive solution:
   $x = 0.14$ cm

1.

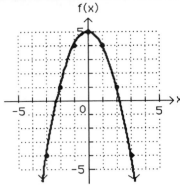

(1-1)

2. (A) Not a function; fails vertical line test

(B) A function

(C) A function

(D) Not a function; fails vertical line test   (1-1)

3. $f(x) = 2x - 1$, $g(x) = x^2 - 2x$

(A) $f(-2) + g(-1) = 2(-2) - 1 + (-1)^2 - 2(-1) = -2$

(B) $f(0) \cdot g(4) = (2 \cdot 0 - 1)(4^2 - 2 \cdot 4) = -8$

(C) $\dfrac{g(2)}{f(3)} = \dfrac{2^2 - 2 \cdot 2}{2 \cdot 3 - 1} = 0$

(D) $\dfrac{f(3)}{g(2)}$ not defined because $g(2) = 0$ (1-1)

4. (A) $y = 4$ (B) $x = 0$ (C) $y = 1$ (D) $x = -1$ or 1

(E) $y = -2$ (F) $x = -5$ or 5 (1-1)

5. (A)

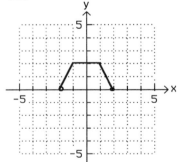

(B)

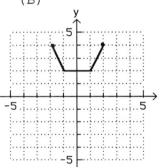

(C)

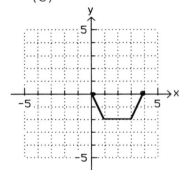

(D)

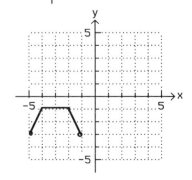

(1-2)

6. (A) (n)   (B) (g)   (C) (m); slope is zero

(D) (f); slope is not defined   (1-3)

7. $y = -\frac{2}{3}x + 6$ (1-3)

8. vertical line: $x = -6$; horizontal line: $y = 5$ (1-3)

9. x intercept: $2x = 18$, $x = 9$;   Graph:
y intercept: $-3y = 18$, $x = -6$;
slope-intercept form:
$y = \frac{2}{3}x - 6$; slope $= \frac{2}{3}$

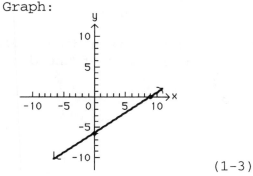

(1-3)

10. $f(x) = -x^2 + 4x = -(x^2 - 4x)$
$$= -(x^2 - 4x + 4) + 4$$
$$= -(x - 2)^2 + 4 \quad \text{(standard form)}$$
The graph of $f(x)$ is the graph of $y = x^2$ reflected in the x axis, then shifted right 2 units and up 4 units. (1-4)

11. (A) g (B) m (C) n (D) f (1-2, 1-4)

12. $y = f(x) = (x + 2)^2 - 4$
(A) x intercepts: $(x + 2)^2 - 4 = 0$
$$(x + 2)^2 = 4$$
$$x + 2 = -2 \text{ or } 2$$
$$x = -4, \ 0$$
y intercept: 0
(B) Vertex: $(-2, -4)$ (C) Minimum: -4 (D) Range: $y \geq -4$ or $[-4, \infty)$
(E) Increasing interval $[-2, \infty)$ (F) Decreasing interval $(-\infty, -2]$
(1-4)

13. (A) This correspondence specifies a function; each person has exactly one mother.

(B) This correspondence does not specify a function; a person may have no children, or two or more children. (1-1)

14.

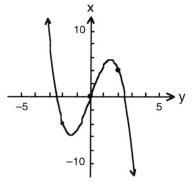

(1-1)

15.

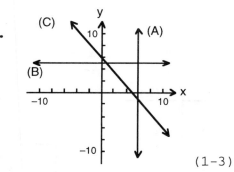

(1-3)

16. Linear function: (a), (c), (e), (f); Constant function: (d) (1-3)

17. (A) $x^2 - x - 6 = 0$ at $x = -2, 3$
Domain: all real numbers except $x = -2, 3$

(B) $5 - x > 0$ for $x < 5$
Domain: $x < 5$ or $(-\infty, 5)$ (1-1)

18. Function g multiplies a domain element by 2 and then subtracts three times the square root of the domain element from the result. (1-1)

19. $f(x) = 4x^2 + 4x - 3 = 4(x^2 + x) - 3$
$$= 4\left(x^2 + x + \frac{1}{4}\right) - 3 - 1$$
$$= 4\left(x + \frac{1}{2}\right)^2 - 4 \quad \text{(standard form)}$$

(A) Intercepts:
y intercept: $f(0) = 4(0)^2 + 4(0) - 3 = -3$
x intercepts: $f(x) = 0$
$$4\left(x + \frac{1}{2}\right)^2 - 4 = 0$$
$$\left(x + \frac{1}{2}\right)^2 = 1$$
$$x + \frac{1}{2} = \pm 1$$
$$x = -\frac{1}{2} \pm 1 = -\frac{3}{2}, \frac{1}{2}$$

(B) Vertex: $\left(-\frac{1}{2}, -4\right)$ (C) Minimum: -4 (D) Range: $y \geq -4$ or $[-4, \infty)$ (1-4)

20. The graph of $x = -3$ is a vertical line 3 units to the *left* of the y axis; $y = 2$ is a horizontal line 2 units *above* the x axis.

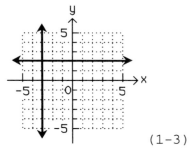

(1-3)

21. $f(x) = 0.4x(x + 4)(2 - x) = 0.4x(8 - 2x - x^2)$
$$= -0.4x^3 - 0.8x^2 + 3.2x$$

(A)

x	$f(x)$
-3	-6
-1	-3.6
1	2
3	-8.4

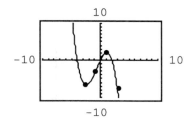

(B) Graph f and the lines $y = 3$, $y = 2$, $y = 1$ in the same coordinate system.

It is now easy to see that $f(x) = 3$ has one solution, $f(x) = 2$ has two solutions, and $f(x) = 1$ has three solutions.

(C) $f(x) = 3$: $x = -4.28$, $f(x) = 2$: $x = -4.19$, 1
$f(x) = 1$: $x = -4.10$, 0.38, 1.75   (1-1)

22. $f(x) = 3 - 2x$
(A) $f(2) = 3 - 2(2) = 3 - 4 = -1$
(B) $f(2 + h) = 3 - 2(2 + h) = 3 - 4 - 2h = -1 - 2h$
(C) $f(2 + h) - f(2) = -1 - 2h - (-1) = -2h$
(D) $\dfrac{f(2 + h) - f(2)}{h} = -\dfrac{2h}{h} = -2$ (1-1)

23. $f(x) = x^2 - 3x + 1$
(A) $f(a) = a^2 - 3a + 1$
(B) $f(a + h) = (a + h)^2 - 3(a + h) + 1 = a^2 + 2ah + h^2 - 3a - 3h + 1$
(C) $f(a + h) - f(a) = a^2 + 2ah + h^2 - 3a - 3h + 1 - (a^2 - 3a + 1)$
$= 2ah + h^2 - 3h$
(D) $\dfrac{f(a + h) - f(a)}{h} = \dfrac{2ah + h^2 - 3h}{h} = \dfrac{h(2a + h - 3)}{h} = 2a + h - 3$ (1-1)

24. The graph of m is the graph of $y = |x|$ reflected on the x axis and shifted 4 units to the right.   (1-2)

25. The graph of g is the graph of $y = x^3$ vertically contracted by a factor of 0.3 and shifted up 3 units.   (1-2)

26. The graph of $y = x^2$ is vertically expanded by a factor of 2, reflected in the x axis and shifted to the left 3 units. Equation: $y = -2(x + 3)^2$ (1-2)

27. Equation: $f(x) = 2\sqrt{x + 3} - 1$ 28.

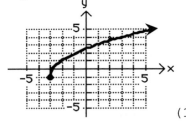

(1-2)

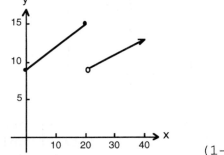

(1-2)

29.

(1-2)

30. Use the point-slope form:

(A) $y - 2 = -\dfrac{2}{3}[x - (-3)]$ (B) $y - 3 = 0(x - 3)$

$\qquad y - 2 = -\dfrac{2}{3}(x + 3)$ $\qquad\qquad y = 3$

$\qquad\qquad y = -\dfrac{2}{3}x$ (1-3)

31. (A) Slope: $\dfrac{-1 - 5}{1 - (-3)} = -\dfrac{3}{2}$ (B) Slope: $\dfrac{5 - 5}{4 - (-1)} = 0$

$\qquad\qquad y - 5 = -\dfrac{3}{2}(x + 3)$ $\qquad\qquad y - 5 = 0(x - 1)$

$\qquad\qquad 3x + 2y = 1$ $\qquad\qquad\qquad y = 5$

(C) Slope: $\dfrac{-2 - 7}{-2 - (-2)}$ not defined since $2 - (-2) = 0$

$\qquad\qquad\qquad\qquad\qquad x = -2$ (1-3)

32. $y = -(x - 4)^2 + 3$ (1-2, 1-4)

33. $f(x) = -0.4x^2 + 3.2x - 1.2 = -0.4(x^2 - 8x + 16) + 7.6$

$\qquad\qquad\qquad\qquad\qquad = -0.4(x - 4)^2 + 7.6$

(A) y intercept: 1.2

$\quad$ x intercepts: $-0.4(x - 4)^2 + 7.6 = 0$

$\qquad\qquad\qquad\qquad (x - 4)^2 = 19$

$\qquad\qquad\qquad\qquad\qquad x = 4 + \sqrt{19} \approx 8.4, \ 4 - \sqrt{19} \approx -0.4$

(B) Vertex: $(4.0, 7.6)$ (C) Maximum: 7.6

(D) Range: $x \leq 7.6$ or $(-\infty, 7.6]$ (1-4)

34.

(A) y intercept: 1.2

$\quad$ x intercepts: $-0.4, 8.4$

(B) Vertex: $(4.0, 7.6)$

(C) Maximum: 7.6

(D) Range: $x \leq 7.6$ or $(-\infty, 7.6]$ (1-4)

35. The graph of $y = \sqrt[3]{x}$ is vertically expanded by a factor of 2, reflected in the x axis, shifted 1 unit to the left and 1 unit down.
Equation: $y = -2\sqrt[3]{x + 1} - 1$ (1-2)

36. The graphs of the pairs $\{y = 2x,\ y = -\frac{1}{2}x\}$ and

$\{y = \frac{2}{3}x + 2,\ y = -\frac{3}{2}x + 2\}$ are shown below:

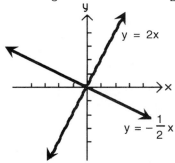 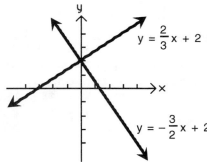

In each case, the graphs appear to be perpendicular to each other. It can be shown that two slant lines are perpendicular if and only if their slopes are negative reciprocals. (1-3)

37. $G(x) = 0.3x^2 + 1.2x - 6.9 = 0.3(x^2 + 4x + 4) - 8.1$
$$= 0.3(x + 2)^2 - 8.1$$

(A) y intercept: -6.9
   x intercepts: $0.3(x + 2)^2 - 8.1 = 0$
$$(x + 2)^2 = 27$$
$$x = -2 + \sqrt{27} \approx 3.2,\ -2 - \sqrt{27} \approx -7.2$$

(B) Vertex: $(-2, -8.1)$ (C) Minimum: -8.1

(D) Range: $x \geq -8.1$ or $[-8.1, \infty)$

(E) Decreasing: $(-\infty, -2]$; Increasing: $[-2, \infty)$ (1-4)

38.

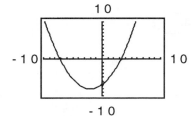

(A) y intercept: -6.9
   x intercept: $-7.2,\ 3.2$

(B) Vertex: $(-2, -8.1)$

(C) Minimum: -8.1

(D) Range: $x \geq -8.1$ or $[-8.1, \infty)$

(E) Decreasing: $(-\infty, -2]$
   Increasing: $[-2, \infty)$

39. (A) $V(0) = 12,000$, $V(8) = 2,000$

Slope: $\dfrac{2,000 - 12,000}{8 - 0} = \dfrac{-10,000}{8} = -1,250$

V intercept: $12,000$

Equation: $V(t) = -1,250t + 12,000$

(B) $V(5) = -1,250(5) + 12,000 = \$5,750$

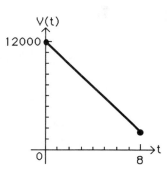

(1-3)

40. (A)

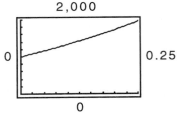

(B) $r = 0.1447$ or 14.7% compounded annually
Alternative algebraic solution:
$$1000(1 + r)^3 = 1500$$
$$(1 + r)^3 = 1.5$$
$$1 + r = \sqrt[3]{1.5} \approx 1.1447$$
$$r = 0.1447$$

(1-1, 1-2)

41. (A) $R(130) = 208$, $R(50) = 80$
Slope: $\dfrac{208 - 80}{130 - 50} = \dfrac{128}{80} = 1.6$
Equation: $R - 80 = 1.6(C - 50)$ or $R = 1.6C$

(B) $R(120) = 1.6(120) = \$192$

(C) $176 = 1.6C$; $C = \$110$

(D) 1.6; The slope gives the change in retail price per unit change in the cost.

(1-3)

42. $f(x) = 0.28x^2 - 6.5x + 274$

(A)

x	0	5	10	15	20
Consumption	271	255	233	236	256
$f(x)$	274	248.5	237	239.5	256

(B)

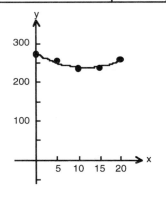

(C) $f(25) = 0.28(25)^2 - 6.5(25) + 274 = 286.5$,
$f(30) = 0.28(30)^2 - 6.5(30) + 274 = 331$

(D) Egg consumption fell annually from 1980 until sometime between 1990 and 1995. From that point on, egg consumption has increased but has not yet reached the 1980 consumption.

(1-4)

43. (A) $S(x) = 3$ if $0 \le x \le 20$;
$S(x) = 3 + 0.057(x - 20)$
$= 0.057x + 1.86$ if $20 < x \le 200$;
$S(200) = 13.36$
$S(x) = 13.36 + 0.0346(x - 200)$
$= 0.0346x + 6.34$ if $200 < x \le 1000$;
$S(1000) = 40.94$

$$S(x) = 40.94 + 0.0217(x - 1000)$$
$$= 0.0217x + 19.24 \quad \text{if} \quad x > 1000$$

Therefore, $S(x) = \begin{cases} 3 & \text{if} \quad 0 \le x \le 20 \\ 0.057x + 1.86 & \text{if} \quad 20 < x \le 200 \\ 0.0346x + 6.34 & \text{if} \quad 200 < x \le 1000 \\ 0.0217x + 19.24 & \text{if} \quad x > 1000 \end{cases}$

(B)

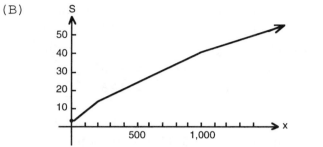

(1-2)

44. Let p = price per bushel
   (A) Price-supply equation: $p(x) = mx + b$;
   at $p = 1.90$, supply: $x = 410$
   at $p = 2.70$, supply: $x = 430$
   Slope: $m = \dfrac{2.70 - 1.90}{430 - 410} = \dfrac{0.80}{20} = 0.04$
   $p - 1.90 = 0.04(x - 410)$
   $\quad\quad p = 0.04x - 14.5$
   Price-demand equation: $p(x) = mx + b$
   at $p = 1.90$, demand: $x = 455$
   at $p = 2.70$, demand: $x = 415$
   Slope: $m = \dfrac{2.70 - 1.90}{415 - 455} = \dfrac{0.80}{-40} = -0.02$
   $p - 1.90 = -0.02(x - 455)$
   $\quad\quad p = -0.02x + 11$

   (B) Equilibrium point: supply = demand
   $0.04x - 14.5 = -0.02x + 11$
   $\quad\quad 0.06x = 25.5$
   $\quad\quad\quad\quad x = 425$
   $\quad p(425) = 0.4(425) - 14.5 = 2.50$
   The equilibrium price is: 425 million bushels at \$2.50 per bushel.

(1-3)

45. (A) Let x = number of video tapes produced.
   $C(x) = 84,000 + 15x$
   $R(x) = 50x$

   (B) $R(x) = C(x)$
   $50x = 84,000 + 15x$
   $35x = 84,000$
   $\quad x = 2,400$ units
   $R < C$ for $0 \le x < 2,400$; $R > C$ for
   $x > 2,400$

   (C) $R = C$ at $x = 2,400$ units
   $R < C$ for $0 \le x < 2,400$; $R > C$ for
   $x > 2,400$

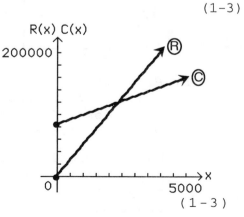

46. $p(x) = 50 - 1.25x$ Price-demand function
$C(x) = 160 + 10x$ Cost function
$R(x) = xp(x)$
$= x(50 - 1.25x)$ Revenue function

(A)

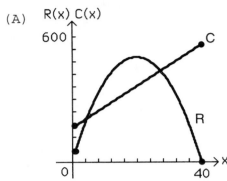

(B) $R = C$
$$x(50 - 1.25x) = 160 + 10x$$
$$-1.25x^2 + 50x = 160 + 10x$$
$$-1.25x^2 + 40x = 160$$
$$-1.25(x^2 - 32x + 256) = 160 - 320$$
$$-1.25(x - 16)^2 = -160$$
$$(x - 16)^2 = 128$$
$$x = 16 + \sqrt{128} \approx 27.314,$$
$$16 - \sqrt{128} \approx 4.686$$

$R = C$ at $x = 4.686$ thousand units
(4,686 units) and $x = 27.314$ thousand units
(27,314 units)
$R < C$ for $1 \leq x < 4.686$ or $27.314 < x \leq 40$
$R > C$ for $4.686 < x < 27.314$

(C) Max Rev: $50x - 1.25x^2 = R$
$$-1.25(x^2 - 40x + 400) + 500 = R$$
$$-1.25(x - 20)^2 + 500 = R$$
Vertex at (20, 500)
Max. Rev. = 500 thousand ($500,000) occurs when <u>output</u> is
20 thousand (20,000 units)
<u>Wholesale price</u> at this output: $p(x) = 50 - 1.25x$
$$p(20) = 50 - 1.25(20)$$
$$= \$25 \qquad\qquad (1\text{-}3, \ 1\text{-}4)$$

47. (A) $P(x) = R(x) - C(x) = x(50 - 1.25x) - (160 + 10x)$
$$= -1.25x^2 + 40x - 160$$

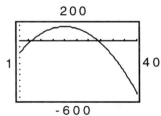

(B) $P = 0$ for $x = 4.686$ thousand units (4,686 units)
and $x = 27.314$ thousand units (27,314 units)
$P < 0$ for $1 \leq x < 4.686$ or $27.314 < x \leq 40$
$P > 0$ for $4.686 < x < 27.314$

(C) Maximum profit is 160 thousand dollars ($160,000), and this occurs
at $x = 16$ thousand units (16,000 units). The wholesale price at this
output is $p(16) = 50 - 1.25(16) = \$30$, which is $5 greater than the
$25 found in 46(C). $\qquad\qquad (1\text{-}4)$

48. (A) The area enclosed by the pens is given by

$$A = (2y)x$$

Now, $3x + 4y = 840$

so $\qquad y = 210 - \dfrac{3}{4}x$

Thus $\qquad A(x) = 2\left(210 - \dfrac{3}{4}x\right)x$

$$= 420x - \dfrac{3}{2}x^2$$

(B) Clearly x and y must be nonnegative; the fact that $y \geq 0$ implies

$$210 - \dfrac{3}{4}x \geq 0$$

and $\qquad 210 \geq \dfrac{3}{4}x$

$$840 \geq 3x$$
$$280 \geq x$$

Thus, domain A: $0 \leq x \leq 280$

(C)

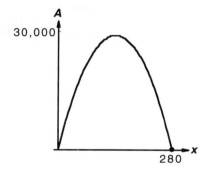

(D) Graph $A(x) = 420x - \dfrac{3}{2}x^2$ and

$y = 25,000$ together.
There are two values of x that will produce storage areas with a combined area of 25,000 square feet, one near $x = 90$ and the other near $x = 190$.

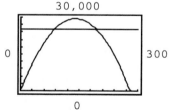

(E) $x = 86$, $x = 194$

(F) $A(x) = 420x - \dfrac{3}{2}x^2 = -\dfrac{3}{2}(x^2 - 280x)$

Completing the square, we have

$$A(x) = -\dfrac{3}{2}(x^2 - 280x + 19,600 - 19,600)$$

$$= -\dfrac{3}{2}[(x - 140)^2 - 19,600]$$

$$= -\dfrac{3}{2}(x - 140)^2 + 29,400$$

The dimensions that will produce the maximum combined area are: $x = 140$ ft, $y = 105$ ft. The maximum area is 29,400 sq. ft. (1-4)

49. (A) We are given $P(0) = 20$ and $m = 15$. Thus, $P(x) = 15x + 20$

(B) 1 PM is 5 hours after 8 AM
$P(5) = 15(5) + 20 = 95$

(C)

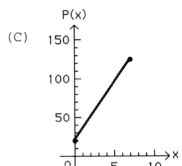

(D) Slope = 15

(1-4)

50. $\dfrac{\Delta s}{s} = k$. For $k = \dfrac{1}{30}$, $\dfrac{\Delta s}{s} = \dfrac{1}{30}$ or $\Delta s = \dfrac{1}{30}s$

(A) When $s = 30$, $\Delta s = \dfrac{1}{30}(30) = 1$ pound.

When $s = 90$, $\Delta s = \dfrac{1}{30}(90) = 3$ pounds.

(B) $\Delta s = \dfrac{1}{30}s$

Slope $m = \dfrac{1}{30}$

y intercept $b = 0$

(C) Slope $m = \dfrac{1}{30}$

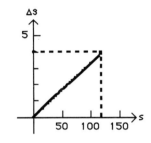

(1-4)

2 ADDITIONAL ELEMENTARY FUNCTIONS

Things to remember:

1. POLYNOMIAL FUNCTION

   A POLYNOMIAL FUNCTION is a function that can be written in the form
   $$f(x) = a_n x^n + a_{n-1} x^{n-1} + \ldots + a_1 x + a_0$$
   for n a nonnegative integer, called the DEGREE of the polynomial. The coefficients a_0, a_1, …, a_n are real numbers with $a_n \neq 0$. The DOMAIN of a polynomial function is the set of all real numbers.

2. TURNING POINT

   A TURNING POINT on a continuous graph is a point that separates an increasing portion from a decreasing portion, or vice versa. The graph of a polynomial function of degree $n \geq 1$ can have at most $n - 1$ turning points and can cross the x axis at most n times.

3. LOCATING THE ZEROS OF A POLYNOMIAL

   If r is a zero of the polynomial
   $$P(x) = x_n + a_{n-1} x^{n-1} + a_{n-2} x^{n-2} + \cdots + a_1 x + a_0$$
   then
   $$|r| < 1 + \max\{|a_{n-1}|, |a_{n-2}|, \ldots, |a_1|, |a_0|\}$$

4. A RATIONAL FUNCTION is any function that can be written in the form
   $$f(x) = \frac{n(x)}{d(x)} \qquad d(x) \neq 0$$
   where $n(x)$ and $d(x)$ are polynomials. The DOMAIN is the set of all real numbers such that $d(x) \neq 0$. We assume that $n(x)$ and $d(x)$ have no real zero in common.

5. ASYMPTOTES OF RATIONAL FUNCTIONS

   Given the rational function
   $$f(x) = \frac{n(x)}{d(x)}$$
   where $n(x)$ and $d(x)$ are polynomials with no real zeros in common.

   (a) If a is a real number such that $d(a) = 0$, then the line $x = a$ is a VERTICAL ASYMPTOTE of the graph of $y = f(x)$.

   (b) HORIZONTAL ASYMPTOTES, if any exist, can be found by dividing each term of the numerator $n(x)$ and denominator $d(x)$ by the highest power of x that appears in $f(x)$.

1. $f(x) = 5x + 3$
    (A) degree 1
    (B) x-intercept: $f(x) = 0$
$$5x + 3 = 0$$
$$x = -\frac{3}{5}$$
    (C) y-intercept: $f(0) = 3$

3. $f(x) = x^2 - 9$
    (A) degree: 2
    (B) x-intercepts: $f(x) = 0$
$$x^2 - 9 = 0$$
$$(x - 3)(x + 3) = 0$$
$$x = 3, \ -3$$
    (C) y-intercept: $f(0) = -9$

5. $f(x) = (x - 2)(x + 3)(x - 5) = x^3 - 4x^2 - 11x + 30$
    (A) degree: 3
    (B) x-intercepts: $f(x) = 0$
$$x = 2, \ -3, \ 5$$
    (C) y-intercept: $f(0) = 30$

7. $f(x) = (2x - 9)(3x + 4) = 6x^2 - 19x - 36$
    (A) degree: 2
    (B) x-intercepts: $f(x) = 0$
$$x = \frac{9}{2}, \ -\frac{4}{3}$$
    (C) y-intercept: $f(0) = -36$

9. $f(x) = x^6 + 1$
    (A) degree: 6
    (B) x-intercepts: $f(x) = 0$
$$x^6 + 1 = 0; \text{ no solutions; no } x\text{-intercepts}$$
    (C) y-intercept: $f(0) = 1$

11. (A) 3   (B) 4   (C) negative   **13.** (A) 4   (B) 5   (C) negative

15. (A) 0   (B) 1   (C) negative   **17.** (A) 5   (B) 6   (C) positive

19. 7   **21.** 10

23. 1; polynomials of odd degree cross the x-axis at least once.

25. $f(x) = \dfrac{x + 2}{x - 2}$

    (A) *Intercepts:*
        x intercepts: $f(x) = 0$ only if $x + 2 = 0$ or $x = -2$.
                The x intercept is -2.
        y intercept: $f(0) = \dfrac{0 + 2}{0 - 2} = -1$
                The y intercept is -1.

    (B) *Domain:* The denominator is 0 at $x = 2$. Thus, the domain is the set of all real numbers except 2.

    (C) *Asymptotes:*
        Vertical asymptotes: $f(x) = \dfrac{x + 2}{x - 2}$
                                The denominator is 0 at $x = 2$. Therefore, the line $x = 2$ is a vertical asymptote.

Horizontal asymptotes: $f(x) = \dfrac{x + 2}{x - 2} = \dfrac{1 + \dfrac{2}{x}}{1 - \dfrac{2}{x}}$

As x increases or decreases without bound, the numerator tends to 1 and the denominator tends to 1. Therefore, the line $y = 1$ is a horizontal asymptote.

(D)

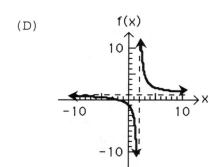

(E)

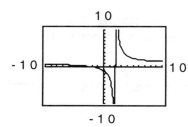

27. $f(x) = \dfrac{3x}{x + 2}$

(A) *Intercepts:*

x intercepts: $f(x) = 0$ only if $3x = 0$ or $x = 0$.
The x intercept is 0.

y intercept: $f(0) = \dfrac{3 \cdot 0}{0 + 2} = 0$
The y intercept is 0.

(B) *Domain:* The denominator is 0 at $x = -2$. Thus, the domain is the set of all real numbers except -2.

(C) *Asymptotes:*

Vertical asymptotes: $f(x) = \dfrac{3x}{x + 2}$

The denominator is 0 at $x = -2$. Therefore, the line $x = -2$ is a vertical asymptote.

Horizontal asymptotes: $f(x) = \dfrac{3x}{x + 2} = \dfrac{3}{1 + \dfrac{2}{x}}$

As x increases or decreases without bound, the numerator is 3 and the denominator tends to 1. Therefore, the line $y = 3$ is a horizontal asymptote.

(D)

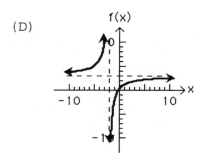

(E)

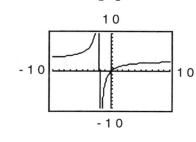

29. $f(x) = \dfrac{4 - 2x}{x - 4}$

   (A) *Intercepts:*

      x intercepts: $f(x) = 0$ only if $4 - 2x = 0$ or $x = 2$.
               The x intercept is 2.

      y intercept: $\quad f(0) = \dfrac{4 - 2 \cdot 0}{0 - 4} = -1$
               The y intercept is -1.

   (B) *Domain:* The denominator is 0 at $x = 4$. Thus, the domain is the set
      of all real numbers except 4.

   (C) *Asymptotes:*

      Vertical asymptotes: $f(x) = \dfrac{4 - 2x}{x - 4}$

               The denominator is 0 at $x = 4$. Therefore, the
               line $x = 4$ is a vertical asymptote.

      Horizontal asymptotes: $f(x) = \dfrac{4 - 2x}{x - 4} = \dfrac{\dfrac{4}{x} - 2}{1 - \dfrac{4}{x}}$

               As x increases or decreases without bound,
               the numerator tends to -2 and the denominator
               tends to 1. Therefore, the line $y = -2$ is a
               horizontal asymptote.

   (D) 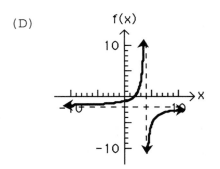   (E)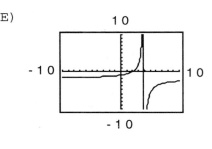

31. The graph of $f(x) = 2x^4 - 5x^2 + x + 2 = 2x^4\left(1 - \dfrac{5}{2x^2} + \dfrac{1}{2x^3} + \dfrac{1}{x^4}\right)$ will

    "look like" the graph of $y = 2x^4$. For large x, $f(x) \approx 2x^4$.

33. The graph of $f(x) = -x^5 + 4x^3 - 4x + 1 = -x^5\left(1 - \dfrac{4}{x^2} + \dfrac{4}{x^4} - \dfrac{1}{x^5}\right)$ will

    "look like" the graph of $y = -x^5$. For large x, $f(x) \approx -x^5$.

35. (A)

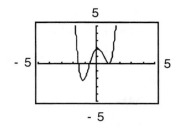

$$y = 2x^4 \qquad\qquad y = 2x^4 - 5x^2 + x + 2$$

(B)

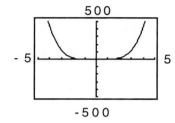

$$y = 2x^4 \qquad\qquad y = 2x^4 - 5x^2 + x + 2$$

37. (A)

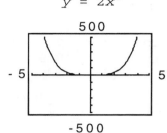

$$y = -x^5 \qquad\qquad y = -x^5 + 4x^3 - 4x + 1$$

(B)

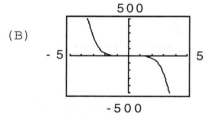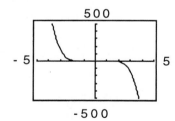

$$y = -x^5 \qquad\qquad y = -x^5 + 4x^3 - 4x + 1$$

39. $P(x) = 2x^3 - x^2 - 7x + 3 = 2\left(x^3 - \dfrac{1}{2}x^2 - \dfrac{7}{2}x + \dfrac{3}{2}\right)$

If r is a zero of $P(x)$, then

$$|r| < 1 + \max\left(\left|-\frac{1}{2}\right|, \left|-\frac{7}{2}\right|, \left|\frac{3}{2}\right|\right) = 1 + \frac{7}{2}$$

Thus, the zeros of $P(x)$ are in $\left[\dfrac{-9}{2}, \dfrac{9}{2}\right]$.

To two decimal places, the real zeros of $P(x)$ are:
$r_1 = -1.84$, $r_2 = 0.42$, $r_3 = 1.92$

41. $P(x) = x^4 + 2x^3 - 3x^2 + 4x + 1$

$\quad |r| < 1 + \max(|2|, |-3|, |4|, |1|), = 1 + 4 = 5$

The zeros of $P(x)$ are in $[-5, 5]$.

To two decimal places, the real zeros of $P(x)$ are:

$r_1 = -2.50$, $r_2 = -1.22$, $r_3 = 0.22$, $r_4 = 1.50$

43. $P(x) = x^5 - 12x^4 + 7x^3 + 15$

$\quad |r| < 1 + \max(|-12|, |7|, |15|) = 1 + 15 = 16$

The zeros of $P(x)$ are in $[-16, 16]$.

To two decimal pieces, the real zeros of $P(x)$ are:

$r_1 = -0.92$, $r_2 = 1.30$, $r_3 = 11.38$

45. The linear regression model for the data set consisting of two points on the line $y = 0.5x + 3$ is simply the line $y = 0.5x + 3$. In general, the linear regression model for two points is the line that passes through the two points.

47. $f(x) = \dfrac{2x^2}{x^2 - x - 6}$

(A) *Intercepts:*

x intercepts: $f(x) = 0$ only if $2x^2 = 0$ or $x = 0$.
The x intercept is 0.

y intercept: $f(0) = \dfrac{2 \cdot 0^2}{0^2 - 0 - 6} = 0$
The y intercept is 0.

(B) *Asymptotes:*

Vertical asymptotes: $f(x) = \dfrac{2x^2}{x^2 - x - 6} = \dfrac{2x^2}{(x - 3)(x + 2)}$

The denominator is 0 at $x = -2$ and $x = 3$.
Thus, the lines $x = -2$ and $x = 3$ are vertical asymptotes.

Horizontal asymptotes: $f(x) = \dfrac{2x^2}{x^2 - x - 6} = \dfrac{2}{1 - \dfrac{1}{x} - \dfrac{6}{x^2}}$

As x increases or decreases without bound, the numerator is 2 and the denominator tends to 1. Therefore, the line $y = 2$ is a horizontal asymptote.

(C)

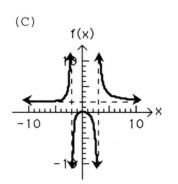

(D)

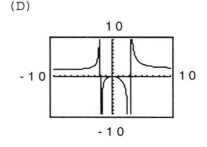

49. $f(x) = \dfrac{6 - 2x^2}{x^2 - 9}$

(A) *Intercepts:*

x intercepts: $f(x) = 0$ only if $6 - 2x^2 = 0$

$$2x^2 = 6$$
$$x^2 = 3$$
$$x = \pm\sqrt{3}$$

The x intercepts are $\pm\sqrt{3}$.

y intercept: $f(0) = \dfrac{6 - 2 \cdot 0^2}{0^2 - 9} = -\dfrac{2}{3}$

The y intercept is $-\dfrac{2}{3}$.

(B) *Asymptotes:*

Vertical asymptotes: $f(x) = \dfrac{6 - 2x^2}{x^2 - 9} = \dfrac{6 - 2x^2}{(x - 3)(x + 3)}$

The denominator is 0 at $x = -3$ and $x = 3$. Thus, the lines $x = -3$ and $x = 3$ are vertical asymptotes.

Horizontal asymptotes: $f(x) = \dfrac{6 - 2x^2}{x^2 - 9} = \dfrac{\dfrac{6}{x^2} - 2}{1 - \dfrac{9}{x^2}}$

As x increases or decreases without bound, the numerator tends to -2 and the denominator tends to 1. Therefore, the line $y = -2$ is a horizontal asymptote.

(C)

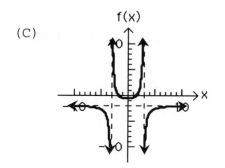

(D)

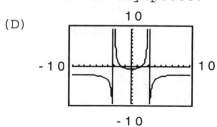

51. $f(x) = \dfrac{-4x}{x^2 + x - 6}$

(A) *Intercepts:*

x intercepts: $f(x) = 0$ only if $-4x = 0$ or $x = 0$.

The x intercept is 0.

y intercept: $f(0) = \dfrac{-4 \cdot 0}{0^2 + 0 - 6} = 0$

The y intercept is 0.

(B) *Asymptotes:*

Vertical asymptotes: $f(x) = \dfrac{-4x}{x^2 + x - 6} = \dfrac{-4x}{(x + 3)(x - 2)}$

The denominator is 0 at $x = -3$ and $x = 2$. Thus, the lines $x = -3$ and $x = 2$ are vertical asymptotes.

Horizontal asymptotes: $f(x) = \dfrac{-4x}{x^2 + x - 6} = \dfrac{-\dfrac{4}{x}}{1 + \dfrac{1}{x} - \dfrac{6}{x^2}}$

As x increases or decreases without bound, the numerator tends to 0 and the denominator tends to 1. Therefore, the line $y = 0$ (the x axis) is a horizontal asymptote.

(C)

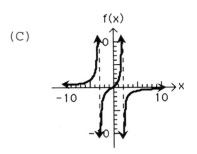

(D)

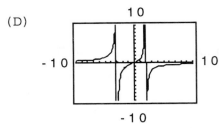

53. The graph has 1 turning point which implies degree $n = 2$. The x intercepts are $x = -1$ and $x = 2$.

Thus, $f(x) = (x + 1)(x - 2) = x^2 - x - 2$.

55. The graph has 2 turning points which implies degree $n = 3$. The x intercepts are $x = -2$, $x = 0$, and $x = 2$. The direction of the graph indicates that leading coefficient is negative

$f(x) = -(x + 2)(x)(x - 2) = 4x - x^3$.

57. (A) Since $C(x)$ is a linear function of x, it can be written in the form

$C(x) = mx + b$

Since the fixed costs are $200, $b = 200$.

Also, $C(20) = 3800$, so

$3800 = m(20) + 200$

$20m = 3600$

$m = 180$

Therefore, $C(x) = 180x + 200$

(B) $\overline{C}(x) = \dfrac{C(x)}{x} = \dfrac{180x + 200}{x}$

(C)

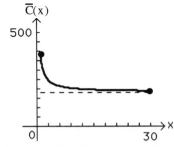

(D) $\overline{C}(x) = \dfrac{180x + 200}{x} = \dfrac{180 + \dfrac{200}{x}}{1}$

As x increases, the numerator tends to 180 and the denominator is 1. Therefore, $\overline{C}(x)$ tends to 180 or $180 per board.

59. (A) $\overline{C}(n) = \dfrac{2500 + 175n + 25n^2}{n}$

(B)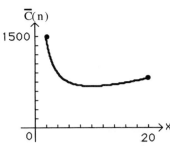

(C) Using the graph, we calculate

$$\overline{C}(8) = \frac{2500 + 175(8) + 25(8)^2}{8} = 687.50$$

$$\overline{C}(9) = \frac{2500 + 175(9) + 25(9)^2}{9} = 677.78$$

$$\overline{C}(10) = \frac{2500 + 175(10) + 25(10)^2}{10} = 675.00$$

$$\overline{C}(11) = \frac{2500 + 175(11) + 25(11)^2}{11} = 677.27$$

$$\overline{C}(12) = \frac{2500 + 175(12) + 25(12)^2}{12} = 683.33$$

Thus, it appears that the average cost per year is a minimum at $n = 10$ years; at 10 years, the average minimum cost is $675.00 per year.

(D) 10 years; $675.00 per year

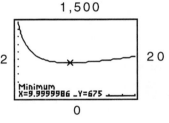

61. (A) $\overline{C}(x) = \dfrac{0.00048(x - 500)^3 + 60,000}{x}$

(B)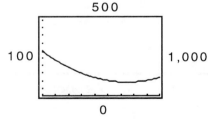

(C) The caseload which yields the minimum average cost per case is 750 cases per month. At 750 cases per month, the average cost per case is $90.

63. (A) Linear regression model for Table 3.

Quadratic regression model for Table 4.

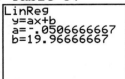

```
LinReg
y=ax+b
a=-.0506666667
b=19.96666667
```

```
QuadReg
y=ax²+bx+c
a=2.4444444E-4
b=-.0065555556
c=2.086111111
```

(B) Graphing the two models, we have

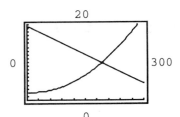

The equilibrium price is $\bar{p}$ = \$10.09 and the equilibrium quantity is $\bar{x}$ = 195.

65. (A) Cubic regression model

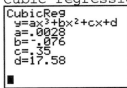

(B) Per capita consumption of ice cream in 2010: $y(30) \approx 35.3$.

67. (A) $v(x) = \dfrac{26 + 0.06x}{x} = \dfrac{\dfrac{26}{x} + 0.06}{1}$

As x increases, the numerator tends to 0.06 and the denominator is 1. Therefore, $v(x)$ approaches 0.06 centimeters per second as x increases.

(B)

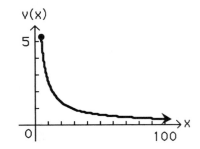

69. (A) Cubic regression model

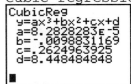

(B) For 2010: $y(50) \approx 7.2$

EXERCISE 2-2

Things to remember:

<u>1</u>. EXPONENTIAL FUNCTION

The equation

$f(x) = b^x$, $b > 0$, $b \neq 1$

defines an EXPONENTIAL FUNCTION for each different constant b, called the BASE. The DOMAIN of f is all real numbers, and the RANGE of f is the set of positive real numbers.

<u>2</u>. BASIC PROPERTIES OF THE GRAPH OF $f(x) = b^x$, $b > 0$, $b \neq 1$

a. All graphs pass through (0,1); b^0 = 1 for any base b.
b. All graphs are continuous curves; there are no holes or jumps.
c. The x-axis is a horizontal asymptote.

d.   If $b > 1$, then b^x increases as x increases.

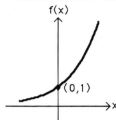

Graph of $f(x) = b^x$, $b > 1$

e.   If $0 < b < 1$, then b^x decreases as x increases.

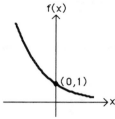

Graph of $f(x) = b^x$, $0 < b < 1$

3.   PROPERTIES OF EXPONENTIAL FUNCTIONS

For a, $b > 0$, $a \neq 1$, $b \neq 1$, and x, y real numbers:

a.   EXPONENT LAWS

   (i) $a^x a^y = a^{x+y}$ (iv) $(ab)^x = a^x b^x$

   (ii) $\dfrac{a^x}{a^y} = a^{x-y}$ (v) $\left(\dfrac{a}{b}\right)^x = \dfrac{a^x}{b^x}$

   (iii) $(a^x)^y = a^{xy}$

b. $a^x = a^y$ if and only if $x = y$.

c.   For $x \neq 0$, $a^x = b^x$ if and only if $a = b$.

4.   EXPONENTIAL FUNCTION WITH BASE $e = 2.71828...$

Exponential functions with base e and base $1/e$ are respectively defined by $y = e^x$ and $y = e^{-x}$.

   Domain: $(-\infty, \infty)$

   Range: $(0, \infty)$

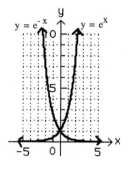

5.   COMPOUND INTEREST

If a principal P (present value) is invested at an annual rate r (expressed as a decimal) compounded m times per year, then the amount A (future value) in the account at the end of t years is given by:

$$A = P\left(1 + \frac{r}{m}\right)^{mt}$$

6. CONTINUOUS COMPOUND INTEREST FORMULA

If a principal P (present value) is invested at an annual rate r (expressed as a decimal) compounded continuously, then the amount A (future value) in the account at the end of t years is given by

$$A = Pe^{rt}$$

7. SUMMARY OF INTEREST FORMULAS

(a) $A = P(1 + rt)$ Simple interest

(b) $A = P\left(1 + \dfrac{r}{m}\right)^{mt}$ Compound interest

(c) $A = Pe^{rt}$ Continuous compound interest

---

1. (A) k (B) g (C) h (D) f

3. $y = 5^x, \ -2 \leq x \leq 2$

x	y
-2	$\frac{1}{25}$
-1	$\frac{1}{5}$
0	1
1	5
2	25

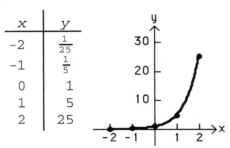

5. $y = \left(\dfrac{1}{5}\right)^x = 5^{-x}, \ -2 \leq x \leq 2$

x	y
-2	25
-1	5
0	1
1	$\frac{1}{5}$
2	$\frac{1}{25}$

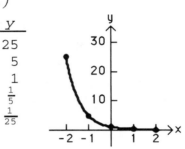

7. $f(x) = -5^x, \ -2 \leq x \leq 2$

x	$f(x)$
-2	$-\frac{1}{25}$
-1	$-\frac{1}{5}$
0	-1
1	-5
2	-25

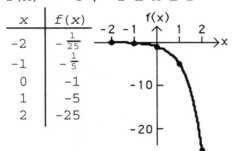

9. $y = -e^{-x}, \ -3 \leq x \leq 3$

x	y
-3	≈ -20
-2	≈ -7.4
-1	≈ -2.7
0	-1
1	≈ -0.4
2	≈ -0.1
3	≈ -0.05

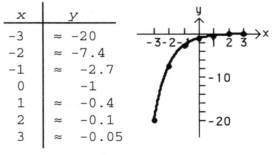

11. $y = 100e^{0.1x}, \ -5 \leq x \leq 5$

x	y
-5	≈ 60
-3	≈ 74
-1	≈ 90
0	100
1	≈ 111
3	≈ 135
5	≈ 165

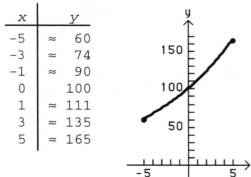

13. $g(t) = 10e^{-0.2t}, \ -5 \leq t \leq 5$

g	$g(t)$
-5	≈ 27.2
-3	≈ 18.2
-1	≈ 12.2
0	10
1	≈ 8.2
3	≈ 5.5
5	≈ 3.7

15. $(4^{3x})^{2y} = 4^{6xy}$

17. $\dfrac{e^{x-3}}{e^{x-4}} = e^{(x-3)-(x-4)} = e^{x-3-x+4} = e$

19. $(2e^{1.2t})^3 = 2^3 e^{3(1.2t)} = 8e^{3.6t}$

21. $g(x) = -f(x)$; the graph of g is the graph of f reflected in the x axis.

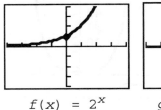   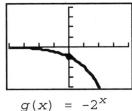

$f(x) = 2^x$ $g(x) = -2^x$

23. $g(x) = f(x+1)$; the graph of g is the graph of f shifted one unit to the left.

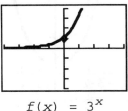   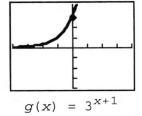

$f(x) = 3^x$ $g(x) = 3^{x+1}$

25. $g(x) = f(x) + 1$; the graph of g is the graph of f shifted one unit up.

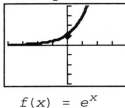   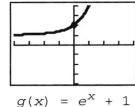

$f(x) = e^x$ $g(x) = e^x + 1$

27. $g(x) = 2f(x+2)$; the graph of g is the graph of f vertically expanded by a factor of 2 and shifted to the left 2 units.

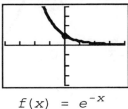   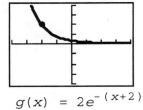

$f(x) = e^{-x}$ $g(x) = 2e^{-(x+2)}$

29. (A) $y = f(x) - 1$ (B) $y = f(x + 2)$ (C) $y = 3f(x) - 2$ (D) $y = 2 - f(x - 3)$

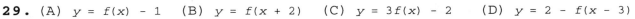

31. $f(t) = 2^{t/10}$, $-30 \le t \le 30$

t	$f(t)$
-30	$\frac{1}{8}$
-20	$\frac{1}{4}$
-10	$\frac{1}{2}$
0	1
10	2
20	4
30	8

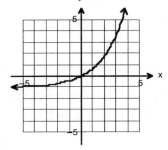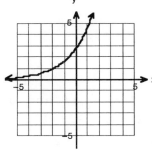

33. $y = -3 + e^{1+x}$, $-4 \le x \le 2$

x	y
-4	≈ -3
-2	≈ -2.6
-1	-2
0	≈ -0.3
1	≈ 4.4
2	≈ 17.1

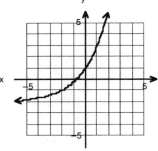

35. $y = e^{|x|}$, $-3 \le x \le 3$

x	y
-3	≈ 20.1
-1	≈ 2.7
0	1
1	≈ 2.7
3	≈ 20.1

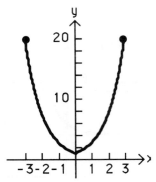

37. $C(x) = \dfrac{e^x + e^{-x}}{2}$, $-5 \le x \le 5$

x	C(x)
-5	≈ 74
-3	≈ 10
0	1
3	≈ 10
5	≈ 74

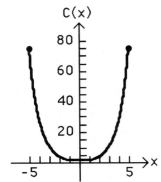

39. $y = e^{-x^2}$, $-3 \le x \le 3$

x	y
-3	0.0001
-2	0.0183
-1	0.3679
0	1
1	0.3679
2	0.0183
3	0.0001

41. Solve

$$a^2 = a^{-2}$$
$$a^2 = \frac{1}{a^2}$$
$$a^4 = 1$$
$$a^4 - 1 = 0$$
$$(a^2 - 1)(a^2 + 1) = 0$$

$a^2 - 1 = 0$ implies $a = 1, -1$
$a^2 + 1 = 0$ has no real solutions

The exponential function property: $a^x = a^y$ if and only if $x = y$ assumes $a > 0$ and $a \ne 1$. Our solutions are $a = 1, -1$; $1^x = 1^y$ for all real numbers x, y, $(-1)^x = (-1)^y$ for all even integers.

43. $10^{2-3x} = 10^{5x-6}$ implies (see <u>3</u>b)
$$2 - 3x = 5x - 6$$
$$-8x = -8$$
$$x = 1$$

45. $4^{5x-x^2} = 4^{-6}$ implies
$$5x - x^2 = -6$$
or $\quad -x^2 + 5x + 6 = 0$
$$x^2 - 5x - 6 = 0$$
$$(x - 6)(x + 1) = 0$$
$$x = 6, -1$$

47. $5^3 = (x + 2)^3$ implies (by property <u>3</u>c)
$$5 = x + 2$$
Thus, $x = 3$.

49. $(x - 3)e^x = 0$

$\quad\quad x - 3 = 0 \quad$ (since $e^x \neq 0$)

$\quad\quad\quad\quad x = 3$

51. $3xe^{-x} + x^2 e^{-x} = 0$

$\quad\quad e^{-x}(3x + x^2) = 0$

$\quad\quad\quad\quad 3x + x^2 = 0 \quad$ (since $e^{-x} \neq 0$)

$\quad\quad\quad\quad x(3 + x) = 0$

$\quad\quad\quad\quad\quad\quad x = 0, \; -3$

53. $h(x) = x2^x, \; -5 \leq x \leq 0$

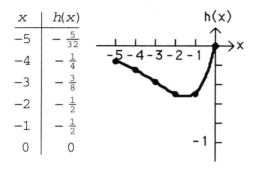

x	$h(x)$
-5	$-\frac{5}{32}$
-4	$-\frac{1}{4}$
-3	$-\frac{3}{8}$
-2	$-\frac{1}{2}$
-1	$-\frac{1}{2}$
0	0

55. $N = \dfrac{100}{1 + e^{-t}}, \; 0 \leq t \leq 5$

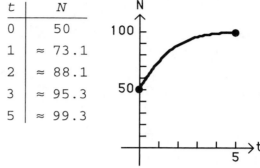

t	N
0	50
1	≈ 73.1
2	≈ 88.1
3	≈ 95.3
5	≈ 99.3

57. $f(x) = 4^x - 7$

$\quad$ Solve $4^x - 7 = 0$

$\quad\quad\quad\quad x \approx 1.40$

59. $f(x) = 2 + 3x + 10^x$

$\quad$ Solve $2 + 3x + 10^x = 0$

$\quad\quad\quad\quad x \approx -0.73$

61. $A = P\left(1 + \dfrac{r}{m}\right)^{mt}$, we have:

(A) $P = 2,500, \; r = 0.07, \; m = 4, \; t = \dfrac{3}{4}$

$\quad A = 2,500\left(1 + \dfrac{0.07}{4}\right)^{4 \cdot 3/4} = 2,500(1 + 0.0175)^3 = 2,633.56$

$\quad$ Thus, $A = \$2,633.56$.

(B) $A = 2,500\left(1 + \dfrac{0.07}{4}\right)^{4 \cdot 15} = 2,500(1 + 0.0175)^{60} = 7079.54$

$\quad$ Thus, $A = \$7,079.54$.

63. With $P = 7,500$ and $r = 0.0835$, we have:

$\quad A = 7,500e^{0.0835t}$

(A) $A = 7,500e^{(0.0835)5.5} = 7,500e^{0.45925} \approx 11,871.65$

$\quad\quad$ Thus, there will be $\$11,871.65$ in the account after 5.5 years.

(B) $A = 7,500e^{(0.0835)12} = 7,500e^{1.002} \approx 20,427.93$

$\quad\quad$ Thus, there will be $\$20,427.93$ in the account after 12 years.

65. Using $A = P\left(1 + \dfrac{r}{m}\right)^{mt}$, we have

$\quad A = 15,000, \; r = 0.0675, \; m = 52, \; t = 5$

$\quad$ Thus, $15,000 = P\left(1 + \dfrac{0.0675}{52}\right)^{52(5)} = P(1 + 0.001298)^{260} \approx P(1.4011)$

$\quad$ and $P = \dfrac{15,000}{1.4011} \approx 10,705.6229$.

$\quad$ Therefore, $P = \$10,706$ to the nearest dollar.

67. For parts (A) and (B), use $A = P\left(1 + \dfrac{r}{m}\right)^{mt}$; $P = 10{,}000$, $t = 1$.

(A) Stonebridge Bank: $r = 0.0215$, $m = 12$

$$A = 10{,}000\left(1 + \frac{0.0215}{12}\right)^{12(1)} \approx 10{,}000(1 + 0.001792)^{12} = \$10{,}217.13$$

(B) Deep Green Bank: $r = 0.0199$, $m = 365$

$$A = 10{,}000\left(1 + \frac{0.0199}{365}\right)^{365(1)} \approx 10{,}000(1 + 0.000055)^{365} = \$10{,}200.99$$

(C) Provident Bank: Use $A = Pe^{rt}$, $r = 0.0195$, $t = 1$.
$$A = 10{,}000e^{0.0195(1)} = 10{,}000e^{0.0195} = \$10{,}196.91$$

69. In $A = Pe^{rt}$, we are given $A = 50{,}000$, $r = 0.08$ and $t = 5.5$. Thus:

$$50{,}000 = Pe^{0.08(5.5)} = Pe^{0.44} \text{ and}$$
$$P = \frac{50{,}000}{e^{0.44}} \approx 32{,}201.82$$

You should be willing to pay $\$32{,}201.82$ for the note.

71. Given $N = 2(1 - e^{-0.037t})$, $0 \le t \le 50$

t	N
0	0
10	≈ 0.62
30	≈ 1.34
50	≈ 1.69

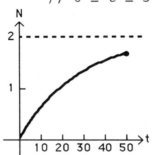

N approaches 2 as t increases without bound.

73. (A) Exponential regression model

```
ExpReg
y=a*b^x
a=643.4738171
b=1.112896033
■
```

$y(20) \approx 5465.410$ thousand or $y(20) \approx \$5{,}465{,}410$.

(B) $y(10) \approx 1875.326$ thousand or $y(10) \approx 1{,}875{,}326$. Inclusion of the Year 2000 data would increase the estimated average salary in 2010 since the actual Year 2000 average salary is higher than that estimated by the model. Inclusion of the Year 2000 data gives an average salary of $\$5{,}652{,}000$ in 2010.

75. Given $I = I_0 e^{-0.23d}$

(A) $I = I_0 e^{-0.23(10)} = I_0 e^{-2.3} \approx I_0(0.10)$

Thus, about 10% of the surface light will reach a depth of 10 feet.

(B) $I = I_0 e^{-0.23(20)} = I_0 e^{-4.6} \approx I_0(0.010)$

Thus, about 1% of the surface light will reach a depth of 20 feet.

77. (A) Model: $N(t) = 60e^{0.08t}$

(B) Infected prior to 1999: $t = -3$

$N(-3) = 60e^{0.08(-3)} = 60e^{-0.24} \approx 47$ million

Infected prior to 2010: $t = 8$

$N(8) = 60e^{0.08(8)} = 60e^{0.64} \approx 114$ million

(C)

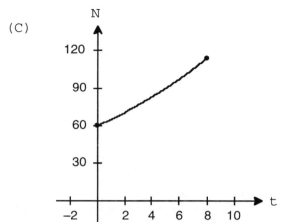

Years since 2002

79. (A) Model: $P(t) = 6.2e^{0.0125t}$

(B) In the year 2010, $t = 8$;

$P(8) = 6.2e^{0.0125(8)}$

$= 6.2e^{0.1} \approx 6.9$ billion

In the year 2030, $t = 28$;

$P(28) = 6.2e^{0.0125(28)}$

$= 6.2e^{0.35}$

≈ 8.8 billion

(C)

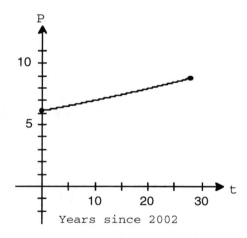

Years since 2002

81. (A) Exponential regression model

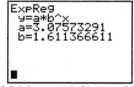

In 2010, $y(16) \approx 6354.164$.
To the nearest million, the number of
hosts in 2010 will be 6,354,000,000.

(B) The model implies
that the number of
internet hosts in
2010 will be only
slightly less than
the world
population in 2010.

EXERCISE 2-3

Things to remember:

<u>1</u>.   ONE-TO-ONE FUNCTIONS

A function f is said to be ONE-TO-ONE if each range value
corresponds to exactly one domain value.

2. INVERSE OF A FUNCTION

If f is a one-to-one function, then the INVERSE of f is the function formed by interchanging the independent and dependent variables for f. Thus, if (a, b) is a point on the graph of f, then (b, a) is a point on the graph of the inverse of f.

Note: If f is not one-to-one, then f DOES NOT HAVE AN INVERSE.

3. LOGARITHMIC FUNCTIONS

The inverse of an exponential function is called a LOGARITHMIC FUNCTION. For $b > 0$ and $b \neq 1$,

Logarithmic form		Exponential form
$y = \log_b x$	is equivalent to	$x = b^y$

The LOG TO THE BASE b OF x is the exponent to which b must be raised to obtain x. [Remember: A logarithm is an exponent.] The DOMAIN of the logarithmic function is the range of the corresponding exponential function, and the RANGE of the logarithmic function is the domain of the corresponding exponential function. Typical graphs of an exponential function and its inverse, a logarithmic function, for $b > 1$, are shown in the figure below:

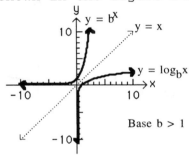

Base b > 1

4. PROPERTIES OF LOGARITHMIC FUNCTIONS

If b, M, and N are positive real numbers, $b \neq 1$, and p and x are real numbers, then:

a. $\log_b 1 = 0$ e. $\log_b MN = \log_b M + \log_b N$

b. $\log_b b = 1$ f. $\log_b \dfrac{M}{N} = \log_b M - \log_b N$

c. $\log_b b^x = x$ g. $\log_b M^p = p \log_b M$

d. $b^{\log_b x} = x,\ x > 0$ h. $\log_b M = \log_b N$ if and only if $M = N$

5. LOGARITHMIC NOTATION; LOGARITHMIC-EXPONENTIAL RELATIONSHIPS

Common logarithm $\log x = \log_{10} x$
Natural logarithm $\ln x = \log_e x$

$\log x = y$ is equivalent to $x = 10^y$
$\ln x = y$ is equivalent to $x = e^y$

1. $27 = 3^3$ (using $\underline{3}$) **3.** $1 = 10^0$ **5.** $8 = 4^{3/2}$

7. $\log_7 49 = 2$ **9.** $\log_4 8 = \dfrac{3}{2}$ **11.** $\log_b A = u$

13. $\log_{10} 1 = y$ is equivalent to $10^y = 1$; $y = 0$.

15. $\log_e e = y$ is equivalent to $e^y = e$; $y = 1$.

17. $\log_{0.2} 0.2 = y$ is equivalent to $(0.2)^y = 0.2$; $y = 1$.

19. $\log_{10} 10^3 = 3$ **21.** $\log_2 2^{-3} = -3$ **23.** $\log_{10} 1{,}000 = \log_{10} 10^3 = 3$
(using $\underline{2}$a)

25. $\log_b \dfrac{P}{Q} = \log_b P - \log_b Q$ **27.** $\log_b L^5 = 5\ \log_b L$

29. $3^{p\,\log_3 q} = 3^{\log_3 q^p} = q^p$. (using $\underline{4}$g and $\underline{4}$d)

31. $\log_3 x = 2$
$x = 3^2$
$x = 9$

33. $\log_7 49 = y$
$\log_7 7^2 = y$
$2 = y$
Thus, $y = 2$.

35. $\log_b 10^{-4} = -4$
$10^{-4} = b^{-4}$
This equality implies $b = 10$ (since the exponents are the same).

37. $\log_4 x = \dfrac{1}{2}$
$x = 4^{1/2}$
$x = 2$

39. $\log_{1/3} 9 = y$
$9 = \left(\dfrac{1}{3}\right)^y$
$3^2 = (3^{-1})^y$
$3^2 = 3^{-y}$

This inequality implies that $2 = -y$ or $y = -2$.

41. $\log_b 1{,}000 = \dfrac{3}{2}$
$\log_b 10^3 = \dfrac{3}{2}$
$3\ \log_b 10 = \dfrac{3}{2}$
$\log_b 10 = \dfrac{1}{2}$
$10 = b^{1/2}$
Square both sides:
$100 = b$, i.e., $b = 100$.

43. False; counterexample: $y = x^2$.

45. True; if g is the inverse of f, then f is the inverse of g so g must be one-to-one.

47. True; if $y = 2x$, then $x = 2y$ implies $y = \dfrac{x}{2}$.

49. False; if $0 < b < 1$, then $\log_b x$ is decreasing.

51. False; $f(x) = \ln x$ is one-to-one; domain of $f = (0,\ \infty)$ range of $f = (-\infty,\ \infty)$.

53. $\log_b x = \dfrac{2}{3}\log_b 8 + \dfrac{1}{2}\log_b 9 - \log_b 6 = \log_b 8^{2/3} + \log_b 9^{1/2} - \log_b 6$

$\qquad = \log_b 4 + \log_b 3 - \log_b 6 = \log_b \dfrac{4 \cdot 3}{6}$

$\log_b x = \log_b 2$

$\qquad x = 2$

55. $\log_b x = \dfrac{3}{2}\log_b 4 - \dfrac{2}{3}\log_b 8 + 2\log_b 2 = \log_b 4^{3/2} - \log_b 8^{2/3} + \log_b 2^2$

$\qquad = \log_b 8 - \log_b 4 + \log_b 4 = \log_b 8$

$\log_b x = \log_b 8$

$\qquad x = 8$

57. $\log_b x + \log_b(x - 4) = \log_b 21$

$\qquad \log_b x(x - 4) = \log_b 21$

Therefore, $x(x - 4) = 21$

$\qquad x^2 - 4x - 21 = 0$

$\qquad (x - 7)(x + 3) = 0$

Thus, $x = 7$.

[Note: $x = -3$ is not a solution since $\log_b(-3)$ is not defined.]

59. $\log_{10}(x - 1) - \log_{10}(x + 1) = 1$

$\qquad \log_{10}\left(\dfrac{x - 1}{x + 1}\right) = 1$

Therefore, $\dfrac{x - 1}{x + 1} = 10^1 = 10$

$\qquad x - 1 = 10(x + 1)$

$\qquad x - 1 = 10x + 10$

$\qquad -9x = 11$

$\qquad x = -\dfrac{11}{9}$

There is *no solution*, since

$\log_{10}\left(-\dfrac{11}{9} - 1\right) = \log_{10}\left(-\dfrac{20}{9}\right)$

is not defined. Similarly,

$\log_{10}\left(-\dfrac{11}{9} + 1\right) = \log_{10}\left(-\dfrac{2}{9}\right)$

is not defined.

61. $y = \log_2(x - 2)$

$\quad x - 2 = 2^y$

$\quad x = 2^y + 2$

x	y
$\frac{9}{4}$	-2
$\frac{5}{2}$	-1
3	0
4	1
6	2
18	4

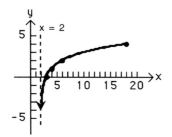

63. The graph of $y = \log_2(x - 2)$ is the graph of $y = \log_2 x$ shifted to the right 2 units.

65. Since logarithmic functions are defined only for positive "inputs", we must have $x + 1 > 0$ or $x > -1$; domain: $(-1, \infty)$. The range of $y = 1 + \ln(x + 1)$ is the set of all real numbers.

67. (A) 3.54743
  (B) -2.16032
  (C) 5.62629
  (D) -3.19704

69. (A) log x = 1.1285
       x = 13.4431
  (B) log x = -2.0497
       x = 0.0089
  (C) ln x = 2.7763
       x = 16.0595
  (D) ln x = -1.8879
       x = 0.1514

71. 10^x = 12 (Take common logarithms of both sides)
   log 10^x = log 12 ≈ 1.0792
       x ≈ 1.0792 (log 10^x = x log 10 = x; log 10 = 1)

73. e^x = 4.304 (Take natural logarithms of both sides)
   ln e^x = ln 4.304 ≈ 1.4595
       x ≈ 1.4595 (ln e^x = x ln e = x; ln e = 1)

75. 1.03^x = 2.475 (Take either common or natural logarithms of both sides;
               we use common logarithms)
   log$(1.03)^x$ = log 2.475
       x = $\dfrac{\log 2.475}{\log 1.03}$ ≈ 30.6589

77. 1.005^{12t} = 3 (Take either common or natural logarithms of both sides;
               here we'll use natural logarithms.)
   ln 1.005^{12t} = ln 3
       $12t$ = $\dfrac{\ln 3}{\ln 1.005}$ ≈ 220.2713
         t = 18.3559

79. y = ln x, x > 0

x	y
0.5	≈ -0.69
1	0
2	≈ 0.69
4	≈ 1.39
5	≈ 1.61

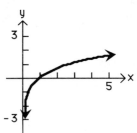

increasing (0, ∞)

81. y = |ln x|, x > 0

x	y
0.5	≈ 0.69
1	0
2	≈ 0.69
4	≈ 1.39
5	≈ 1.6

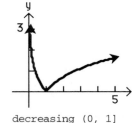

decreasing (0, 1]
increasing [1, ∞)

83. $y = 2 \ln(x + 2)$, $x > -2$

x	y
-1.5	$\approx$ -1.39
-1	0
0	$\approx$ 1.39
1	$\approx$ 2.2
5	$\approx$ 3.89
10	$\approx$ 4.61

increasing $(-2, \infty)$

85. $y = 4 \ln x - 3$, $x > 0$

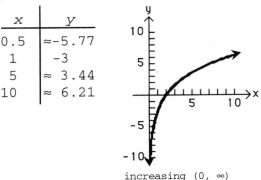

x	y
0.5	$\approx$ -5.77
1	-3
5	$\approx$ 3.44
10	$\approx$ 6.21

increasing $(0, \infty)$

87. For any number b, $b > 0$, $b \neq 1$, $\log_b 1 = y$ is equivalent to $b^y = 1$ which implies $y = 0$. Thus, $\log_b 1 = 0$ for any permissible base b.

89. $\log_{10} y - \log_{10} c = 0.8x$

$\log_{10} \dfrac{y}{c} = 0.8x$

Therefore, $\dfrac{y}{c} = 10^{0.8x}$ (using $\underline{1}$)

and $y = c \cdot 10^{0.8x}$.

91.

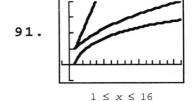

$1 \leq x \leq 16$

A function f is "larger than" a function g on an interval $[a, b]$ if $f(x) > g(x)$ for $a \leq x \leq b$. $r(x) > q(x) > p(x)$ for $1 \leq x \leq 16$, that is $x > \sqrt{x} > \ln x$ for $1 < x \leq 16$

93. From the compound interest formula $A = P(1 + r)^t$, we have:
$2P = P(1 + 0.2136)^t$ or $(1.2136)^t = 2$
Take the natural log of both sides of this equation:
$\ln(1.2136)^t = \ln 2$ [Note: the common log could have been used instead of the natural log.]

$t \ln(1.2136) = \ln 2$

$t = \dfrac{\ln 2}{\ln 1.2136} \approx \dfrac{0.69135}{0.19359} = 3.58 \approx 4$ years

95. $A = P\left(1 + \dfrac{r}{m}\right)^{mt}$, $r = 0.06$, $m = 4$, $P = 1000$, $A = 1800$.

$$1800 = 1000\left(1 + \frac{0.06}{4}\right)^{4t} = 1000(1.015)^{4t}$$

$$(1.015)^{4t} = \frac{1800}{1000} = 1.8$$

$$4t \ln(1.015) = \ln(1.8)$$

$$t = \frac{\ln(1.8)}{4 \ln(1.015)} \approx 9.87$$

$1000 at 6% compounded quarterly will grow to $1800 in 9.87 years.
$A = Pe^{rt}$, $r = 0.06$, $P = 1000$, $A = 1800$

$$1000e^{0.06t} = 1800$$

$$e^{0.06t} = 1.8$$

$$0.06t = \ln 1.8$$

$$t = \frac{\ln 1.8}{0.06} \approx 9.80$$

$1000 at 6% compounded continuously will grow to $1800 in 9.80 years.

97. $A = Pe^{rt}$, $P = 20,000$, $A = 30,000$, $t = 6$

$$30,000 = 20,000e^{6r}$$

$$e^{6r} = 1.5$$

$$6r = \ln 1.5$$

$$r = \frac{\ln 1.5}{6} \approx 0.06758$$

$20,000 invested at an annual rate of 6.758% compounded continuously will yield $30,000 after 6 years.

99. (A) Logarithmic regression model, Table 1:

```
LnReg
  y=a+blnx
  a=256.4659159
  b=-24.03812068
```

To estimate the demand at a price level of $50, we solve the equation
$a + b \ln x = 50$
for x. The result is $x \approx 5.373$ screwdrivers per month.

(B) Logarithmic regression model, Table 2:

```
LnReg
  y=a+blnx
  a=-127.8085281
  b=20.01315349
```

To estimate the supply at a price level of $50, we solve
$a + b \ln x = 50$
for x. The result is $x \approx 7,220$ screwdrivers per month.

(C) The condition is not stable, the price is likely to decrease since the demand at a price level of $50 is much lower than the supply at this level.

101. $I = I_0 10^{N/10}$

Take the common log of both sides of this equation. Then:

$\log I = \log(I_0 10^{N/10}) = \log I_0 + \log 10^{N/10}$

$\qquad = \log I_0 + \dfrac{N}{10} \log 10 = \log I_0 + \dfrac{N}{10}$ (since $\log 10 = 1$)

So, $\dfrac{N}{10} = \log I - \log I_0 = \log\left(\dfrac{I}{I_0}\right)$ and $N = 10 \log\left(\dfrac{I}{I_0}\right)$.

103. Logarithmic regression model, Table 3.

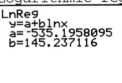

The yield in 2010: $y(110) \approx 147.5$ bushels/acre.

105. Assuming that the current population is 6.2 billion and that the growth rate is 1.25% compounded continuously, the population after t years will be

$$P(t) = 6.2e^{0.0125t}$$

Given that there are $1.68 \times 10^{14} = 168{,}000$ billion square yards of land, solve

$$6.2e^{0.0125t} = 168{,}000$$

for t:

$$e^{0.0125t} \approx 27{,}097$$

$$0.0125t = \ln(27{,}097) \approx 10.2072$$

$$t \approx 817$$

It will take approximately 817 years.

CHAPTER 2 REVIEW

1. $u = e^v$
  $v = \ln u$ (2-3)

2. $x = 10^y$
  $y = \log x$ (2-3)

3. $\operatorname{Ln} M = N$
  $M = e^N$ (2-3)

4. $\log u = v$
  $u = 10^v$ (2-3)

5. $\dfrac{5^{x+4}}{5^{4-x}} = 5^{x+4-(4-x)} = 5^{2x}$ (2-2)

6. $\left(\dfrac{e^u}{e^{-u}}\right)^u = (e^{u+u})^u = (e^{2u})^u = e^{2u^2}$ (2-2)

7. $\log_3 x = 2$
  $x = 3^2$
  $x = 9$ (2-3)

8. $\log_x 36 = 2$
  $x^2 = 36$
  $x = 6$ (2-3)

9. $\log_2 16 = x$
  $2^x = 16$
  $x = 4$ (2-3)

10. $10^x = 143.7$
  $x = \log 143.7$
  $x \approx 2.157$ (2-3)

11. $e^x = 503{,}000$
  $x = \ln 503{,}000 \approx 13.128$ (2-3)

12. $\log x = 3.105$
  $x = 10^{3.105} \approx 1273.503$ (2-3)

13. $\ln x = -1.147$

$x = e^{-1.147} \approx 0.318$ (2-3)

14. (A) 2   (B) 3   (C) positive   (2-1)

15. (A) 3   (B) 4   (C) negative   (2-1)

16. $f(x) = \dfrac{x + 4}{x - 2}$

   (A) *Intercepts:*

       x intercepts: $f(x) = 0$ only if $x + 4 = 0$ or $x = -4$.

                            The x intercept is -4.

       y intercepts: $f(0) = \dfrac{0 + 4}{0 - 2} = -2$

                            The y intercept is -2.

   (B) *Domain:* The denominator is 0 at $x = 2$. Thus, the domain is the set of all real numbers except 2.

   (C) *Asymptotes:*

       Vertical asymptotes: $f(x) = \dfrac{x + 4}{x - 2}$

                           The denominator is 0 at $x = 2$. Therefore, the line $x = 2$ is a vertical asymptote.

       Horizontal asymptotes: $f(x) = \dfrac{x + 4}{x - 2} = \dfrac{1 + \dfrac{4}{x}}{1 - \dfrac{2}{x}}$

                           As x increases or decreases without bound, the numerator tends to 1 and the denominator tends to 1. Therefore, the line $y = 1$ is a horizontal asymptote.

   (D)

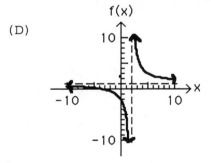

   (E)

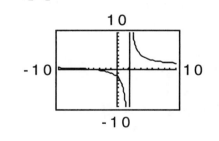

                                                                                 (2-1)

17. $f(x) = \dfrac{3x - 4}{2 + x}$

   (A) *Intercepts:*

       x intercepts: $f(x) = 0$ only if $3x - 4 = 0$ or $x = \dfrac{4}{3}$.

                            The x intercept is $\dfrac{4}{3}$.

       y intercepts: $f(0) = \dfrac{3 \cdot 0 - 4}{2 + 0} = -2$

                            The y intercept is -2.

(B) *Domain:* The denominator is 0 at $x = -2$. Thus, the domain is the set of all real numbers except -2.

(C) *Asymptotes:*

Vertical asymptotes: $f(x) = \dfrac{3x - 4}{x + 2}$

The denominator is 0 at $x = -2$. Therefore, the line $x = -2$ is a vertical asymptote.

Horizontal asymptotes: $f(x) = \dfrac{3x - 4}{x + 2} = \dfrac{3 - \dfrac{4}{x}}{1 + \dfrac{2}{x}}$

As x increases or decreases without bound, the numerator tends to 3 and the denominator tends to 1. Therefore, the line $y = 3$ is a horizontal asymptote.

(D)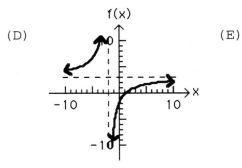

(E)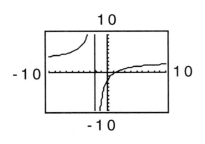

(2-1)

---

18. $\log(x + 5) = \log(2x - 3)$
$$x + 5 = 2x - 3$$
$$-x = -8$$
$$x = 8 \qquad (2\text{-}3)$$

19. $2 \ln(x - 1) = \ln(x^2 - 5)$
$$\ln(x - 1)^2 = \ln(x^2 - 5)$$
$$(x - 1)^2 = x^2 - 5$$
$$x^2 - 2x + 1 = x^2 - 5$$
$$-2x = -6$$
$$x = 3 \qquad (2\text{-}3)$$

20.
$$9^{x-1} = 3^{1+x}$$
$$(3^2)^{x-1} = 3^{1+x}$$
$$3^{2x-2} = 3^{1+x}$$
$$2x - 2 = 1 + x$$
$$x = 3 \qquad (2\text{-}2)$$

21.
$$e^{2x} = e^{x^2-3}$$
$$2x = x^2 - 3$$
$$x^2 - 2x - 3 = 0$$
$$(x - 3)(x + 1) = 0$$
$$x = 3, -1 \qquad (2\text{-}2)$$

22. $2x^2 e^x = 3xe^x$
$$2x^2 = 3x \text{ (divide both sides by } e^x)$$
$$2x^2 - 3x = 0$$
$$x(2x - 3) = 0$$
$$x = 0, \frac{3}{2} \qquad (2\text{-}2)$$

23. $\log_{1/3} 9 = x$
$$\left(\frac{1}{3}\right)^x = 9$$
$$\frac{1}{3^x} = 9$$
$$3^x = \frac{1}{9}$$
$$x = -2$$
$$(2\text{-}3)$$

24. $\log_x 8 = -3$
$$x^{-3} = 8$$
$$\frac{1}{x^3} = 8$$
$$x^3 = \frac{1}{8}$$
$$x = \frac{1}{2} \qquad (2\text{-}3)$$

25. $\log_9 x = \dfrac{3}{2}$

$9^{3/2} = x$

$x = 27$ (2-3)

26. $x = 3(e^{1.49}) \approx 13.3113$ (2-3)

27. $x = 230(10^{-0.161}) \approx 158.7552$ (2-3)

28. $\log x = -2.0144$

$x \approx 0.0097$ (2-3)

29. $\text{Ln } x = 0.3618$

$x \approx 1.4359$ (2-3)

30. $35 = 7(3^x)$

$3^x = 5$

$\ln 3^x = \ln 5$

$x \ln 3 = \ln 5$

$x = \dfrac{\ln 5}{\ln 3} \approx 1.4650$ (2-3)

31. $0.01 = e^{-0.05x}$

$\ln(0.01) = \ln(e^{-0.05x}) = -0.05x$

Thus, $x = \dfrac{\ln(0.01)}{-0.05} \approx 92.1034$ (2-3)

32. $8,000 = 4,000(1.08)^x$

$(1.08)^x = 2$

$\ln(1.08)^x = \ln 2$

$x \ln 1.08 = \ln 2$

$x = \dfrac{\ln 2}{\ln 1.08} \approx 9.0065$

    (2-3)

33. $5^{2x-3} = 7.08$

$\ln(5^{2x-3}) = \ln 7.08$

$(2x - 3)\ln 5 = \ln 7.08$

$2x \ln 5 - 3 \ln 5 = \ln 7.08$

$x = \dfrac{\ln 7.08 + 3 \ln 5}{2 \ln 5}$

$= \dfrac{\ln 7.08 + \ln 5^3}{2 \ln 5}$

$= \dfrac{\ln[7.08(125)]}{2 \ln 5} \approx 2.1081$ (2-3)

34. $x = \log_2 7 = \dfrac{\log 7}{\log 2} \approx 2.8074$

or $x = \log_2 7 = \dfrac{\ln 7}{\ln 2} \approx 2.8074$

    (2-3)

35. $x = \log_{0.2} 5.321 = \dfrac{\log 5.321}{\log 0.2} \approx -1.0387$

or $x = \log_{0.2} 5.321 = \dfrac{\ln 5.321}{\ln 0.2} \approx -1.0387$

    (2-3)

36. The graph of $f(x) = x^4 - 4x^2 + 1 = x^4\left(1 - \dfrac{4}{x^2} + \dfrac{1}{x^4}\right)$ will "look like" the

graph of $y = x^4$; for large x, $f(x) \approx x^4$.   (2-1)

37. (A)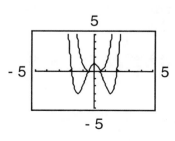

(B)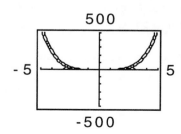

    (2-1)

38. $p(x) = 2x^4 - 11x^3 - 15x^2 - 14x - 16$

Let $q(x) = \frac{1}{2}p(x) = x^4 - \frac{11}{2}x^3 - \frac{15}{2}x^2 - 7x - 8$; $p(x)$ and $q(x)$ have the same zeros. If x is a zero of $q(x)$, then

$$|x| < 1 + \max \left\{ \left|-\frac{11}{2}\right|, \left|-\frac{15}{2}\right|, |-7|, |-8| \right\} = 1 + 8 = 9$$

Graph $p(x)$ on $[-9, 9]$.

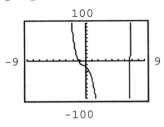

$p(x) = 0$ at $x \approx -1.14, 6.78$

(2-1)

39. $f(x) = e^x - 1$, $g(x) = \ln(x + 2)$

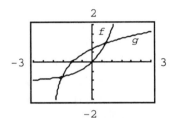

Points of intersection:
$(-1.54, -0.79)$, $(0.69, 0.99)$

(2-2, 2-3)

40. True; $p(x) = \frac{p(x)}{1}$ is a rational function for every polynomial p. (2-1)

41. False; $f(x) = \frac{1}{x} = x^{-1}$ is not a polynomial function. (2-1)

42. False; $f(x) = \frac{1}{x^2 + 1}$ has no vertical asymptotes. (2-1)

43. True: let $f(x) = b^x$, $(b > 0, b \neq 1)$, then the positive x-axis is a horizontal asymptote if $0 < b < 1$, and the negative x-axis is a horizontal asymptote if $b > 1$. (2-2)

44. True: let $f(x) = \log_b x$ $(b > 0, b \neq 1)$. If $0 < b < 1$, then the positive y-axis is a vertical asymptote; if $b > 1$, then the negative y-axis is a vertical asymptote. (2-3)

45. False; as x increases without bound, $\log_b x \to \infty$ if $b > 1$ and $\log_b x \to -\infty$ if $0 < b < 1$. (2-3)

46. True; $f(x) = \frac{x}{x - 1}$ has vertical asymptote $x = 1$ and horizontal asymptote $y = 1$. (2-1)

47. False; the domain of $f(x) = b^x$ $(b > 0,\ b \neq 1)$ is $(-\infty,\ \infty)$. (2-2)

48. $y = 2^{x-1}$, $-2 \leq x \leq 4$

x	y
-2	$\frac{1}{8}$
-1	$\frac{1}{4}$
0	$\frac{1}{2}$
1	1
2	2
4	8

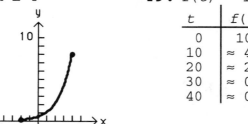

increasing [-2, 4]
(2-2)

49. $f(t) = 10e^{-0.08t}$, $t \geq 0$

t	$f(t)$
0	10
10	≈ 4.5
20	≈ 2
30	≈ 0.9
40	≈ 0.4

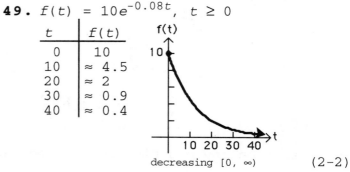

decreasing [0, ∞) (2-2)

50. $y = \ln(x + 1)$, $-1 < x \leq 10$

x	y
-0.5	≈ -0.7
0	0
4	≈ 1.6
8	≈ 2.2
10	≈ 2.4

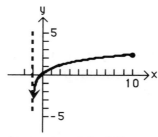

increasing (-1, 10] (2-2)

51. $\log 10^{\pi} = \pi \log 10 = \pi$ (see logarithm properties $\underline{4}$.b & g, Section 2-3)
$10^{\log \sqrt{2}} = y$ is equivalent to $\log y = \log \sqrt{2}$
which implies $y = \sqrt{2}$

Similarly, $\ln e^{\pi} = \pi \ln e = \pi$ (Section 2-3, $\underline{4}$.b & g) and $e^{\ln \sqrt{2}} = y$
implies $\ln y = \ln \sqrt{2}$ and $y = \sqrt{2}$. (2-3)

52. $\log x - \log 3 = \log 4 - \log(x + 4)$
$$\log \frac{x}{3} = \log \frac{4}{x + 4}$$
$$\frac{x}{3} = \frac{4}{x + 4}$$
$$x(x + 4) = 12$$
$$x^2 + 4x - 12 = 0$$
$$(x + 6)(x - 2) = 0$$
$$x = -6,\ 2$$

Since $\log(-6)$ and $\log(-2)$ are not defined, -6 is not a solution.
Therefore, the solution is $x = 2$. (2-3)

53. $\ln(2x - 2) - \ln(x - 1) = \ln x$
$$\ln\left(\frac{2x - 2}{x - 1}\right) = \ln x$$
$$\ln\left[\frac{2(x - 1)}{x - 1}\right] = \ln x$$
$$\ln 2 = \ln x$$
$$x = 2 \quad (2-3)$$

54. $\ln(x + 3) - \ln x = 2 \ln 2$
$$\ln\left(\frac{x + 3}{x}\right) = \ln(2^2)$$
$$\frac{x + 3}{x} = 4$$
$$x + 3 = 4x$$
$$3x = 3$$
$$x = 1 \quad (2-3)$$

55.
$$\log 3x^2 = 2 + \log 9x$$
$$\log 3x^2 - \log 9x = 2$$
$$\log\left(\frac{3x^2}{9x}\right) = 2$$
$$\log\left(\frac{x}{3}\right) = 2$$
$$\frac{x}{3} = 10^2 = 100$$
$$x = 300 \qquad (2\text{-}3)$$

56.
$$\ln y = -5t + \ln c$$
$$\ln y - \ln c = -5t$$
$$\ln\frac{y}{c} = -5t$$
$$\frac{y}{c} = e^{-5t}$$
$$y = ce^{-5t} \qquad (2\text{-}3)$$

57. Let x be *any* positive real number and suppose $\log_1 x = y$.   Then $1^y = x$.

But, $1^y = 1$, so $x = 1$, i.e., $x = 1$ for all positive real numbers x.
This is clearly impossible. (2-3)

58. $A = Pe^{rt}$
We let $P = 5,000$, $r = 0.0355$, and $t = 5$. Then:
$A = 5,000e^{0.0355(5)} = 5,000e^{0.1775} \approx 5,971.14$
After 5 years, the CD will be worth $5,971.14. (2-2)

59. $A = P\left(1 + \dfrac{r}{m}\right)^{mt}$
We let $P = 5,000$, $r = 0.0362$, $m = 365$, and $t = 5$.
Then:
$$A = 5,000\left(1 + \frac{0.0362}{365}\right)^{365(5)} \approx 5,992.02.$$
After 5 years, the CD will be worth $5,992.02. (2-2)

60. $A = Pe^{rt}$, $r = 0.0659$
Solve $3P = Pe^{0.0659t}$ *for* t:
$e^{0.0659t} = 3$
Take the natural log of both sides of this equation
$0.0659t = \ln 3$
$$t = \frac{\ln 3}{0.0659} \approx \frac{1.0968}{0.0659} \approx 16.7 \text{ years} \qquad (2\text{-}3)$$

61. $A = P\left(1 + \dfrac{r}{m}\right)^{mt}$, $r = 0.0658$, $m = 365$

Solve $2P = P\left(1 + \dfrac{0.0658}{365}\right)^{365t}$ for t

$(1.00018)^{365t} = 2$
Take the natural log of both sides of this equation
$\ln(1.00018)^{365t} = \ln 2$
$(365t)\ln(1.00018) = \ln 2$
$$t = \frac{\ln 2}{365 \ln(1.00018)} \approx \frac{0.69315}{0.06569} \approx 10.6 \text{ years} \qquad (2\text{-}3)$$

62. (A) Since $C(x)$ is a linear function of x, it can be written in the form
$$C(x) = mx + b$$
Since the fixed costs are $300, b = 300.
Also, $C(100) = 4300$, so
$$4300 = 100m + 300$$
$$100m = 4000$$
$$m = 40$$
Therefore,
$$C(x) = 40x + 300$$
and $$\overline{C}(x) = \frac{40x + 300}{x}$$

(B)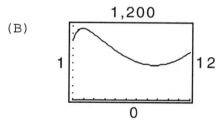

(C) $\overline{C}(x) = \dfrac{40x + 300}{x} = \dfrac{40 + \dfrac{300}{x}}{1}$, $5 \leq x \leq 200$

As x increases, the numerator tends to 40 and the denominator is 1. Therefore, $\overline{C}(x)$ approaches 40; The line $y = 40$ is a horizontal asymptote.

(D) $\overline{C}(x)$ approaches $40 per pair as production increases. (2-1)

63. (A) $\overline{C}(x) = \dfrac{C(x)}{x} = \dfrac{20x^3 - 360x^2 + 2,300x - 1,000}{x}$

(B)
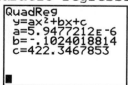

(C) From the graph, $\overline{C}(x)$ has a minimum at $x \approx 8.667$. Thus, the minimum average cost occurs when 8.667 thousand (8,667) cases are handled per year.
$$\overline{C}(8.667) = \frac{20(8.667)^3 - 360(8.667)^2 + 2300(8.667) - 1000}{8.667}$$
$$\approx \$567 \text{ per case}$$
(2-1)

64. (A) Quadratic regression model,

```
QuadReg
y=ax²+bx+c
a=5.9477212E⁻6
b=-.1024018814
c=422.3467853

■
```

To estimate the demand at price level of $180, we solve the equation
$$ax^2 + bx + c = 180$$
for x. The result is
$$x \approx 2,833 \text{ sets.}$$

(B) Linear regression model,
Table 2:

To estimate the supply at a price level of $180, we solve the equation
$$ax + b = 180$$
for x. The result is $x \approx 4{,}836$ sets.

(C) The condition is not stable; the price is likely to decrease since the supply at the price level of $180 exceeds the demand at this level.

(D) Equilibrium price: $131.59
Equilibrium quantity: 3,587 cookware sets
(2-1)

65. (A) Exponential regression model

```
ExpReg
y=a*b^x
a=4.917029881
b=1.346213923
```

(B) In 2006, $y(16) \approx 572{,}000{,}000$ subscribers which is much greater than the analysts' estimate.

In 2010, $y(20) \approx 1{,}879{,}000{,}000$ subscribers.
(2-2)

66. (A) $N(0) = 1$
$N\left(\dfrac{1}{2}\right) = 2$
$N(1) = 4 = 2^2$
$N\left(\dfrac{3}{2}\right) = 8 = 2^3$
$N(2) = 16 = 2^4$

$\vdots$

Thus, we conclude that
$N(t) = 2^{2t}$ or $N = 4^t$.

(B) We need to solve:
$$2^{2t} = 10^9$$
$$\log 2^{2t} = \log 10^9 = 9$$
$$2t \log 2 = 9$$
$$t = \frac{9}{2 \log 2} \approx 14.95$$

Thus, the mouse will die in 15 days.
(2-2, 2-3)

67. Given $I = I_0 e^{-kd}$. When $d = 73.6$, $I = \dfrac{1}{2} I_0$. Thus, we have:

$$\frac{1}{2} I_0 = I_0 e^{-k(73.6)}$$

$$e^{-k(73.6)} = \frac{1}{2}$$

$$-k(73.6) = \ln \frac{1}{2}$$

$$k = \frac{\ln(0.5)}{-73.6} \approx 0.00942$$

Thus, $k \approx 0.00942$.

To find the depth at which 1% of the surface light remains, we set $I = 0.01I_0$ and solve

$$0.01I_0 = I_0 e^{-0.00942d}$$

for d:

$$0.01 = e^{-0.00942d}$$

$$-0.00942d = \ln 0.01$$

$$d = \frac{\ln 0.01}{-0.00942} \approx 488.87$$

Thus, 1% of the surface light remains at approximately 489 feet.

(2-2, 2-3)

68. (A) Logarithmic regression model

In 2010, $y(70) \approx 6,747,000$ cows.

(B) $\ln(0)$ is not defined.

(2-3)

69. Using the continuous compounding model, we have:

$$2P_0 = P_0 e^{0.03t}$$

$$2 = e^{0.03t}$$

$$0.03t = \ln 2$$

$$t = \frac{\ln 2}{0.03} \approx 23.1$$

Thus, the model predicts that the population will double in approximately 23.1 years.

(2-2, 2-3)

70. (A) Exponential regression model   Total expenditures 2010:

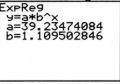 $y(30) \approx \$886$ billion

(B) To find when the total expenditures will reach $500 billion, solve the equation $ab^x = 500$ for x. The result is $x \approx 24.5$ years; that is, at mid-year in 2004.

(2-2)

71. (A) Exponential regression model

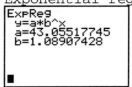

Total expenditures in 2010: $y(30) \approx \$557$ billion.

(B) To find when the total expenditures will reach $500 billion, solve

$$ab^x = 500$$

for x. The result is $x \approx 28.7$; that is in August 2008.

(2-2)

3 THE DERIVATIVE

EXERCISE 3-1

Things to remember:

1. **LIMIT**

   We write
   $$\lim_{x \to c} f(x) = L \text{ or } f(x) \to L \text{ as } x \to c$$
   if the functional value $f(x)$ is close to the single real number L whenever x is close to but not equal to c (on either side of c).

   [Note: The existence of a limit at c has nothing to do with the value of the function at c. In fact, c may not even be in the domain of f. However, the function must be defined on both sides of c.]

2. **ONE-SIDED LIMITS**

   We write $\lim_{x \to c^-} f(x) = K$ [$x \to c^-$ is read "x approaches c from the left" and means $x \to c$ and $x < c$] and call K the LIMIT FROM THE LEFT or LEFT-HAND LIMIT if $f(x)$ is close to K whenever x is close to c, but to the left of c on the real number line.

   We write $\lim_{x \to c^+} f(x) = L$ [$x \to c^+$ is read "x approaches c from the right" and means $x \to c$ and $x > c$] and call L the LIMIT FROM THE RIGHT or RIGHT-HAND LIMIT if $f(x)$ is close to L whenever x is close to c, but to the right of c on the real number line.

3. **EXISTENCE OF A LIMIT**

   In order for a limit to exist, the limit from the left and the limit from the right must both exist, and must be equal. That is, $\lim_{x \to c} f(x) = L$ if and only if $\lim_{x \to c^-} f(x) = \lim_{x \to c^+} f(x) = L$.

4. **PROPERTIES OF LIMITS**

   Let f and g be two functions and assume that
   $$\lim_{x \to c} f(x) = L \qquad \lim_{x \to c} g(x) = M$$

   where L and M are real numbers (both limits exist). Then:

   (a) $\lim_{x \to c} [f(x) + g(x)] = \lim_{x \to c} f(x) + \lim_{x \to c} g(x) = L + M$.

   (b) $\lim_{x \to c} [f(x) - g(x)] = \lim_{x \to c} f(x) - \lim_{x \to c} g(x) = L - M$.

(c) $\lim\limits_{x \to c} kf(x) = k \lim\limits_{x \to c} f(x) = kL$ for any constant k.

(d) $\lim\limits_{x \to c} [f(x)g(x)] = \left(\lim\limits_{x \to c} f(x)\right)\left(\lim\limits_{x \to c} g(x)\right) = LM.$

(e) $\lim\limits_{x \to c} \dfrac{f(x)}{g(x)} = \dfrac{L}{M}$ if $M \neq 0$; $\lim\limits_{x \to c} \dfrac{f(x)}{g(x)}$ does not exist if $L \neq 0$

and $M = 0$; $\lim\limits_{x \to c} \dfrac{f(x)}{g(x)}$ is a 0/0 INDETERMINATE FORM if $L = M = 0$.

(f) $\lim\limits_{x \to c} \sqrt[n]{f(x)} = \sqrt[n]{\lim\limits_{x \to c} f(x)} = \sqrt[n]{L}$ ($L \geq 0$ for n even).

5. LIMITS OF POLYNOMIAL AND RATIONAL FUNCTIONS

(a) $\lim\limits_{x \to c} f(x) = f(c)$ f any polynomial function

(b) $\lim\limits_{x \to c} r(x) = r(c)$ r any rational function with a nonzero denominator at $x = c$.

6. DIFFERENCE QUOTIENT
Let the function f be defined in an open interval containing the number a. The expression

$$\frac{f(a + h) - f(a)}{h}$$

is called the DIFFERENCE QUOTIENT. One of the most important limits in calculus is the limit of the difference quotient:

$$\lim\limits_{h \to 0} \frac{f(a + h) - f(a)}{h}$$

---

1. (A) $\lim\limits_{x \to 0^-} f(x) = 2$ (B) $\lim\limits_{x \to 0^+} f(x) = 2$ (C) $\lim\limits_{x \to 0} f(x) = 2$ (D) $f(0) = 2$

3. (A) $\lim\limits_{x \to 2^-} f(x) = 1$ (B) $\lim\limits_{x \to 2^+} f(x) = 2$ (C) $\lim\limits_{x \to 2} f(x)$ does not exist

(D) $f(2) = 2$ (E) No, because $\lim\limits_{x \to 2^-} f(x) = 1 \neq \lim\limits_{x \to 2^+} f(x) = 2$

5. (A) $\lim\limits_{x \to 1^-} g(x) = 1$ (B) $\lim\limits_{x \to 1^+} g(x) = 2$ (C) $\lim\limits_{x \to 1} g(x) =$ does not exist

(D) $g(1)$ does not exist   (E) No, because $\lim\limits_{x \to 1^-} f(x) = 1 \neq \lim\limits_{x \to 1^+} f(x) = 2$

7. (A) $\lim\limits_{x \to 3^-} g(x) = 1$ (B) $\lim\limits_{x \to 3^+} g(x) = 1$ (C) $\lim\limits_{x \to 3} g(x) = 1$ (D) $g(3) = 3$
(E) Yes, define $f(3) = 1$.

9. (A) $\lim\limits_{x \to -3^+} f(x) = -2$ (B) $\lim\limits_{x \to -3^-} f(x) = -2$ (C) $\lim\limits_{x \to -3} f(x) = -2$
(D) $f(-3) = 1$ (E) Yes, set $f(-3) = -2$.

11. (A) $\lim\limits_{x \to 0^+} f(x) = 2$ (B) $\lim\limits_{x \to 0^-} f(x) = 2$ (C) $\lim\limits_{x \to 0} f(x) = 2$
(D) $f(0)$ does not exist.   (E) Yes, define $f(0) = 2$.

13. $\lim\limits_{x \to 3} 4x = 4 \cdot 3 = 12$ (use $\underline{5}$)   **15.** $\lim\limits_{x \to -4} (x + 5) = -4 + 5 = 1$ (use $\underline{5}$)

17. $\lim\limits_{x \to 2} x(x - 4) = 2(2 - 4) = 2(-2) = -4$ (use $\underline{4}$c and $\underline{5}$)

19. $\lim\limits_{x \to -3} \dfrac{x}{x + 5} = \dfrac{-3}{-3 + 5} = -\dfrac{3}{2} = -1.5$ (use $\underline{4}$e and $\underline{5}$)

21. $\lim\limits_{x \to 1} \sqrt{5x + 4} = \sqrt{5 + 4} = \sqrt{9} = 3$ (use $\underline{4}$f and $\underline{5}$)

23. $\lim\limits_{x \to 1} -3f(x) = -3 \lim\limits_{x \to 1} f(x) = -3(-5) = 15$

25. $\lim\limits_{x \to 1} [2f(x) + g(x)] = 2 \lim\limits_{x \to 1} f(x) + \lim\limits_{x \to 1} g(x) = 2(-5) + 4 = -6$

27. $\lim\limits_{x \to 1} \dfrac{2 - f(x)}{x + g(x)} = \dfrac{\lim\limits_{x \to 1}[2 - f(x)]}{\lim\limits_{x \to 1}[x + g(x)]} = \dfrac{2 - \lim\limits_{x \to 1} f(x)}{1 + \lim\limits_{x \to 1} g(x)} = \dfrac{2 - (-5)}{1 + 4} = \dfrac{7}{5}$

29. $\lim\limits_{x \to 1} f(x)[2 - g(x)] = \lim\limits_{x \to 1} f(x) \cdot \lim\limits_{x \to 1} [2 - g(x)]$
$= (-5)(2 - 4) = 10$

31. $\lim\limits_{x \to 1} \sqrt{g(x) - f(x)} = \sqrt{\lim\limits_{x \to 1}[g(x) - f(x)]} = \sqrt{\lim\limits_{x \to 1} g(x) - \lim\limits_{x \to 1} f(x)}$
$= \sqrt{4 - (-5)} = \sqrt{9} = 3$

33. $\lim\limits_{x \to 1} [f(x) + 1]^2 = (\lim\limits_{x \to 1} [f(x) + 1])^2 = [-5 + 1]^2 = 16$

35.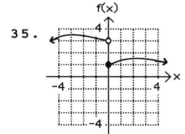

37.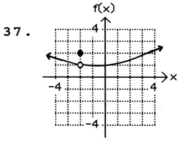

39. $f(x) = \begin{cases} 1 - x^2 & \text{if } x \le 0 \\ 1 + x^2 & \text{if } x > 0 \end{cases}$

(A) $\lim\limits_{x \to 0^+} f(x) = \lim\limits_{x \to 0^+} (1 + x^2) = 1$ (B) $\lim\limits_{x \to 0^-} f(x) = \lim\limits_{x \to 0^-} (1 - x^2) = 1$

(C) $\lim\limits_{x \to 0} f(x) = 1$ (D) $f(0) = 1$

41. $f(x) = \begin{cases} x^2 & \text{if} \quad x < 1 \\ 2x & \text{if} \quad x > 1 \end{cases}$

(A) $\lim\limits_{x \to 1^+} f(x) = \lim\limits_{x \to 1^+} 2x = 2$

(B) $\lim\limits_{x \to 1^-} f(x) = \lim\limits_{x \to 1^-} x^2 = 1$

(C) $\lim\limits_{x \to 1} f(x)$ does not exist

(D) $f(1)$ does not exist

43. $f(x) = \begin{cases} \dfrac{x^2 - 9}{x + 3} & \text{if} \quad x < 0 \\ \dfrac{x^2 - 9}{x - 3} & \text{if} \quad x > 0 \end{cases}$

(A) $\lim\limits_{x \to -3} f(x) = \lim\limits_{x \to -3} \dfrac{x^2 - 9}{x + 3} = \lim\limits_{x \to -3} \dfrac{(x - 3)(x + 3)}{x + 3} = \lim\limits_{x \to -3} (x - 3) = -6$

(B) $\lim\limits_{x \to 0^-} f(x) = \lim\limits_{x \to 0^-} \dfrac{x^2 - 9}{x + 3} = \dfrac{\lim\limits_{x \to 0^-}(x^2 - 9)}{\lim\limits_{x \to 0^-}(x + 3)} = \dfrac{-9}{3} = -3$

$\lim\limits_{x \to 0^+} f(x) = \lim\limits_{x \to 0^+} \dfrac{x^2 - 9}{x - 3} = \dfrac{\lim\limits_{x \to 0^+}(x^2 - 9)}{\lim\limits_{x \to 0^+}(x - 3)} = \dfrac{-9}{-3} = 3$

$\lim\limits_{x \to 0} f(x)$ does not exist

(C) $\lim\limits_{x \to 3} f(x) = \lim\limits_{x \to 3} \dfrac{x^2 - 9}{x - 3} = \lim\limits_{x \to 3} \dfrac{(x - 3)(x + 3)}{x - 3} = \lim\limits_{x \to 3} (x + 3) = 6$

45. $f(x) = \dfrac{|x - 1|}{x - 1}$

(A) For $x > 1$, $|x - 1| = x - 1$.

Thus, $\lim\limits_{x \to 1^+} \dfrac{|x - 1|}{x + 1} = \lim\limits_{x \to 1^+} \dfrac{x - 1}{x - 1} = \lim\limits_{x \to 1^+} 1 = 1$.

(B) For $x < 1$, $|x - 1| = -(x - 1)$.

Thus, $\lim\limits_{x \to 1^-} \dfrac{|x - 1|}{x - 1} = \lim\limits_{x \to 1^-} \dfrac{-(x - 1)}{x - 1} = \lim\limits_{x \to 1^-} -1 = -1$.

(C) $\lim\limits_{x \to 1} f(x)$ does not exist

(D) $f(1)$ does not exist

47. $f(x) = \dfrac{x - 2}{x^2 - 2x} = \dfrac{x - 2}{x(x - 2)} = \dfrac{1}{x}$, $x \neq 2$; $f(2)$ does not exist.

(A) $\lim\limits_{x \to 0} f(x) = \lim\limits_{x \to 0} \dfrac{1}{x}$ does not exist

(B) $\lim\limits_{x \to 2} f(x) = \lim\limits_{x \to 2} \dfrac{1}{x} = \dfrac{1}{2}$

(C) $\lim\limits_{x \to 4} f(x) = \lim\limits_{x \to 4} \dfrac{1}{x} = \dfrac{1}{4}$

49. $f(x) = \dfrac{x^2 - x - 6}{x + 2} = \dfrac{(x - 3)(x + 2)}{x + 2} = x - 3,\ x \neq -2;\ f(-2)$ does not exist

    (A) $\lim\limits_{x \to -2} f(x) = \lim\limits_{x \to -2} (x - 3) = -5$

    (B) $\lim\limits_{x \to 0} f(x) = \lim\limits_{x \to 0} (x - 3) = -3$

    (C) $\lim\limits_{x \to 3} f(x) = \lim\limits_{x \to 3} (x - 3) = 0$

51. $f(x) = \dfrac{(x + 2)^2}{x^2 - 4} = \dfrac{(x + 2)^2}{(x - 2)(x + 2)} = \dfrac{x + 2}{x - 2},\ x \neq -2;\ f(-2)$ does not exist

    (A) $\lim\limits_{x \to -2} f(x) = \lim\limits_{x \to -2} \dfrac{x + 2}{x - 2} = \dfrac{0}{-4} = 0$

    (B) $\lim\limits_{x \to 0} f(x) = \lim\limits_{x \to 0} \dfrac{x + 2}{x - 2} = \dfrac{2}{-2} = -1$

    (C) $\lim\limits_{x \to 2} f(x) = \lim\limits_{x \to 2} \dfrac{x + 2}{x - 2}$ does not exist

53. $f(x) = \dfrac{2x^2 - 3x - 2}{x^2 + x - 6} = \dfrac{(2x + 1)(x - 2)}{(x + 3)(x - 2)} = \dfrac{2x + 1}{x + 3},\ x \neq 2;\ f(2)$ does not exist

    (A) $\lim\limits_{x \to 2} f(x) = \lim\limits_{x \to 2} \dfrac{2x + 1}{x + 3} = \dfrac{5}{5} = 1$

    (B) $\lim\limits_{x \to 0} f(x) = \lim\limits_{x \to 0} \dfrac{2x + 1}{x + 3} = \dfrac{1}{3}$

    (C) $\lim\limits_{x \to 1} f(x) = \lim\limits_{x \to 1} \dfrac{2x + 1}{x + 3} = \dfrac{3}{4}$

55. $f(x) = 3x + 1$

$$\lim\limits_{h \to 0} \dfrac{f(2 + h) - f(2)}{h} = \lim\limits_{h \to 0} \dfrac{3(2 + h) + 1 - (3 \cdot 2 + 1)}{h}$$

$$= \lim\limits_{h \to 0} \dfrac{6 + 3h + 1 - 7}{h} = \lim\limits_{h \to 0} \dfrac{3h}{h} = \lim\limits_{h \to 0} 3 = 3$$

57. $f(x) = x^2 + 1$

$$\lim_{h \to 0} \frac{f(2 + h) - f(2)}{h} = \lim_{h \to 0} \frac{(2 + h)^2 + 1 - (2^2 + 1)}{h}$$

$$= \lim_{h \to 0} \frac{4 + 4h + h^2 + 1 - 5}{h} = \lim_{h \to 0} \frac{4h + h^2}{h}$$

$$= \lim_{h \to 0} (4 + h) = 4$$

59. $f(x) = \sqrt{x} - 2$

$$\lim_{h \to 0} \frac{f(2 + h) - f(2)}{h} = \lim_{h \to 0} \frac{\sqrt{2 + h} - 2 - (\sqrt{2} - 2)}{h} = \lim_{h \to 0} \frac{\sqrt{2 + h} - \sqrt{2}}{h}$$

$$= \lim_{h \to 0} \frac{\sqrt{2 + h} - \sqrt{2}}{h} \cdot \frac{\sqrt{2 + h} + \sqrt{2}}{\sqrt{2 + h} + \sqrt{2}} = \lim_{h \to 0} \frac{2 + h - 2}{h(\sqrt{2 + h} + \sqrt{2})}$$

$$= \lim_{h \to 0} \frac{h}{h(\sqrt{2 + h} + \sqrt{2})} = \lim_{h \to 0} \frac{1}{\sqrt{2 + h} + \sqrt{2}} = \frac{1}{2\sqrt{2}}$$

61. $f(x) = |x - 2| - 3$

$$\lim_{h \to 0} \frac{f(2 + h) - f(2)}{h} = \lim_{h \to 0} \frac{|(2 + h) - 2| - 3 - (|2 - 2| - 3)}{h}$$

$$= \lim_{h \to 0} \frac{|h| - 3 + 3}{h} = \lim_{h \to 0} \frac{|h|}{h} \text{ does not exist.}$$

63. $f(x) = \dfrac{2}{x - 1}$

$$\lim_{h \to 0} \frac{f(2 + h) - f(2)}{h} = \lim_{h \to 0} \frac{\dfrac{2}{2 + h - 1} - \dfrac{2}{2 - 1}}{h} = \lim_{h \to 0} \frac{\dfrac{2}{1 + h} - 2}{h}$$

$$= \lim_{h \to 0} \frac{\dfrac{2 - 2(1 + h)}{1 + h}}{h} = \lim_{h \to 0} \frac{-2h}{h(1 + h)}$$

$$= \lim_{h \to 0} \frac{-2}{1 + h} = -2$$

65. (A) $\displaystyle\lim_{x \to 1^-} f(x) = \lim_{x \to 1^-} (1 + x) = 2$

$\displaystyle\lim_{x \to 1^+} f(x) = \lim_{x \to 1^+} (4 - x) = 3$

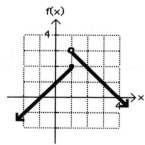

(B) $\lim\limits_{x \to 1^-} f(x) = \lim\limits_{x \to 1^-} (1 + 2x) = 3$

$\lim\limits_{x \to 1^+} f(x) = \lim\limits_{x \to 1^+} (4 - 2x) = 2$

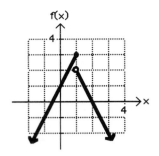

(C) $\lim\limits_{x \to 1^-} f(x) = \lim\limits_{x \to 1^-} (1 + mx) = 1 + m$

$\lim\limits_{x \to 1^+} f(x) = \lim\limits_{x \to 1^+} (4 - mx) = 4 - m$

$1 + m = 4 - m$

$2m = 3$

$m = \dfrac{3}{2}$

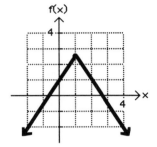

(D) The graph in (A) is broken at $x = 1$; it jumps up from $(1, 2)$ to $(1, 3)$.

The graph in (B) is also broken at $x = 1$; it jumps down from $(1, 3)$ to $(1, 2)$.

The graph in (C) is not broken; the two pieces meet at $\left(1, \dfrac{5}{2}\right)$.

67. $\lim\limits_{h \to 0} \dfrac{(a + h)^2 - a^2}{h} = \lim\limits_{h \to 0} \dfrac{a^2 + 2ah + h^2 - a^2}{h}$

$= \lim\limits_{h \to 0} \dfrac{2ah + h^2}{h} = \lim\limits_{h \to 0} (2a + h) = 2a$

69. $\lim\limits_{h \to 0} \dfrac{\sqrt{a + h} - \sqrt{a}}{h} = \lim\limits_{h \to 0} \dfrac{\sqrt{a + h} - \sqrt{a}}{h} \cdot \dfrac{\sqrt{a + h} + \sqrt{a}}{\sqrt{a + h} + \sqrt{a}} = \lim\limits_{h \to 0} \dfrac{(a + h) - a}{h(\sqrt{a + h} + \sqrt{a})}$

$= \lim\limits_{h \to 0} \dfrac{1}{\sqrt{a + h} + \sqrt{a}} = \dfrac{1}{2\sqrt{a}}$

71. (A) $F(x) = \begin{cases} 0.99 & \text{if } 0 < x \le 20 \\ 0.07(x - 20) + 0.99 & \text{if } x > 20 \end{cases}$ (B)

$= \begin{cases} 0.99 & \text{if } 0 < x \le 20 \\ 0.07x - 0.41 & \text{if } x > 20 \end{cases}$

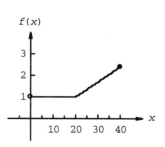

(C) $\lim\limits_{x \to 20^-} F(x) = 0.99 = \lim\limits_{x \to 20^+} F(x)$

Therefore, $\lim\limits_{x \to 20} F(x) = 0.99$

73. At $x = 20$ minutes, the first service charge is \$0.99 and the second service charge is \$2.70. Also, after 20 minutes, the first service charge is \$0.07 per minute versus \$0.09 per minute for the second service. The second service is much more expensive than the first.

75. (A) $D(x) = \begin{cases} x & \text{if} & 0 \le x < 300 \\ 0.97x & \text{if} & 300 \le x < 1,000 \\ 0.95x & \text{if} & 1,000 \le x < 3,000 \\ 0.93x & \text{if} & 3,000 \le x < 5,000 \\ 0.90x & \text{if} & 5,000 \le x \end{cases}$

(B) $\displaystyle \lim_{x \to 1000^-} D(x) = \lim_{x \to 1000^-} 0.97x = 970$,

$\displaystyle \lim_{x \to 1000^+} D(x) = \lim_{x \to 1000^+} 0.95x = 950$,

$\displaystyle \lim_{x \to 1000} D(x)$ does not exist;

$\displaystyle \lim_{x \to 3000^-} D(x) = \lim_{x \to 3000^-} 0.95x = 2850$,

$\displaystyle \lim_{x \to 3000^+} D(x) = \lim_{x \to 3000^+} 0.93x = 2790$,

$\displaystyle \lim_{x \to 3000} D(x)$ does not exist.

77. (A) $F(x) = \begin{cases} 20x & \text{if} & 0 \le x \le 4,000 \\ 80,000 & \text{if} & x > 4,000 \end{cases}$

(B) $\displaystyle \lim_{x \to 4000^-} F(x) = \lim_{x \to 4000^-} 20x = 80,000$,

$\displaystyle \lim_{x \to 4000^+} F(x) = \lim_{x \to 4000^+} 80,000 = 80,000$.

Therefore, $\displaystyle \lim_{x \to 4000} F(x) = 80,000$.

$\displaystyle \lim_{x \to 8000} F(x) = \lim_{x \to 8000} 80,000 = 80,000$.

79. $\displaystyle \lim_{x \to 5^-} f(x) = \lim_{x \to 5^-} 0 = 0$,

$\displaystyle \lim_{x \to 5^+} f(x) = \lim_{x \to 5^+} (0.8 - 0.08x) = 0.4$.

Therefore, $\displaystyle \lim_{x \to 5} f(x)$ does not exist.

$\displaystyle \lim_{x \to 5^-} g(x) = \lim_{x \to 5^-} 0 = 0$,

$\displaystyle \lim_{x \to 5^+} g(x) = \lim_{x \to 5^+} (0.8x - 0.04x^2 - 3) = 0$.

Therefore, $\displaystyle \lim_{x \to 5} g(x) = 0$.

$$\lim_{x \to 10^-} f(x) = \lim_{x \to 10^-} (0.8 - 0.08x) = 0,$$

$$\lim_{x \to 10^+} f(x) = \lim_{x \to 10^+} 0 = 0.$$

Therefore, $\lim_{x \to 10} f(x) = 0.$

$$\lim_{x \to 10^-} g(x) = \lim_{x \to 10^-} (0.8x - 0.04x^2 - 3) = 1,$$

$$\lim_{x \to 10^+} g(x) = \lim_{x \to 0^+} 1 = 1.$$

Therefore, $\lim_{x \to 10} g(x) = 1.$

EXERCISE 3-2

Things to remember:

1. CONTINUITY

   A function f is CONTINUOUS AT THE POINT $x = c$ if:

   (a) $\lim_{x \to c} f(x)$ exists;

   (b) $f(c)$ exists;

   (c) $\lim_{x \to c} f(x) = f(c)$

   If one or more of the three conditions fails, then f is DISCONTINUOUS at $x = c$.

   A function is CONTINUOUS ON THE OPEN INTERVAL (a, b) if it is continuous at each point on the interval.

2. ONE-SIDED CONTINUITY

   A function f is CONTINUOUS ON THE LEFT AT $x = c$ if $\lim_{x \to c^-} f(x) = f(c)$; f is CONTINUOUS ON THE RIGHT AT $x = c$ if $\lim_{x \to c^+} f(x) = f(c)$.

   The function f is continuous on the closed interval $[a, b]$ if it is continuous on the open interval (a, b), and is continuous on the right at a and continuous on the left at b.

3. CONTINUITY PROPERTIES OF SOME SPECIFIC FUNCTIONS

   (a) A constant function, $f(x) = k$, is continuous for all x.

   (b) For n a positive integer, $f(x) = x^n$ is continuous for all x.

   (c) A polynomial function
   $$P(x) = a_n x^n + a_{n-1} x^{n-1} + \ldots + a_1 x + a_0$$
   is continuous for all x.

(d) A rational function

$$R(x) = \frac{P(x)}{Q(x)} \ ,$$

P and Q polynomial functions, is continuous for all x except those numbers $x = c$ such that $Q(c) = 0$.

(e) For n an odd positive integer, $n > 1$, $\sqrt[n]{f(x)}$ is continuous wherever f is continuous.

(f) For n an even positive integer, $\sqrt[n]{f(x)}$ is continuous wherever f is continuous and non-negative.

4. VERTICAL ASYMPTOTES

Suppose that the limit of a function f fails to exist as x approaches c from the left because the values of $f(x)$ are becoming very large positive numbers (or very large negative numbers). This is denoted

$$\lim_{x \to c^-} f(x) = \infty \quad (\text{or } -\infty)$$

If this happens as x approaches c from the right, then

$$\lim_{x \to c^+} f(x) = \infty \quad (\text{or } -\infty)$$

If both one-sided limits exhibit the same behavior, then

$$\lim_{x \to c} f(x) = \infty \quad (\text{or } -\infty)$$

If any of the above hold, the line $x = c$ is a VERTICAL ASYMPTOTE for the graph of $y = f(x)$.

5. SIGN PROPERTIES ON AN INTERVAL (a, b)

If f is continuous or (a, b) and $f(x) \neq 0$ for all x in (a, b), then either $f(x) > 0$ for all x in (a, b) or $f(x) < 0$ for all x in (a, b).

6. CONSTRUCTING SIGN CHARTS

Given a function f:

Step 1. Find all partition numbers. That is:

(A) Find all numbers where f is discontinuous. (Rational functions are discontinuous for values of x that make a denominator 0.)

(B) Find all numbers where $f(x) = 0$. (For a rational function, this occurs where the numerator is 0 and the denominator is not 0.)

Step 2. Plot the numbers found in step 1 on a real number line, dividing the number line into intervals.

Step 3. Select a test number in each open interval determined in step 2, and evaluate $f(x)$ at each test number to determine whether $f(x)$ is positive (+) or negative (−) in each interval.

Step 4. Construct a sign chart using the real number line in step 2. This will show the sign of $f(x)$ on each open interval.

[*Note*: From the sign chart, it is easy to find the solution for the inequality $f(x) < 0$ or $f(x) > 0$.]

---

1. f is continuous at $x = 1$, since $\lim\limits_{x \to 1} f(x) = f(1) = 2$

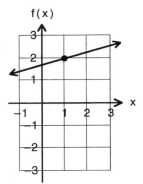

3. f is discontinuous at $x = 1$, since $\lim\limits_{x \to 1} f(x) \neq f(1)$

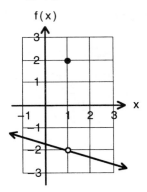

5. $\lim\limits_{x \to 1^-} f(x) = 2$, $\lim\limits_{x \to 1^+} f(x) = -2$
implies $\lim\limits_{x \to 1} f(x)$ does not exist;

f is discontinuous at $x = 1$,
since $\lim\limits_{x \to 1} f(x)$ does not exist

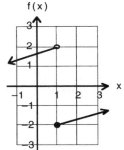

7. (A) $\lim\limits_{x \to 1^-} f(x) = 2$ (B) $\lim\limits_{x \to 1^+} f(x) = 1$

   (C) $\lim\limits_{x \to 1} f(x)$ does not exist   (D) $f(1) = 1$

   (E) No, because $\lim\limits_{x \to 1} f(x)$ does not exist.

9. (A) $\lim\limits_{x \to -2^-} f(x) = 1$ (B) $\lim\limits_{x \to -2^+} f(x) = 1$

   (C) $\lim\limits_{x \to -2} f(x) = 1$ (D) $f(-2) = 3$

   (E) No, because $\lim\limits_{x \to -2} f(x) \neq f(-2)$.

11. (A) $\lim\limits_{x \to -3^-} g(x) = 1$ (B) $\lim\limits_{x \to -3^+} g(x) = 1$

(C) $\lim\limits_{x \to -3} g(x) = 1$ (D) $g(-3) = 3$

(E) No, because $\lim\limits_{x \to -3} g(x) \neq g(-3)$.

13. (A) $\lim\limits_{x \to 2^-} g(x) = 2$ (B) $\lim\limits_{x \to 2^+} g(x) = -1$

(C) $\lim\limits_{x \to 2} g(x)$ does not exist   (D) $g(2) = 2$

(E) No, because $\lim\limits_{x \to 2} g(x)$ does not exist.

15. $f(x) = 3x - 4$ is a polynomial function. Therefore, f is continuous for all x [$\underline{3}$(c)].

17. $g(x) = \dfrac{3x}{x + 2}$ is a rational function and the denominator $x + 2$ is 0 at $x = -2$. Thus, g is continuous for all x except $x = -2$ [$\underline{3}$(d)].

19. $m(x) = \dfrac{x + 1}{(x - 1)(x + 4)}$ is a rational function and the denominator $(x - 1)(x + 4)$ is 0 at $x = 1$ or $x = -4$. Thus, m is continuous for all x except $x = 1$, $x = -4$ [$\underline{3}$(d)].

21. $F(x) = \dfrac{2x}{x^2 + 9}$ is a rational function and the denominator $x^2 + 9 \neq 0$ for all x. Thus, F is continuous for all x.

23. $M(x) = \dfrac{x - 1}{4x^2 - 9}$ is a rational function and the denominator $4x^2 - 9 = 0$ at $x = \dfrac{3}{2}, -\dfrac{3}{2}$. Thus, M is continuous for all x except $x = \pm\dfrac{3}{2}$.

25. $f(x) = \begin{cases} 2 \text{ if } x \text{ is an integer} \\ 1 \text{ if } x \text{ is not an integer} \end{cases}$

(A) The graph of f is:

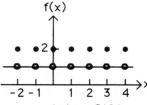

(B) $\lim\limits_{x \to 2} f(x) = 1$ (C) $f(2) = 2$

(D) f is not continuous at $x = 2$ since $\lim\limits_{x \to 2} f(x) \neq f(2)$.

(E) f is discontinuous at $x = n$ for all integers n.

27. $x^2 - x - 12 < 0$

Let $f(x) = x^2 - x - 12 = (x - 4)(x + 3)$. Then f is continuous for all x and $f(-3) = f(4) = 0$. Thus, $x = -3$ and $x = 4$ are partition numbers.

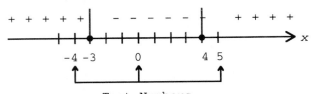

Test Numbers	
x	$f(x)$
-4	$8\ (+)$
0	$-12\ (-)$
5	$8\ (+)$

Thus, $x^2 - x - 12 < 0$ for:

$-3 < x < 4$ (inequality notation)

$(-3, 4)$ (interval notation)

29. $x^2 + 21 > 10x$ or $x^2 - 10x + 21 > 0$

Let $f(x) = x^2 - 10x + 21 = (x - 7)(x - 3)$. Then f is continuous for all x and $f(3) = f(7) = 0$. Thus, $x = 3$ and $x = 7$ are partition numbers.

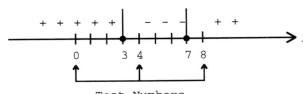

Test Numbers	
x	$f(x)$
0	$21\ (+)$
4	$-3\ (-)$
8	$5\ (+)$

Thus, $x^2 - 10x + 21 > 0$ for:

$x < 3$ or $x > 7$ (inequality notation)

$(-\infty, 3) \cup (7, \infty)$ (interval notation)

31. $x^3 < 4x$ or $x^3 - 4x < 0$

Let $f(x) = x^3 - 4x = x(x^2 - 4) = x(x - 2)(x + 2)$. Then f is continuous for all x and $f(-2) = f(0) = f(2) = 0$. Thus, $x = -2$, $x = 0$ and $x = 2$ are partition numbers.

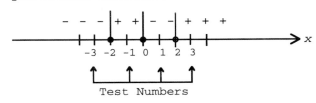

Test Numbers	
x	$f(x)$
-3	$-15\ (-)$
-1	$3\ (+)$
1	$-3\ (-)$
3	$15\ (+)$

Thus, $x^3 < 4x$ for:

$-\infty < x < -2$ or $0 < x < 2$ (inequality notation)

$(-\infty, -2) \cup (0, 2)$ (interval notation)

33. $\dfrac{x^2 + 5x}{x - 3} > 0$

Let $f(x) = \dfrac{x^2 + 5x}{x - 3} = \dfrac{x(x + 5)}{x - 3}$. Then f is discontinuous at $x = 3$ and $f(0) = f(-5) = 0$. Thus, $x = -5$, $x = 0$, and $x = 3$ are partition numbers.

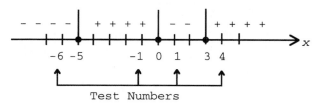

Test Numbers	
x	$f(x)$
-6	$-\frac{2}{3}$ (−)
-1	1 (+)
1	-3 (−)
4	36 (+)

Thus, $\dfrac{x^2 + 5x}{x - 3} > 0$ for: $-5 < x < 0$ or $x > 3$ (inequality notation)

$(-5, 0) \cup (3, \infty)$ (interval notation)

35. (A) $f(x) > 0$ on $(-4, -2) \cup (0, 2) \cup (4, \infty)$

(B) $f(x) < 0$ on $(-\infty, -4) \cup (-2, 0) \cup (2, 4)$

37. $f(x) = x^4 - 6x^2 + 3x + 5$
Partition numbers: $x_1 \approx -2.5308$, $x_2 \approx -0.7198$

(A) $f(x) > 0$ on $(-\infty, -2.5308) \cup (-0.7198, \infty)$

(B) $f(x) < 0$ on $(-2.5308, -0.7198)$

39. $f(x) = \dfrac{3 + 6x - x^3}{x^2 - 1}$
Partition numbers: $x_1 \approx -2.1451$, $x_2 = -1$, $x_3 \approx -0.5240$,
$\qquad\qquad\qquad x_4 = 1$, $x_5 \approx 2.6691$

(A) $f(x) > 0$ on $(-\infty, -2.1451) \cup (-1, -0.5240) \cup (1, 2.6691)$

(B) $f(x) < 0$ on $(-2.1451, -1) \cup (-0.5240, 1) \cup (2.6691, \infty)$

41. $f(x) = x - 6$ is continuous for all x since it is a polynomial function. Therefore, $g(x) = \sqrt{x - 6}$ is continuous for all x such that $x - 6 \geq 0$, that is, for all x in $[6, \infty)$ [see 3(f)].

43. $f(x) = 5 - x$ is continuous for all x since it is a polynomial function. Therefore, $F(x) = \sqrt[3]{5 - x}$ is continuous for all x, that is, for all x in $(-\infty, \infty)$.

45. $f(x) = x^2 - 9$ is continuous for all x since it is a polynomial function. Therefore, $g(x) = \sqrt{x^2 - 9}$ is continuous for all x such that $x^2 - 9 = (x - 3)(x + 3) \geq 0$.

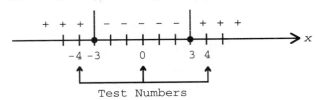

Test Numbers	
x	$f(x)$
0	−9
−4	7
4	7

$\sqrt{x^2 - 9}$ is continuous on $(-\infty, -3] \cup [3, \infty)$.

47. $f(x) = x^2 + 1$ is continuous for all x since it is a polynomial function. Also $x^2 + 1 \geq 1 > 0$ for all x. Therefore, $\sqrt{x^2 + 1}$ is continuous for all x, that is, for all x in $(-\infty, \infty)$.

49. The graph of f is shown at the right. This function is discontinuous at $x = 1$. [$\lim_{x \to 1} f(x)$ does not exist.]

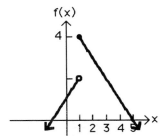

51. The graph of f is:

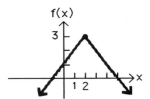

This function is continuous for all x. $\left[\lim_{x \to 2} f(x) = f(2) = 3. \right]$

53. The graph of f is:

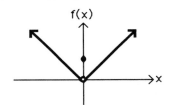

This function is discontinuous at $x = 0$. $\left[\lim_{x \to 0} f(x) = 0 \neq f(0) = 1. \right]$

55. f is discontinuous at $x = 2$: f is not defined at 2, $\lim_{x \to 2^-} f(x) = 0$ and $\lim_{x \to 2^+} 4$.

57. f is discontinuous at $x = -1$ and $x = 1$ because f is not defined at these points. However, $\lim_{x \to -1} f(x) = 2$ and $\lim_{x \to 1} f(x) = 2$.

59. (A) Yes; g is continuous on $(-1, 2)$.

(B) Since $\lim_{x \to -1^+} g(x) = -1 = g(-1)$, g is continuous from the right at $x = -1$

(C) Since $\lim_{x \to 2^-} g(x) = 2 = g(2)$, g is continuous from the left at $x = 2$.

(D) Yes; g is continuous on the closed interval $[-1, 2]$.

61. (A) Since $\lim\limits_{x \to 0^+} f(x) = f(0) = 0$, f is continuous from the right at $x = 0$.

(B) Since $\lim\limits_{x \to 0^-} f(x) = -1 \neq f(0) = 0$, f is not continuous from the left at $x = 0$.

(C) f is continuous on the open interval $(0, 1)$.

(D) f is *not* continuous on the closed interval $[0, 1]$ since $\lim\limits_{x \to 1^-} f(x) = 0 \neq f(1) = 1$, i.e., f is not continuous from the left at $x = 1$.

(E) f is continuous on the half-closed interval $[0, 1)$.

63. x intercepts:
$x = -5, 2$

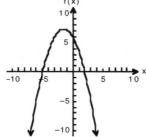

65. x intercepts:
$x = -6, -1, 4$

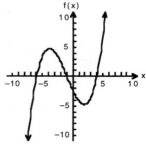

67. $f(x) = \dfrac{2}{1 - x} \neq 0$ for all x. This does not contradict Theorem 2 because f is not continuous on $(-1, 3)$; f is discontinuous at $x = 1$.

69. The following sketches illustrate that either condition is possible. Theorem 2 implies that one of these two conditions must occur.

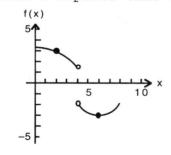

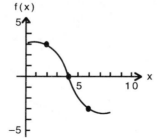

71. (A)
$$P(x) = \begin{cases} 0.37 & \text{if } 0 < x \leq 1 \\ 0.60 & \text{if } 1 < x \leq 2 \\ 0.83 & \text{if } 2 < x \leq 3 \\ 1.06 & \text{if } 3 < x \leq 4 \\ 1.29 & \text{if } 4 < x \leq 5 \end{cases}$$

(B)

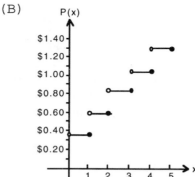

(C) P is continuous at $x = 4.5$ since P is a continuous function on $(4, 5]$; $P(x) = 1.29$ for $4 < x \leq 5$.
P is not continuous at $x = 4$ since
$\lim\limits_{x \to 4^-} P(x) = 1.06 \neq \lim\limits_{x \to 4^+} P(x) = 1.29$.

73. (A) Q is defined for all real numbers whereas P is defined only for $x > 0$.

(B) For each positive integer n, $P(n) = 0.37 + (n - 1)(0.23)$ while $Q(n) = 0.37 + n(0.23)$; for each positive number x, x not an integer $P(x) = Q(x)$.

75. (A) $\quad S(x) = 5.00 + 0.63x$ if $0 \le x \le 50$;
$\qquad S(50) = 36.50$;
$\qquad S(x) = 36.50 + 0.45(x - 50)$
$\qquad \qquad = 14 + 0.45x$ if $x > 50$

Therefore, $S(x) = \begin{cases} 36.50 + 0.50x & \text{if} \quad 0 \le x \le 50 \\ 14.00 + 0.45x & \text{if} \quad x > 50 \end{cases}$

(B)

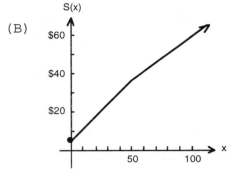

(C) $S(x)$ is continuous at $x = 50$;
$$\lim_{x \to 50^-} S(x) = \lim_{x \to 50^+} S(x)$$
$$= \lim_{x \to 50} S(x)$$
$$= S(50) = 36.5.$$

77. (A) $E(s) = \begin{cases} 1000, & 0 \le s \le 10{,}000 \\ 1000 + 0.05(s - 10{,}000), & 10{,}000 < s < 20{,}000 \\ 1500 + 0.05(s - 10{,}000), & s \ge 20{,}000 \end{cases}$

The graph of E is:

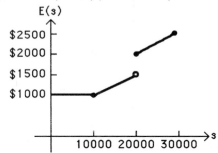

(B) From the graph, $\lim\limits_{s \to 10{,}000} E(s) = \$1000$ and $E(10{,}000) = \$1000$.

(C) From the graph, $\lim\limits_{s \to 20{,}000} E(s)$ does not exist. $E(20{,}000) = \$2000$.

(D) E is continuous at $10{,}000$; E is not continuous at $20{,}000$.

79. (A) From the graph, N is discontinuous at $t = t_2$, $t = t_3$, $t = t_4$, $t = t_6$, and $t = t_7$.

(B) From the graph, $\lim\limits_{t \to t_5} N(t) = 7$ and $N(t_5) = 7$.

(C) From the graph, $\lim\limits_{t \to t_3} N(t)$ does not exist; $N(t_3) = 4$.

Things to remember:

1. AVERAGE RATE OF CHANGE

   For $y = f(x)$, the AVERAGE RATE OF CHANGE FROM $x = a$ TO $x = a + h$ is

   $$\frac{f(a + h) - f(a)}{(a + h) - a} = \frac{f(a + h) - f(a)}{h} \qquad h \neq 0$$

   The expression $\dfrac{f(a + h) - f(a)}{h}$ is called the DIFFERENCE QUOTIENT.

2. INSTANTANEOUS RATE OF CHANGE

   For $y = f(x)$, the INSTANTANEOUS RATE OF CHANGE AT $x = a$ is

   $$\lim_{h \to 0} \frac{f(a + h) - f(a)}{h}$$

   if the limit exists.

3. SECANT LINE

   A line through two points on the graph of a function is called a SECANT LINE. If $(a, f(a))$ and $((a + h), f(a + h))$ are two points on the graph of $y = f(x)$, then

   $$\text{Slope of secant line} = \frac{f(a + h) - f(a)}{h} \qquad \text{[Difference quotient]}$$

4. SLOPE OF A GRAPH

   For $y = f(x)$, the SLOPE OF THE GRAPH at the point $(a, f(a))$ is given by

   $$\lim_{h \to 0} \frac{f(a + h) - f(a)}{h}$$

   provided the limit exists. The slope of the graph is also the SLOPE OF THE TANGENT LINE at the point $(a, f(a))$.

5. THE DERIVATIVE

   For $y = f(x)$, we define THE DERIVATIVE OF f AT x, denoted by $f'(x)$, to be

   $$f'(x) = \lim_{h \to 0} \frac{f(x + h) - f(x)}{h} \qquad \text{if the limit exists.}$$

   If $f'(x)$ exists for each x in the open interval (a, b), then f is said to be DIFFERENTIABLE OVER (a, b).

<u>6</u>. INTERPRETATIONS OF THE DERIVATIVE

The derivative of a function f is a new function f'. The domain of f' is a subset of the domain of f. Interpretations of the derivative are:

a. Slope of the tangent line. For each x in the domain of f', $f'(x)$ is the slope of the line tangent to the graph of f at the point $(x, f(x))$.

b. Instantaneous rate of change. For each x in the domain of f', $f'(x)$ is the instantaneous rate of change of $y = f(x)$ with respect to x.

c. <u>Velocity</u>. If $f(x)$ is the position of a moving object at time x, then $v = f'(x)$ is the velocity of the object at that time.

<u>7</u>. THE FOUR STEP PROCESS FOR FINDING THE DERIVATIVE OF A FUNCTION f.

<u>Step 1</u>. Find $f(x + h)$.

<u>Step 2</u>. Find $f(x + h) - f(x)$.

<u>Step 3</u>. Find $\dfrac{f(x + h) - f(x)}{h}$.

<u>Step 4</u>. Find $\lim\limits_{h \to 0} \dfrac{f(x + h) - f(x)}{h}$.

---

1. (A) $\dfrac{f(2) - f(1)}{2 - 1} = \dfrac{1 - 4}{1} = -3$ is the slope of the secant line through $(1, f(1))$ and $(2, f(2))$.

(B) $\dfrac{f(1 + h) - f(1)}{h} = \dfrac{5 - (1 + h)^2 - 4}{h} = \dfrac{5 - [1 + 2h + h^2] - 4}{h}$

$= \dfrac{-2h - h^2}{h} = -2 - h;$

slope of the secant line through $(1, f(1))$ and $(1 + h, f(1 + h))$

(C) $\lim\limits_{h \to 0} \dfrac{f(1 + h) - f(1)}{h} = \lim\limits_{h \to 0} (-2 - h) = -2;$

slope of the tangent line at $(1, f(1))$

3. $f(x) = 3x^2$

(A) Average rate of change: $\dfrac{f(4) - f(1)}{4 - 1} = \dfrac{3(4)^2 - 3(1)^2}{3} = \dfrac{48 - 3}{3} = 15.$

(B) Slope of the secant line: $\dfrac{f(4) - f(1)}{4 - 1} = 15.$

(C) $\dfrac{f(1 + h) - f(1)}{1 + h - 1} = \dfrac{3(1 + h)^2 - 3(1)^2}{h} = \dfrac{3(1 + 2h + h^2) - 3}{h}$

$= \dfrac{6h + 3h^2}{h} = 6 + 3h.$

(D) $\lim\limits_{h \to 0} \dfrac{f(1 + h) - f(1)}{h} = \lim\limits_{h \to 0} (6 + 3h) = 6.$

(E) 6.

(F) 6.

(G) $f(1) = 3$, $f'(1) = 6$; tangent line: $y - 3 = 6(x - 1)$ or $y = 6x - 3$.

5. $f(x) = -5$

Step 1. Find $f(x + h)$:

$\quad f(x + h) = -5$

Step 2. Find $f(x + h) - f(x)$:

$\quad f(x + h) - f(x) = -5 - (-5) = 0$

Step 3. Find $\dfrac{f(x + h) - f(x)}{h}$:

$\quad \dfrac{f(x + h) - f(x)}{h} = \dfrac{0}{h} = 0$

Step 4. Find $\lim\limits_{h \to 0} \dfrac{f(x + h) - f(x)}{h}$:

$\quad \lim\limits_{h \to 0} \dfrac{f(x + h) - f(x)}{h} = \lim\limits_{h \to 0} 0 = 0$

$\quad$ Thus, $f'(x) = 0.$

$\quad f'(1) = 0$, $f'(2) = 0$, $f'(3) = 0$

7. $f(x) = 3x - 7$

Step 1. Find $f(x + h)$:

$\quad f(x + h) = 3(x + h) - 7 = 3x + 3h - 7$

Step 2. Find $f(x + h) - f(x)$:

$\quad f(x + h) - f(x) = 3x + 3h - 7 - (3x - 7) = 3h$

Step 3. Find $\dfrac{f(x + h) - f(x)}{h}$:

$\quad \dfrac{f(x + h) - f(x)}{h} = \dfrac{3h}{h} = 3$

Step 4. Find $\lim\limits_{h \to 0} \dfrac{f(x + h) - f(x)}{h}$:

$\quad \lim\limits_{h \to 0} \dfrac{f(x + h) - f(x)}{h} = \lim\limits_{h \to 0} 3 = 3$

$\quad$ Thus, $f'(x) = 3.$

$\quad f'(1) = 3$, $f'(2) = 3$, $f'(3) = 3$

9. $f(x) = 2 - 3x^2$

Step 1. Find $f(x + h)$:

$\quad f(x + h) = 2 - 3(x + h)^2 = 2 - 3(x^2 + 2xh + h^2)$
$\qquad\qquad = 2 - 3x^2 - 6xh - 3h^2$

Step 2. Find $f(x + h) - f(x)$:

$$f(x + h) - f(x) = 2 - 3x^2 - 6xh - 3h^2 - (2 - 3x^2) = -6xh - 3h^2$$

Step 3. Find $\dfrac{f(x + h) - f(x)}{h}$:

$$\frac{f(x + h) - f(x)}{h} = \frac{-6xh - 3h^2}{h} = -6x - 3h$$

Step 4. Find $\lim\limits_{h \to 0} \dfrac{f(x + h) - f(x)}{h}$:

$$\lim_{h \to 0} \frac{f(x + h) - f(x)}{h} = \lim_{h \to 0} (-6x - 3h) = -6x$$

Thus, $f'(x) = -6x$.

$f'(1) = -6$, $f'(2) = -12$, $f'(3) = -18$

11. $f(x) = x^2 + 6x - 10$

Step 1. Find $f(x + h)$:

$$f(x + h) = (x + h)^2 + 6(x + h) - 10 = x^2 + 2xh + h^2 + 6x + 6h - 10$$

Step 2. Find $f(x + h) - f(x)$:

$$f(x + h) - f(x) = x^2 + 2xh + h^2 + 6x + 6h - 10 - (x^2 + 6x - 10)$$
$$= 2xh + h^2 + 6h$$

Step 3. Find $\dfrac{f(x + h) - f(x)}{h}$:

$$\frac{f(x + h) - f(x)}{h} = \frac{2xh + h^2 + 6h}{h} = 2x + h + 6$$

Step 4. Find $\lim\limits_{h \to 0} \dfrac{f(x + h) - f(x)}{h}$:

$$\lim_{h \to 0} \frac{f(x + h) - f(x)}{h} = \lim_{h \to 0} (2x + h + 6) = 2x + 6$$

Thus, $f'(x) = 2x + 6$.

$f'(1) = 8$, $f'(2) = 10$, $f'(3) = 12$

13. $f(x) = 2x^2 - 7x + 3$

Step 1. Find $f(x + h)$:

$$f(x + h) = 2(x + h)^2 - 7(x + h) + 3$$
$$= 2(x^2 + 2xh + h^2) - 7x - 7h + 3$$
$$= 2x^2 + 4xh + 2h^2 - 7x - 7h + 3$$

Step 2. Find $f(x + h) - f(x)$:

$$f(x + h) - f(x) = 2x^2 + 4xh + 2h^2 - 7x - 7h + 3 - (2x^2 - 7x + 3)$$
$$= 4xh + 2h^2 - 7h$$

Step 3. Find $\dfrac{f(x+h)-f(x)}{h}$:

$$\dfrac{f(x+h)-f(x)}{h} = \dfrac{4xh + 2h^2 - 7h}{h} = 4x + 2h - 7$$

Step 4. Find $\lim\limits_{h\to 0} \dfrac{f(x+h)-f(x)}{h}$:

$$\lim\limits_{h\to 0} \dfrac{f(x+h)-f(x)}{h} = \lim\limits_{h\to 0}(4x + 2h - 7) = 4x - 7$$

Thus, $f'(x) = 4x - 7$.
$f'(1) = -3$, $f'(2) = 1$, $f'(3) = 5$

15. $f(x) = -x^2 + 4x - 9$

Step 1. Find $f(x+h)$:

$$\begin{aligned}
f(x+h) &= -(x+h)^2 + 4(x+h) - 9 \\
&= -(x^2 + 2xh + h^2) + 4x + 4h - 9 \\
&= -x^2 - 2xh - h^2 + 4x + 4h - 9
\end{aligned}$$

Step 2. Find $f(x+h) - f(x)$:

$$\begin{aligned}
f(x+h) - f(x) &= -x^2 - 2xh - h^2 + 4x + 4h - 9 - (-x^2 + 4x - 9) \\
&= -2xh - h^2 + 4h
\end{aligned}$$

Step 3. Find $\dfrac{f(x+h)-f(x)}{h}$:

$$\dfrac{f(x+h)-f(x)}{h} = \dfrac{-2xh - h^2 + 4h}{h} = -2x - h + 4$$

Step 4. Find $\lim\limits_{h\to 0} \dfrac{f(x+h)-f(x)}{h}$:

$$\lim\limits_{h\to 0} \dfrac{f(x+h)-f(x)}{h} = \lim\limits_{h\to 0}(-2x - h + 4) = -2x + 4$$

Thus, $f'(x) = -2x + 4$.
$f'(1) = 2$, $f'(2) = 0$, $f'(3) = -2$

17. $f(x) = 2x^3 + 1$

Step 1. Find $f(x+h)$:

$$\begin{aligned}
f(x+h) &= 2(x+h)^3 + 1 = 2(x^3 + 3x^2h + 3xh^2 + h^3) + 1 \\
&= 2x^3 + 6x^2h + 6xh^2 + 2h^3 + 1
\end{aligned}$$

Step 2. Find $f(x+h) - f(x)$:

$$\begin{aligned}
f(x+h) - f(x) &= 2x^3 + 6x^2h + 6xh^2 + 2h^3 + 1 - (2x^3 + 1) \\
&= 6x^2h + 6xh^2 + 2h^3
\end{aligned}$$

Step 3. Find $\dfrac{f(x+h)-f(x)}{h}$:

$$\dfrac{f(x+h)-f(x)}{h} = \dfrac{6x^2h + 6xh^2 + 2h^3}{h} = 6x^2 + 6xh + 2h^2$$

Step 4. Find $\lim\limits_{h \to 0} \dfrac{f(x + h) - f(x)}{h}$:

$$\lim\limits_{h \to 0} \dfrac{f(x + h) - f(x)}{h} = \lim\limits_{h \to 0} (6x^2 + 6xh + 2h^2) = 6x^2$$

Thus, $f'(x) = 6x^2$.

$f'(1) = 6, \quad f'(2) = 24, \quad f'(3) = 54$

19. $f(x) = 4 + \dfrac{4}{x}$

Step 1. Find $f(x + h)$:

$$f(x + h) = 4 + \dfrac{4}{x + h}$$

Step 2. Find $f(x + h) - f(x)$:

$$f(x + h) - f(x) = 4 + \dfrac{4}{x + h} - \left(4 + \dfrac{4}{x}\right) = \dfrac{4}{x + h} - \dfrac{4}{x}$$

$$= \dfrac{4x - 4(x + h)}{x(x + h)} = -\dfrac{4h}{x(x + h)}$$

Step 3. Find $\dfrac{f(x + h) - f(x)}{h}$:

$$\dfrac{f(x + h) - f(x)}{h} = \dfrac{-\dfrac{4h}{x(x + h)}}{h} = -\dfrac{4}{x(x + h)}$$

Step 4. Find $\lim\limits_{h \to 0} \dfrac{f(x + h) - f(x)}{h}$:

$$\lim\limits_{h \to 0} \dfrac{f(x + h) - f(x)}{h} = \lim\limits_{h \to 0} -\dfrac{4}{x(x + h)} = -\dfrac{4}{x^2}$$

Thus, $f'(x) = -\dfrac{4}{x^2}$.

$$f'(1) = -4, \quad f'(2) = -1, \quad f'(3) = -\dfrac{4}{9}$$

21. $f(x) = 5 + 3\sqrt{x}$

Step 1. Find $f(x + h)$:

$$f(x + h) = 5 + 3\sqrt{x + h}$$

Step 2. Find $f(x + h) - f(x)$:

$$f(x + h) - f(x) = 5 + 3\sqrt{x + h} - (5 + 3\sqrt{x})$$
$$= 3(\sqrt{x + h} - \sqrt{x})$$

Step 3. Find $\dfrac{f(x + h) - f(x)}{h}$:

$$\dfrac{f(x + h) - f(x)}{h} = \dfrac{3(\sqrt{x + h} - \sqrt{x})}{h} = \dfrac{3(\sqrt{x + h} - \sqrt{x})}{h} \cdot \dfrac{(\sqrt{x + h} + \sqrt{x})}{(\sqrt{x + h} + \sqrt{x})}$$

$$= \dfrac{3(x + h - x)}{h(\sqrt{x + h} + \sqrt{x})} = \dfrac{3h}{h(\sqrt{x + h} + \sqrt{x})} = \dfrac{3}{\sqrt{x + h} + \sqrt{x}}$$

Find $\lim\limits_{h \to 0} \dfrac{f(x + h) - f(x)}{h}$:

$$\lim_{h \to 0} \frac{f(x + h) - f(x)}{h} = \lim_{h \to 0} \frac{3}{\sqrt{x + h} + \sqrt{x}} = \frac{3}{2\sqrt{x}}$$

Thus, $f'(x) = \dfrac{3}{2\sqrt{x}}$.

$$f'(1) = \frac{3}{2}, \quad f'(2) = \frac{3}{2\sqrt{2}} = \frac{3\sqrt{2}}{4}, \quad f'(3) = \frac{3}{2\sqrt{3}} = \frac{\sqrt{3}}{2}$$

23. $f(x) = 10\sqrt{x + 5}$

Step 1. Find $f(x + h)$:
$$f(x + h) = 10\sqrt{x + h + 5}$$

Step 2. Find $f(x + h) - f(x)$:
$$f(x + h) - f(x) = 10\sqrt{x + h + 5} - 10\sqrt{x + 5}$$
$$= 10\left(\sqrt{x + h + 5} - \sqrt{x + 5}\right)$$

Step 3. Find $\dfrac{f(x + h) - f(x)}{h}$:

$$\frac{f(x + h) - f(x)}{h} = \frac{10\left(\sqrt{x + h + 5} - \sqrt{x + 5}\right)}{h}$$

$$= \frac{10\left(\sqrt{x + h + 5} - \sqrt{x + 5}\right)}{h} \cdot \frac{\left(\sqrt{x + h + 5} + \sqrt{x + 5}\right)}{\left(\sqrt{x + h + 5} + \sqrt{x + 5}\right)}$$

$$= \frac{10[x + h + 5 - (x + 5)]}{h\left(\sqrt{x + h + 5} + \sqrt{x + 5}\right)} = \frac{10h}{h\left(\sqrt{x + h + 5} + \sqrt{x + 5}\right)}$$

$$= \frac{10}{\sqrt{x + h + 5} + \sqrt{x + 5}}$$

Step 4. Find $\lim\limits_{h \to 0} \dfrac{f(x + h) - f(x)}{h}$:

$$\lim_{h \to 0} \frac{f(x + h) - f(x)}{h} = \lim_{h \to 0} \frac{10}{\sqrt{x + h + 5} + \sqrt{x + 5}} = \frac{10}{2\sqrt{x + 5}} = \frac{5}{\sqrt{x + 5}}$$

Thus, $f'(x) = \dfrac{5}{\sqrt{x + 5}}$.

$$f'(1) = \frac{5}{\sqrt{6}} = \frac{5\sqrt{6}}{6}, \quad f'(2) = \frac{5}{\sqrt{7}} = \frac{5\sqrt{7}}{7}, \quad f'(3) = \frac{5}{\sqrt{8}} = \frac{5}{2\sqrt{2}} = \frac{5\sqrt{2}}{4}$$

25. $f(x) = \dfrac{3x}{x + 2}$

Step 1. Find $f(x + h)$:
$$f(x + h) = \frac{3(x + h)}{x + h + 2}$$

<u>Step 2</u>. Find $f(x + h) - f(x)$:

$$f(x + h) - f(x) = \frac{3(x + h)}{x + h + 2} - \frac{3x}{x + 2}$$

$$= \frac{3(x + h)(x + 2) - 3x(x + h + 2)}{(x + h + 2)(x + 2)}$$

$$= \frac{3x^2 + 3xh + 6x + 6h - 3x^2 - 3xh - 6x}{(x + h + 2)(x + 2)}$$

$$= \frac{6h}{(x + h + 2)(x + 2)}$$

<u>Step 3</u>. Find $\dfrac{f(x + h) - f(x)}{h}$:

$$\frac{f(x + h) - f(x)}{h} = \frac{\dfrac{6h}{(x + h + 2)(x + 2)}}{h} = \frac{6}{(x + h + 2)(x + 2)}$$

<u>Step 4</u>. Find $\displaystyle\lim_{h \to 0} \frac{f(x + h) - f(x)}{h}$:

$$\lim_{h \to 0} \frac{f(x + h) - f(x)}{h} = \lim_{h \to 0} \frac{6}{(x + h + 2)(x + 2)} = \frac{6}{(x + 2)^2}$$

Thus, $f'(x) = \dfrac{6}{(x + 2)^2}$.

$$f'(1) = \frac{2}{3}, \quad f'(2) = \frac{3}{8}, \quad f'(3) = \frac{6}{25}$$

27. $y = f(x) = x^2 + x$

(A) $f(1) = 1^2 + 1 = 2$, $f(3) = 3^2 + 3 = 12$

Slope of secant line: $\dfrac{f(3) - f(1)}{3 - 1} = \dfrac{12 - 2}{2} = 5$

(B) $f(1) = 2$, $f(1 + h) = (1 + h)^2 + (1 + h) = 1 + 2h + h^2 + 1 + h$
$$= 2 + 3h + h^2$$

Slope of secant line: $\dfrac{f(1 + h) - f(1)}{h} = \dfrac{2 + 3h + h^2 - 2}{h} = 3 + h$

(C) Slope of tangent line at $(1, f(1))$:
$$\lim_{h \to 0} \frac{f(1 + h) - f(1)}{h} = \lim_{h \to 0} (3 + h) = 3$$

(D) Equation of tangent line at $(1, f(1))$:
$y - f(1) = f'(1)(x - 1)$ or $y - 2 = 3(x - 1)$ and $y = 3x - 1$.

29. $f(x) = x^2 + x$

(A) Average velocity: $\dfrac{f(3) - f(1)}{3 - 1} = \dfrac{3^2 + 3 - (1^2 + 1)}{2} = \dfrac{12 - 2}{2}$
$$= 5 \text{ meters/sec.}$$

(B) Average velocity: $\dfrac{f(1 + h) - f(1)}{h} = \dfrac{(1 + h)^2 + (1 + h) - (1^2 + 1)}{h}$

$$= \dfrac{1 + 2h + h^2 + 1 + h - 2}{h}$$

$$= \dfrac{3h + h^2}{h} = 3 + h \text{ meters/sec.}$$

(C) Instantaneous velocity: $\lim\limits_{h \to 0} \dfrac{f(1 + h) - f(1)}{h} = \lim\limits_{h \to 0} (3 + h) = 3 \text{ m/sec.}$

31. $F'(x)$ does exist at $x = a$.

33. $F'(x)$ does not exist at $x = c$; the graph has a vertical tangent line at $(c,\ F(c))$.

35. $F'(x)$ does exist at $x = e$; $F'(e) = 0$.

37. $F'(x)$ does exist at $x = g$.

39. $f(x) = x^2 - 4x$

   (A) <u>Step 1</u>. Find $f(x + h)$:

   $\qquad f(x + h) = (x + h)^2 - 4(x + h) = x^2 + 2xh + h^2 - 4x - 4h$

   <u>Step 2</u>. Find $f(x + h) - f(x)$:

   $\qquad f(x + h) - f(x) = x^2 + 2xh + h^2 - 4x - 4h - (x^2 - 4x)$

   $\qquad\qquad\qquad\qquad = 2xh + h^2 - 4h$

   <u>Step 3</u>. Find $\dfrac{f(x + h) - f(x)}{h}$:

   $\qquad \dfrac{f(x + h) - f(x)}{h} = \dfrac{2xh + h^2 - 4h}{h} = 2x + h - 4$

   <u>Step 4</u>. Find $\lim\limits_{h \to 0} \dfrac{f(x + h) - f(x)}{h}$:

   $\qquad \lim\limits_{h \to 0} \dfrac{f(x + h) - f(x)}{h} = \lim\limits_{h \to 0} (2x + h - 4) = 2x - 4$

   $\qquad$ Thus, $f'(x) = 2x - 4$.

   (B) $f'(0) = -4$, $f'(2) = 0$,
   $f'(4) = 4$

   (C) Since f is a quadratic
   function, the graph of f is
   a parabola.

   y intercept: $y = 0$
   x intercepts: $x = 0$, $x = 4$
   Vertex: $(2, -4)$

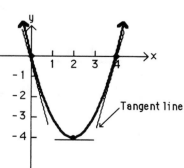

41. To find $v = f'(x)$, use the four-step process on the position function $f(x) = 4x^2 - 2x$.

Step 1. Find $f(x + h)$:
$$f(x + h) = 4(x + h)^2 - 2(x + h) = 4(x^2 + 2xh + h^2) - 2x - 2h$$
$$= 4x^2 + 8xh + 4h^2 - 2x - 2h$$

Step 2. Find $f(x + h) - f(x)$:
$$f(x + h) - f(x) = 4x^2 + 8xh + 4h^2 - 2x - 2h - (4x^2 - 2x)$$
$$= 8xh + 4h^2 - 2h$$

Step 3. Find $\dfrac{f(x + h) - f(x)}{h}$:
$$\frac{f(x + h) - f(x)}{h} = \frac{8xh + 4h^2 - 2h}{h} = 8x + 4h - 2$$

Step 4. Find $\lim\limits_{h \to 0} \dfrac{f(x + h) - f(x)}{h}$:
$$\lim_{h \to 0} \frac{f(x + h) - f(x)}{h} = \lim_{h \to 0}(8x + 4h - 2) = 8x - 2$$

Thus, the velocity, $v(x) = f'(x) = 8x - 2$

$f'(1) = 8 \cdot 1 - 2 = 6$ ft/sec
$f'(3) = 8 \cdot 3 - 2 = 22$ ft/sec
$f'(5) = 8 \cdot 5 - 2 = 38$ ft/sec

43. (A) The graphs of g and h are vertical translations of the graph of f. All three functions should have the same derivative.

(B) $m(x) = x^2 + C$

Step 1. Find $m(x + h)$:
$$m(x + h) = (x + h)^2 + C$$

Step 2. Find $m(x + h) - m(x)$:
$$m(x + h) - m(x) = (x + h)^2 + C - (x^2 + C)$$
$$= x^2 + 2xh + h^2 + C - x^2 + C$$
$$= 2xh + h^2$$

Step 3. Find $\dfrac{m(x + h) - m(x)}{h}$:
$$\frac{m(x + h) - m(x)}{h} = \frac{2xh + h^2}{h} = 2x + h$$

Step 4. $\lim\limits_{h \to 0} \dfrac{m(x + h) - m(x)}{h}$:
$$\lim_{h \to 0} \frac{m(x + h) - m(x)}{h} = \lim_{h \to 0}(2x + h) = 2x$$

Thus, $m'(x) = 2x$.

45. (A) The graph of $f(x) = C$, C a constant, is a horizontal line C units above or below the x axis depending on the sign of C. At any given point on the graph, the slope of the tangent line is 0.

(B) $f(x) = C$

Step 1. Find $f(x + h)$:

$$f(x + h) = C$$

Step 2. Find $f(x + h) - f(x)$:

$$f(x + h) - f(x) = C - C = 0$$

Step 3. Find $\dfrac{f(x + h) - f(x)}{h}$:

$$\frac{f(x + h) - f(x)}{h} = \frac{0}{h} = 0$$

Step 4. Find $\lim\limits_{h \to 0} \dfrac{f(x + h) - f(x)}{h}$:

$$\lim_{h \to 0} \frac{f(x + h) - f(x)}{h} = \lim_{h \to 0} 0 = 0$$

Thus, $f'(x) = 0$.

47. The graph of $f(x) = \begin{Bmatrix} 2x, & x < 1 \\ 2, & x \ge 1 \end{Bmatrix}$ is:

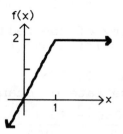

f is not differentiable at $x = 1$ because the graph of f has a sharp corner at this point.

49. $f(x) = \begin{cases} x^2 + 1 & \text{if } x < 0 \\ 1 & \text{if } x \ge 0 \end{cases}$

It is clear that $f'(x) = \begin{cases} 2x & \text{if } x < 0 \\ 0 & \text{if } x > 0 \end{cases}$

Thus, the only question is $f'(0)$. Since

$$\lim_{x \to 0^-} f'(x) = \lim_{x \to 0^-} 2x = 0 \quad \text{and} \quad \lim_{x \to 0^+} f'(x) = \lim_{x \to 0^+} 0 = 0$$

f is differentiable at 0 as well; f is differentiable for real numbers.

51. $f(x) = |x|$

$$\lim_{h \to 0} \frac{f(0 + h) - f(0)}{h} = \lim_{h \to 0} \frac{|0 + h| - |0|}{h} = \lim_{h \to 0} \frac{|h|}{h}$$

The limit does not exist. Thus, f is not differentiable at $x = 0$.

53. $f(x) = \sqrt[3]{x} = x^{1/3}$

$$\lim_{h \to 0} \frac{f(0 + h) - f(0)}{h} = \lim_{h \to 0} \frac{(0 + h)^{1/3} - 0^{1/3}}{h} = \lim_{h \to 0} \frac{h^{1/3}}{h} = \lim_{h \to 0} \frac{1}{h^{2/3}}$$

The limit does not exist. Thus, f is not differentiable at $x = 0$.

55. $f(x) = \sqrt{1 - x^2}$

$$\frac{f(0 + h) - f(0)}{h} = \frac{\sqrt{1 - h^2} - 1}{h} = \frac{\sqrt{1 - h^2} - 1}{h} \cdot \frac{\sqrt{1 - h^2} + 1}{\sqrt{1 - h^2} + 1}$$

$$= \frac{1 - h^2 - 1}{h\left(\sqrt{1 - h^2} + 1\right)} = \frac{-h}{\sqrt{1 - h^2} + 1}$$

$$\lim_{h \to 0} \frac{f(0 + h) - f(0)}{h} = \lim_{h \to 0} \frac{-h}{\sqrt{1 - h^2} + 1} = 0$$

f is differentiable at 0; $f'(0) = 0$.

57. The height of the ball at x seconds is $h(x) = 576 - 16x^2$. To find when the ball hits the ground, we solve:

$$576 - 16x^2 = 0$$
$$16x^2 = 576$$
$$x^2 = 36$$
$$x = 6 \text{ seconds}$$

The velocity of the ball is given by $h'(x) = -32x$. The velocity at impact is $h'(6) = -32(6) = -192$; the ball hits the ground at 192 ft/sec.

59. $R(x) = 60x - 0.025x^2 \qquad 0 \le x \le 2,400$.
(A) Average rate of change:

$$\frac{R(1,050) - R(1,000)}{1,050 - 1,000}$$

$$= \frac{60(1,050) - 0.025(1,050)^2 - [60(1,000) - 0.025(1,000)^2]}{50}$$

$$= \frac{35,437.50 - 35,000}{50} = \$8.75$$

(B) <u>Step 1</u>. Find $R(x + h)$:

$$R(x + h) = 60(x + h) - 0.025(x + h)^2$$
$$= 60x + 60h - 0.025(x^2 + 2xh + h^2)$$
$$= 60x + 60h - 0.025x^2 - 0.050xh - 0.025h^2$$

<u>Step 2</u>. Find $R(x + h) - R(x)$:

$$R(x + h) - R(x) = 60x + 60h - 0.025x^2 - 0.050xh - 0.025h^2$$
$$- (60x - 0.025x^2)$$
$$= 60h - 0.050xh - 0.025h^2$$

<u>Step 3</u>. Find $\dfrac{R(x + h) - R(x)}{h}$:

$$\frac{R(x + h) - R(x)}{h} = \frac{60h - 0.050xh - 0.025h^2}{h}$$

$$= 60 - 0.050x - 0.025h$$

Step 4. Find $\lim\limits_{h \to 0} \dfrac{R(x + h) - R(x)}{h}$:

$$\lim\limits_{h \to 0} \dfrac{R(x + h) - R(x)}{h} = \lim\limits_{h \to 0}(60 - 0.050x - 0.025h)$$
$$= 60 - 0.050x$$

Thus, $R'(x) = 60 - 0.050x$.

(C) $R(1,000) = 60(1,000) - 0.025(1,000)^2 = \$35,000$;
   $R'(1,000) = 60 - 0.05(1,000) = \$10$;
   at a production level of 1,000 car seats, the revenue is $35,000 and is increasing at the rate of $10 per seat.

61. (A) $S(t) = 2\sqrt{t + 10}$

Step 1. Find $S(t + h)$:
   $$S(t + h) = 2\sqrt{t + h + 10}$$

Step 2. Find $S(t + h) - S(t)$:
   $$S(t + h) - S(t) = 2\sqrt{t + h + 10} - 2\sqrt{t + 10}$$
   $$= 2(\sqrt{t + h + 10} - \sqrt{t + 10})$$

Step 3. Find $\dfrac{S(t + h) - S(t)}{h}$:

$$\dfrac{S(t + h) - S(t)}{h} = \dfrac{2(\sqrt{t + h + 10} - \sqrt{t + 10})}{h}$$

$$= \dfrac{2(\sqrt{t + h + 10} - \sqrt{t + 10})}{h} \cdot \dfrac{(\sqrt{t + h + 10} + \sqrt{t + 10})}{(\sqrt{t + h + 10} + \sqrt{t + 10})}$$

$$= \dfrac{2[t + h + 10 - (t + 10)]}{h(\sqrt{t + h + 10} + \sqrt{t + 10})} = \dfrac{2h}{h(\sqrt{t + h + 10} + \sqrt{t + 10})}$$

$$= \dfrac{2}{\sqrt{t + h + 10} + \sqrt{t + 10}}$$

Step 4. Find $\lim\limits_{h \to 0} \dfrac{S(t + h) - S(t)}{h}$:

$$\lim\limits_{h \to 0} \dfrac{S(t + h) - S(t)}{h} = \lim\limits_{h \to 0} \dfrac{2}{\sqrt{t + h + 10} + \sqrt{t + 10}} = \dfrac{1}{\sqrt{t + 10}}$$

Thus, $S'(t) = \dfrac{1}{\sqrt{t + 10}}$.

(B) $S(15) = 2\sqrt{15 + 10} = 2\sqrt{25} = 10$;
   $$S'(15) = \dfrac{1}{\sqrt{15 + 10}} = \dfrac{1}{\sqrt{25}} = \dfrac{1}{5} = 0.2$$

   After 15 months, the total sales are $10 million and are INCREASING at the rate of $0.2 million = $200,000 per month.

(C) The estimated total sales are $10.2 million after 16 months and $10.4 million after 17 months.

63. $p(t) = 14t^2 - 6.6t + 602.4$

(A) Step 1. Find $p(t + h)$:
$$p(t + h) = 14(t + h)^2 - 6.6(t + h) + 602.4$$

Step 2. Find $p(t + h) - p(t)$:
$$p(t + h) - p(t) = 14(t + h)^2 - 6.6(t + h) + 602.4$$
$$- (14t^2 - 6.6t + 602.4)$$
$$= 28th + 14h^2 - 6.6h$$

Step 3. Find $\dfrac{p(t + h) - p(t)}{h}$:
$$\frac{p(t + h) - p(t)}{h} = \frac{28th + 14h^2 - 6.6h}{h} = 28t + 14h - 6.6$$

Step 4. Find $\lim\limits_{h \to 0} \dfrac{p(t + h) - p(t)}{h}$:
$$\lim_{h \to 0} \frac{p(t + h) - p(t)}{h} = \lim_{h \to 0}(28t + 14h - 6.6) = 28t - 6.6$$
Thus, $p'(t) = 28t - 6.6$.

(B) The year 2010 corresponds to $t = 15$.
$p(15) = 14(15)^2 - 6.6(15) + 602.4 = 3,653.4$ thousand tons;
$p'(t) = 28t - 6.6$,
$p'(15) = 28(15) - 6.6 = 413.4$;
in 2010 the US will produce 3,653.4 thousand tons of zinc and this quantity is increasing at the rate of 413.4 thousand tons per year.

65. (A)
```
QuadReg
 y=ax2+bx+c
 a=.5303030303
 b=20.68181818
 c=921.0181818
```

(B) $R(20) \approx 1,546.8$; $R'(20) \approx 41.9$
Interpretation: In 2010, retail sales will be 1,546.8 billion kilowatt hours and will be INCREASING at the rate of 41.9 billion kilowatt hours per year.

67. (A) $P(t) = 80 + 12t - t^2$

Step 1. Find $P(t + h)$:
$$P(t + h) = 80 + 12(t + h) - (t + h)^2$$
$$= 80 + 12t + 12h - (t + h)^2$$

Step 2. Find $P(t + h) - P(t)$:
$$P(t + h) - P(t) = 80 + 12t + 12h - (t + h)^2 - (80 + 12t - t^2)$$
$$= 12h - 2th - h^2$$

Step 3. Find $\dfrac{P(t + h) - P(t)}{h}$:
$$\frac{P(t + h) - P(t)}{h} = \frac{12h - 2th - h^2}{h} = 12 - 2t - h$$

Step 4. Find $\lim\limits_{h \to 0} \dfrac{P(t + h) - P(t)}{h}$:

$$\lim_{h \to 0} \frac{P(t + h) - P(t)}{h} = \lim_{h \to 0} (12 - 2t - h) = 12 - 2t$$

Thus, $P'(t) = 12 - 2t$.

(B) $P(3) = 80 + 12(3) - (3)^2 = 107$; $P'(3) = 12 - 2(3) = 6$

After 3 hours, the ozone level is 107 ppb and is INCREASING at the rate of 6 ppb per hour.

69. (A) $f(t) = 0.011t^2 - t + 29.8$

Step 1. Find $f(t + h)$:
$$f(t + h) = 0.011(t + h)^2 - (t + h) + 29.8$$

Step 2. Find $f(t + h) - f(t)$:
$$f(t + h) - f(t) = 0.011(t + h)^2 - t - h + 29.8$$
$$- (0.011t^2 - t + 29.8)$$
$$= 0.022th + 0.011h^2 - h$$

Step 3. Find $\dfrac{f(t + h) - f(t)}{h}$:
$$\frac{f(t + h) - f(t)}{h} = \frac{0.022th + 0.011h^2 - h}{h}$$
$$= 0.022t + 0.011h - 1$$

Step 4. Find $\lim\limits_{h \to 0} \dfrac{f(t + h) - f(t)}{h}$:
$$\lim_{h \to 0} \frac{f(t + h) - f(t)}{h} = \lim_{h \to 0} (0.022t + 0.011h - 1) = 0.022t - 1$$
Thus, $f'(t) = 0.022t - 1$.

(B) The year 2000 corresponds to $t = 40$.
$f(40) = 0.011(40)^2 - 40 + 29.8 = 7.4$;
$f'(t) = 0.022t - 1$, $f'(40) = 0.022(40) - 1 = -0.12$;

The number of infant male deaths per 100,000 births was 7.4 and was decreasing at the rate of 0.12 deaths per 100,000 births per year.

EXERCISE 3-4

Things to remember:

1. DERIVATIVE NOTATION

   Given $y = f(x)$, then

   $$f'(x), \quad y', \quad \frac{dy}{dx}$$

   all represent the derivative of f at x.

2. CONSTANT FUNCTION RULE

If $f(x) = C$, C a constant, then $f'(x) = 0$. Also

$$y' = 0 \text{ and } \frac{dy}{dx} = 0.$$

3. POWER RULE

If $f(x) = x^n$, n any real number, then

$$f'(x) = nx^{n-1}.$$

Also, $y' = nx^{n-1}$ and $\dfrac{dy}{dx} = nx^{n-1}$

4. CONSTANT MULTIPLE PROPERTY

If $y = f(x) = ku(x)$, where k is a constant, then

$$f'(x) = ku'(x).$$

Also,

$$y' = ku' \text{ and } \frac{dy}{dx} = k\frac{du}{dx}.$$

5. SUM AND DIFFERENCE PROPERTY

If $y = f(x) = u(x) \pm v(x)$, then

$$f'(x) = u'(x) \pm v'(x).$$

Also,

$$y' = u' \pm v' \text{ and } \frac{dy}{dx} = \frac{du}{dx} \pm \frac{dv}{dx}$$

[Note: This rule generalizes to the sum and difference of any given number of functions.]

---

1. $f(x) = 7$; $f'(x) = 0$ (using 2)

3. $y = x^9$; $\dfrac{dy}{dx} = 9x^8$ (using 3)

5. $\dfrac{d}{dx}x^3 = 3x^2$ (using 3)

7. $y = x^{-4}$; $y' = -4x^{-5}$ (using 3)

9. $g(x) = x^{8/3}$; $g'(x) = \dfrac{8}{3}x^{5/3}$ (using 3)

11. $y = \dfrac{1}{x^{10}}$; $\dfrac{dy}{dx} = -10x^{-11} = \dfrac{-10}{x^{11}}$

13. $f(x) = 5x^2$; $f'(x) = 5(2x) = 10x$ (using 4)

15. $y = 0.4x^7$; $y' = 0.4(7x^6) = 2.8x^6$

17. $\dfrac{d}{dx}\left(\dfrac{x^3}{18}\right) = \dfrac{1}{18}(3x^2) = \dfrac{1}{6}x^2$

19. $h(x) = 4f(x)$; $h'(2) = 4 \cdot f'(2) = 4(3) = 12$

21. $h(x) = f(x) + g(x)$; $h'(2) = f'(2) + g'(2) = 3 + (-1) = 2$

23. $h(x) = 2f(x) - 3g(x) + 7$; $h'(2) = 2f'(2) - 3g'(2)$
$$= 2(3) - 3(-1) = 9$$

25. $\dfrac{d}{dx}(2x - 5) = \dfrac{d}{dx}(2x) - \dfrac{d}{dx}(5) = 2$

27. $f(t) = 2t^2 - 3t + 1$; $f'(t) = (2t^2)' - (3t)' + (1)' = 4t - 3$

29. $y = 5x^{-2} + 9x^{-1}$; $y' = -10x^{-3} - 9x^{-2}$

31. $\dfrac{d}{du}(5u^{0.3} - 4u^{2.2}) = \dfrac{d}{du}(5u^{0.3}) - \dfrac{d}{du}(4u^{2.2}) = 1.5u^{-0.7} - 8.8u^{1.2}$

33. $h(t) = 2.1 + 0.5t - 1.1t^3$; $h'(t) = 0.5 - (1.1)3t^2 = 0.5 - 3.3t^2$

35. $y = \dfrac{2}{5x^4} = \dfrac{2}{5}x^{-4}$; $y' = \dfrac{2}{5}(-4x^{-5}) = -\dfrac{8}{5}x^{-5} = \dfrac{-8}{5x^5}$

37. $\dfrac{d}{dx}\left(\dfrac{3x^2}{2} - \dfrac{7}{5x^2}\right) = \dfrac{d}{dx}\left(\dfrac{3}{2}x^2\right) - \dfrac{d}{dx}\left(\dfrac{7}{5}x^{-2}\right) = 3x - \dfrac{14}{5}x^{-3} = 3x - \dfrac{14}{5x^3}$

39. $G(w) = \dfrac{5}{9w^4} + 5\sqrt[3]{w} = \dfrac{5}{9}w^{-4} + 5w^{1/3}$;

$G'(w) = -\dfrac{20}{9}w^{-5} + \dfrac{5}{3}w^{-2/3} = \dfrac{-20}{9w^5} + \dfrac{5}{3w^{2/3}}$

41. $\dfrac{d}{du}(3u^{2/3} - 5u^{1/3}) = \dfrac{d}{du}(3u^{2/3}) - \dfrac{d}{du}(5u^{1/3})$

$$= 2u^{-1/3} - \dfrac{5}{3}u^{-2/3} = \dfrac{2}{u^{1/3}} - \dfrac{5}{3u^{2/3}}$$

43. $h(t) = \dfrac{3}{t^{3/5}} - \dfrac{6}{t^{1/2}} = 3t^{-3/5} - 6t^{-1/2}$;

$h'(t) = 3\left(-\dfrac{3}{5}t^{-8/5}\right) - 6\left(-\dfrac{1}{2}t^{-3/2}\right) = -\dfrac{9}{5}t^{-8/5} + 3t^{-3/2} = \dfrac{-9}{5t^{8/5}} + \dfrac{3}{t^{3/2}}$

45. $y = \dfrac{1}{\sqrt[3]{x}} = \dfrac{1}{x^{1/3}} = x^{-1/3}$; $y' = -\dfrac{1}{3}x^{-4/3} = \dfrac{-1}{3x^{4/3}}$

47. $\dfrac{d}{dx}\left(\dfrac{1.2}{\sqrt{x}} - 3.2x^{-2} + x\right) = \dfrac{d}{dx}(1.2x^{-1/2} - 3.2x^{-2} + x)$

$$= \dfrac{d}{dx}(1.2x^{-1/2}) - \dfrac{d}{dx}(3.2x^{-2}) + \dfrac{d}{dx}(x)$$

$$= -0.6x^{-3/2} + 6.4x^{-3} + 1 = \dfrac{-0.6}{x^{3/2}} + \dfrac{6.4}{x^3} + 1$$

49. $f(x) = 6x - x^2$

(A) $f'(x) = 6 - 2x$

(B) Slope of the graph of f at $x = 2$: $f'(2) = 6 - 2(2) = 2$
Slope of the graph of f at $x = 4$: $f'(4) = 6 - 2(4) = -2$

(C) Tangent line at $x = 2$: $y - y_1 = m(x - x_1)$

$x_1 = 2$

$y_1 = f(2) = 6(2) - 2^2 = 8$

$m = f'(2) = 2$

Thus, $y - 8 = 2(x - 2)$ or $y = 2x + 4$.

Tangent line at $x = 4$: $y - y_1 = m(x - x_1)$

$x_1 = 4$

$y_1 = f(4) = 6(4) - 4^2 = 8$

$m = f'(4) = -2$

Thus, $y - 8 = -2(x - 4)$ or $y = -2x + 16$

(D) The tangent line is horizontal at the values $x = c$ such that $f'(c) = 0$. Thus, we must solve the following:

$$f'(x) = 6 - 2x = 0$$
$$2x = 6$$
$$x = 3$$

51. $f(x) = 3x^4 - 6x^2 - 7$

(A) $f'(x) = 12x^3 - 12x$

(B) Slope of the graph of $x = 2$: $f'(2) = 12(2)^3 - 12(2) = 72$
Slope of the graph of $x = 4$: $f'(4) = 12(4)^3 - 12(4) = 720$

(C) Tangent line at $x = 2$: $y - y_1 = m(x - x_1)$, where $x_1 = 2$,

$y_1 = f(2) = 3(2)^4 - 6(2)^2 - 7 = 17$, $m = 72$.

$y - 17 = 72(x - 2)$ or $y = 72x - 127$

Tangent line at $x = 4$: $y - y_1 = m(x - x_1)$, where $x_1 = 4$,

$y_1 = f(4) = 3(4)^4 - 6(4)^2 - 7 = 665$, $m = 720$.

$y - 665 = 720(x - 4)$ or $y = 720x - 2215$

(D) Solve $f'(x) = 0$ for x:

$$12x^3 - 12x = 0$$
$$12x(x^2 - 1) = 0$$
$$12x(x - 1)(x + 1) = 0$$
$$x = -1, \ x = 0, \ x = 1$$

53. $f(x) = 176x - 16x^2$

    (A) $v = f'(x) = 176 - 32x$ (B) $v\big|_{x=0} = f'(0) = 176$ ft/sec.

    (C) Solve $v = f'(x) = 0$ $v\big|_{x=3} = f'(3) = 176 - 32(3) = 80$ ft/sec.
        for x:
        $176 - 32x = 0$
            $32x = 176$
               $x = 5.5$ sec.

55. $f(x) = x^3 - 9x^2 + 15x$

    (A) $v = f'(x) = 3x^2 - 18x + 15$

    (B) $v\big|_{x=0} = f'(0) = 15$ feet/sec.

        $v\big|_{x=3} = f'(3) = 3(3)^2 - 18(3) + 15 = -12$ feet/sec.

    (C) Solve $v = f'(x) = 0$ for x:
        $3x^2 - 18x + 15 = 0$
        $3(x^2 - 6x + 5) = 0$
        $3(x - 5)(x - 1) = 0$
              $x = 1, \; x = 5$

57. $f(x) = x^2 - 3x - 4\sqrt{x} = x^2 - 3x - 4x^{1/2}$

$f'(x) = 2x - 3 - 2x^{-1/2}$

The graph of f has a horizontal tangent line at the value(s) of x where $f'(x) = 0$. Thus, we need to solve the equation
      $2x - 3 - 2x^{-1/2} = 0$

By graphing the function $y = 2x - 3 - 2x^{-1/2}$, we see that there is one zero. To four decimal places, it is $x = 2.1777$.

59. $f(x) = 3\sqrt[3]{x^4} - 1.5x^2 - 3x = 3x^{4/3} - 1.5x^2 - 3x$

$f'(x) = 4x^{1/3} - 3x - 3$

The graph of f has a horizontal tangent line at the value(s) of x where $f'(x) = 0$. Thus, we need to solve the equation
      $4x^{1/3} - 3x - 3 = 0$

Graphing the function $y = 4x^{1/3} - 3x - 3$, we see that there is one zero. To four decimal places, it is $x = -2.9018$.

61. $f(x) = 0.05x^4 - 0.1x^3 - 1.5x^2 - 1.6x + 3$

$f'(x) = 0.2x^3 + 0.3x^2 - 3x - 1.6$

The graph of f has a horizontal tangent line at the value(s) of x where $f'(x) = 0$. Thus, we need to solve the equation
      $0.2x^3 + 0.3x^2 - 3x - 1.6 = 0$

By graphing the function $y = 0.2x^3 + 0.3x^2 - 3x - 1.6$ we see that there are three zeros. To four decimal places, they are
      $x_1 = -4.4607, \; x_2 = -0.5159, \; x_3 = 3.4765$

63. $f(x) = 0.2x^4 - 3.12x^3 + 16.25x^2 - 28.25x + 7.5$

$f'(x) = 0.8x^3 - 9.36x^2 + 32.5x - 28.25$

The graph of f has a horizontal tangent line at the value(s) of x where $f'(x) = 0$. Thus, we need to solve the equation

$$0.8x^3 - 9.36x^2 + 32.5x - 28.25 = 0$$

Graphing the function $y = 0.8x^3 - 9.36x^2 + 32.5x - 28.25$, we see that there is one zero. To four decimal places, it is $x = 1.3050$.

65. $f(x) = ax^2 + bx + c$; $f'(x) = 2ax + b$.

The derivative is 0 at the vertex of the parabola:

$$2ax + b = 0$$
$$x = -\frac{b}{2a}$$

67. (A) $f(x) = x^3 + x$ (B) $f(x) = x^3$ (C) $f(x) = x^3 - x$

69. $f(x) = (2x - 1)^2 = 4x^2 - 4x + 1$

$f'(x) = 8x - 4$

71. $\dfrac{d}{dx}\left(\dfrac{10x + 20}{x}\right) = \dfrac{d}{dx}\left(10 + \dfrac{20}{x}\right) = \dfrac{d}{dx}(10) + \dfrac{d}{dx}(20x^{-1}) = -20x^{-2} = -\dfrac{20}{x^2}$

73. $y = \dfrac{3x - 4}{12x^2} = \dfrac{3x}{12x^2} - \dfrac{4}{12x^2} = \dfrac{1}{4}x^{-1} - \dfrac{1}{3}x^{-2}$

$\dfrac{dy}{dx} = -\dfrac{1}{4}x^{-2} + \dfrac{2}{3}x^{-3} = -\dfrac{1}{4x^2} + \dfrac{2}{3x^3}$

75. $y = \dfrac{x^4 - 3x^3 + 5}{x^2} = x^2 - 3x + 5x^{-2}$; $y' = 2x - 3 - 10x^{-3} = 2x - 3 - \dfrac{10}{x^3}$

77. $f(x) = x^3$

<u>Step 1</u>. Find $f(x + h)$:

$$f(x + h) = (x + h)^3 = x^3 + 3x^2h + 3xh^2 + h^3$$

<u>Step 2</u>. Find $f(x + h) - f(x)$:

$$f(x + h) - f(x + h) = x^3 + 3x^3h + 3xh^2 + h^3 - x^3$$
$$= 3x^2h + 3xh^2 + h^3$$

<u>Step 3</u>. Find $\dfrac{f(x + h) - f(x)}{h}$:

$$\dfrac{f(x + h) - f(x)}{h} = \dfrac{3x^2h + 3xh^2 + h^3}{h} = 3x^2 + 3xh + h^2$$

<u>Step 4</u>. Find $\lim\limits_{h \to 0} \dfrac{f(x + h) - f(x)}{h}$:

$$\lim\limits_{h \to 0} \dfrac{f(x + h) - f(x)}{h} = \lim\limits_{h \to 0}(3x^2 + 3xh + h^2) = 3x^2$$

Thus, $\dfrac{d}{dx}(x^3) = 3x^2$.

79. $f(x) = x^{1/3}$; $f'(x) = \frac{1}{3}x^{-2/3} = \frac{1}{3x^{2/3}}$

The domain of f' is the set of all real numbers except $x = 0$. The graph of f is smooth, but it has a vertical tangent line at $(0, 0)$.

81. (A) $S(t) = 0.03t^3 + 0.5t^2 + 2t + 3$
$S'(t) = 0.09t^2 + t + 2$

(B) $S(5) = 0.03(5)^3 + 0.5(5)^2 + 2(5) + 3 = 29.25$
$S'(5) = 0.09(5)^2 + 5 + 2 = 9.25$

After 5 months, sales are \$29.25 million and are increasing at the rate of \$9.25 million per month.

(C) $S(10) = 0.03(10)^3 + 0.5(10)^2 + 2(10) + 3 = 103$
$S'(10) = 0.09(10)^2 + 10 + 2 = 21$

After 10 months, sales are \$103 million and are increasing at the rate of \$21 million per month.

83. (A) $N(x) = 1,000 - \frac{3,780}{x} = 1,000 - 3,780x^{-1}$
$N'(x) = 3,780x^{-2} = \frac{3,780}{x^2}$

(B) $N'(10) = \frac{3,780}{(10)^2} = 37.8$

At the \$10,000 level of advertising, sales are INCREASING at the rate of 37.8 boats per \$1000 spent on advertising.

$N'(20) = \frac{3,780}{(20)^2} = 9.45$

At the \$20,000 level of advertising, sales are INCREASING at the rate of 9.45 boats per \$1000 spent on advertising.

85. (A)

```
CubicReg
y=ax³+bx²+cx+d
a=6.266666667
b=-194.5714286
c=1544.761905
d=2571.428571
```

(B) $L(12) \approx 3,919.09$ or 3,900 rounded to the nearest hundred; $L'(12) = -417.75$ or -400. Interpretation: In 1992, 3,900 limousines were produced and limousine production was DECREASING at the rate of 400 limousines per year.

(C) $L(18) \approx 3,883.2$ or 3,900 rounded to the nearest hundred; $L'(18) \approx 631.39$ or 600.
Interpretation: In 1998, 3,900 limousines were produced and limousine production was INCREASING at the rate of 600 limousines per year.

87. $y = 590x^{-1/2}$, $30 \leq x \leq 75$

First, find $\dfrac{dy}{dx} = \dfrac{d}{dx}590x^{-1/2} = -295x^{-3/2} = \dfrac{-295}{x^{3/2}}$, the instantaneous rate

of change of pulse when a person is x inches tall.

(A) The instantaneous rate of change of pulse rate at $x = 36$ is:

$\dfrac{-295}{(36)^{3/2}} = \dfrac{-295}{216} = -1.37$ (1.37 decrease in pulse rate)

(B) The instantaneous rate of change of pulse rate at $x = 64$ is:

$\dfrac{-295}{(64)^{3/2}} = \dfrac{-295}{512} = -0.58$ (0.58 decrease in pulse rate)

89. $y = 50\sqrt{x}$, $0 \leq x \leq 9$

First, find $y' = (50\sqrt{x})' = (50x^{1/2})' = 25x^{-1/2}$

$= \dfrac{25}{\sqrt{x}}$, the rate of learning at the end of x hours.

(A) Rate of learning at the end of 1 hour: $\dfrac{25}{\sqrt{1}} = 25$ items/hr

(B) Rate of learning at the end of 9 hours: $\dfrac{25}{\sqrt{9}} = \dfrac{25}{3} = 8.33$ items/hr

---

EXERCISE 3-5

Things to remember:

1. PRODUCT RULE

   If

   $y = f(x) = F(x)S(x)$

   and if $F'(x)$ and $S'(x)$ exist, then

   $f'(x) = F(x)S'(x) + S(x)F'(x)$.

   Also,

   $y' = FS' + SF'$;

   $\dfrac{dy}{dx} = F\dfrac{dS}{dx} + S\dfrac{dF}{dx}$.

2. QUOTIENT RULE

   If

   $y = f(x) = \dfrac{T(x)}{B(x)}$

   and if $T'(x)$ and $B'(x)$ exist, then

   $f'(x) = \dfrac{B(x)T'(x) - T(x)B'(x)}{[B(x)]^2}$.

   Also,

   $y' = \dfrac{BT' - TB'}{B^2}$;

   $\dfrac{dy}{dx} = \dfrac{B\left(\dfrac{dT}{dx}\right) - T\left(\dfrac{dB}{dx}\right)}{B^2}$.

1. $f(x) = 2x^3(x^2 - 2)$

$f'(x) = 2x^3(x^2 - 2)' + (x^2 - 2)(2x^3)'$ [using $\underline{1}$ with $F(x) = 2x^3$,

$\quad\quad = 2x^3(2x) + (x^2 - 2)(6x^2)$ $S(x) = x^2 - 2]$

$\quad\quad = 4x^4 + 6x^4 - 12x^2$

$\quad\quad = 10x^4 - 12x^2$

3. $f(x) = (x - 3)(2x - 1)$

$f'(x) = (x - 3)(2x - 1)' + (2x - 1)(x - 3)'$ (using $\underline{1}$)

$\quad\quad = (x - 3)(2) + (2x - 1)(1)$

$\quad\quad = 2x - 6 + 2x - 1$

$\quad\quad = 4x - 7$

5. $f(x) = \dfrac{x}{x - 3}$

$f'(x) = \dfrac{(x - 3)(x)' - x(x - 3)'}{(x - 3)^2}$ [using $\underline{2}$ with $T(x) = x$, $B(x) = x - 3$]

$\quad\quad = \dfrac{(x - 3)(1) - x(1)}{(x - 3)^2} = \dfrac{-3}{(x - 3)^2}$

7. $f(x) = \dfrac{2x + 3}{x - 2}$

$f'(x) = \dfrac{(x - 2)(2x + 3)' - (2x + 3)(x - 2)'}{(x - 2)^2}$ (using $\underline{2}$)

$\quad\quad = \dfrac{(x - 2)(2) - (2x + 3)(1)}{(x - 2)^2} = \dfrac{2x - 4 - 2x - 3}{(x - 2)^2} = \dfrac{-7}{(x - 2)^2}$

9. $f(x) = (x^2 + 1)(2x - 3)$

$f'(x) = (x^2 + 1)(2x - 3)' + (2x - 3)(x^2 + 1)'$ (using $\underline{1}$)

$\quad\quad = (x^2 + 1)(2) + (2x - 3)(2x)$

$\quad\quad = 2x^2 + 2 + 4x^2 - 6x$

$\quad\quad = 6x^2 - 6x + 2$

11. $f(x) = (0.4x + 2)(0.5x - 5)$

$f'(x) = (0.4x + 2)(0.5x - 5)' + (0.5x - 5)(0.4x + 2)'$

$\quad\quad = (0.4x + 2)(0.5) + (0.5x - 5)(0.4)$

$\quad\quad = 0.2x + 1 + 0.2x - 2 = 0.4x - 1$

13. $f(x) = \dfrac{x^2 + 1}{2x - 3}$

$f'(x) = \dfrac{(2x - 3)(x^2 + 1)' - (x^2 + 1)(2x - 3)'}{(2x - 3)^2}$ (using $\underline{2}$)

$\quad\quad = \dfrac{(2x - 3)(2x) - (x^2 + 1)(2)}{(2x - 3)^2}$

$\quad\quad = \dfrac{4x^2 - 6x - 2x^2 - 2}{(2x - 3)^2} = \dfrac{2x^2 - 6x - 2}{(2x - 3)^2}$

15. $f(x) = (x^2 + 2)(x^2 - 3)$

$\quad f'(x) = (x^2 + 2)(x^2 - 3)' + (x^2 - 3)(x^2 + 2)'$

$\qquad = (x^2 + 2)(2x) + (x^2 - 3)(2x)$

$\qquad = 2x^3 + 4x + 2x^3 - 6x$

$\qquad = 4x^3 - 2x$

17. $f(x) = \dfrac{x^2 + 2}{x^2 - 3}$

$\quad f'(x) = \dfrac{(x^2 - 3)(x^2 + 2)' - (x^2 + 2)(x^2 - 3)'}{(x^2 - 3)^2}$

$\qquad = \dfrac{(x^2 - 3)(2x) - (x^2 + 2)(2x)}{(x^2 - 3)^2} = \dfrac{2x^3 - 6x - 2x^3 - 4x}{(x^2 - 3)^2} = \dfrac{-10x}{(x^2 - 3)^2}$

19. $h(x) = xf(x); \quad h'(x) = xf'(x) + f(x)$

21. $h(x) = x^3 f(x); \quad h'(x) = x^3 f'(x) + f(x)(3x^2) = x^3 f'(x) + 3x^2 f(x)$

23. $h(x) = \dfrac{f(x)}{x^2}; \quad h'(x) = \dfrac{x^2 f'(x) - f(x)(2x)}{(x^2)^2} = \dfrac{x^2 f'(x) - 2xf(x)}{x^4} = \dfrac{xf'(x) - 2f(x)}{x^3}$

$\quad$ or $h(x) = x^{-2} f(x); \quad h'(x) = x^{-2} f'(x) + f(x)(-2x^{-3}) = \dfrac{xf'(x) - 2f(x)}{x^3}$

25. $h(x) = \dfrac{x}{f(x)}; \quad h'(x) = \dfrac{f(x) - xf'(x)}{[f(x)]^2}$

27. $f(x) = (2x + 1)(x^2 - 3x)$

$\quad f'(x) = (2x + 1)(x^2 - 3x)' + (x^2 - 3x)(2x + 1)'$

$\qquad = (2x + 1)(2x - 3) + (x^2 - 3x)(2)$

$\qquad = 6x^2 - 10x - 3$

29. $y = (2.5t - t^2)(4t + 1.4)$

$\quad \dfrac{dy}{dx} = (2.5t - t^2)\dfrac{d}{dt}(4t + 1.4) + (4t + 1.4)\dfrac{d}{dt}(2.5t - t^2)$

$\qquad = (2.5t - t^2)(4) + (4t + 1.4)(2.5 - 2t)$

$\qquad = 10t - 4t^2 + 10t - 2.8t + 3.5 - 8t^2$

$\qquad = -12t^2 + 17.2t + 3.5$

31. $y = \dfrac{5x - 3}{x^2 + 2x}$

$\quad y' = \dfrac{(x^2 + 2x)(5x - 3)' - (5x - 3)(x^2 + 2x)'}{(x^2 + 2x)^2}$

$\qquad = \dfrac{(x^2 + 2x)(5) - (5x - 3)(2x + 2)}{(x^2 + 2x)^2} = \dfrac{-5x^2 + 6x + 6}{(x^2 + 2x)^2}$

33. $\dfrac{d}{dw}\left[\dfrac{w^2 - 3w + 1}{w^2 - 1}\right] = \dfrac{(w^2 - 1)\dfrac{d}{dw}(w^2 - 3w + 1) - (w^2 - 3w + 1)\dfrac{d}{dw}(w^2 - 1)}{(w^2 - 1)^2}$

$$= \dfrac{(w^2 - 1)(2w - 3) - (w^2 - 3w + 1)(2w)}{(w^2 - 1)^2}$$

$$= \dfrac{3w^2 - 4w + 3}{(w^2 - 1)^2}$$

35. $f(x) = (1 + 3x)(5 - 2x)$

First find $f'(x)$:

$f'(x) = (1 + 3x)(5 - 2x)' + (5 - 2x)(1 + 3x)'$
$= (1 + 3x)(-2) + (5 - 2x)(3)$
$= -2 - 6x + 15 - 6x$
$= 13 - 12x$

An equation for the tangent line at $x = 2$ is:

$y - y_1 = m(x - x_1)$

where $x_1 = 2$, $y_1 = f(x_1) = f(2) = 7$, and $m = f'(x_1) = f'(2) = -11$.

Thus, we have:

$y - 7 = -11(x - 2)$ or $y = -11x + 29$

37. $f(x) = \dfrac{x - 8}{3x - 4}$

First find $f'(x)$:

$f'(x) = \dfrac{(3x - 4)(x - 8)' - (x - 8)(3x - 4)'}{(3x - 4)^2}$

$= \dfrac{(3x - 4)(1) - (x - 8)(3)}{(3x - 4)^2} = \dfrac{20}{(3x - 4)^2}$

An equation for the tangent line at $x = 2$ is: $y - y_1 = m(x - x_1)$

where $x_1 = 2$, $y_1 = f(x_1) = f(2) = -3$, and $m = f'(x_1) = f'(2) = 5$.

Thus, we have: $y - (-3) = 5(x - 2)$ or $y = 5x - 13$

39. $f(x) = (2x - 15)(x^2 + 18)$

$f'(x) = (2x - 15)(x^2 + 18)' + (x^2 + 18)(2x - 15)'$
$= (2x - 15)(2x) + (x^2 + 18)(2)$
$= 6x^2 - 30x + 36$

To find the values of x where $f'(x) = 0$, set: $f'(x) = 6x^2 - 30x + 36 = 0$

or $x^2 - 5x + 6 = 0$
$(x - 2)(x - 3) = 0$

Thus, $x = 2$, $x = 3$.

41. $f(x) = \dfrac{x}{x^2 + 1}$

$f'(x) = \dfrac{(x^2 + 1)(x)' - x(x^2 + 1)'}{(x^2 + 1)^2} = \dfrac{(x^2 + 1)(1) - x(2x)}{(x^2 + 1)^2} = \dfrac{1 - x^2}{(x^2 + 1)^2}$

Now, set $f'(x) = \dfrac{1 - x^2}{(x^2 + 1)^2} = 0$

$\quad\quad$ or $\quad\quad\quad\quad 1 - x^2 = 0$

$\quad\quad\quad\quad\quad (1 - x)(1 + x) = 0$

Thus, $x = 1$, $x = -1$.

43. $f(x) = x^3(x^4 - 1)$

First, we use the product rule:

$f'(x) = x^3(x^4 - 1)' + (x^4 - 1)(x^3)'$

$\quad\quad = x^3(4x^3) + (x^4 - 1)(3x^2)$

$\quad\quad = 7x^6 - 3x^2$

Next, simplifying $f(x)$, we have $f(x) = x^7 - x^3$. Thus, $f'(x) = 7x^6 - 3x^2$.

45. $f(x) = \dfrac{x^3 + 9}{x^3}$

First, we use the quotient rule:

$f'(x) = \dfrac{x^3(x^3 + 9)' - (x^3 + 9)(x^3)'}{(x^3)^2} = \dfrac{x^3(3x^2) - (x^3 + 9)(3x^2)}{x^6}$

$\quad\quad = \dfrac{-27x^2}{x^6} = \dfrac{-27}{x^4}$

Next, simplifying $f(x)$, we have $f(x) = \dfrac{x^3 + 9}{x^3} = 1 + \dfrac{9}{x^3} = 1 + 9x^{-3}$

Thus, $f'(x) = -27x^{-4} = -\dfrac{27}{x^4}$.

47. $f(w) = (3w^2 - 1)^2 = (3w^2 - 1)(3w^2 - 1)$

$f'(w) = (3w^2 - 1)(6w) + (3w^2 - 1)(6w)$

$\quad\quad = 12w(3w^2 - 1) = 36w^3 - 12w$

49. $\dfrac{d}{dx} \dfrac{3x^2 - 2x + 3}{4x^2 + 5x - 1}$

$= \dfrac{(4x^2 + 5x - 1)\dfrac{d}{dx}(3x^2 - 2x + 3) - (3x^2 - 2x + 3)\dfrac{d}{dx}(4x^2 + 5x - 1)}{(4x^2 + 5x - 1)^2}$

$= \dfrac{(4x^2 + 5x - 1)(6x - 2) - (3x^2 - 2x + 3)(8x + 5)}{(4x^2 + 5x - 1)^2}$

$= \dfrac{24x^3 + 30x^2 - 6x - 8x^2 - 10x + 2 - 24x^3 + 16x^2 - 24x - 15x^2 + 10x - 15}{(4x^2 + 5x - 1)^2}$

$= \dfrac{23x^2 - 30x - 13}{(4x^2 + 5x - 1)^2}$

51. $y = 9x^{1/3}(x^3 + 5)$

$$\frac{dy}{dx} = 9x^{1/3}\frac{d}{dx}(x^3 + 5) + (x^3 + 5)\frac{d}{dx}(9x^{1/3})\frac{d}{dx}(9x^{1/3})$$

$$= 9x^{1/3}(3x^2) + (x^3 + 5)\left(9 \cdot \frac{1}{3}x^{-2/3}\right) = 27x^{7/3} + (x^3 + 5)(3x^{-2/3})$$

$$= 27x^{7/3} + \frac{3x^3 + 15}{x^{2/3}} = \frac{30x^3 + 15}{x^{2/3}}$$

53. $f(x) = \dfrac{6\sqrt[3]{x}}{x^2 - 3} = \dfrac{6x^{1/3}}{x^2 - 3}$

$$f'(x) = \frac{(x^2 - 3)(6x^{1/3})' - 6x^{1/3}(x^2 - 3)'}{(x^2 - 3)^2}$$

$$= \frac{(x^2 - 3)\left(6 \cdot \frac{1}{3}x^{-2/3}\right) - 6x^{1/3}(2x)}{(x^2 - 3)^2} = \frac{(x^2 - 3)(2x^{-2/3}) - 12x^{4/3}}{(x^2 - 3)^2}$$

$$= \frac{\frac{2(x^2 - 3)}{x^{2/3}} - 12x^{4/3}}{(x^2 - 3)^2} = \frac{2x^2 - 6 - 12x^2}{(x^2 - 3)^2 x^{2/3}} = \frac{-10x^2 - 6}{(x^2 - 3)^2 x^{2/3}}$$

55. $g(t) = \dfrac{0.2t}{3t^2 - 1}$; $g'(t) = \dfrac{(3t^2 - 1)(0.2) - (0.2t)(6t)}{(3t^2 - 1)^2} = \dfrac{-0.6t^2 - 0.2}{(3t^2 - 1)^2}$

57. $\dfrac{d}{dx}\dfrac{x^3 - 2x^2}{\sqrt[3]{x^2}} = \dfrac{d}{dx}\dfrac{x^3 - 2x^2}{x^{2/3}}$

$$= \frac{x^{2/3}\frac{d}{dx}(x^3 - 2x^2) - (x^3 - 2x^2)\frac{d}{dx}(x^{2/3})}{(x^{2/3})^2}$$

$$= \frac{x^{2/3}(3x^2 - 4x) - (x^3 - 2x^2)\left(\frac{2}{3}x^{-1/3}\right)}{x^{4/3}}$$

$$= x^{-2/3}(3x^2 - 4x) - \frac{2}{3}x^{-5/3}(x^3 - 2x^2)$$

$$= 3x^{4/3} - 4x^{1/3} - \frac{2}{3}x^{4/3} + \frac{4}{3}x^{1/3}$$

$$= -\frac{8}{3}x^{1/3} + \frac{7}{3}x^{4/3}$$

59. $f(x) = \dfrac{(2x^2 - 1)(x^2 + 3)}{x^2 + 1}$

$$f'(x) = \frac{(x^2 + 1)[(2x^2 - 1)(x^2 + 3)]' - (2x^2 - 1)(x^2 + 3)(x^2 + 1)'}{(x^2 + 1)^2}$$

$$= \frac{(x^2 + 1)[(2x^2 - 1)(x^2 + 3)' + (x^2 + 3)(2x^2 - 1)'] - (2x^2 - 1)(x^2 + 3)(2x)}{(x^2 + 1)^2}$$

$$= \frac{(x^2 + 1)[(2x^2 - 1)(2x) + (x^2 + 3)(4x)] - (2x^2 - 1)(x^2 + 3)(2x)}{(x^2 + 1)^2}$$

$$= \frac{(x^2 + 1)\,[4x^3 - 2x + 4x^3 + 12x] - [2x^4 + 5x^2 - 3]\,(2x)}{(x^2 + 1)^2}$$

$$= \frac{(x^2 + 1)\,(8x^3 + 10x) - 4x^5 - 10x^3 + 6x}{(x^2 + 1)^2}$$

$$= \frac{8x^5 + 10x^3 + 8x^3 + 10x - 4x^5 - 10x^3 + 6x}{(x^2 + 1)^2}$$

$$= \frac{4x^5 + 8x^3 + 16x}{(x^2 + 1)^2}$$

61. $f(x) = (x^2 + 4)\,(x^2 - 2x)$

$f'(x) = (x^2 + 4)\,(2x - 2) + (x^2 - 2x)\,2x = 4x^3 - 6x^2 + 8x - 8$

Set $f'(x) = 4x^3 - 6x^2 + 8x - 8 = 0$ and solve using a root-approximation routine on a graphing utility: $f'(x) = 0$ at $x = 1.2117$.

63. $f(x) = \dfrac{x^3 + 17x - 2}{x^2 + 1}$

$f'(x) = \dfrac{(x^2 + 1)\,(3x^2 + 17) - (x^3 + 17x - 2)\,(2x)}{(x^2 + 1)^2} = \dfrac{x^4 - 14x^2 + 4x + 17}{(x^2 + 1)^2}$;

$f'(x) = 0$ implies $x^4 - 14x^2 + 4x + 17 = 0$.

Solve using a root-approximation routine on a graphing utility: $f'(x) = 0$ at $x = -3.7212$, $x = -1$, $x = 1.3586$, $x = 3.3626$.

65. $S(t) = \dfrac{90t^2}{t^2 + 50}$

(A) $S'(t) = \dfrac{(t^2 + 50)\,(180t) - 90t^2\,(2t)}{(t^2 + 50)^2} = \dfrac{9000t}{(t^2 + 50)^2}$

(B) $S(10) = \dfrac{90(10)^2}{(10)^2 + 50} = \dfrac{9000}{150} = 60$;

$S'(10) = \dfrac{9000(10)}{[\,(10)^2 + 50]^2} = \dfrac{90,000}{22,500} = 4$

After 10 months, the total sales are 60,000 CD's and the sales are INCREASING at the rate of 4,000 CD's per month.

(C) The total sales after 11 months will be approximately 64,000 CD's.

67. $x = \dfrac{4,000}{0.1p + 1}$, $10 \le p \le 70$

(A) $\dfrac{dx}{dp} = \dfrac{(0.1p + 1)\,(0) - 4,000(0.1)}{(0.1p + 1)^2} = \dfrac{-400}{(0.1p + 1)^2}$

(B) $x(40) = \dfrac{4,000}{0.1(40) + 1} = \dfrac{4,000}{5} = 800;$

$\dfrac{dx}{dp} = \dfrac{-400}{[0.1(40) + 1]^2} = \dfrac{-400}{25} = -16$

At a price level of \$40, the demand is 800 CD players and the demand is DECREASING at the rate of 16 CD players per dollar.

(C) At a price of \$41, the demand will be approximately 784 CD players.

69. $C(t) = \dfrac{0.14t}{t^2 + 1}$

(A) $C'(t) = \dfrac{(t^2 + 1)(0.14t)' - (0.14t)(t^2 + 1)'}{(t^2 + 1)^2}$

$= \dfrac{(t^2 + 1)(0.14) - (0.14t)(2t)}{(t^2 + 1)^2} = \dfrac{0.14 - 0.14t^2}{(t^2 + 1)^2} = \dfrac{0.14(1 - t^2)}{(t^2 + 1)^2}$

(B) $C'(0.5) = \dfrac{0.14(1 - [0.5]^2)}{([0.5]^2 + 1)^2} = \dfrac{0.14(1 - 0.25)}{(1.25)^2} = 0.0672$

Interpretation: At $t = 0.5$ hours, the concentration is increasing at the rate of 0.0672 units per hour.

$C'(3) = \dfrac{0.14(1 - 3^2)}{(3^2 + 1)^2} = \dfrac{0.14(-8)}{100} = -0.0112$

Interpretation: At $t = 3$ hours, the concentration is decreasing at the rate of 0.0112 units per hour.

71. $N(x) = \dfrac{100x + 200}{x + 32}$

(A) $N'(x) = \dfrac{(x + 32)(100x + 200)' - (100x + 200)(x + 32)'}{(x + 32)^2}$

$= \dfrac{(x + 32)(100) - (100x + 200)(1)}{(x + 32)^2}$

$= \dfrac{100x + 3200 - 100x - 200}{(x + 32)^2} = \dfrac{3000}{(x + 32)^2}$

(B) $N'(4) = \dfrac{3000}{(36)^2} = \dfrac{3000}{1296} \approx 2.31;\quad N'(68) = \dfrac{3000}{(100)^2} = \dfrac{3000}{10,000} = \dfrac{3}{10} = 0.30$

Things to remember:

1. GENERAL POWER RULE

    If $u(x)$ is a differentiable function, n is any real number, and

    $$y = f(x) = [u(x)]^n$$

    then

    $$f'(x) = n[u(x)]^{n-1}u'(x)$$

    This rule is often written more compactly as

    $$y' = nu^{n-1}u' \quad \text{or} \quad \frac{d}{dx}u^n = nu^{n-1}\frac{du}{dx}, \quad u = u(x)$$

---

1. $3; \quad \dfrac{d}{dx}(3x + 4)^4 = 4(3x + 4)^3(3) \quad = 12(3x + 4)^3$

3. $-4x; \quad \dfrac{d}{dx}(4 - 2x^2)^3 = 3(4 - 2x^2)^2(-4x) \quad = -12x(4 - 2x^2)^2$

5. $2 + 6x; \quad \dfrac{d}{dx}(1 + 2x + 3x^2)^7 = 7(1 + 2x + 3x^2)^6(2 + 6x)$

$$= 7(2 + 6x)(1 + 2x + 3x^2)^6$$

7. $f(x) = (2x + 5)^3$

$f'(x) = 3(2x + 5)^2(2x + 5)'$

$ = 3(2x + 5)^2(2)$

$ = 6(2x + 5)^2$

9. $f(x) = (5 - 2x)^4$

$f'(x) = 4(5 - 2x)^3(5 - 2x)'$

$ = 4(5 - 2x)^3(-2)$

$ = -8(5 - 2x)^3$

11. $f(x) = (4 + 0.2x)^5$

$f'(x) = 5(4 + 0.2x)^4(4 + 0.2x)' = 5(4 + 0.2x)^4(0.2)$

$$= (4 + 0.2x)^4$$

13. $f(x) = (3x^2 + 5)^5$

$f'(x) = 5(3x^2 + 5)^4(3x^2 + 5)'$

$ = 5(3x^2 + 5)^4(6x)$

$ = 30x(3x^2 + 5)^4$

15. $f(x) = (x^3 - 2x^2 + 2)^8$

$f'(x) = 8(x^3 - 2x^2 + 2)^7(x^3 - 2x^2 + 2)'$

$ = 8(x^3 - 2x^2 + 2)^7(3x^2 - 4x)$

17. $f(x) = (2x - 5)^{1/2}$

$f'(x) = \dfrac{1}{2}(2x - 5)^{-1/2}(2x - 5)'$

$ = \dfrac{1}{2}(2x - 5)^{-1/2}(2) = \dfrac{1}{(2x - 5)^{1/2}}$

19. $f(x) = (x^4 + 1)^{-2}$

$f'(x) = -2(x^4 + 1)^{-3}(x^4 + 1)'$

$\qquad = -2(x^4 + 1)^{-3}(4x^3)$

$\qquad = -8x^3(x^4 + 1)^{-3} = \dfrac{-8x^3}{(x^4 + 1)^3}$

21. $f(x) = (2x - 1)^3$

$f'(x) = 3(2x - 1)^2(2) = 6(2x - 1)^2$

Tangent line at $x = 1$: $y - y_1 = m(x - x_1)$ where $x_1 = 1$, $y_1 = f(1) =$

$(2(1) - 1)^3 = 1$, $m = f'(1) = 6[2(1) - 1]^2 = 6$. Thus, $y - 1 = 6(x - 1)$

or $y = 6x - 5$.

The tangent line is horizontal at the value(s) of x such that $f'(x) = 0$:

$6(2x - 1)^2 = 0$

$\qquad 2x - 1 = 0$

$\qquad\qquad x = \dfrac{1}{2}$

23. $f(x) = (4x - 3)^{1/2}$

$f'(x) = \dfrac{1}{2}(4x - 3)^{-1/2}(4) = \dfrac{2}{(4x - 3)^{1/2}}$

Tangent line at $x = 3$: $y - y_1 = m(x - x_1)$ where $x_1 = 3$, $y_1 = f(3) =$

$(4 \cdot 3 - 3)^{1/2} = 3$, $f'(3) = \dfrac{2}{(4 \cdot 3 - 3)^{1/2}} = \dfrac{2}{3}$. Thus, $y - 3 = \dfrac{2}{3}(x - 3)$ or

$y = \dfrac{2}{3}x + 1$.

The tangent line is horizontal at the value(s) of x such that $f'(x) = 0$.

Since $\dfrac{2}{(4x - 3)^{1/2}} \neq 0$ for all x $\left(x \neq \dfrac{3}{4}\right)$, there are no values of x where

the tangent line is horizontal.

25. $y = 3(x^2 - 2)^4$

$\dfrac{dy}{dx} = 3 \cdot 4(x^2 - 2)^3(2x) = 24x(x^2 - 2)^3$

27. $\dfrac{d}{dt}[2(t^2 + 3t)^{-3}] = 2(-3)(t^2 + 3t)^{-4}(2t + 3) = \dfrac{-6(2t + 3)}{(t^2 + 3t)^4}$

29. $h(w) = \sqrt{w^2 + 8} = (w^2 + 8)^{1/2}$;

$h'(w) = \dfrac{1}{2}(w^2 + 8)^{-1/2}(2w) = \dfrac{w}{(w^2 + 8)^{1/2}} = \dfrac{w}{\sqrt{w^2 + 8}}$.

31. $g(x) = \sqrt[3]{3x + 4} = (3x + 4)^{1/3}$

$g'(x) = \dfrac{1}{3}(3x + 4)^{-2/3}(3) = \dfrac{1}{(3x + 4)^{2/3}} = \dfrac{1}{\sqrt[3]{(3x + 4)^2}}$.

33. $\dfrac{d}{dx} = (\sqrt[4]{0.8x + 3.6}) = \dfrac{d}{dx}[(0.8x + 3.6)^{1/4}]$

$$= \frac{1}{4}(0.8x + 3.6)^{-3/4}(0.8)$$

$$= \frac{0.2}{(0.8x + 3.6)^{3/4}} = \frac{0.2}{\sqrt[4]{(0.8x + 3.6)^3}}$$

35. $F(t) = (t^2 - 4t + 2)^{1/2}$; $F'(t) = \dfrac{1}{2}(t^2 - 4t + 2)^{-1/2}(2t - 4)$

$$= \frac{t - 2}{(t^2 - 4t + 2)^{1/2}} = \frac{t - 2}{\sqrt{t^2 - 4t + 2}}.$$

37. $y = \dfrac{1}{2x + 4} = (2x + 4)^{-1}$; $y' = -1(2x + 4)^{-2}(2) = \dfrac{-2}{(2x + 4)^2}$.

39. $\dfrac{d}{dw}\left[\dfrac{1}{(w^3 + 4)^5}\right] = \dfrac{d}{dw}[(w^3 + 4)^{-5}]$

$$= -5(w^3 + 4)^{-6}(3w^2) = \frac{-15w^2}{(w^3 + 4)^6}.$$

41. $y = (3\sqrt{x} - 1)^5 = (3x^{1/2} - 1)^5$;

$\dfrac{dy}{dx} = 5(3x^{1/2} - 1)^4(3)\left(\dfrac{1}{2}x^{-1/2}\right) = \dfrac{15(3x^{1/2} - 1)^4}{2x^{1/2}} = \dfrac{15(3\sqrt{x} - 1)^4}{2\sqrt{x}}.$

43. $f(t) = \dfrac{4}{\sqrt{t^2 - 3t}} = 4(t^2 - 3t)^{-1/2}$;

$f'(t) = 4\left(-\dfrac{1}{2}\right)(t^2 - 3t)^{-3/2}(2t - 3) = \dfrac{-2(2t - 3)}{(t^2 - 3t)^{3/2}} = \dfrac{-2(2t - 3)}{\sqrt{(t^2 - 3t)^3}}$

45. $f(x) = x(4 - x)^3$

$f'(x) = x[(4 - x)^3]' + (4 - x)^3(x)'$

$\quad = x(3)(4 - x)^2(-1) + (4 - x)^3(1)$

$\quad = (4 - x)^3 - 3x(4 - x)^2 = (4 - x)^2[4 - x - 3x] = 4(4 - x)^2(1 - x)$

An equation for the tangent line to the graph of f at $x = 2$ is:

$y - y_1 = m(x - x_1)$ where $x_1 = 2$, $y_1 = f(x_1) = f(2) = 16$, and

$m = f'(x_1) = f'(2) = -16$. Thus, $y - 16 = -16(x - 2)$ or $y = -16x + 48$.

47. $f(x) = \dfrac{x}{(2x - 5)^3}$

$f'(x) = \dfrac{(2x - 5)^3(1) - x(3)(2x - 5)^2(2)}{[(2x - 5)^3]^2}$

$\quad = \dfrac{(2x - 5)^3 - 6x(2x - 5)^2}{(2x - 5)^6} = \dfrac{(2x - 5) - 6x}{(2x - 5)^4} = \dfrac{-4x - 5}{(2x - 5)^4}$

An equation for the tangent line to the graph of f at $x = 3$ is:

$y - y_1 = m(x - x_1)$ where $x_1 = 3$, $y_1 = f(x_1) = f(3) = 3$, and

$m = f'(x_1) = f'(3) = -17$. Thus, $y - 3 = -17(x - 3)$ or $y = -17x + 54$.

49. $f(x) = x\sqrt{2x + 2} = x(2x + 2)^{1/2}$

$f'(x) = x[(2x + 2)^{1/2}]' + (2x + 2)^{1/2}(x)'$

$\quad = x\left(\dfrac{1}{2}\right)(2x + 2)^{-1/2}(2) + (2x + 2)^{1/2}(1) = \dfrac{x}{(2x + 2)^{1/2}} + (2x + 2)^{1/2}$

$\quad\quad\quad\quad\quad\quad\quad\quad\quad\quad\quad\quad\quad\quad\quad = \dfrac{3x + 2}{(2x + 2)^{1/2}}$

An equation for the tangent line to the graph of f at $x = 1$ is:

$y - y_1 = m(x - x_1)$ where $x_1 = 1$, $y_1 = f(x_1) = f(1) = 2$, and

$m = f'(x_1) = f'(1) = \dfrac{5}{2}$. Thus, $y - 2 = \dfrac{5}{2}(x - 1)$ or $y = \dfrac{5}{2}x - \dfrac{1}{2}$.

51. $f(x) = x^2(x - 5)^3$

$f'(x) = x^2[(x - 5)^3]' + (x - 5)^3(x^2)'$

$\quad = x^2(3)(x - 5)^2(1) + (x - 5)^3(2x)$

$\quad = 3x^2(x - 5)^2 + 2x(x - 5)^3 = 5x(x - 5)^2(x - 2)$

The tangent line to the graph of f is horizontal at the values of x such that $f'(x) = 0$. Thus, we set $5x(x - 5)^2(x - 2) = 0$ and $x = 0$, $x = 2$, $x = 5$.

53. $f(x) = \dfrac{x}{(2x + 5)^2}$

$f'(x) = \dfrac{(2x + 5)^2(x)' - x[(2x + 5)^2]'}{[(2x + 5)^2]^2}$

$\quad = \dfrac{(2x + 5)^2(1) - x(2)(2x + 5)(2)}{(2x + 5)^4} = \dfrac{2x + 5 - 4x}{(2x + 5)^3} = \dfrac{5 - 2x}{(2x + 5)^3}$

The tangent line to the graph of f is horizontal at the values of x such that $f'(x) = 0$. Thus, we set

$\dfrac{5 - 2x}{(2x + 5)^3} = 0$

$5 - 2x = 0$

and $x = \dfrac{5}{2}$.

55. $f(x) = \sqrt{x^2 - 8x + 20} = (x^2 - 8x + 20)^{1/2}$

$f'(x) = \dfrac{1}{2}(x^2 - 8x + 20)^{-1/2}(2x - 8)$

$\quad = \dfrac{x - 4}{(x^2 - 8x + 20)^{1/2}}$

The tangent line to the graph of f is horizontal at the values of x such that $f'(x) = 0$. Thus, we set

$\dfrac{x - 4}{(x^2 - 8x + 20)^{1/2}} = 0$

$x - 4 = 0$

and $x = 4$.

57. $f(x) = x(x - 1)(x^2 - 5) = x(x^3 - x^2 - 5x + 5) = x^4 - x^3 - 5x^2 + 5x$

$f'(x) = 4x^3 - 3x^2 - 10x + 5$

The tangent line to the graph of f is horizontal at the values of x where $f'(x) = 0$. Solve this equation using a root-approximation routine on a graphing utility:

$f'(x) = 0$ at $x = -1.4903$, $x = 0.4752$, $x = 1.7651$.

59. $f(x) = (x^3 - 2x^2)(x^2 + 1)$

$f'(x) = (x^3 - 2x^2)2x + (x^2 + 1)(3x^2 - 4x)$

$\qquad = 5x^4 - 8x^3 + 3x^2 - 4x$

The tangent line to the graph of f is horizontal at the values of x where $f'(x) = 0$. Solve this equation using a root-approximation routine on a graphing utility:

$f'(x) = 0$ at $x = 0$, $x = 1.5465$.

61. $f(x) = \sqrt{x^4 - 6x^2 + x + 12} = (x^4 - 6x^2 + x + 12)^{1/2}$

$f'(x) = \dfrac{1}{2}(x^4 - 6x^2 + x + 12)^{-1/2}(4x^3 - 12x + 1)$

$\qquad = \dfrac{4x^3 - 12x + 1}{2\sqrt{x^4 - 6x^2 + x + 12}}$

The tangent line to the graph of f is horizontal at the values of x where $f'(x) = 0$, that is at the values of x where $4x^3 - 12x + 1 = 0$. Solve this equation using a root-approximation routine on a graphing utility:

$f'(x) = 0$ at $x = -1.7723$, $x = 0.0835$, $x = 1.6888$.

63. $\dfrac{d}{dx}[3x(x^2 + 1)^3] = 3x\dfrac{d}{dx}(x^2 + 1)^3 + (x^2 + 1)^3\dfrac{d}{dx}3x$

$\qquad\qquad = 3x \cdot 3(x^2 + 1)^2(2x) + (x^2 + 1)^3(3)$

$\qquad\qquad = 18x^2(x^2 + 1)^2 + 3(x^2 + 1)^3$

$\qquad\qquad = (x^2 + 1)^2[18x^2 + 3(x^2 + 1)]$

$\qquad\qquad = (x^2 + 1)^2(21x^2 + 3)$

$\qquad\qquad = 3(x^2 + 1)^2(7x^2 + 1)$

65. $\dfrac{d}{dx}\dfrac{(x^3 - 7)^4}{2x^3} = \dfrac{2x^3\dfrac{d}{dx}(x^3 - 7)^4 - (x^3 - 7)^4\dfrac{d}{dx}2x^3}{(2x^3)^2}$

$\qquad\qquad = \dfrac{2x^3 \cdot 4(x^3 - 7)^3(3x^2) - (x^3 - 7)^4 6x^2}{4x^6}$

$\qquad\qquad = \dfrac{3(x^3 - 7)^3 x^2[8x^3 - 2(x^3 - 7)]}{4x^6}$

$\qquad\qquad = \dfrac{3(x^3 - 7)^3(6x^3 + 14)}{4x^4} = \dfrac{3(x^3 - 7)^3(3x^3 + 7)}{2x^4}$

67. $\dfrac{d}{dx}[(2x-3)^2(2x^2+1)^3]$

$$= (2x-3)^2\dfrac{d}{dx}(2x^2+1)^3 + (2x^2+1)^3\dfrac{d}{dx}(2x-3)^2$$

$$= (2x-3)^2\,3(2x^2+1)^2(4x) + (2x^2+1)^3\,2(2x-3)(2)$$

$$= 12x(2x-3)^2(2x^2+1)^2 + 4(2x^2+1)^3(2x-3)$$

$$= 4(2x-3)(2x^2+1)^2[3x(2x-3)+(2x^2+1)]$$

$$= 4(2x-3)(2x^2+1)^2(6x^2-9x+2x^2+1)$$

$$= 4(2x-3)(2x^2+1)^2(8x^2-9x+1)$$

69. $\dfrac{d}{dx}[4x^2\sqrt{x^2-1}] = \dfrac{d}{dx}[\sqrt{16x^4(x^2-1)}] = \dfrac{d}{dx}[(16x^6-16x^4)^{1/2}]$

$$= \dfrac{1}{2}(16x^6-16x^4)^{-1/2}(96x^5-64x^3)$$

$$= \dfrac{96x^5-64x^3}{2(16x^6-16x^4)^{1/2}} = \dfrac{8x^2(12x^3-8x)}{2\cdot 4x^2(x^2-1)^{1/2}} = \dfrac{12x^3-8x}{(x^2-1)^{1/2}}$$

or $\dfrac{d}{dx}[4x^2\sqrt{x^2-1}] = \dfrac{d}{dx}[4x^2(x^2-1)^{1/2}]$

$$= 4x^2\cdot\dfrac{1}{2}(x^2-1)^{-1/2}(2x) + (x^2-1)^{1/2}(8x)$$

$$= \dfrac{4x^3}{(x^2-1)^{1/2}} + 8x(x^2-1)^{1/2}$$

$$= \dfrac{4x^3+8x(x^2-1)}{(x^2-1)^{1/2}} = \dfrac{4x^3+8x^3-8x}{(x^2-1)^{1/2}} = \dfrac{12x^3-8x}{(x^2-1)^{1/2}}$$

71. $\dfrac{d}{dx}\dfrac{2x}{\sqrt{x-3}} = \dfrac{(x-3)^{1/2}(2) - 2x\cdot\dfrac{1}{2}(x-3)^{-1/2}}{(x-3)}$

$$= \dfrac{2(x-3)^{1/2} - \dfrac{x}{(x-3)^{1/2}}}{(x-3)} = \dfrac{2(x-3)-x}{(x-3)(x-3)^{1/2}}$$

$$= \dfrac{2x-6-x}{(x-3)^{3/2}} = \dfrac{x-6}{(x-3)^{3/2}}$$

73. $\dfrac{d}{dx}\sqrt{(2x-1)^3(x^2+3)^4} = \dfrac{d}{dx}[(2x-1)^3(x^2+3)^4]^{1/2}$

$$= \dfrac{d}{dx}(2x-1)^{3/2}(x^2+3)^2$$

$$= (2x-1)^{3/2}\dfrac{d}{dx}(x^2+3)^2 + (x^2+3)^2\dfrac{d}{dx}(2x-1)^{3/2}$$

$$= (2x-1)^{3/2}\,2(x^2+3)(2x) + (x^2+3)^2\cdot\dfrac{3}{2}(2x-1)^{1/2}(2)$$

$$= (2x-1)^{1/2}(x^2+3)[4x(2x-1)+3(x^2+3)]$$

$$= (2x-1)^{1/2}(x^2+3)(8x^2-4x+3x^2+9)$$

$$= (2x-1)^{1/2}(x^2+3)(11x^2-4x+9)$$

75. $C(x) = 10 + \sqrt{2x + 16} = 10 + (2x + 16)^{1/2}, \ 0 \leq x \leq 50$

(A) $C'(x) = \dfrac{1}{2}(2x + 16)^{-1/2}(2) = \dfrac{1}{(2x + 16)^{1/2}}$

(B) $C'(24) = \dfrac{1}{[2(24) + 16]^{1/2}} = \dfrac{1}{(64)^{1/2}} = \dfrac{1}{8}$ or \$12.50; at a production
level of 24 calculators, total costs are INCREASING at the rate of \$12.50 per calculator; also, the cost of producing the 25th calculator is approximately \$12.50.

$C'(42) = \dfrac{1}{[2(42) + 16]^{1/2}} = \dfrac{1}{(100)^{1/2}} = \dfrac{1}{10}$ or \$10.00; at a production
level of 42 calculators, total costs are INCREASING at the rate of \$10.00 per calculator; also the cost of producing the 43rd calculator is approximately \$10.00.

77. $x = 80\sqrt{p + 25} - 400 = 80(p + 25)^{1/2} - 400, \ 20 \leq p \leq 100$

(A) $\dfrac{dx}{dp} = 80\left(\dfrac{1}{2}\right)(p + 25)^{-1/2}(1) = \dfrac{40}{(p + 25)^{1/2}}$

(B) At $p = 75$, $x = 80\sqrt{75 + 25} - 400 = 400$ and
$\dfrac{dx}{dp} = \dfrac{40}{(75 + 25)^{1/2}} = \dfrac{40}{(100)^{1/2}} = 4.$

At a price of \$75, the supply is 400 speakers, and the supply is INCREASING at a rate of 4 speakers per dollar.

79. $A = 1000\left(1 + \dfrac{1}{12}r\right)^{48}$

$\dfrac{dA}{dr} = 1000(48)\left(1 + \dfrac{1}{12}r\right)^{47}\left(\dfrac{1}{12}\right) = 4000\left(1 + \dfrac{1}{12}r\right)^{47}$

81. $y = (3 \times 10^6)\left[1 - \dfrac{1}{\sqrt[3]{(x^2 - 1)^2}}\right] = (3 \times 10^6)[1 - (x^2 - 1)^{-2/3}]$

$\dfrac{dy}{dx} = -(3 \times 10^6)\left(-\dfrac{2}{3}\right)(x^2 - 1)^{-5/3}(2x) = \dfrac{(4 \times 10^6)x}{(x^2 - 1)^{5/3}}$

83. $T = f(n) = 2n\sqrt{n - 2} = 2n(n - 2)^{1/2}$

(A) $f'(n) = 2n[(n - 2)^{1/2}]' + (n - 2)^{1/2}(2n)'$

$= 2n\left(\dfrac{1}{2}\right)(n - 2)^{-1/2}(1) + (n - 2)^{1/2}(2)$

$= \dfrac{n}{(n - 2)^{1/2}} + 2(n - 2)^{1/2}$

$= \dfrac{n + 2(n - 2)}{(n - 2)^{1/2}} = \dfrac{3n - 4}{(n - 2)^{1/2}}$

(B) $f'(11) = \dfrac{29}{3} = 9.67$; when the list contains 11 items, the learning time is increasing at the rate of 9.67 minutes per item;

$f'(27) = \dfrac{77}{5} = 15.4$; when the list contains 27 items, the learning time is increasing at the rate of 15.4 minutes per item.

EXERCISE 3-7

Things to remember:

<u>1</u>. MARGINAL COST, REVENUE, AND PROFIT

If x is the number of units of a product produced in some time interval, then:

Total Cost = $C(x)$
Marginal Cost = $C'(x)$
Total Revenue = $R(x)$
Marginal Revenue = $R'(x)$
Total Profit = $P(x) = R(x) - C(x)$
Marginal Profit = $P'(x) = R'(x) - C'(x)$
                          = (Marginal Revenue) − (Marginal Cost)

Marginal cost (or revenue or profit) is the instantaneous rate of change of cost (or revenue or profit) relative to production at a given production level.

<u>2</u>. MARGINAL COST AND EXACT COST

If $C(x)$ is the cost of producing x items, then the marginal cost function approximates the exact cost of producing the $(x + 1)$st item:

  Marginal Cost   Exact Cost
    $C'(x)$ $\approx$ $C(x + 1) - C(x)$

Similar interpretations can be made for total revenue and total profit functions.

<u>3</u>. BREAK-EVEN POINTS

The BREAK-EVEN POINTS are the points where total revenue equals total cost.

<u>4</u>. MARGINAL AVERAGE COST, REVENUE, AND PROFIT

If x is the number of units of a product produced in some time interval, then:

Average Cost = $\overline{C}(x) = \dfrac{C(x)}{x}$ Cost per unit

Marginal Average Cost = $\overline{C}'(x)$

Average Revenue = $\overline{R}(x) = \dfrac{R(x)}{x}$ Revenue per unit

Marginal Average Revenue = $\overline{R}'(x)$

Average Profit = $\overline{P}(x) = \dfrac{P(x)}{x}$ Profit per unit

Marginal Average Profit = $\overline{P}'(x)$

1. $C(x) = 2000 + 50x - 0.5x^2$

(A) The exact cost of producing the 21st food processor is:

$$C(21) - C(20) = 2000 + 50(21) - \frac{(21)^2}{2} - \left[2000 + 50(20) - \frac{(20)^2}{2}\right]$$
$$= 2829.50 - 2800$$
$$= 29.50 \text{ or } \$29.50$$

(B) $C'(x) = 50 - x$
$C'(20) = 50 - 20 = 30 \text{ or } \$30$

3. $C(x) = 60,000 + 300x$

(A) $\overline{C}(x) = \frac{60,000 + 300x}{x} = \frac{60,000}{x} + 300 = 60,000x^{-1} + 300$

$\overline{C}(500) = \frac{60,000 + 300(500)}{500} = \frac{210,000}{500} = 420 \text{ or } \$420$

(B) $\overline{C}'(x) = -60,000x^{-2} = \frac{-60,000}{x^2}$

$\overline{C}'(500) = \frac{-60,000}{(500)^2} = -0.24 \text{ or } \$0.24$

Interpretation: At a production level of 500 frames, average cost is decreasing at the rate of 24¢ per frame.

(C) The average cost per frame if 501 frames are produced is approximately $420 - $0.24 = $419.76.

5. $P(x) = 30x - 0.3x^2 - 250, \ 0 \leq x \leq 100$

(A) The exact profit from the sale of the 26th skateboard is:
$$P(26) - P(25) = 30(26) - 0.3(26)^2 - 250 - [30(25) - 0.3(25)^2 - 250]$$
$$= 327.20 - 312.50 = \$14.70$$

(B) Marginal profit: $P'(x) = 30 - 0.6x$
$P'(25) = \$15$

7. $P(x) = 5x - \frac{x^2}{200} - 450$

$P'(x) = 5 - \frac{x}{100}$

(A) $P'(450) = 5 - \frac{450}{100} = 0.5 \text{ or } \$0.50$

Interpretation: At a production level of 450 cassettes, profit is increasing at the rate of 50¢ per cassette.

(B) $P'(750) = 5 - \frac{750}{100} = -2.5 \text{ or } -\$2.50$

Interpretation: At a production level of 750 cassettes, profit is decreasing at the rate of $2.50 per cassette.

9. $P(x) = 30x - 0.03x^2 - 750$

Average profit: $\overline{P}(x) = \dfrac{P(x)}{x} = 30 - 0.03x - \dfrac{750}{x} = 30 - 0.03x - 750x^{-1}$

(A) At $x = 50$, $\overline{P}(50) = 30 - (0.03)50 - \dfrac{750}{50} = 13.50$ or \$13.50.

(B) $\overline{P}'(x) = -0.03 + 750x^{-2} = -0.03 + \dfrac{750}{x^2}$

$\overline{P}'(50) = -0.03 + \dfrac{750}{(50)^2} = -0.03 + 0.3 = 0.27$ or \$0.27; at a
production level of 50 mowers, the average profit per mower is
INCREASING at the rate of \$0.27 per mower.

(C) The average profit per mower if 51 mowers are produced is
approximately \$13.50 + \$0.27 = \$13.77.

11. $x = 4,000 - 40p$

(A) Solving the given equation for p, we get

$40p = 4,000 - x$

and $p = 100 - \dfrac{1}{40}x$ or $p = 100 - 0.025x$

Since $p \geq 0$, the domain is: $0 \leq x \leq 4,00$

(B) $R(x) = xp = 100x - 0.025x^2$, $0 \leq x \leq 4,000$

(C) $R'(x) = 100 - 0.05x$; $R'(1,600) = 100 - 80 = 20$
At a production level of 1,600 radios, revenue is INCREASING at the
rate of \$20 per radio.

(D) $R'(2,500) = 100 - 125 = -25$
At a production level of 2,500 radios, revenue is DECREASING at the
rate of \$25 per radio.

13. Price-demand equation: $x = 6,000 - 30p$
Cost function: $C(x) = 72,000 + 60x$

(A) Solving the price-demand equation for p, we get

$p = 200 - \dfrac{1}{30}x$; domain: $0 \leq x \leq 6,000$

(B) Marginal cost: $C'(x) = 60$

(C) Revenue function: $R(x) = 200x - \dfrac{1}{30}x^2$; domain: $0 \leq x \leq 6,000$

(D) Marginal revenue: $R'(x) = 200 - \dfrac{1}{15}x$

(E) $R'(1,500) = 100$; at a production level of 1,500 saws, revenue is
INCREASING at the rate of \$100 per saw.

$R'(4,500) = -100$; at a production level of 4,500 saws, revenue is
DECREASING at the rate of \$100 per saw.

(F)

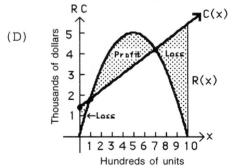

(G) Profit function: $P(x) = R(x) - C(x)$

$$= 200x - \frac{1}{30}x^2 - [72{,}000 + 60x]$$

$$= 140x - \frac{1}{30}x^2 - 72{,}000$$

(H) Marginal profit: $P'(x) = 140 - \frac{1}{15}x$

(I) $P'(1{,}500) = 140 - 100 = 40$; at a production level of 1,500 saws, profit is INCREASING at the rate of \$40 per saw.

$P'(3000) = 140 - 200 = -60$; at a production level of 3,000 saws, profit is DECREASING at the rate of \$60 per saw.

15. (A) Assume $p = mx + b$. We are given

$$16 = m \cdot 200 + b$$

and $\quad 14 = m \cdot 300 + b$

Subtracting the second equation from the first, we get

$$-100m = 2 \quad \text{so} \quad m = -\frac{1}{50} = -0.02$$

Substituting this value into either equation yields $b = 20$. Therefore, $P = 20 - 0.02x$; domain: $0 \le x \le 1{,}000$

(B) Revenue function: $R(x) = xp = 20x - 0.02x^2$, domain: $0 \le x \le 1{,}000$.

(C) $C(x) = mx + b$. From the finance department's estimates, $m = 4$ and $b = 1{,}400$. Thus, $C(x) = 4x + 1{,}400$.

(D)

(E) Profit function: $P(x) = R(x) - C(x)$

$$= 20x - 0.02x^2 - [4x + 1{,}400]$$

$$= 16x - 0.02x^2 - 1{,}400$$

(F) Marginal profit: $P'(x) = 16 - 0.04x$

$P'(250) = 16 - 10 = 6$; at a production level of 250 toasters, profit is INCREASING at the rate of $6 per toaster.

$P'(475) = 16 - 19 = -3$; at a production level of 475 toasters, profit is DECREASING at the rate of $3 per toaster.

17. Total cost: $C(x) = 24x + 21,900$

Total revenue: $R(x) = 200x - 0.2x^2$, $0 \le x \le 1,000$

(A) $R'(x) = 200 - 0.4x$

The graph of R has a horizontal tangent line at the value(s) of x where $R'(x) = 0$, i.e.,

$$200 - 0.4x = 0$$
$$\text{or } x = 500$$

(B) $P(x) = R(x) - C(x) = 200x - 0.2x^2 - (24x + 21,900)$
$$= 176x - 0.2x^2 - 21,900$$

(C) $P'(x) = 176 - 0.4x$. Setting $P'(x) = 0$, we have

$$176x - 0.4x = 0$$
$$\text{or } x = 440$$

(D) The graphs of C, R and P are shown below.

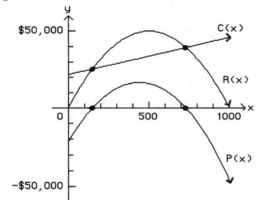

Break-even points: $R(x) = C(x)$

$$200x - 0.2x^2 = 24x + 21,900$$
$$0.2x^2 - 176x + 21,900 = 0$$
$$x = \frac{176 \pm \sqrt{(176)^2 - (4)(0.2)(21,900)}}{2(0.2)} \quad \text{(quadratic formula)}$$
$$= \frac{176 \pm \sqrt{30,976 - 17,520}}{0.4}$$
$$= \frac{176 \pm \sqrt{13,456}}{0.4} = \frac{176 \pm 116}{0.4} = 730, \ 150$$

Thus, the break-even points are: (730, 39,420) and (150, 25,500).

x-intercepts for P: $-0.2x^2 + 17.6x - 21,900 = 0$
$$\text{or } 0.2x^2 - 176x + 21,900 = 0$$

which is the same as the equation above.

Thus, $x = 150$ and $x = 730$.

19. Demand equation: $p = 20 - \sqrt{x} = 20 - x^{1/2}$

Cost equation: $C(x) = 500 + 2x$

(A) Revenue $R(x) = xp = x(20 - x^{1/2})$

or $R(x) = 20x - x^{3/2}$

(B) The graphs for R and C for $0 \le x \le 400$ are shown at the right.

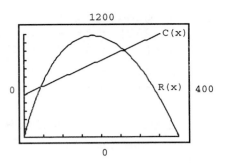

Break-even points $(44, 588)$ and $(258, 1,016)$.

21. (A)
```
QuadReg
y=ax²+bx+c
a=1.4101002E-5
b=-.2732556676
c=1320.924694
```

(B) Fixed costs $\approx \$721,680$; variable costs $\approx \$121$
```
LinReg
y=ax+b
a=120.7047281
b=721680.1282
r=.9934384133
```

(C) Let $y = p(x)$ be the quadratic regression equation found in part (A) and let $y = C(x)$ be the linear regression equation found in part (B). Then revenue $R(x) = xp(x)$, and the break-even points are the points where $R(x) = C(x)$.

break-even points: $(713, 807,703)$, $(5,423, 1,376,227)$

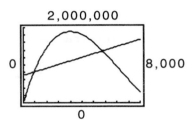

(D) The company will make a profit when $713 \le x \le 5,423$. From part (A), $p(713) \approx 1,133$ and $p(5,423) \approx 254$. Thus, the company will make a profit for the price range $\$254 \le p \le \$1,133$.

CHAPTER 3 REVIEW

1. (A) $f(3) - f(1) = 2(3)^2 + 5 - [2(1)^2 + 5] = 16$

(B) Average rate of change: $\dfrac{f(3) - f(1)}{3 - 1} = \dfrac{16}{2} = 8$

(C) Slope of secant line: $\dfrac{f(3) - f(1)}{3 - 1} = \dfrac{16}{2} = 8$

(D) Instantaneous rate of change at $x = 1$:

Step 1. $\dfrac{f(1 + h) - f(1)}{h} = \dfrac{2(1 + h)^2 + 5 - [2(1)^2 + 5]}{h}$

$= \dfrac{2(1 + 2h + h^2) + 5 - 7}{h} = \dfrac{4h + 2h^2}{h} = 4 + 2h$

Step 2. $\lim\limits_{h \to 0} \dfrac{f(1 + h) - f(1)}{h} = \lim\limits_{h \to 0} (4 + 2h) = 4$

(E) Slope of the tangent line at $x = 1$: 4

(F) $f'(1) = 4$

(3-1, 3-3, 3-4)

2. $f(x) = -3x + 2$

Step 1. Simplify $\dfrac{f(x + h) - f(x)}{h}$

$$\dfrac{f(x + h) - f(x)}{h} = \dfrac{-3(x + h) + 2 - (-3x + 2)}{h}$$

$$= \dfrac{-3x - 3h + 2 + 3x - 2}{h} = -3$$

Step 2. Evaluate $\lim\limits_{h \to 0} \dfrac{f(x + h) - f(x)}{h}$.

$$\lim\limits_{h \to 0} \dfrac{f(x + h) - f(x)}{h} = \lim\limits_{h \to 0} (-3) = -3 \tag{3-3}$$

3. (A) $\lim\limits_{x \to 1} (5f(x) + 3g(x)) = 5\lim\limits_{x \to 1} f(x) + 3\lim\limits_{x \to 1} g(x) = 5 \cdot 2 + 3 \cdot 4 = 22$

(B) $\lim\limits_{x \to 1} [f(x)g(x)] = [\lim\limits_{x \to 1} f(x)][\lim\limits_{x \to 1} g(x)] = 2 \cdot 4 = 8$

(C) $\lim\limits_{x \to 1} \dfrac{g(x)}{f(x)} = \dfrac{\lim\limits_{x \to 1} g(x)}{\lim\limits_{x \to 1} f(x)} = \dfrac{4}{2} = 2$

(D) $\lim\limits_{x \to 1} [5 + 2x - 3g(x)] = \lim\limits_{x \to 1} 5 + \lim\limits_{x \to 1} 2x - 3\lim\limits_{x \to 1} g(x)$

$$= 5 + 2 - 3(4) = -5 \tag{3-2}$$

4. (A) $\lim\limits_{x \to 1^-} f(x) = 1$　　(B) $\lim\limits_{x \to 1^+} f(x) = 1$　　(C) $\lim\limits_{x \to 1} f(x) = 1$

(D) $f(1) = 1$ $\tag{3-2}$

5. (A) $\lim\limits_{x \to 2^-} f(x) = 2$　　(B) $\lim\limits_{x \to 2^+} f(x) = 3$　　(C) $\lim\limits_{x \to 2} f(x)$ does not exist

(D) $f(2) = 3$ $\tag{3-2}$

6. (A) $\lim\limits_{x \to 3^-} f(x) = 4$　　(B) $\lim\limits_{x \to 3^+} f(x) = 4$　　(C) $\lim\limits_{x \to 3} f(x) = 4$

(D) $f(3)$ does not exist $\tag{3-2}$

7. (A) From the graph, $\lim\limits_{x \to 1} f(x)$ does not exist since
$\lim\limits_{x \to 1^-} f(x) = 2 \neq \lim\limits_{x \to 1^+} f(x) = 3$.

(B) $f(1) = 3$

(C) f is NOT continuous at $x = 1$, since $\lim\limits_{x \to 1} f(x)$ does not exist. $\tag{3-2}$

8. (A) $\lim\limits_{x \to 2} f(x) = 2$　　　　(B) $f(2)$ is not defined

(C) f is NOT continuous at $x = 2$ since $f(2)$ is not defined. $\tag{3-2}$

9. (A) $\lim\limits_{x \to 3} f(x) = 1$ (B) $f(3) = 1$

    (C) f is continuous at $x = 3$ since $\lim\limits_{x \to 3} f(x) = f(3)$.   (3-2)

10. $f(x) = 5x^2$

Step 1. Simplify $\dfrac{f(x + h) - f(x)}{h}$.

$$\frac{f(x + h) - f(x)}{h} = \frac{5(x + h)^2 - 5x^2}{h} = \frac{5(x^2 + 2xh + h^2) - 5x^2}{h}$$

$$= \frac{10xh + 5h^2}{h} = 10x + 5h$$

Step 2. Evaluate $\lim\limits_{h \to 0} \dfrac{f(x + h) - f(x)}{h}$.

$$\lim_{h \to 0} \frac{f(x + h) - f(x)}{h} = \lim_{h \to 0}(10x + 5h) = 10x \tag{3-3}$$

11. (A) $h(x) = 2f(x) + 3g(x); \quad h'(5) = 2f'(5) + 3g'(5) = 2(-1) + 3(-3) = -11$

    (B) $h(x) = f(x)g(x); \quad h'(5) = f(5)g'(5) + g(5)f'(5) = 4(-3) + 2(-1) = -14$

    (C) $h(x) = \dfrac{f(x)}{g(x)}; \quad h'(5) = \dfrac{g(5)f'(5) - f(5)g'(5)}{[g(5)]^2} = \dfrac{2(-1) - 4(-3)}{2^2} = \dfrac{10}{4} = \dfrac{5}{2}$

    (D) $h(x) = [f(x)]^2; \quad h'(5) = 2f(5)f'(5) = 2(4)(-1) = -8$

    (E) $h(x) = x^2 f(x); \quad h'(x) = x^2 f'(x) + f(x)(2x);$
        $h'(5) = 25f'(5) + f(5)(10) = 25(-1) + 4(10) = 15$

    (F) $h(x) = \dfrac{g(x)}{x + 2}; \quad h'(x) = \dfrac{(x + 2)g'(x) - g(x)(1)}{(x + 2)^2};$
        $h'(5) = \dfrac{7(-3) - 2(1)}{7^2} = \dfrac{-23}{49}$ (3-4, 3-5, 3-6)

12. $6x + 4; \quad \dfrac{d}{dx}(3x^2 + 4x + 1)^5 = 5(3x^2 + 4x + 1)^4(6x + 4)$ (3-6)

13. $f(x) = \dfrac{1}{3}x^3 - 5x^2 + 1; \quad f'(x) = x^2 - 10x$ (3-4)

14. $f(x) = 2x^{1/2} - 3x$
    $f'(x) = 2 \cdot \dfrac{1}{2}x^{-1/2} - 3 = \dfrac{1}{x^{1/2}} - 3$ (3-4)

15. $f(x) = 5$ **16.** $f(x) = \dfrac{3}{2x} + \dfrac{5x^3}{4} = \dfrac{3}{2}x^{-1} + \dfrac{5}{4}x^3;$
    $f'(x) = 0$

        (3-4) $f'(x) = -\dfrac{3}{2}x^{-2} + \dfrac{15}{4}x^2 = -\dfrac{3}{2x^2} + \dfrac{15}{4}x^2$ (3-4)

17. $f(x) = \dfrac{0.5}{x^4} + 0.25x^4 = 0.5x^{-4} + 0.25x^4$

$f'(x) = 0.5(-4)x^{-5} + 0.25(4x^3) = -2x^{-5} + x^3 = -\dfrac{2}{x^5} + x^3$ 　　　(3-4)

18. $f(x) = (2x - 1)(3x + 2)$
$f'(x) = (2x - 1)(3) + (3x + 2)(2)$
　　$= 6x - 3 + 6x + 4$
　　$= 12x + 1$ 　　　(3-5)

19. $f(x) = (x^2 - 1)(x^3 - 3)$
$f'(x) = (x^2 - 1)(3x^2) + (x^3 - 3)(2x) = 3x^4 - 3x^2 + 2x^4 - 6x = 5x^4 - 3x^2 - 6x$ 　　　(3-5)

20. $f(x) = (0.2x - 1.5)(0.5x + 0.4)$
$f'(x) = (0.2x - 1.5)(0.5x + 0.4)' + (0.5x + 0.4)(0.2x - 1.5)'$
　　$= (0.2x - 1.5)(0.5) + (0.5x + 0.4)(0.2)$
　　$= 0.1x - 0.75 + 0.1x + 0.08 = 0.2x - 0.67$ 　　　(3-5)

21. $f(x) = \dfrac{2x}{x^2 + 2}$

$f'(x) = \dfrac{(x^2 + 2)(2) - 2x(2x)}{(x^2 + 2)^2} = \dfrac{2x^2 + 4 - 4x^2}{(x^2 + 2)^2} = \dfrac{4 - 2x^2}{(x^2 + 2)^2}$ 　　　(3-5)

22. $f(x) = \dfrac{1}{3x + 2} = (3x + 2)^{-1}$

$f'(x) = -1(3x + 2)^{-2}(3) = \dfrac{-3}{(3x + 2)^2}$ 　　　(3-6)

23. $f(x) = (2x - 3)^3$
$f'(x) = 3(2x - 3)^2(2) = 6(2x - 3)^2$ 　　　(3-6)

24. $f(x) = (x^2 + 2)^{-2}$

$f'(x) = -2(x^2 + 2)^{-3}(2x) = \dfrac{-4x}{(x^2 + 2)^3}$ 　　　(3-6)

25. From the graph:
　(A) $\lim\limits_{x \to 2^-} f(x) = 4$ 　　　　　(B) $\lim\limits_{x \to 2^+} f(x) = 6$

　(C) $\lim\limits_{x \to 2} f(x)$ does not exist since $\lim\limits_{x \to 2^-} f(x) \neq \lim\limits_{x \to 2^+} f(x)$

　(D) $f(2) = 6$ 　　　　　(E) No, since $\lim\limits_{x \to 2} f(x)$ does not exist. 　　(3-2)

26. From the graph:
　(A) $\lim\limits_{x \to 5^-} f(x) = 3$ 　(B) $\lim\limits_{x \to 5^+} f(x) = 3$ 　(C) $\lim\limits_{x \to 5} f(x) = 3$ 　(D) $f(5) = 3$

　(E) Yes, since $\lim\limits_{x \to 5} f(x) = f(5) = 3$. 　　　(3-2)

27. (A) $f(x) < 0$ on $(8, \infty)$
　　(B) $f(x) \geq 0$ on $[0, 8]$ 　　　(3-2)

28. $x^2 - x < 12$ or $x^2 - x - 12 < 0$

Let $f(x) = x^2 - x - 12 = (x + 3)(x - 4)$. Then f is continuous for all x and $f(-3) = f(4) = 0$. Thus, $x = -3$ and $x = 4$ are partition numbers.

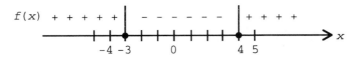

Test Numbers

x	$f(x)$
-4	8 (+)
0	-12 (−)
5	8 (+)

Thus, $x^2 - x < 12$ for: $-3 < x < 4$ or $(-3, 4)$. (3-2)

29. $\dfrac{x - 5}{x^2 + 3x} > 0$ or $\dfrac{x - 5}{x(x + 3)} > 0$

Let $f(x) = \dfrac{x - 5}{x(x + 3)}$. Then f is discontinuous at $x = 0$ and $x = -3$, and $f(5) = 0$. Thus, $x = -3$, $x = 0$, and $x = 5$ are partition numbers.

Test Numbers

x	$f(x)$
-4	$-\frac{9}{4}$ (−)
-1	3 (+)
1	-1 (−)
6	$\frac{1}{54}$ (+)

Thus, $\dfrac{x - 5}{x^2 + 3x} > 0$ for $-3 < x < 0$ or $x > 5$

or $(-3, 0) \cup (5, \infty)$. (3-2)

30. $x^3 + x^2 - 4x - 2 > 0$

Let $f(x) = x^3 + x^2 - 4x - 2$. The f is continuous for all x and $f(x) = 0$ at $x = -2.3429$, -0.4707 and 1.8136.

$f(x)$ $\quad$ $-\,-\,-\,0\,+\,+\,+\,0\,-\,-\,-\,-\,0\,+\,+\,+$

$-2.34 \quad -0.470 \quad 1.81$

Thus, $x^3 + x^2 - 4x - 2 > 0$ for $-2.3429 < x < -0.4707$ or $1.8136 < x < \infty$, or $(-2.3429, -0.4707) \cup (1.8136, \infty)$. (3-2)

31. $f(x) = 0.5x^2 - 5$

(A) $\dfrac{f(4) - f(2)}{4 - 2} = \dfrac{0.5(4)^2 - 5 - [0.5(2)^2 - 5]}{2} = \dfrac{8 - 2}{2} = 3$

(B) $\dfrac{f(2 + h) - f(2)}{h} = \dfrac{0.5(2 + h)^2 - 5 - [0.5(2)^2 - 5]}{h}$

$= \dfrac{0.5(4 + 4h + h^2) - 5 + 3}{h}$

$= \dfrac{2h + 0.5h^2}{h} = \dfrac{h(2 + 0.5h)}{h} = 2 + 0.5h$

(C) $\lim\limits_{h \to 0} \dfrac{f(2 + h) - f(2)}{h} = \lim\limits_{h \to 0} (2 + 0.5h) = 2$ (3-3)

32. $y = \dfrac{1}{3}x^{-3} - 5x^{-2} + 1; \quad \dfrac{dy}{dx} = -x^{-4} + 10x^{-3}$ (3-4)

33. $y = (2x^2 - 3x + 2)(x^2 + 2x - 1)$

$y' = (2x^2 - 3x + 2)(2x + 2) + (x^2 + 2x - 1)(4x - 3)$

$= 4x^3 - 6x^2 + 4x + 4x^2 - 6x + 4 + 4x^3 + 8x^2 - 4x - 3x^2 - 6x + 3$

$= 8x^3 + 3x^2 - 12x + 7$ (3-5)

34. $f(x) = \dfrac{2x - 3}{(x - 1)^2}$

$f'(x) = \dfrac{(x - 1)^2 2 - (2x - 3)2(x - 1)}{(x - 1)^4} = \dfrac{(x - 1)[2(x - 1) - 4x + 6]}{(x - 1)^4}$

$= \dfrac{(2x - 2 - 4x + 6)}{(x - 1)^3} = \dfrac{4 - 2x}{(x - 1)^3}$ (3-5)

35. $y = \dfrac{3\sqrt{x}}{2} + \dfrac{5}{3\sqrt{x}} = \dfrac{3}{2}x^{1/2} + \dfrac{5}{3}x^{-1/2};$

$y' = \dfrac{3}{2}\left(\dfrac{1}{2}x^{-1/2}\right) + \dfrac{5}{3}\left(-\dfrac{1}{2}x^{-3/2}\right) = \dfrac{3}{4x^{1/2}} - \dfrac{5}{6x^{3/2}} = \dfrac{3}{4\sqrt{x}} - \dfrac{5}{6\sqrt{x^3}}$ (3-4)

36. $g(x) = 1.8\sqrt[3]{x} + \dfrac{0.9}{\sqrt[3]{x}} = 1.8x^{1/3} + 0.9x^{-1/3}$

$g'(x) = 1.8\left(\dfrac{1}{3}x^{-2/3}\right) + 0.9\left(-\dfrac{1}{3}x^{-4/3}\right)$

$= 0.6x^{-2/3} - 0.3x^{-4/3} = \dfrac{0.6}{x^{2/3}} - \dfrac{0.3}{x^{4/3}}$ (3-4)

37. $\dfrac{d}{dx}[(x^2 - 1)(2x + 1)^2] = (x^2 - 1)\dfrac{d}{dx}(2x + 1)^2 + (2x + 1)^2\dfrac{d}{dx}(x^2 - 1)$

$= (x^2 - 1)[2(2x + 1)(2)] + (2x + 1)^2(2x)$

$= 2(2x + 1)[2(x^2 - 1) + x(2x + 1)]$

$= 2(2x + 1)(2x^2 - 2 + 2x^2 + x)$

$= 2(2x + 1)(4x^2 + x - 2)$ (3-5, 3-6)

38. $\dfrac{d}{dx}(x^3 - 5)^{1/3} = \dfrac{1}{3}(x^3 - 5)^{-2/3}(3x^2) = \dfrac{x^2}{(x^3 - 5)^{2/3}}$ (3-6)

39. $y = \dfrac{2x^3 - 3}{5x^3} = \dfrac{2}{5} - \dfrac{3}{5}x^{-3}; \quad y' = -\dfrac{3}{5}(-3x^{-4}) = \dfrac{9}{5x^4}$ (3-4)

40. $\dfrac{d}{dx}\dfrac{(x^2+2)^4}{2x-3} = \dfrac{(2x-3)4(x^2+2)^3(2x)-(x^2+2)^4(2)}{(2x-3)^2}$

$= \dfrac{2(x^2+2)^3[4x(2x-3)-(x^2+2)]}{(2x-3)^2}$

$= \dfrac{2(x^2+2)^3(8x^2-12x-x^2-2)}{(2x-3)^2} = \dfrac{2(x^2+2)^3(7x^2-12x-2)}{(2x-3)^2}$

$(3-5, 3-6)$

41. $f(x) = x^2 + 4$
$f'(x) = 2x$

(A) The slope of the graph at $x = 1$ is $m = f'(1) = 2$.

(B) $f(1) = 1^2 + 4 = 5$
The tangent line at $(1, 5)$, where the slope $m = 2$, is:
$(y - 5) = 2(x - 1)$ [Note: $(y - y_1) = m(x - x_1)$.]

$y = 5 + 2x - 2$
$y = 2x + 3$

$(3-3, 3-4)$

42. $f(x) = x^3(x+1)^2$

$f'(x) = x^3(2)(x+1)(1) + (x+1)^2(3x^2)$
$= 2x^3(x+1) + 3x^2(x+1)^2$

(A) The slope of the graph of f at $x = 1$ is:
$f'(1) = 2 \cdot 1^3(1+1) + 3 \cdot 1^2(1+1)^2 = 16$

(B) $f(1) = 1^3(1+1)^2 = 4$

An equation for the tangent line to the graph of f at $x = 1$ is
$y - 4 = 16(x - 1)$ or $y = 16x - 12$. $(3-3, 3-5)$

43. $f(x) = 10x - x^2$
$f'(x) = 10 - 2x$
The tangent line is horizontal at the values of x such that $f'(x) = 0$:
$10 - 2x = 0$
$x = 5$

$(3-4)$

44. $f(x) = (x+3)(x^2-45)$

$f'(x) = (x+3)(2x) + (x^2-45)(1) = 3x^2 + 6x - 45$
Set $f'(x) = 0$:
$3x^2 + 6x - 45 = 0$
$x^2 + 2x - 15 = 0$
$(x-3)(x+5) = 0$
$x = 3, \; x = -5$ $(3-5)$

45. $f(x) = \dfrac{x}{x^2+4}$

$f'(x) = \dfrac{(x^2+4)(1) - x(2x)}{(x^2+4)^2} = \dfrac{4-x^2}{(x^2+4)^2}$

Set $f'(x) = 0$: $\dfrac{4-x^2}{(x^2+4)^2} = 0$

$4 - x^2 = 0$
$(2-x)(2+x) = 0$
$x = 2, \; x = -2$ $(3-5)$

46. $f(x) = x^2(2x - 15)^3$

$f'(x) = x^2(3)(2x - 15)^2(2) + (2x - 15)^3(2x)$

$\quad = (2x - 15)^2[6x^2 + 4x^2 - 30x]$

$\quad = (2x - 15)^2 10x(x - 3)$

Set $f'(x) = 0$:

$10x(x - 3)(2x - 15)^2 = 0$

$$x = 0, \ x = 3, \ x = \frac{15}{2} \qquad\qquad (3-5)$$

47. $f(x) = x^4 - 2x^3 - 5x^2 + 7x$

$f'(x) = 4x^3 - 6x^2 - 10x + 7$

Set $f'(x) = 4x^3 - 6x^2 - 10x + 7 = 0$ and solve for x using a root-approximation routine on a graphing utility:

$f'(x) = 0$ at $x = -1.34$, $x = 0.58$, $x = 2.26$ $\qquad\qquad (3-4)$

48. $f(x) = \dfrac{x^3 - 5x + 10}{x^2 + 2}$

$$f'(x) = \frac{(x^2 + 2)(3x^2 - 5) - (x^3 - 5x + 10)2x}{(x^2 + 2)^2} = \frac{x^4 + 11x^2 - 20x - 10}{(x^2 + 2)^2}$$

Set $f'(x) = 0$: $\dfrac{x^4 + 11x^2 - 20x - 10}{(x^2 + 2)^2} = 0$ implies $x^4 + 11x^2 - 20x - 10 = 0$

Use a root-approximation routine on a graphing utility:

$f'(x) = 0$ at $x = -0.41$, $x = 1.80$. $\qquad\qquad (3-5)$

49. $f(x) = \dfrac{5x^4 - 40x^2}{(x^2 + 1)^2}$

$$f'(x) = \frac{(x^2 + 1)^2(20x^3 - 80x) - (5x^4 - 40x^2)(2)(x^2 + 1)2x}{(x^2 + 1)^4}$$

$$= \frac{(x^2 + 1)(20x^3 - 80x) - 4x(5x^4 - 40x^2)}{(x^2 + 1)^3}$$

$$= \frac{100x^3 - 80x}{(x^2 + 1)^3} = \frac{20x(5x^2 - 4)}{(x^2 + 1)^3}$$

$f'(x) = 0$ implies $20x(5x^2 - 4) = 0$ and $x = 0, \ \pm\dfrac{2}{\sqrt{5}}$ or $x = -0.89$, $x = 0$,

$x = 0.89$ to two decimal places. $\qquad\qquad (3-5, \ 3-6)$

50. $y = f(x) = 8x^2 - 4x + 1$

(A) Instantaneous velocity function; $v(x) = f'(x) = 16x - 4$.

(B) $v(3) = 16(3) - 4 = 44$ ft/sec. $\qquad\qquad (3-4)$

51. $y = f(x) = -5x^2 + 16x + 3$

   (A) Instantaneous velocity function: $v(x) = f'(x) = -10x + 16$.

   (B) $v(x) = 0$ when $-10x + 16 = 0$

$$10x = 16$$
$$x = 1.6 \text{ sec}$$

                                                           (3-4)

52. (A) $f(x) = x^3$, $g(x) = (x - 4)^3$, $h(x) = (x + 3)^3$

     The graph of g is the graph of f shifted 4 units to the right;
     the graph of h is the graph of f shifted 3 units to the left.

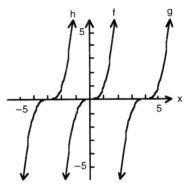

   (B) $f'(x) = 3x^2$, $g'(x) = 3(x - 4)^2$, $h'(x) = 3(x + 3)^2$

     The graph of g' is the graph of f' shifted 4 units to the right;
     the graph of h' is the graph of f' shifted 3 units to the left.

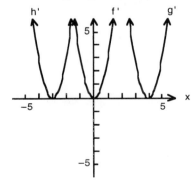

                                                               (1-2, 3-6)

53. (A) $g(x) = f(x + k)$; $g'(x) = f'(x + k)(1) = f'(x + k)$

     The graph of g is a horizontal translation of the graph of f.
     The graph of g' is a horizontal translation of the graph of f'.

   (B) $g(x) = f(x) + k$, $g'(x) = f'(x)$

     The graph of g is a vertical translation of the graph of f
     (up k units if $k > 0$, down k units if $k < 0$). The graph of g' is
     the same as the graph of f'.   (1-2, 3-6)

54. $f(x) = x^2 - 4$ is a polynomial function; f is continuous on $(-\infty, \infty)$.

                                                                   (3-2)

55. $f(x) = \dfrac{x+1}{x-2}$ is a rational function and the denominator $x - 2$ is 0 at $x = 2$. Thus f is continuous for all x such that $x \neq 2$, i.e., on $(-\infty, 2) \cup (2, \infty)$. (3-2)

56. $f(x) = \dfrac{x+4}{x^2 + 3x - 4}$ is a rational function and the denominator $x^2 + 3x - 4 = (x + 4)(x - 1)$ is 0 at $x = -4$ and $x = 1$. Thus, f is continuous for all x except $x = -4$ and $x = 1$, i.e., on $(-\infty, -4) \cup (-4, 1) \cup (1, \infty)$. (3-2)

57. $f(x) = \sqrt[3]{4 - x^2}$; $g(x) = 4 - x^2$ is continuous for all x since it is a polynomial function. Therefore, $f(x) = \sqrt[3]{g(x)}$ is continuous for all x, i.e., on $(-\infty, \infty)$. (3-2)

58. $f(x) = \sqrt{4 - x^2}$; $g(x) = 4 - x^2$ is continuous for all x and $g(x)$ is nonnegative for $-2 \leq x \leq 2$. Therefore, $f(x) = \sqrt{g(x)}$ is continuous for $-2 \leq x \leq 2$, i.e., on $[-2, 2]$. (3-2)

59. $f(x) = \dfrac{2x}{x^2 - 3x} = \dfrac{2x}{x(x-3)} = \dfrac{2}{x-3}$, $x \neq 0$

   (A) $\displaystyle\lim_{x \to 1} f(x) = \lim_{x \to 1} \dfrac{2}{x-3} = \dfrac{\displaystyle\lim_{x \to 1} 2}{\displaystyle\lim_{x \to 1}(x-3)} = \dfrac{2}{-2} = -1$

   (B) $\displaystyle\lim_{x \to 3} f(x) = \lim_{x \to 3} \dfrac{2}{x-3}$ does not exist since $\displaystyle\lim_{x \to 3} 2 = 2$ and $\displaystyle\lim_{x \to 3}(x-3) = 0$

   (C) $\displaystyle\lim_{x \to 0} f(x) = \lim_{x \to 0} \dfrac{2}{x-3} = -\dfrac{2}{3}$ (3-1)

60. $f(x) = \dfrac{x+1}{(3-x)^2}$

   (A) $\displaystyle\lim_{x \to 1} \dfrac{x+1}{(3-x)^2} = \dfrac{\displaystyle\lim_{x \to 1}(x+1)}{\displaystyle\lim_{x \to 1}(3-x)^2} = \dfrac{2}{2^2} = \dfrac{1}{2}$

   (B) $\displaystyle\lim_{x \to -1} \dfrac{x+1}{(3-x)^2} = \dfrac{\displaystyle\lim_{x \to -1}(x+1)}{\displaystyle\lim_{x \to -1}(3-x)^2} = \dfrac{0}{4^2} = 0$

   (C) $\displaystyle\lim_{x \to 3} \dfrac{x+1}{(3-x)^2}$ does not exist since $\displaystyle\lim_{x \to 3}(x+1) = 4$ and $\displaystyle\lim_{x \to 3}(3-x)^2 = 0$ (3-1)

61. $f(x) = \dfrac{|x - 4|}{x - 4} = \begin{cases} -1 & \text{if } x < 4 \\ 1 & \text{if } x > 4 \end{cases}$

(A) $\lim\limits_{x \to 4^-} f(x) = -1$ (B) $\lim\limits_{x \to 4^+} f(x) = 1$

(C) $\lim\limits_{x \to 4} f(x)$ does not exist.   (3-1)

62. $f(x) = \dfrac{x - 3}{9 - x^2} = \dfrac{x - 3}{(3 + x)(3 - x)} = \dfrac{-(3 - x)}{(3 + x)(3 - x)} = \dfrac{-1}{3 + x}, \quad x \neq 3$

(A) $\lim\limits_{x \to 3} f(x) = \lim\limits_{x \to 3} \dfrac{-1}{3 + x} = -\dfrac{1}{6}$

(B) $\lim\limits_{x \to -3} f(x) = \lim\limits_{x \to -3} \dfrac{-1}{3 + x}$ does not exist

(C) $\lim\limits_{x \to 0} f(x) = \lim\limits_{x \to 0} \dfrac{-1}{3 + x} = -\dfrac{1}{3}$ (3-1)

63. $f(x) = \dfrac{x^2 - x - 2}{x^2 - 7x + 10} = \dfrac{(x - 2)(x + 1)}{(x - 2)(x - 5)} = \dfrac{x + 1}{x - 5}, \quad x \neq 2$

(A) $\lim\limits_{x \to -1} f(x) = \lim\limits_{x \to -1} \dfrac{x + 1}{x - 5} = 0$

(B) $\lim\limits_{x \to 2} f(x) = \lim\limits_{x \to 2} \dfrac{x + 1}{x - 5} = \dfrac{3}{-3} = -1$

(C) $\lim\limits_{x \to 5} f(x) = \lim\limits_{x \to 5} \dfrac{x + 1}{x - 5}$ does not exist   (3-1)

64. $f(x) = x^2 + 4$

$\lim\limits_{h \to 0} \dfrac{f(2 + h) - f(2)}{h} = \lim\limits_{h \to 0} \dfrac{[(2 + h)^2 + 4] - [2^2 + 4]}{h}$

$= \lim\limits_{h \to 0} \dfrac{4 + 4h + h^2 + 4 - 8}{h} = \lim\limits_{h \to 0} \dfrac{4h + h^2}{h}$

$= \lim\limits_{h \to 0} (4 + h) = 4$ (3-1)

65. Let $f(x) = \dfrac{1}{x + 2}$

$\lim\limits_{h \to 0} \dfrac{f(x + h) - f(x)}{h} = \lim\limits_{h \to 0} \dfrac{\dfrac{1}{(x + h) + 2} - \dfrac{1}{x + 2}}{h}$

$= \lim\limits_{h \to 0} \dfrac{x + 2 - (x + h + 2)}{h(x + h + 2)(x + 2)}$

$= \lim\limits_{h \to 0} \dfrac{-h}{h(x + h + 2)(x + 2)}$

$= \lim\limits_{h \to 0} \dfrac{-1}{(x + h + 2)(x - 2)} = \dfrac{-1}{(x + 2)^2}$ (3-1)

66. (A) $\lim\limits_{x \to -2^-} f(x) = -6,\quad \lim\limits_{x \to -2^+} f(x) = 6;\quad \lim\limits_{x \to -2} f(x)$ does not exist

(B) $\lim\limits_{x \to 0} f(x) = 4$

(C) $\lim\limits_{x \to 2^-} f(x) = 2,\quad \lim\limits_{x \to 2^+} f(x) = -2;\quad \lim\limits_{x \to 2} f(x)$ does not exist

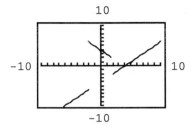

(3-1)

67. $f(x) = x^2 - x$

Step 1. Simplify $\dfrac{f(x + h) - f(x)}{h}$.

$$\dfrac{f(x + h) - f(x)}{h} = \dfrac{[(x + h)^2 - (x + h)] - (x^2 - x)}{h}$$

$$= \dfrac{x^2 + 2xh + h^2 - x - h - x^2 + x}{h}$$

$$= \dfrac{2xh + h^2 - h}{h} = 2x + h - 1$$

Step 2. Evaluate $\lim\limits_{h \to 0} \dfrac{f(x + h) - f(x)}{h}$.

$$\lim\limits_{h \to 0} \dfrac{f(x + h) - f(x)}{h} = \lim\limits_{h \to 0} (2x + h - 1) = 2x - 1$$

Thus, $f'(x) = 2x - 1$.

(3-3)

68. $f(x) = \sqrt{x} - 3$

Step 1. Simplify $\dfrac{f(x + h) - f(x)}{h}$.

$$\dfrac{f(x + h) - f(x)}{h} = \dfrac{[\sqrt{x + h} - 3] - (\sqrt{x} - 3)}{h}$$

$$= \dfrac{\sqrt{x + h} - \sqrt{x}}{h} \cdot \dfrac{\sqrt{x + h} + \sqrt{x}}{\sqrt{x + h} + \sqrt{x}} = \dfrac{x + h - x}{h[\sqrt{x + h} + \sqrt{x}]}$$

$$= \dfrac{1}{\sqrt{x + h} + \sqrt{x}}$$

Step 2. Evaluate $\lim\limits_{h \to 0} \dfrac{f(x + h) - f(x)}{h}$.

$$\lim\limits_{h \to 0} \dfrac{f(x + h) - f(x)}{h} = \lim\limits_{h \to 0} \dfrac{1}{\sqrt{x + h} + \sqrt{x}} = \dfrac{1}{2\sqrt{x}}$$

(3-3)

69. f is not differentiable at $x = 0$, since f is not continuous at 0.   (3-3)

70. f is not differentiable at $x = 1$; the curve has a vertical tangent line at this point. (3-3)

71. f is not differentiable at $x = 2$; the curve has a "corner" at this point. (3-3)

72. f is differentiable at $x = 3$. In fact, $f'(3) = 0$. (3-3)

73. $f(x) = (x - 4)^4(x + 3)^3$

$$f'(x) = (x - 4)^4(3)(x + 3)^2(1) + (x + 3)^3(4)(x - 4)^3(1)$$
$$= (x - 4)^3(x + 3)^2[3(x - 4) + 4(x + 3)]$$
$$= 7x(x - 4)^3(x + 3)^2 \qquad (3\text{-}5, \ 3\text{-}6)$$

74. $f(x) = 5x^3(x^2 - 1)^2$; $f'(x) = 5x^3(2)(x^2 - 1)(2x) + (x^2 - 1)^2(15x^2)$
$$= 5x^2(x^2 - 1)[4x^2 + 3(x^2 - 1)]$$
$$= 5x^2(x^2 - 1)(7x^2 - 3) \qquad (3\text{-}5, \ 3\text{-}6)$$

75. $f(x) = \dfrac{x^5}{(2x + 1)^4}$

$$f'(x) = \frac{(2x + 1)^4(5x^4) - x^5(4)(2x + 1)^3(2)}{[(2x + 1)^4]^2}$$

$$= \frac{(2x + 1)(5x^4) - 8x^5}{(2x + 1)^5} = \frac{2x^5 + 5x^4}{(2x + 1)^5} = \frac{x^4(2x + 5)}{(2x + 1)^5} \qquad (3\text{-}5, \ 3\text{-}6)$$

76. $f(x) = \dfrac{\sqrt{x^2 - 1}}{x} = \dfrac{(x^2 - 1)^{1/2}}{x}$

$$f'(x) = \frac{x\left(\dfrac{1}{2}\right)(x^2 - 1)^{-1/2}(2x) - (x^2 - 1)^{1/2}(1)}{x^2} = \frac{\dfrac{x^2}{(x^2 - 1)^{1/2}} - (x^2 - 1)^{1/2}}{x^2}$$

$$= \frac{1}{x^2(x^2 - 1)^{1/2}} = \frac{1}{x^2\sqrt{x^2 - 1}} \qquad (3\text{-}5, \ 3\text{-}6)$$

77. $f(x) = \dfrac{x}{\sqrt{x^2 + 4}} = \dfrac{x}{(x^2 + 4)^{1/2}}$

$$f'(x) = \frac{(x^2 + 4)^{1/2}(1) - x\left(\dfrac{1}{2}\right)(x^2 + 4)^{-1/2}(2x)}{[(x^2 + 4)^{1/2}]^2}$$

$$= \frac{(x^2 + 4)^{1/2} - \dfrac{x^2}{(x^2 + 4)^{1/2}}}{(x^2 + 4)} = \frac{4}{(x^2 + 4)^{3/2}} \qquad (3\text{-}5, \ 3\text{-}6)$$

78. $f(x) = x^{1/5};\ f'(x) = \dfrac{1}{5}x^{-4/5} = \dfrac{1}{5x^{4/5}}$

The domain of f' is all real numbers except $x = 0$. At $x = 0$, the graph of f is smooth, but the tangent line to the graph at $(0, 0)$ is vertical.

(3-3)

79. $f(x) = \begin{cases} x^2 - m & \text{if } x \le 1 \\ -x^2 + m & \text{if } x > 1 \end{cases}$

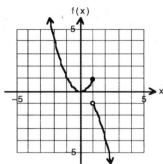
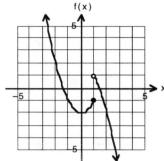

$\lim\limits_{x \to 1^-} f(x) = 1,\quad \lim\limits_{x \to 1^+} f(x) = -1$
$\qquad$
$\lim\limits_{x \to 1^-} f(x) = -1,\quad \lim\limits_{x \to 1^+} f(x) = 1$

(C) $\lim\limits_{x \to 1^-} f(x) = 1 - m,\quad \lim\limits_{x \to 1^+} f(x) = -1 + m$

We want $1 - m = -1 + m$ which implies $m = 1$.

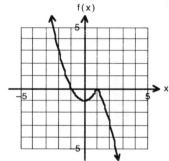

(D) The graphs in (A) and (B) have jumps at $x = 1$; the graph in (C) does not.

(3-1)

80. $f(x) = 1 - |x - 1|,\ 0 \le x \le 2$

(A) $\lim\limits_{h \to 0^-} \dfrac{f(1 + h) - f(1)}{h} = \lim\limits_{h \to 0^-} \dfrac{1 - |1 + h - 1| - 1}{h} = \lim\limits_{h \to 0^-} \dfrac{-|h|}{h}$

$\qquad\qquad = \lim\limits_{h \to 0^-} \dfrac{h}{h} = 1 \quad (|h| = -h \text{ if } h < 0)$

(B) $\lim\limits_{h \to 0^+} \dfrac{f(1 + h) - f(1)}{h} = \lim\limits_{h \to 0^-} \dfrac{1 - |1 + h - 1| - 1}{h} = \lim\limits_{h \to 0^+} \dfrac{-|h|}{h}$

$\qquad\qquad = \lim\limits_{h \to 0^+} \dfrac{-h}{h} = -1 \quad (|h| = h \text{ if } h > 0)$

(C) $\lim\limits_{h \to 0} \dfrac{f(1 + h) - f(1)}{h}$ does not exist, since the left limit and the right limit are not equal.

(D) $f'(1)$ does not exist.

(3-3)

81. (A) $S(x) = 7.47 + 0.4000x$ for $0 \leq x \leq 90$;
$S(90) = 43.47$;
$S(x) = 43.47 + 0.2076 (x - 90)$
$= 24.786 + 0.2076x, \ x > 90$

Therefore,

$$S(x) = \begin{cases} 7.47 + 0.4000x & \text{if} \quad 0 \leq x \leq 90 \\ 24.786 + 0.2076x & \text{if} \quad x > 90 \end{cases}$$

(B)

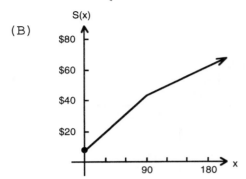

(C) $\lim\limits_{x \to 90^-} S(x) = \lim\limits_{x \to 90^+} S(x) = 43.47 = S(90)$;
$S(x)$ is continuous at $x = 90$.

(3-2)

82. $C(x) = 10,000 + 200x - 0.1x^2$

(A) $C(101) - C(100) = 10,000 + 200(101) - 0.1(101)^2$
$\qquad - [10,000 + 200(100) - 0.1(100)^2]$
$= 29,179.90 - 29,000$
$= \$179.90$

(B) $C'(x) = 200 - 0.2x$
$C'(100) = 200 - 0.2(100)$
$= 200 - 20$
$= \$180$

(3-7)

83. $C(x) = 5,000 + 40x + 0.05x^2$

(A) Cost of producing 100 bicycles:
$C(100) = 5,000 + 40(100) + 0.05(100)^2$
$= 9000 + 500 = 9500$
Marginal cost:
$C'(x) = 40 + 0.1x$
$C'(100) = 40 + 0.1(100) = 40 + 10 = 50$

Interpretation: At a production level of 100 bicycles, the total cost is \$9,500 and is increasing at the rate of \$50 per additional bicycle.

(B) Average cost: $\overline{C}(x) = \dfrac{C(x)}{x} = \dfrac{5000}{x} + 40 + 0.05x$

$\overline{C}(100) = \dfrac{5000}{100} + 40 + 0.05(100) = 50 + 40 + 5 = 95$

Marginal average cost: $\overline{C}'(x) = -\dfrac{5000}{x^2} + 0.05$

and $\overline{C}'(100) = -\dfrac{5000}{(100)^2} + 0.05 = -0.5 + 0.05 = -0.45$

Interpretation: At a production level of 100 bicycles, the average cost is \$95 and the marginal average cost is decreasing at a rate of \$0.45 per additional bicycle.

(3-7)

84. The approximate cost of producing the 201st printer is greater than that of producing the 601st printer (the slope of the tangent line at $x = 200$ is greater than the slope of the tangent line at $x = 600$). Since the marginal costs are decreasing, the manufacturing process is becoming more efficient. (3-7)

85. $p = 25 - 0.1x$, $C(x) = 2x + 9,000$

(A) Marginal cost: $C'(x) = 2$

Average cost: $\overline{C}(x) = \dfrac{C(x)}{x} = 2 + \dfrac{9,000}{x}$

Marginal cost: $\overline{C}'(x) = -\dfrac{9,000}{x^2}$

(B) Revenue: $R(x) = xp = 25x - 0.01x^2$
Marginal revenue: $R'(x) = 25 - 0.02x$

Average revenue: $\overline{R}(x) = \dfrac{R(x)}{x} = 25 - 0.01x$

Marginal average revenue: $\overline{R}'(x) = -0.01$

(C) Profit: $P(x) = R(x) - C(x) = 25x - 0.01x^2 - (2x + 9,000)$
$$= 23x - 0.01x^2 - 9,000$$
Marginal profit: $P'(x) = 23 - 0.02x$

Average profit: $\overline{P}(x) = \dfrac{P(x)}{x} = 23 - 0.01x - \dfrac{9,000}{x}$

Marginal average profit: $\overline{P}'(x) = -0.01 + \dfrac{9,000}{x^2}$

(D) Break-even points: $R(x) = C(x)$
$$25x - 0.01x^2 = 2x + 9,000$$
$$0.01x^2 - 23x + 9,000 = 0$$
$$x^2 - 2,300x + 900,000 = 0$$
$$(x - 500)(x - 1,800) = 0$$

Thus, the break-even points are: $x = 500$, $x = 1,800$.

(E) $P'(1,000) = 23 - 0.02(1000) = 3$; profit is increasing at the rate of \$3 per umbrella.

$P'(1,150) = 23 - 0.02(1,150) = 0$; profit is flat.

$P'(1,400) = 23 - 0.02(1,400) = -5$; profit is decreasing at the rate of \$5 per umbrella.

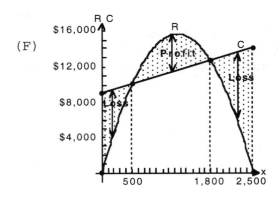

(F)

(3-7)

86. $N(t) = \dfrac{40t}{t + 2}$

(A) Average rate of change from $t = 3$ to $t = 6$:

$$\frac{N(6) - N(3)}{6 - 3} = \frac{\dfrac{40 \cdot 6}{6 + 2} - \dfrac{40 \cdot 3}{3 + 2}}{3} = \frac{30 - 24}{3} = 2 \text{ components per day}$$

(B) $N'(t) = \dfrac{(t + 2)(40) - 40t(1)}{(t + 2)^2} = \dfrac{80}{(t + 2)^2}$

$N'(3) = \dfrac{80}{25} = 3.2$ components per day   (3-5)

87. $N(t) = t\sqrt{4 + t} = t(4 + t)^{1/2}$

$$N'(t) = t\left(\frac{1}{2}\right)(4 + t)^{-1/2} + (4 + t)^{1/2} = \frac{t}{2(4 + t)^{1/2}} + \frac{(4 + t)^{1/2}}{1}$$

$$= \frac{t + 2(4 + t)}{2(4 + t)^{1/2}} = \frac{8 + 3t}{2(4 + t)^{1/2}}$$

$N(5) = 5\sqrt{4 + 5} = 15$; $N'(t) = \dfrac{8 + 3(5)}{2(4 + 5)^{1/2}} = \dfrac{23}{6} = 3.833$;

After 5 months, the total sales are 15,000 pools and sales are
INCREASING at the rate of 3,833 pools per month.   (3-6)

88. (A)
```
CubicReg
 y=ax³+bx²+cx+d
 a=.001225
 b=-.0819285714
 c=1.564642857
 d=12.08428571
```

(B) $N(50) \approx 38.6$, $N'(50) \approx 2.6$; in 1020, natural
gas consumption will be 38.6 trillion cubic
feet and will be INCREASING at the rate of
2.6 trillion cubic feet per year.   (3-3)

89. (A)
```
LinReg
 y=ax+b
 a=-.0384180791
 b=13.59887006
 r=-.9897782666
```

(B) Fixed costs: $484.21; variable cost per
kringle: $2.11.
```
LinReg
 y=ax+b
 a=2.107344633
 b=484.2090395
 r=.9939318704
```

(C) Let $p(x)$ be the linear regression equation found in part (A) and let $C(x)$ be the linear regression equation found in part (B). Then revenue $R(x) = xp(x)$ and the break-even points are the points where $R(x) = C(x)$.

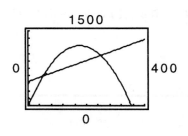

Using an intersection routine on a graphing utility, the break-even points are: (51, 591.15) and (248, 1,007.62).

(D) The bakery will make a profit when $51 < x < 248$. From the regression equation in part (A), $p(51) = 11.64$ and $p(248) = 4.07$. Thus, the bakery will make a profit for the price range $\$4.07 < p < \$11.64$.

(3-7)

90. $C(x) = 500(x + 1)^{-2}$

The instantaneous rate of change of concentration at x meters is:

$C'(x) = 500(-2)(x + 1)^{-3}$

$\qquad = -1000(x + 1)^{-3} = \dfrac{-1000}{(x + 1)^3}$

The rate of change of concentration at 9 meters is:

$C'(9) = \dfrac{-1000}{(9 + 1)^3} = \dfrac{-1000}{10^3} = -1$ part per million per meter

The rate of change of concentration at 99 meters is:

$C'(99) = \dfrac{-1000}{(99 + 1)^3} = \dfrac{-1000}{100^3} = \dfrac{-10^3}{10^6} = -10^{-3}$ or $= -\dfrac{1}{1000}$

$\qquad\qquad\qquad\qquad = -0.001$ parts per million per meter   (3-4)

91. $F(t) = 98 + \dfrac{4}{\sqrt{t + 1}} = 98 + 4(t + 1)^{-1/2}$,

$F'(t) = 4\left(-\dfrac{1}{2}\right)(t + 1)^{-3/2} = \dfrac{-2}{(t + 1)^{3/2}}$

$F(3) = 98 + \dfrac{4}{\sqrt{3 + 1}} = 100$; $F'(3) = \dfrac{-2}{(3 + 1)^{3/2}} = -\dfrac{1}{4} = -0.25$

After 3 hours, the body temperature of the patient is $100°$ and is DECREASING at the rate of $0.25°$ per hour.   (3-6)

92. $N(t) = 20\sqrt{t} = 20t^{1/2}$

The rate of learning is $N'(t) = 20\left(\dfrac{1}{2}\right)t^{-1/2} = 10t^{-1/2} = \dfrac{10}{\sqrt{t}}$.

(A) The rate of learning after one hour is $N'(1) = \dfrac{10}{\sqrt{1}}$

$\qquad\qquad\qquad\qquad\qquad\qquad\qquad = 10$ items per hour.

(B) The rate of learning after four hours is $N'(4) = \dfrac{10}{\sqrt{4}} = \dfrac{10}{2}$

$\qquad\qquad\qquad\qquad\qquad\qquad\qquad = 5$ items per hour.

(3-4)

4 GRAPHING AND OPTIMIZATION

EXERCISE 4-1

Things to remember:

1. INCREASING AND DECREASING FUNCTIONS

    For the interval (a, b):

$f'(x)$	$f(x)$	Graph of f	Examples
+	Increases ↗	Rises ↗	
−	Decreases ↘	Falls ↘	

2. CRITICAL VALUES

    The values of x in the domain of f where $f'(x) = 0$ or where $f'(x)$ does not exist are called the CRITICAL VALUES of f.

    The critical values of f are always in the domain of f and are also partition numbers for f', but f' may have partition numbers that are not critical values.

    If f is a polynomial, then both the partition numbers for f' and the critical values of f are the solutions of $f'(x) = 0$.

3. LOCAL EXTREMA

    Given a function f. The value $f(c)$ is a LOCAL MAXIMUM of f if there is an interval (m, n) containing c such that $f(x) \leq f(c)$ for all x in (m, n). The value $f(e)$ is a LOCAL MINIMUM of f if there is an interval (p, q) containing e such that $f(x) \geq f(e)$ for all x in (p, q). Local maxima and local minima are called LOCAL EXTREMA.

    A point on the graph where a local extremum occurs is also called a TURNING POINT.

4. FIRST DERIVATIVE TEST FOR LOCAL EXTREMA

    Let c be a critical value of f [$f(c)$ is defined and either $f'(c) = 0$ or $f'(c)$ is not defined.]

    Construct a sign chart for $f'(x)$ close to and on either side of c.

Sign Chart		$f(c)$

$f'(x)$ $\quad$ --- $\vdots$ +++ $\longrightarrow x$
$\qquad m \qquad c \qquad n$

$f(x)$ Decreasing $\vdots$ Increasing

$f(c)$ is a local minimum.
If $f'(x)$ changes from negative to positive at c, then $f(c)$ is a local minimum.

$f'(x)$ $\quad$ +++ $\vdots$ --- $\longrightarrow x$
$\qquad m \qquad c \qquad n$

$f(x)$ Increasing $\vdots$ Decreasing

$f(c)$ is a local maximum.
If $f'(x)$ changes from positive to negative at c, then $f(c)$ is a local maximum.

$f'(x)$ $\quad$ --- $\vdots$ --- $\longrightarrow x$
$\qquad m \qquad c \qquad n$

$f(x)$ Decreasing $\vdots$ Decreasing

$f(c)$ is not a local extremum.
If $f'(x)$ does not change sign at c, then $f(c)$ is neither a local maximum nor a local minimum.

$f'(x)$ $\quad$ +++ $\vdots$ +++ $\longrightarrow x$
$\qquad m \qquad c \qquad n$

$f(x)$ Increasing $\vdots$ Increasing

$f(c)$ is not a local extremum.
If $f'(x)$ does not change sign at c, then $f(c)$ is neither a local maximum nor a local minimum.

<u>5</u>. INTERCEPTS AND LOCAL EXTREMA FOR POLYNOMIAL FUNCTIONS

If $f(x) = a_n x^n + a_{n-1} x^{n-1} + \ldots + a_1 x + a_0$, $a_n \neq 0$ is an nth degree polynomial then f has at most n x intercepts and at most $n-1$ local extrema.

---

1. (a, b), (d, f), (g, h) $\qquad\qquad$ **3.** (b, c), (c, d), (f, g)

5. $x = c, d, f$ $\qquad\qquad\qquad\qquad$ **7.** $x = b, f$

9. f has a local maximum at $x = a$, and a local minimum at $x = c$; f does not have a local extremum at $x = b$ or at $x = d$.

11. e $\qquad\qquad$ **13.** d $\qquad\qquad$ **15.** f $\qquad\qquad$ **17.** c

19. $f(x) = 2x^2 - 4x$; domain of f: $(-\infty, \infty)$
$f'(x) = 4x - 4$; f' is continuous for all x.
$f'(x) = 4x - 4 = 0$
$\qquad\qquad x = 1$

Thus, $x = 1$ is a partition number for f', and since 1 is in the domain of f, $x = 1$ is a critical value of f.

Sign chart for f':

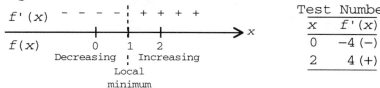

Test Numbers	
x	$f'(x)$
0	-4 $(-)$
2	4 $(+)$

Therefore, f is decreasing on $(-\infty, 1)$; f is increasing on $(1, \infty)$; $f(1) = -2$ is a local minimum.

21. $f(x) = -2x^2 - 16x - 25$; domain of f: $(-\infty, \infty)$
$f'(x) = -4x - 16$; f' is continuous for all x and
$$f'(x) = -4x - 16 = 0$$
$$x = -4$$
Thus, $x = -4$ is a partition number for f', and since -4 is in the domain of f, $x = -4$ is a critical value for f.
Sign chart for f':

Test Numbers	
x	$f'(x)$
-5	$4\,(+)$
0	$-16\,(-)$

Therefore, f is increasing on $(-\infty, -4)$; f is decreasing on $(-4, \infty)$; f has a local maximum at $x = -4$.

23. $f(x) = x^3 + 4x - 5$; domain of f: $(-\infty, \infty)$
$f'(x) = 3x^2 + 4 \geq 4 > 0$ for all x; f is increasing on $(-\infty, \infty)$; f has no local extrema.

25. $f(x) = x^3 - 6x^2 + 1$; domain of f: $(-\infty, \infty)$
$f'(x) = 3x^2 - 12x$; f' is continuous for all x.
$$f'(x) = 3x^2 - 12x = 0$$
$$3x(x - 4) = 0$$
$$x = 0,\ 4$$
The partition numbers for f' are $x = 0$ and $x = 4$. Since 0 and 4 are in the domain of f, $x = 0$, $x = 4$ are critical values of f.
Sign chart for f':

Test Numbers	
x	$f'(x)$
-1	$15\,(+)$
1	$-9\,(-)$
5	$15\,(+)$

Therefore, f is increasing on $(-\infty, 0)$ and $(4, \infty)$; f is decreasing on $(0, 4)$; $f(0) = 1$ is a local maximum, $f(4) = -31$ is a local minimum.

27. $f(x) = 2x^3 - 3x^2 - 36x$; domain of f: $(-\infty, \infty)$
$f'(x) = 6x^2 - 6x - 36$; f' is continuous for all x and
$$f'(x) = 6(x^2 - x - 6) = 0$$
$$6(x - 3)(x + 2) = 0$$
$$x = -2,\ 3$$
The partition numbers for f are $x = -2$ and $x = 3$. Since -2 and 3 are in the domain of f, $x = -2$, $x = 3$ are critical values for f.
Sign chart for f':

Test Numbers	
x	$f'(x)$
-3	$36\,(+)$
0	$-36\,(-)$
4	$36\,(+)$

Therefore, f is increasing on $(-\infty, -2)$ and $(3, \infty)$; f is decreasing on $(-2, 3)$; f has a local maximum at $x = -2$ and a local minimum at $x = 3$.

29. $f(x) = 3x^4 - 4x^3 + 5$; domain of f: $(-\infty, \infty)$

$f'(x) = 12x^3 - 12x^2$; f' is continuous for all x.

$f'(x) = 12x^3 - 12x^2 = 0$

$\qquad 12x^2(x - 1) = 0$

$\qquad\qquad x = 0, 1$

The partition numbers for f' are $x = 0$ and $x = 1$. Since 0 and 1 are in the domain of f, $x = 0$, $x = 1$ are critical values of f.

Sign chart for f':

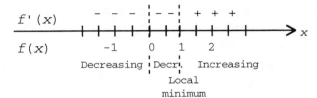

Test Numbers	
x	$f'(x)$
-1	$-24\ (-)$
$\frac{1}{2}$	$-\frac{3}{2}\ (-)$
2	$48\ (+)$

Therefore, f is decreasing on $(-\infty, 1)$; f is increasing on $(1, \infty)$; $f(1) = 4$ is a local minimum.

31. $f(x) = -x^4 + 32x$; domain of f: $(-\infty, \infty)$

$f'(x) = -4x^3 + 32$; f' is continuous for all x and

$f'(x) = -4x^3 + 32 = 0$

$\qquad\qquad x^3 = 8$

$\qquad\qquad x = 2$

$x = 2$ is a partition number for f' and since 2 is in the domain of f, $x = 2$ is a critical value for f.

Sign chart for f':

Test Numbers	
x	$f'(x)$
0	$32\ (+)$
3	$-76\ (-)$

Therefore, f is increasing on $(-\infty, 2)$ and decreasing on $(2, \infty)$; f has a local maximum at $x = 2$.

33. $f(x) = x^4 + x^2 + x$; domain of f: $(-\infty, \infty)$

$f'(x) = 4x^3 + 2x + 1$; f' is continuous for all x, so we must solve $f'(x) = 4x^3 + 2x + 1 = 0$ using a root-approximation routine, $f'(x) = 0$ at $x = -0.39$ (to two decimal places); critical value.

Sign chart for f':

Test Numbers	
x	$f'(x)$
-1	$-5\ (-)$
0	$1\ (+)$

f is decreasing on $(-\infty, -0.39)$; increasing on $(-0.39, \infty)$; f has a local minimum at $x = -0.39$.

35. $f(x) = x^4 - 4x^3 + 9x$; domain of f: $(-\infty, \infty)$
$f'(x) = 4x^3 - 12x^2 + 9$; f is continuous for all x. Using a root-approximation routine, $f'(x) = 0$ at $x = -0.77$, $x = 1.08$, and $x = 2.69$; critical values.

Sign chart for f':

f is decreasing on $(-\infty, -0.77)$ and $(1.08, 2.69)$; increasing on $(-0.77, 1.08)$ and $(2.69, \infty)$; f has a local minima at $x = -0.77$ and $x = 2.69$, f has a local maximum at $x = 1.08$.

37. $f(x) = x^4 - 2x^3 - 5x^2 + 4x$; domain of f: $(-\infty, \infty)$
$f'(x) = 4x^3 - 6x^2 - 10x + 4$; f is continuous for all x. Using a root-approximation routine, $f'(x) = 0$ at $x = -1.22$, $x = 0.35$, and $x = 2.38$; critical values.

Sign chart for f':

f is decreasing on $(-\infty, -1.22)$ and $(0.35, 2.38)$; f is increasing on $(-1.22, 0.35)$ and $(2.38, \infty)$; f has local minima at $x = -1.22$ and $x = 2.38$, f has a local maximum at $x = 0.35$.

39. $f(x) = 4 + 8x - x^2$
$f'(x) = 8 - 2x$
f' is continuous for all x and
$f'(x) = 8 - 2x = 0$
$x = 4$
Thus, $x = 4$ is a partition number for f'.

The sign chart for f' is:

Test Numbers	
x	$f'(x)$
0	8 (+)
5	−2 (−)

Therefore, f is increasing on $(-\infty, 4)$ and decreasing on $(4, \infty)$; f has a local maximum at $x = 4$.

x	$f'(x)$	f	GRAPH OF f
$(-\infty, 4)$	+	Increasing	Rising
$x = 4$	0	Local maximum	Horizontal tangent
$(4, \infty)$	−	Decreasing	Falling

x	$f(x)$
0	4
4	20

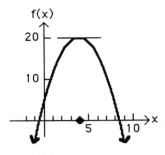

41. $f(x) = x^3 - 3x + 1$

$f'(x) = 3x^2 - 3$

f' is continuous for all x and

$f'(x) = 3x^2 - 3 = 0$

$\qquad 3(x^2 - 1) = 0$

$3(x + 1)(x - 1) = 0$

Thus, $x = -1$ and $x = 1$ are partition numbers for f'.
The sign chart for f' is:

$f'(x) + + + + + + 0 - - - - - - - 0 + + + + +$

```
      +----------●--------◆--------●--------+------→ x
     -2         -1        0        1        2
```

$f(x)$ Increasing ┆ Decreasing ┆ Increasing

Test Numbers

x	$f'(x)$
-2	9 (+)
0	-3 (−)
2	9 (+)

Therefore, f is increasing on $(-\infty, -1)$ and on $(1, \infty)$, f is decreasing on $(-1, 1)$; f has a local maximum at $x = -1$ and a local minimum at $x = 1$.

x	$f'(x)$	f	GRAPH OF f
$(-\infty, -1)$	+	Increasing	Rising
$x = -1$	0	Local maximum	Horizontal tangent
$(-1, 1)$	−	Decreasing	Falling
$x = 1$	0	Local minimum	Horizontal tangent
$(1, \infty)$	+	Increasing	Rising

x	$f(x)$
-1	3
0	1
1	-1

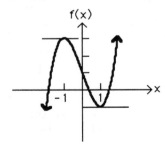

43. $f(x) = 10 - 12x + 6x^2 - x^3$

$f'(x) = -12 + 12x - 3x^2$

f' is continuous for all x and

$f'(x) = -12 + 12x - 3x^2 = 0$

$\qquad -3(x^2 - 4x + 4) = 0$

$\qquad\qquad -3(x - 2)^2 = 0$

Thus, $x = 2$ is a partition number for f'.

The sign chart for f' is:

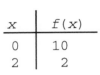

$f'(x)$ $\qquad$ $- - - - - 0 - - - - -$

$f(x)$ $\qquad$ Decreasing ┊ Decreasing

Test Numbers	
x	$f'(x)$
0	−12 (−)
3	−3 (−)

Therefore, f is decreasing for all x, i.e., on $(-\infty, \infty)$, and there is a horizontal tangent line at $x = 2$.

x	$f'(x)$	f	GRAPH of f
$(-\infty, 2)$	−	Decreasing	Falling
$x = 2$	0		Horizontal tangent
$x > 2$	−	Decreasing	Falling

x	$f(x)$
0	10
2	2

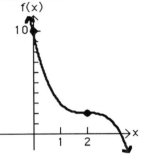

45. $f(x) = x^4 - 18x^2$

$f'(x) = 4x^3 - 36x$

f' is continuous for all x and

$f'(x) = 4x^3 - 36x = 0$

$\qquad 4x(x^2 - 9) = 0$

$4x(x - 3)(x + 3) = 0$

Thus, $x = -3$, $x = 0$, and $x = 3$ are partition numbers for f'.

Sign chart for f':

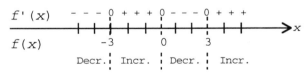

$f'(x)$ $\quad - - - 0 + + + 0 - - - 0 + + +$

$f(x)$ $\qquad -3 \quad\quad 0 \quad\quad 3$

$\qquad$ Decr.┊ Incr. ┊ Decr.┊ Incr.

Test Numbers	
x	$f'(x)$
−4	−196 (−)
−1	32 (+)
1	−32 (−)
4	196 (+)

Therefore, f is increasing on $(-3, 0)$ and on $(3, \infty)$; f is decreasing on $(-\infty, -3)$ and on $(0, 3)$; f has a local maximum at $x = 0$ and local minima at $x = -3$ and $x = 3$.

x	$f'(x)$	f	GRAPH of f
$(-\infty, -3)$	−	Decreasing	Falling
$x = -3$	0	Local minimum	Horizontal tangent
$(-3, 0)$	+	Increasing	Rising
$x = 0$	0	Local maximum	Horizontal tangent
$(0, 3)$	−	Decreasing	Falling
$x = 3$	0	Local minimum	Horizontal tangent
$(3, \infty)$	+	Increasing	Rising

x	$f(x)$
0	0
−3	−81
3	−81

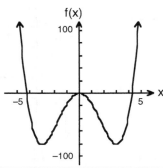

47.

x	$f'(x)$	$f(x)$	GRAPH OF f
$(-\infty, -1)$	+	Increasing	Rising
$x = -1$	0	Neither local maximum nor local minimum	Horizontal tangent
$(-1, 1)$	+	Increasing	Rising
$x = 1$	0	Local maximum	Horizontal tangent
$(1, \infty)$	−	Decreasing	Falling

Using this information together with the points $(-2, -1)$, $(-1, 1)$, $(0, 2)$, $(1, 3)$, $(2, 1)$ on the graph, we have

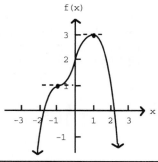

49.

x	$f'(x)$	$f(x)$	GRAPH OF $f(x)$
$(-\infty, -1)$	−	Decreasing	Falling
$x = -1$	0	Local minimum	Horizontal tangent
$(-1, 0)$	+	Increasing	Rising
$x = 0$	Not defined	Local maximum	Vertical tangent line
$(0, 2)$	−	Decreasing	Falling
$x = 2$	0	Neither local maximum nor local minimum	Horizontal tangent
$(2, \infty)$	−	Decreasing	Falling

Using this information together with the points $(-2, 2)$, $(-1, 1)$, $(0, 2)$, $(2, 1)$, $(4, 0)$ on the graph, we have

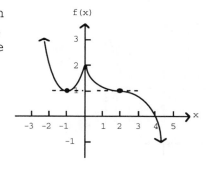

51.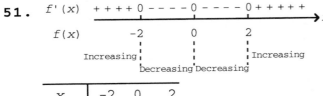

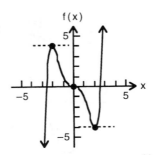

x	-2	0	2
$f(x)$	4	0	-4

53.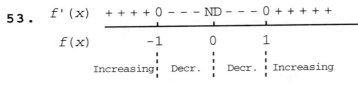

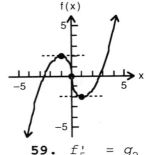

x	-1	0	1
$f(x)$	2	0	2

55. $f_1' = g_4$

57. $f_3' = g_6$

59. $f_5' = g_2$

61. Increasing on $(-1, 2)$ $[f'(x) > 0]$; decreasing on $(-\infty, -1)$ and on $(2, \infty)$ $[f'(x) < 0]$; local minimum at $x = -1$; local maximum at $x = 2$.

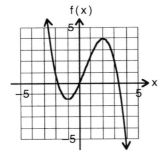

63. Increasing on $(-1, 2)$ and on $(2, \infty)$ $[f'(x) > 0]$; decreasing on $(-\infty, -1)$ $[f'(x) < 0]$; local minimum at $x = -1$.

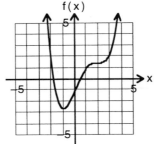

65. Increasing on $(-2, 0)$ and $(3, \infty)$ $[f'(x) > 0]$; decreasing on $(-\infty, -2)$ and $(0, 3)$ $[f'(x) < 0]$; local minima at $x = -2$ and $x = 3$, local maximum at $x = 0$.

67. $f'(x) > 0$ on $(-\infty, -1)$ and on $(3, \infty)$; $f'(x) < 0$ on $(-1, 3)$; $f'(x) = 0$ at $x = -1$ and $x = 3$.

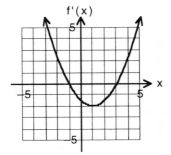

69. $f'(x) > 0$ on $(-2, 1)$ and on $(3, \infty)$; $f'(x) < 0$ on $(-\infty, -2)$ and on $(1, 3)$: $f'(x) = 0$ at $x = -2$, $x = 1$, and $x = 3$.

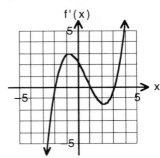

71. $f(x) = x + \dfrac{4}{x}$ [<u>Note</u>: f is not defined at $x = 0$.]

$f'(x) = 1 - \dfrac{4}{x^2}$

Critical values: $x = 0$ is *not* a critical value of f since 0 is not in the domain of f, but $x = 0$ is a partition number for f'.

$f'(x) = 1 - \dfrac{4}{x^2} = 0$

$\qquad\quad x^2 - 4 = 0$

$(x + 2)(x - 2) = 0$

Thus, the critical values are $x = -2$ and $x = 2$; $x = -2$ and $x = 2$ are also partition numbers for f'.

The sign chart for f' is:

Test Numbers	
x	$f'(x)$
-3	$\frac{5}{9}$ (+)
-1	-3 (−)
1	-3 (−)
3	$\frac{5}{9}$ (+)

$f'(x)$ + + 0 − − ND − − 0 + +

$f(x)$ −3 −2 −1 0 1 2 3

Increasing ┊ Decreasing ┊ Increasing

Therefore, f is increasing on $(-\infty, -2)$ and on $(2, \infty)$, f is decreasing on $(-2, 0)$ and on $(0, 2)$; f has a local maximum at $x = -2$ and a local minimum at $x = 2$.

73. $f(x) = 1 + \dfrac{1}{x} + \dfrac{1}{x^2}$ [<u>Note</u>: f is not defined at $x = 0$.]

$f'(x) = -\dfrac{1}{x^2} - \dfrac{2}{x^3}$

Critical values: $x = 0$ is not a critical value of f since 0 is not in the domain of f; $x = 0$ is a partition number for f'.

$f'(x) = -\dfrac{1}{x^2} - \dfrac{2}{x^3} = 0$

$\qquad\quad -x - 2 = 0$

$\qquad\qquad x = -2$

Thus, the critical value is $x = -2$; -2 is also a partition number for f'.

The sign chart for f' is:

Test Numbers	
x	$f'(x)$
-3	$-\frac{1}{27}$ (−)
-1	1 (+)
1	-3 (−)

$f'(x)$ − − − − − 0 + + + + + ND − − − − −

$\qquad\quad$ −3 −2 −1 0 1

$f(x)$ Decreasing ┊ Increasing ┊ Decreasing

Therefore, f is increasing on $(-2, 0)$ and f is decreasing on $(-\infty, -2)$ and on $(0, \infty)$; f has a local minimum at $x = -2$.

75. $f(x) = \dfrac{x^2}{x-2}$ [Note: f is not defined at $x = 2$.]

$f'(x) = \dfrac{(x-2)(2x) - x^2(1)}{(x-2)^2} = \dfrac{x^2 - 4x}{(x-2)^2}$

Critical values: $x = 2$ is *not* a critical value of f since 2 is not in the domain of f; $x = 2$ is a partition number for f'.

$f'(x) = \dfrac{x^2 - 4x}{(x-2)^2} = 0$

$x^2 - 4x = 0$

$x(x - 4) = 0$

Thus, the critical values are $x = 0$ and $x = 4$; 0 and 4 are also partition numbers for f'.

The sign chart for f' is:

Test Numbers	
x	$f'(x)$
-1	$\frac{5}{9}$ (+)
1	-3 (−)
3	-3 (−)
5	$\frac{5}{9}$ (+)

Therefore, f is increasing on $(-\infty, 0)$ and on $(4, \infty)$, f is decreasing on $(0, 2)$ and on $(2, 4)$; f has a local maximum at $x = 0$ and a local minimum at $x = 4$.

77. $f(x) = x^4(x - 6)^2$

$f'(x) = x^4(2)(x - 6)(1) + (x - 6)^2(4x^3)$

$\quad = 2x^3(x - 6)[x + 2(x - 6)]$

$\quad = 2x^3(x - 6)(3x - 12)$

$\quad = 6x^3(x - 4)(x - 6)$

Thus, the critical values of f are $x = 0$, $x = 4$, and $x = 6$.

Now we construct the sign chart for f' ($x = 0$, $x = 4$, $x = 6$ are partition numbers).

Test Numbers	
x	$f'(x)$
-1	-210 (−)
1	90 (+)
5	-750 (−)
7	+

Therefore, f is increasing on $(0, 4)$ and on $(6, \infty)$, f is decreasing on $(-\infty, 0)$ and on $(4, 6)$; f has a local maximum at $x = 4$ and local minima at $x = 0$ and $x = 6$.

79. $f(x) = 3(x - 2)^{2/3} + 4$

$f'(x) = 3\left(\dfrac{2}{3}\right)(x - 2)^{-1/3} = \dfrac{2}{(x - 2)^{1/3}}$

Critical values: f' is not defined at $x = 2$. [<u>Note</u>: $f(2)$ is defined, $f(2) = 4$.] $f'(x) \neq 0$ for all x. Thus, the critical value for f is $x = 2$; $x = 2$ is also a partition number for f'.

Test Numbers	
x	$f'(x)$
1	-2 $(-)$
3	2 $(+)$

Therefore, f is increasing on $(2, \infty)$ and decreasing on $(-\infty, 2)$; f has a local minimum at $x = 2$.

81. $f(x) = \dfrac{2x^2}{x^2 + 1}$; domain of f: $(-\infty, \infty)$

$f'(x) = \dfrac{(x^2 + 1)4x - 2x^2(2x)}{(x^2 + 1)^2} = \dfrac{4x}{(x^2 + 1)^2}$

Critical values:

$f'(x) = \dfrac{4x}{(x^2 + 1)^2} = 0$

$4x = 0$

$x = 0$

Thus, the critical value is $x = 0$.

The sign chart for f' is:

Test Numbers	
x	$f'(x)$
-1	-1 $(-)$
1	1 $(+)$

Therefore, f is increasing on $(0, \infty)$; f is decreasing on $(-\infty, 0)$; $f(0) = 0$ is a local minimum.

83. Let $f(x) = x^3 + kx$

(A) $k > 0$

  $f'(x) = 3x^2 + k > 0$ for all x.
  There are no critical values and no local extrema; f is increasing on $(-\infty, \infty)$.

(B) $k < 0$

  $f'(x) = 3x^2 + k$; $3x^2 + k = 0$

  $$x^2 = -\frac{k}{3}$$

  $$x = \pm\sqrt{-\frac{k}{3}}$$

Critical values: $x = -\sqrt{-\dfrac{k}{3}}$, $x = \sqrt{-\dfrac{k}{3}}$;

$f'(x)$ $+ + + + + 0 - - - - - - - - 0 + + + + +$

$-\sqrt{-\dfrac{k}{3}}$ 0 $\sqrt{-\dfrac{k}{3}}$

f is increasing on $\left(-\infty, -\sqrt{-\dfrac{k}{3}}\right)$ and on $\left(\sqrt{-\dfrac{k}{3}}, \infty\right)$; f is decreasing

on $\left(-\sqrt{-\dfrac{k}{3}}, \sqrt{-\dfrac{k}{3}}\right)$; f has a local maximum at $x = -\sqrt{-\dfrac{k}{3}}$ and a local

minimum at $x = \sqrt{-\dfrac{k}{3}}$.

(C) The only critical value is $x = 0$. There are no extrema, the function is increasing for all x.

85. (A) The marginal profit function, P', is positive on $(0, 600)$, zero at $x = 600$, and negative on $(600, 1{,}000)$.

(B)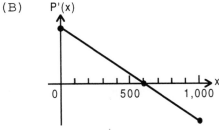

87. (A) The price function, $B(t)$, decreases for the first 15 months to a local minimum, increases for the next 40 months to a local maximum, and then decreases for the remaining 15 months.

(B)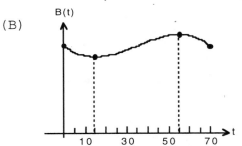

89. $C(x) = \dfrac{x^2}{20} + 20x + 320$

(A) $\overline{C}(x) = \dfrac{C(x)}{x} = \dfrac{x}{20} + 20 + \dfrac{320}{x}$

(B) Critical values:

$$\overline{C}'(x) = \dfrac{1}{20} - \dfrac{320}{x^2} = 0$$

$$x^2 - 320(20) = 0$$

$$x^2 - 6400 = 0$$

$$(x - 80)(x + 80) = 0$$

Thus, the critical value of $\overline{C}$ on the interval $(0, 150)$ is $x = 80$.

Next, construct the sign chart for $\overline{C}'$ ($x = 80$ is a partition number for $\overline{C}'$).

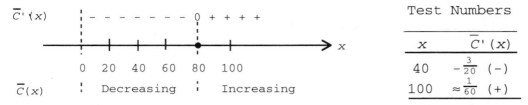

x	$\overline{C}'(x)$
40	$-\frac{3}{20}$ (−)
100	$\approx \frac{1}{60}$ (+)

Therefore, $\overline{C}$ is increasing for $80 < x < 150$ and decreasing for $0 < x < 80$; $\overline{C}$ has a local minimum at $x = 80$.

91. $P(x) = R(x) - C(x)$

$P'(x) = R'(x) - C'(x)$

Thus, if $R'(x) > C'(x)$ on the interval (a, b), then $P'(x) = R'(x) - C'(x) > 0$ on this interval and P is increasing.

93. $C(t) = \dfrac{0.28t}{t^2 + 4}$, $0 < t < 24$

$C'(t) = \dfrac{(t^2 + 4)(0.28) - 0.28t(2t)}{(t^2 + 4)^2} = \dfrac{0.28(4 - t^2)}{(t^2 + 4)^2}$

Critical values: C' is continuous for all t on the interval $(0, 24)$.

$C'(t) = \dfrac{0.28(4 - t^2)}{(t^2 + 4)^2} = 0$

$4 - t^2 = 0$

$(2 - t)(2 + t) = 0$

Thus, the critical value of C on the interval $(0, 24)$ is $t = 2$. The sign chart for C' ($t = 2$ is a partition number) is:

t	$C'(t)$
1	(+)
3	(−)

Therefore, C is increasing on $(0, 2)$ and decreasing on $(2, 24)$; $C(2) = 0.07$ is a local maximum.

95. $P(t) = \dfrac{8.4t}{t^2 + 49} + 0.1$, $0 < t < 24$

$P'(t) = \dfrac{(t^2 + 49)(8.4) - 8.4t(2t)}{(t^2 + 49)^2} = \dfrac{8.4(49 - t^2)}{(t^2 + 49)^2}$

Critical values: P is continuous for all t on the interval $(0, 24)$:

$P'(t) = \dfrac{8.4(49 - t^2)}{(t^2 + 49)^2} = 0$

$49 - t^2 = 0$

$(7 - t)(7 + t) = 0$

Thus, the critical value of P on $(0, 24)$ is $t = 7$.

The sign chart for P' ($t = 7$ is a partition number for P') is:

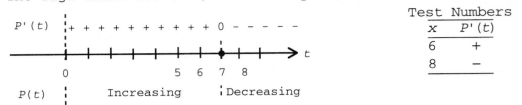

Test Numbers	
x	$P'(t)$
6	+
8	−

Therefore, P is increasing for $0 < t < 7$ and decreasing for $7 < t < 24$; P has a local maximum at $t = 7$.

___

EXERCISE 4-2

Things to remember:

1. CONCAVITY

    The graph of a function f is concave upward on the interval (a, b) if $f'(x)$ is *increasing* on (a, b) and is concave downward on the interval (a, b) if $f'(x)$ is *decreasing* on (a, b).

    For the interval (a, b):

$f''(x)$	$f'(x)$	Graph of $y = f(x)$	Example
+	Increasing	Concave upward	$\smile$
−	Decreasing	Concave downward	$\frown$

2. SECOND DERIVATIVE

    For $y = f(x)$, the SECOND DERIVATIVE of f, provided it exists, is:
    $$f''(x) = \frac{d}{dx} f'(x)$$
    Other notations for $f''(x)$ are:
    $$\frac{d^2 y}{dx^2} \quad \text{and} \quad y''.$$

3. INFLECTION POINT

    An INFLECTION POINT is a point on the graph of a function where the concavity changes (from upward to downward, or from downward to upward).

4. STRATEGY FOR GRAPHING A POLYNOMIAL

Step 1. Analyze $f(x)$.

Find the intercepts. The x intercepts are the solutions to $f(x) = 0$, if they exist, and the y intercept is $f(0)$.

Step 2. Analyze $f'(x)$.

Find the zeros of $f'(x)$. Construct a sign chart for $f'(x)$, determine the intervals where $f(x)$ is increasing and decreasing, and find local maxima and minima.

Step 3. Analyze $f''(x)$.

Find the zeros of $f''(x)$. Construct a sign chart for $f''(x)$, determine where the graph of f is concave upward and concave downward, and find any inflection points.

Step 4. Sketch the graph of f.

---

1. (A) The graph of f is concave upward on (a, c), (c, d), and (e, g).
   (B) The graph of f is concave downward on (d, e) and (g, h).
   (C) $f''(x) < 0$ on (d, e) and (g, h).
   (D) $f''(x) > 0$ on (a, c), (c, d), and (e, g).
   (E) $f'(x)$ is increasing on (a, c), (c, d), and (e, g).
   (F) $f'(x)$ is decreasing on (d, e) and (g, h).
   (G) Inflection points occur at $x = d$, $x = e$, and $x = g$.
   (H) The local extrema occur at $x = b$, $x = c$, and $x = f$.

3. $f'(x) > 0$, $f''(x) > 0$; (c)

5. $f'(x) < 0$, $f''(x) > 0$; (d)

7. $f(x) = 2x^3 - 4x^2 + 5x - 6$
   $f'(x) = 6x^2 - 8x + 5$
   $f''(x) = 12x - 8$

9. $h(x) = 2x^{-1} - 3x^{-2}$
   $h'(x) = -2x^{-2} + 6x^{-3}$
   $h''(x) = 4x^{-3} - 18x^{-4}$

11. $y = x^2 - 18x^{1/2}$
    $\dfrac{dy}{dx} = 2x - 9x^{-1/2}$
    $\dfrac{d^2y}{dx^2} = 2 + \dfrac{9}{2}x^{-3/2}$

13. $y = (x^2 + 9)^4$
    $y' = 4(x^2 + 9)^3(2x) = 8x(x^2 + 9)^3$
    $y'' = 24x(x^2 + 9)^2(2x) + 8(x^2 + 9)^3$
    $\quad = 48x^2(x^2 + 9)^2 + 8(x^2 + 9)^3 = 8(x^2 + 9)^2(7x^2 + 9)$

15. $f(x) = x^4 + 6x^2$
    $f'(x) = 4x^3 + 12x$
    $f''(x) = 12x^2 + 12 \geq 12 > 0$
    The graph of f is concave upward for all x; there are no inflection points.

17. $f(x) = x^3 - 4x^2 + 5x - 2$
    $f'(x) = 3x^2 - 8x + 5$
    $f''(x) = 6x - 8$
    $f''(x) = 0$: $6x - 8 = 0$
    $\qquad\qquad\qquad x = \dfrac{4}{3}$

Sign chart for f'' $\left(\text{partition number is } \dfrac{4}{3}\right)$:

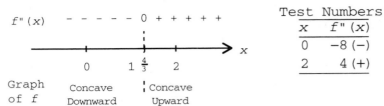

Test Numbers	
x	$f''(x)$
0	$-8\ (-)$
2	$4\ (+)$

Therefore, the graph of f is concave downward on $\left(-\infty, \dfrac{4}{3}\right)$ and concave upward on $\left(\dfrac{4}{3}, \infty\right)$; there is an inflection point at $x = \dfrac{4}{3}$.

19. $f(x) = -x^4 + 12x^3 - 12x + 24$
$f'(x) = -4x^3 + 36x^2 - 12$
$f''(x) = -12x^2 + 72x$
$f''(x) = 0:\ -12x^2 + 72x = 0$
$\qquad\qquad\quad -12x(x - 6) = 0$
$\qquad\qquad\qquad\qquad x = 0,\ 6$

Sign chart for f'' (partition numbers 0, 6):

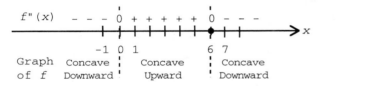

Test Numbers	
x	$f''(x)$
-1	$-84\ (-)$
1	$60\ (+)$
7	$-84\ (-)$

Therefore, the graph of f is concave downward on $(-\infty, 0)$ and $(6, \infty)$; concave upward on $(0, 6)$; there are inflection points at $x = 0$ and $x = 6$.

21.

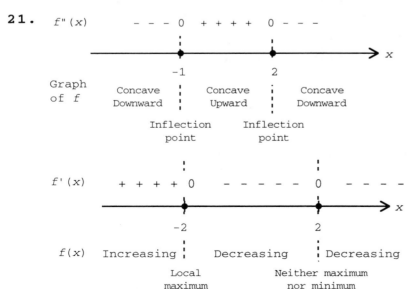

Using this information together with the points (-4, 0), (-2, 3), (-1, 1.5), (0, 0), (2, -1), (4, -3) on the graph, we have

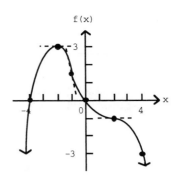

23.

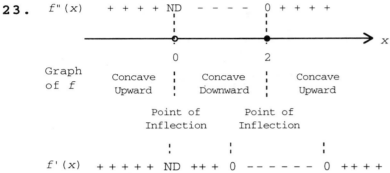

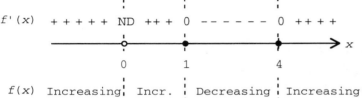

Local
maximum

Local
minimum

Using this information together with the points (-3, -4), (0, 0), (1, 2), (2, 1), (4, -1), (5, 0) on the graph, we have

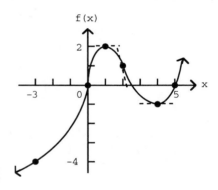

25.

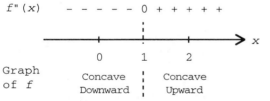

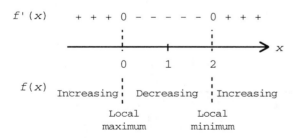

Local
maximum

Local
minimum

x	0	1	2
$f(x)$	2	0	-2

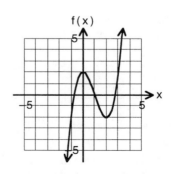

27.

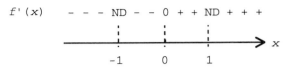

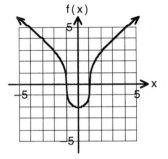

x	-1	0	1
$f(x)$	0	-2	0

29. $f(x) = x^3 - 6x^2 + 16$

Step 1. Analyze $f(x)$.

x-intercept(s): $f(x) = 0$

$$x^3 - 6x^2 + 16 = 0$$
$$(x - 2)(x^2 - 4x - 8) = 0$$
$$x = 2,\ 2 \pm 2\sqrt{3}$$

y-intercept: $f(0) = 16$

Step 2. Analyze $f'(x)$. $f'(x) = 3x^2 - 12x = 3x(x - 4)$

Zeros for $f'(x)$: 0 and 4.

Sign chart for $f'(x)$:

f'(x) + + + 0 – – – – – 0 + + +

f(x)   -1 0 1 2 3 4 5

Increasing ┊ Decreasing ┊ Increasing

Local maximum   Local minimum

Test Numbers	
x	$f'(x)$
−1	10 (+)
2	−12 (−)
5	15 (+)

Thus, $f(x)$ is increasing on $(-\infty, 0)$ and on $(4, \infty)$; $f(x)$ is decreasing on $(0, 4)$; f has a local maximum at $x = 0$ and a local minimum at $x = 4$.

Step 3. Analyze $f''(x)$. $f''(x) = 6x - 12 = 6(x - 2)$

Partition numbers for $f''(x)$: $x = 2$

Sign chart for $f''(x)$:

f''(x)   – – – – – 0 + + + +

0 1 2 3

Graph of f Concave Downward ┊ Concave Upward

Test Numbers	
x	$f''(x)$
0	−12 (−)
3	6 (+)

The graph of f is concave upward on $(2, \infty)$, concave downward on $(-\infty, 2)$; and has an inflection point at $x = 2$.

Step 4. Sketch the graph of f.

x	$f(x)$
0	16
2	0
4	-16

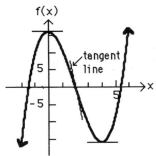

31. $f(x) = x^3 + x + 2$

Step 1. Analyze $f(x)$:

x-intercept(s): $f(x) = 0$

$$x^3 + x + 2 = 0$$
$$(x + 1)(x^2 - x + 2) = 0$$
$$x = -1 \text{ (the quadratic factor does not have real roots)}$$

y-intercept: $f(0) = 2$

Step 2. Analyze $f'(x)$: $f'(x) = 3x^2 + 1 > 0$ for all x.

Zeros of $f'(x)$: $f'(x)$ does not have any zeros.

Sign chart for $f'(x)$:

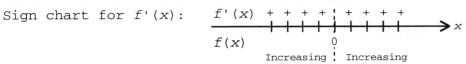

Thus, $f(x)$ is increasing on $(-\infty, \infty)$.

Step 3. Analyze $f''(x)$: $f''(x) = 6x$

Partition numbers for $f''(x)$: $x = 0$

Sign chart for $f''(x)$:

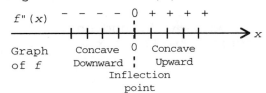

Test Numbers

x	$f''(x)$
-1	-6 (−)
1	6 (+)

Thus, the graph of f is concave upward on $(0, \infty)$ and concave downward on $(-\infty, 0)$; the graph has an inflection point at $x = 0$.

Step 4. Sketch the graph of f:

x	$f(x)$
-1	0
0	2
1	4

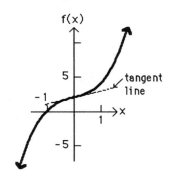

33. $f(x) = -0.25x^4 + x^3 = -\frac{1}{4}x^4 + x^3$

Step 1. Analyze $f(x)$:
x-intercept(s): $f(x) = 0$
$$-\frac{1}{4}x^4 + x^3 = 0$$
$$x^3\left(-\frac{1}{4}x + 1\right) = 0$$
$$x = 0,\ 4$$
y-intercept: $f(0) = 0$

Step 2. Analyze $f'(x)$: $f'(x) = -x^3 + 3x^2 = -x^2(x - 3)$
Zeros of $f'(x)$: $x = 0,\ 3$
Sign chart for $f'(x)$:

```
              + + + 0 + + + + + 0 - - -
  f'(x)  _____|_____|_____→ x
  f(x)   _____|___|___|___|___|_____
              0   1   2   3   4
          Increasing ┆ Increasing ┆ Decreasing
```

Test Numbers	
x	$f'(x)$
−1	4 (+)
2	4 (+)
4	−16 (−)

Thus, f is increasing on $(-\infty, 3)$; f is decreasing on $(3, \infty)$; f has a local maximum at $x = 3$.

Step 3. Analyze $f''(x)$: $f''(x) = -3x^2 + 6x = -3x(x - 2)$
Partition numbers for $f''(x)$: $x = 0,\ 2$
Sign chart for $f''(x)$:

```
              - - - 0 + + + 0 - - -
  f''(x)  _____|_____|_____→ x
  Graph   ___|___|___|___|___|___|___
  of f    -1  0   1   2   3   4
          Concave ┆ Concave ┆ Concave
          Downward ┆ Upward ┆ Downward
          Inflection  Inflection
            point       point
```

Test Numbers	
x	$f''(x)$
−1	−9 (−)
1	3 (+)
3	−9 (−)

Thus, the graph of f is concave downward on $(-\infty, 0)$ and on $(2, \infty)$; concave upward on $(0, 2)$, and has inflection points at $x = 0,\ 2$.

Step 4. Sketch the graph of f:

x	$f(x)$
0	0
2	4
3	$\frac{27}{4}$
4	0

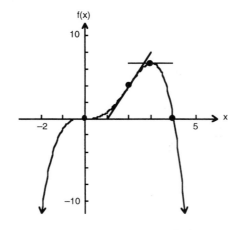

35. $f(x) = 16x(x - 1)^3$

Step 1. Analyze $f(x)$:

x-intercept(s): $f(x) = 0$

$$16x(x - 1)^3 = 0$$
$$x = 0, 1$$

y-intercept: $f(0) = 0$

Step 2. Analyze $f'(x)$: $f'(x) = 16x(3)(x - 1)^2 + 16(x - 1)^3$

$$= 16(x - 1)^2(3x + x - 1)$$
$$= 16(x - 1)^2(4x - 1)$$

Zeros of $f'(x)$: $x = 0, \frac{1}{4}$

Sign chart for $f'(x)$:

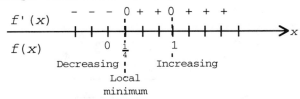

Test Numbers	
x	$f'(x)$
0	-16 $(-)$
$\frac{1}{2}$	4 $(+)$
$\frac{3}{2}$	20 $(+)$

Thus, f is increasing on $\left(\frac{1}{4}, \infty\right)$; decreasing on $\left(-\infty, \frac{1}{4}\right)$; and has a local minimum at $x = \frac{1}{4}$.

Step 3. Analyze $f''(x)$: $f''(x) = 16(x - 1)^2 4 + 32(x - 1)(4x - 1)$

$$= 32(x - 1)[2(x - 1) + 4x - 1]$$
$$= 32(x - 1)(6x - 3) \cdot$$

Partition numbers for $f''(x)$: $x = 1, \frac{1}{2}$

Sign chart for $f''(x)$:

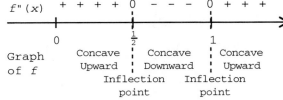

Test Numbers	
x	$f''(x)$
0	96 $(+)$
$\frac{3}{4}$	-12 $(-)$
$\frac{3}{2}$	96 $(+)$

Thus, the graph of f is concave upward on $\left(-\infty, \frac{1}{2}\right)$ and on $(1, \infty)$, concave downward on $\left(\frac{1}{2}, 1\right)$, and has inflection points at $x = \frac{1}{2}, 1$.

Step 4. Sketch the graph of f:

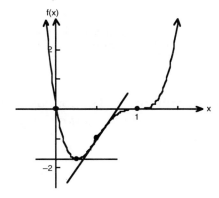

37. $f(x) = (x^2 + 3)(9 - x^2)$

Step 1. Analyze $f(x)$:

Intercepts: y-intercept: $f(0) = 3(9) = 27$

x-intercepts: $(x^2 + 3)(9 - x^2) = 0$

$(3 - x)(3 + x) = 0$

$x = 3, -3$

Step 2. Analyze $f'(x)$:

$f'(x) = (x^2 + 3)(-2x) + (9 - x^2)(2x)$

$= 2x[9 - x^2 - (x^2 + 3)]$

$= 2x(6 - 2x^2)$

$= 4x(\sqrt{3} + x)(\sqrt{3} - x)$

Zeros of $f'(x)$: $x = 0$, $x = -\sqrt{3}$, $x = \sqrt{3}$

Sign chart for f':

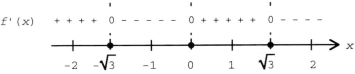

Test Numbers	
x	$f'(x)$
-2	8 (+)
-1	-8 (-)
1	8 (+)
2	-8 (-)

Thus, f is increasing on $(-\infty, -\sqrt{3})$ and on $(0, \sqrt{3})$; f is decreasing on $(-\sqrt{3}, 0)$ and on $(\sqrt{3}, \infty)$; f has local maxima at $x = -\sqrt{3}$ and $x = \sqrt{3}$ and a local minimum at $x = 0$.

Step 3. Analyze $f''(x)$:

$f''(x) = 2x(-4x) + (6 - 2x^2)(2) = 12 - 12x^2 = -12(x - 1)(x + 1)$

Partition numbers for f'': $x = 1$, $x = -1$

Sign chart for f'':

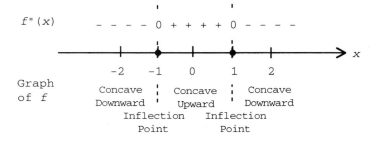

Test Numbers	
x	$f''(x)$
-2	-36 (-)
0	12 (+)
2	-36 (-)

Thus, the graph of f is concave downward on $(-\infty, -1)$ and on $(1, \infty)$; the graph of f is concave upward on $(-1, 1)$; the graph has inflection points at $x = -1$ and $x = 1$.

Step 4. Sketch the graph of f:

x	$f(x)$
$-\sqrt{3}$	36
-1	32
0	27
1	32
$\sqrt{3}$	36

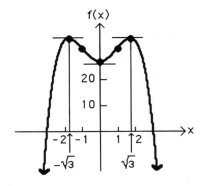

39. $f(x) = (x^2 - 4)^2$

Step 1. Analyze $f(x)$:

Intercepts: y-intercept: $f(0) = (-4)^2 = 16$

           x-intercepts: $(x^2 - 4)^2 = 0$

                      $[(x - 2)(x + 2)]^2 = 0$

                      $(x - 2)^2 (x + 2)^2 = 0$

                      $x = 2, -2$

Step 2. Analyze $f'(x)$:

$f'(x) = 2(x^2 - 4)(2x) = 4x(x - 2)(x + 2)$
Zeros of $f'(x)$: $x = 0$, $x = 2$, $x = -2$
Sign chart for f':

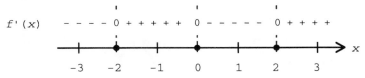

Test Numbers	
x	$f'(x)$
-3	-60 $(-)$
-1	12 $(+)$
1	-12 $(-)$
3	60 $(+)$

Thus, f is decreasing on $(-\infty, -2)$ and on $(0, 2)$; f is increasing on $(-2, 0)$ and on $(2, \infty)$; f has local minima at $x = -2$ and $x = 2$ and a local maximum at $x = 0$.

Step 3. Analyze $f''(x)$:

$f''(x) = 4x(2x) + (x^2 - 4)(4) = 12x^2 - 16 = 12\left(x^2 - \dfrac{4}{3}\right)$

$= 12\left(x - \dfrac{2\sqrt{3}}{3}\right)\left(x + \dfrac{2\sqrt{3}}{3}\right)$

Partition numbers for f'': $x = \dfrac{2\sqrt{3}}{3}$, $x = \dfrac{-2\sqrt{3}}{3}$

Sign chart for f'':

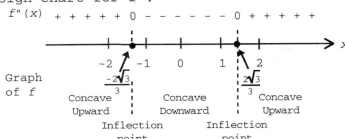

$f''(x)$ + + + + + 0 − − − − − − 0 + + + + +

Test Numbers	
x	$f''(x)$
−2	32 (+)
0	−16 (−)
2	32 (+)

Graph of f

Concave Upward   Concave Downward   Concave Upward

Inflection point   Inflection point

Thus, the graph of f is concave upward on $\left(-\infty, \dfrac{-2\sqrt{3}}{3}\right)$ and on $\left(\dfrac{2\sqrt{3}}{3}, \infty\right)$;

the graph of f is concave downward on $\left(\dfrac{-2\sqrt{3}}{3}, \dfrac{2\sqrt{3}}{3}\right)$; the graph has

inflection points at $x = \dfrac{-2\sqrt{3}}{3}$ and $x = \dfrac{2\sqrt{3}}{3}$.

Step 4. Sketch the graph of f:

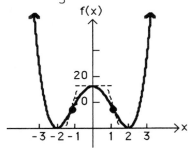

x	$f(x)$
−2	0
$-\dfrac{2\sqrt{3}}{3}$	$\dfrac{64}{9}$
0	16
$\dfrac{2\sqrt{3}}{3}$	$\dfrac{64}{9}$
2	0

41. $f(x) = 2x^6 - 3x^5$

Step 1. Analyze $f(x)$:

Intercepts: y-intercept: $f(0) = 2 \cdot 0^6 - 3 \cdot 0^5 = 0$

x-intercepts: $2x^6 - 3x^5 = 0$

$$x^5(2x - 3) = 0$$

$$x = 0, \ \frac{3}{2}$$

Step 2. Analyze $f'(x)$:

$$f'(x) = 12x^5 - 15x^4 = 12x^4\left(x - \frac{5}{4}\right)$$

Zeros of $f'(x)$: $x = 0$, $x = \dfrac{5}{4}$

Sign chart for f':

$f'(x)$ − − − − 0 − − − − − − 0 + + + +

Test Numbers	
x	$f'(x)$
−1	−27 (−)
1	−3 (−)
2	144 (+)

$f(x)$ Decreasing   Decreasing   Increasing

Local minimum

Thus, f is decreasing on $(-\infty, 0)$ and $\left(0, \dfrac{5}{4}\right)$; f is increasing on $\left(\dfrac{5}{4}, \infty\right)$;

f has a local minimum at $x = \dfrac{5}{4}$.

<u>Step 3.</u> <u>Analyze $f''(x)$:</u>

$f''(x) = 60x^4 - 60x^3 = 60x^3(x - 1)$

Partition numbers for f'': $x = 0$, $x = 1$

Sign chart for f'':

$f''(x)$ $\qquad + + + + 0 - - - - 0 + + + +$

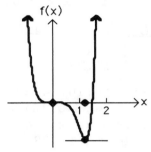

	Test Numbers	
x	$f''(x)$	
-1	120	$(+)$
$\frac{1}{2}$	$-\frac{15}{4}$	$(-)$
2	480	$(+)$

Graph of f: Concave Upward | Concave Downward | Concave Upward

Inflection point   Inflection point

Thus, the graph of f is concave upward on $(-\infty, 0)$ and on $(1, \infty)$; the graph of f is concave downward on $(0, 1)$; the graph has inflection points at $x = 0$ and $x = 1$.

<u>Step 4.</u> <u>Sketch the graph of f:</u>

x	$f(x)$
0	0
1	-1
$\frac{5}{4}$	≈ -1.5

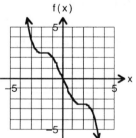

43.

x	$f'(x)$	$f(x)$
$-\infty < x < -1$	Positive and decreasing	Decreasing and concave downward
$x = -1$	x-intercept	Local maximum
$-1 < x < 0$	Negative and decreasing	Decreasing and concave downward
$x = 0$	Local minimum	Inflection point
$0 < x < 2$	Negative and increasing	Decreasing and concave upward
$x = 2$	Local maximum	Inflection point
$2 < x < \infty$	Negative and decreasing	Decreasing and concave downward

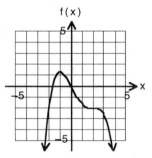

45.

x	$f'(x)$	$f(x)$
$-\infty < x < -2$	Negative and increasing	Decreasing and concave upward
$x = -2$	Local maximum	Inflection point
$-2 < x < 0$	Negative and decreasing	Decreasing and concave downward
$x = 0$	Local minimum	Inflection point
$0 < x < 2$	Negative and increasing	Decreasing and concave upward
$x = 2$	Local maximum	Inflection point
$2 < x < \infty$	Negative and decreasing	Decreasing and concave downward

47. $f(x) = x^4 - 5x^3 + 3x^2 + 8x - 5$

<u>Step 1.</u> <u>Analyze $f(x)$:</u>

Intercepts: y-intercept: $f(0) = -5$

x-intercepts: $x \approx -1.18, 0.61, 1.87, 3.71$

Step 2. Analyze $f'(x)$: $f'(x) = 4x^3 - 15x^2 + 6x + 8$

Zeros of $f'(x)$: $x \approx -0.53, 1.24, 3.04$

f is decreasing on $(-\infty, -0.53)$ and $(1.24, 3.04)$; f is increasing on $(-0.53, 1.24)$ and $(3.04, \infty)$; f has local minima at $x = -0.53$ and 3.04; f has a local maximum at $x = 1.24$

Step 3. Analyze $f''(x)$: $f''(x) = 12x^2 - 30x + 6$

The graph of f is concave upward on $(-\infty, 0.22)$ and $(2.28, \infty)$; the graph of f is concave downward on $(0.22, 2.28)$; the graph has inflection points at $x = 0.22$ and 2.28.

49. $f(x) = x^4 - 21x^3 + 100x^2 + 20x + 100$

Part 1. Analyze $f(x)$:

Intercepts: y-intercept: $f(0) = 100$

x-intercept: $x \approx 8.01, 13.36$

Part 2. Analyze $f'(x)$: $f'(x) = 4x^3 - 63x^2 + 200x + 20$

Zeros of $f'(x)$:

$\quad x \approx -0.10, 4.57, 11.28$

f is increasing on $(-0.10, 4.57)$ and $(11.28, \infty)$; f is decreasing on $(-\infty, -0.10)$ and $(4.57, 11.28)$; f has a local maximum at $x = 4.57$; f has local minima at $x = -0.10$ and 11.28.

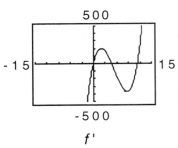

f'

Part 3. Analyze $f''(x)$: $f''(x) = 12x^2 - 126x + 200$

The graph of f is concave upward on $(-\infty, 1.95)$ and $(8.55, \infty)$; the graph of f is concave downward on $(1.95, 8.55)$; the graph has inflection points at $x = 1.95$ and $x = 8.55$.

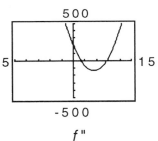

f''

51. $f(x) = -x^4 - x^3 + 2x^2 - 2x + 3$

Step 1. Analyze $f(x)$:

Intercepts: y-intercept: $f(0) = 3$

x-intercepts: $x \approx -2.40, 1.16$

Step 2. Analyze $f'(x)$: $f'(x) = -4x^3 - 3x^2 + 4x - 2$

Zeros of $f'(x)$: $x \approx -1.58$

f is increasing on $(-\infty, -1.58)$; f is decreasing on $(-1.58, \infty)$; f has a local maximum at $x = -1.58$

Step 3. Analyze $f''(x)$: $f''(x) = -12x^2 - 6x + 4$

The graph of f is concave downward on $(-\infty, -0.88)$ and $(0.38, \infty)$; the graph of f is concave upward on $(-0.88, 0.38)$; the graph has inflection points at $x = -0.88$ and $x = 0.38$.

53. $f(x) = 0.1x^5 + 0.3x^4 - 4x^3 - 5x^2 + 40x + 30$

Part 1. Analyze $f(x)$:

Intercepts: y-intercept: $f(0) = 3$
            x-intercepts: $x \approx -6.68, -3.64, -0.72$

Part 2. Analyze $f'(x)$:

$f'(x) = 0.5x^4 + 1.2x^3 - 12x^2 - 10x + 40$
Zeros of $f'(x)$: $x \approx -5.59, -2.27, 1.65, 3.82$
f is increasing on $(-\infty, -5.59)$, $(-2.27, 1.65)$, and $(3.82, \infty)$; f is decreasing on $(-5.59, -2.27)$ and $(1.65, 3.82)$; f has local minima at $x = -2.27$ and 3.82; f has local maxima at $x = -5.59$ and 1.65

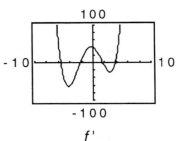

f'

Part 3. Analyze $f''(x)$: $f''(x) = 2x^3 + 3.6x^2 - 24x - 10$
The graph of f is concave downward on $(-\infty, -4.31)$ and $(-0.40, 2.91)$; the graph of f is concave upward on $(-4.31, -0.40)$ and $(2.91, \infty)$; the graph has inflection points at $x = -4.31, -0.40$ and 2.91.

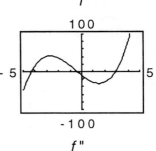

f''

55. If $f'(x)$ has a local extremum at $x = c$, then $f'(x)$ must change from increasing to decreasing, or from decreasing to increasing at $x = c$. It follows from this that the graph of f must change its concavity at $x = c$ and so there must be an inflection point at $x = c$.

57. If there is an inflection point on the graph of f at $x = c$, then the graph changes its concavity at $x = c$. Consequently, f' must change from increasing to decreasing, or from decreasing to increasing at $x = c$ and so $x = c$ is a local extremum of f'.

59. The graph of the CPI is concave up.

61. The graph of C is increasing and concave down. Therefore, the graph of C' is positive and decreasing. Since the marginal costs are decreasing, the production process is becoming more efficient.

63. $R(x) = xp = 1296x - 0.12x^3$, $0 < x < 80$
$R'(x) = 1296 - 0.36x^2$
Critical values: $R'(x) = 1296 - 0.36x^2 = 0$
$$x^2 = \frac{1296}{0.36} = 3600$$
$$x = \pm 60$$
Thus, $x = 60$ is the only critical value on the interval $(0, 80)$.
$R''(x) = -0.72x$
$R''(60) = -43.2 < 0$
(A) R has a local maximum at $x = 60$.
(B) Since $R''(x) = -0.72x < 0$ for $0 < x < 80$, R is concave downward on this interval.

65. $T(x) = -0.25x^4 + 5x^3 = -\frac{1}{4}x^4 + 5x^3$, $0 \le x \le 15$

$T'(x) = -x^3 + 15x^2$

$T''(x) = -3x^2 + 30x = -3x(x - 10)$

Partition numbers for $T''(x)$: $x = 10$

Sign chart for $T''(x)$:

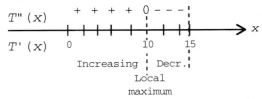

Test Numbers	
x	$T''(x)$
9	27 (+)
11	−33 (−)

Thus, T' is increasing on $(0, 10)$ and decreasing on $(10, 15)$; the point of diminishing returns is $x = 10$; the maximum rate of change is $T'(10) = 500$.

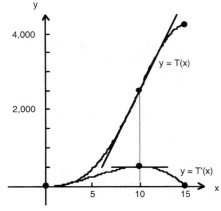

67. $N(x) = -0.25x^4 + 23x^3 - 540x^2 + 80,000$, $24 \le x \le 45$

$N'(x) = -x^3 + 69x^2 - 1080x$

$N''(x) = -3x^2 + 138x - 1080 = -3(x^2 - 46x + 360)$

$\qquad\qquad\qquad\qquad\qquad = -3(x - 10)(x - 36)$

Partition numbers for $N''(x)$: $x = 36$

Sign chart for $N''(x)$:

Test Numbers	
x	$N''(x)$
35	75 (+)
37	−111 (−)

Thus, N' is increasing on $(24, 36)$ and decreasing on $(36, 45)$; the point of diminishing returns is $x = 36$; the maximum rate of change is

$N'(36) = -(36)^3 + 69(36)^2 - 1080(36)$

$\qquad\quad = 3888$.

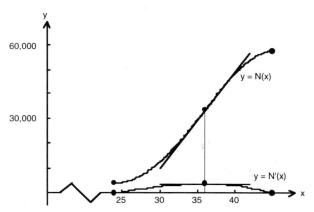

69. (A)

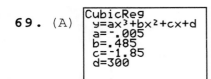

```
CubicReg
y=ax³+bx²+cx+d
a=-.005
b=.485
c=-1.85
d=300
```

(B) From part (A),
$$y(x) = -0.005x^3 + 0.485x^2 - 1.85x + 300$$
so $y'(x) = -0.015x^2 + 0.970x - 1.85$

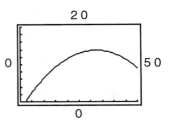

The graph of $y'(x)$ is shown at the right and the maximum value of y' occurs at $x \approx 32$; and $y(32) \approx 574$.

The manager should place 32 ads each month to maximize the rate of change of sales; the manager can expect to sell 574 cars.

71. $N(t) = 1000 + 30t^2 - t^3$, $0 \leq t \leq 20$

$N'(t) = 60t - 3t^2$

$N''(t) = 60 - 6t$

(A) To determine when N' is increasing or decreasing, we must solve the inequalities $N''(t) > 0$ and $N''(t) < 0$, respectively. Now
$$N''(t) = 60 - 6t = 0$$
$$t = 10$$

The sign chart for N'' (partition number is 10) is:

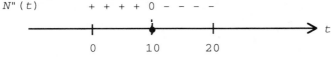

Test Numbers	
t	$N''(t)$
0	60 (+)
20	-60 (-)

Thus, N' is increasing on (0, 10) and decreasing on (10, 20).

(B) From the results in (A), the graph of N has an inflection point at $t = 10$.

(C)

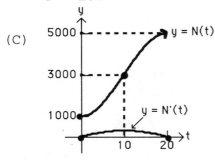

(D) Using the results in (A), N' has a local maximum at
$t = 10$:
$N'(10) = 300$

73. $T(n) = 0.08n^3 - 1.2n^2 + 6n$, $n \geq 0$

$T'(n) = 0.24n^2 - 2.4n + 6$, $n \geq 0$

$T''(n) = 0.48n - 2.4$

(A) To determine when the rate of change of T, i.e., T', is increasing or decreasing, we must solve the inequalities $T''(n) > 0$ and $T''(n) < 0$, respectively. Now
$$T''(n) = 0.48n - 2.4 = 0$$
$$n = 5$$

The sign chart for T'' (partition number is 5) is:

$T''(n)$ - - - - 0 + + + +

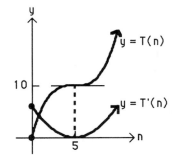

Test Numbers	
t	$N''(t)$
1	-1.92 (-)
10	2.4 (+)

$T'(n)$ Decreasing ┊ Increasing

Thus, T' is increasing on $(5, \infty)$ and decreasing on $(0, 5)$.

(B) Using the results in (A), the graph of T has an inflection point at $n = 5$. The graphs of T and T' are shown at the right.

(C) Using the results in (A), T' has a local minimum at $n = 5$:

$T'(5) = 0.24(5)^2 - 2.4(5) + 6 = 0$

EXERCISE 4-3

Things to remember:

1. RATIONAL FUNCTIONS

   A RATIONAL FUNCTION is any function that can be written in the form

   $$f(x) = \frac{n(x)}{d(x)} \qquad d(x) \neq 0$$

   where $n(x)$ and $d(x)$ are polynomials. The DOMAIN of f is the set of all real numbers such that $d(x) \neq 0$.

2. VERTICAL ASYMPTOTES

   The vertical line $x = a$ is a VERTICAL ASYMPTOTE for the graph of $y = f(x)$ if

   $$f(x) \to \infty \text{ or } f(x) \to -\infty \text{ as } x \to a^+ \text{ or } x \to a^-$$

   (that is, if $f(x)$ either increases or decreases without bound as x approaches a from the right or from the left).

3. LOCATING VERTICAL ASYMPTOTES OF RATIONAL FUNCTIONS

   If $f(x) = \dfrac{n(x)}{d(x)}$ is a rational function, $d(c) = 0$ and $n(c) \neq 0$, then the line $x = c$ is a vertical asymptote of the graph of f.

4. HORIZONTAL ASYMPTOTES

   The line $y = b$ is a HORIZONTAL ASYMPTOTE for the graph of $y = f(x)$ if

   $$\lim_{x \to \infty} f(x) = b \quad \text{or} \quad \lim_{x \to -\infty} f(x) = b$$

5. HORIZONTAL ASYMPTOTES FOR RATIONAL FUNCTIONS

Let $f(x) = \dfrac{a_m x^m + a_{m-1}x^{m-1} + \ldots + a_1 x + a_0}{b_n x^n + b_{n-1}x^{n-1} + \ldots + b_1 x + b_0}$

1. If $m < n$, then $y = 0$ (the x axis) is a horizontal asymptote for $f(x)$.

2. If $m = n$, then the line $y = \dfrac{a_m}{b_n}$ is a horizontal asymptote for $f(x)$.

3. If $m > n$, then $f(x)$ does not have a horizontal asymptote.

6. STRATEGY FOR GRAPHING A RATIONAL FUNCTION

Step 1. Analyze $f(x)$.
(A) Find the domain of f.
(B) Find intercepts.
(C) Find asymptotes.

Step 2. Analyze $f'(x)$.
Find the zeros of $f'(x)$. Construct a sign chart for $f'(x)$, determine the intervals where $f(x)$ is increasing and decreasing, and find local maxima and minima.

Step 3. Analyze $f''(x)$.
Find the zeros of $f''(x)$. Construct a sign chart for $f''(x)$, determine where the graph of f is concave upward and concave downward, and find any inflection points.

Step 4. Sketch the graph of f.
Draw asymptotes and locate intercepts, local maxima and minima, and inflection points. Sketch in what you know from steps 1—3. In regions of uncertainty, use point-by-point plotting to complete the graph.

---

1. (A) $f'(x) < 0$ on $(-\infty, b)$, $(0, e)$, (e, g)

(B) $f'(x) > 0$ on (b, d), $(d, 0)$, (g, ∞)

(C) $f(x)$ is increasing on (b, d), $(d, 0)$, (g, ∞)

(D) $f(x)$ is decreasing on $(-\infty, b)$, $(0, e)$, (e, g)

(E) $f(x)$ has a local maximum at $x = 0$

(F) $f(x)$ has local minima at $x = b$ and $x = g$

(G) $f''(x) < 0$ on $(-\infty, a)$, (d, e), (h, ∞)

(H) $f''(x) > 0$ on (a, c), (e, h)

(I) The graph of f is concave upward on (a, c) and (e, h).

(J) The graph of f is concave downward on $(-\infty, a)$, (d, e), and (h, ∞).

(K) Inflection points at $x = a$, $x = h$

(L) Horizontal asymptote: $y = L$

(M) Vertical asymptotes: $x = d$, $x = e$

3. $f(x) = \dfrac{3x - 4}{x}$

Horizontal asymptote: $\dfrac{a_m x^m}{b_n x^n} = \dfrac{3x}{x} = 3$

$y = 3$ is a horizontal asymptote [4b].

Vertical asymptotes: Let $n(x) = 3x - 4$, $d(x) = x$; $d(0) = 0$ and $n(0) = 4 \neq 0$. Therefore, $x = 0$ is a vertical asymptote [5].

5. $f(x) = \dfrac{x^2 - 4}{x^2 + 4}$

Horizontal asymptote: $\dfrac{a_m x^m}{b_n x^n} = \dfrac{x^2}{x^2} = 1$

$y = 1$ is a horizontal asymptote [4b].

Vertical asymptotes: Let $n(x) = x^2 - 4$, $d(x) = x^2 + 4$.

Since $x^2 + 4 \geq 4 > 0$ for all x, $d(x) \neq 0$ for all x; there are no vertical asymptotes [5].

7. $f(x) = \dfrac{x}{x^2 - 1}$

Horizontal asymptote: $\dfrac{a_m x^m}{b_n x^n} = \dfrac{x}{x^2} = \dfrac{1}{x}$

$y = 0$ is a horizontal asymptote [4a].

Vertical asymptotes: Let $n(x) = x$, $d(x) = x^2 - 1 = (x - 1)(x + 1)$. Since $d(1) = 0$ and $n(1) = 1 \neq 0$, $x = 1$ is a vertical asymptote; since $d(-1) = 0$ and $n(-1) = -1 \neq 0$, $x = -1$ is a vertical asymptote [5].

9. $f(x) = \dfrac{x^3}{x^2 - 16}$

Horizontal asymptote: $\dfrac{a_m x^m}{b_n x^n} = \dfrac{x^3}{x^2} = x$;

there is no horizontal asymptote [4c].

Vertical asymptotes: Let $n(x) = x^3$, $d(x) = x^2 - 16 = (x - 4)(x + 4)$. Since $d(4) = 0$ and $n(4) = 64 \neq 0$, $x = 4$ is a vertical asymptote; since $d(-4) = 0$ and $n(-4) = -64 \neq 0$, $x = -4$ is a horizontal asymptote [5].

11. $f(x) = \dfrac{2x^2 + x - 3}{x^2 - 2x + 1}$

Horizontal asymptote: $\dfrac{a_m x^m}{b_n x^n} = \dfrac{2x^2}{x^2} = 2$;

$y = 2$ is a horizontal asymptote.

Vertical asymptotes: Let $n(x) = 2x^2 + x - 3 = (2x + 3)(x - 1)$ and $d(x) = x^2 - 2x + 1 = (x - 1)^2$. Then $\dfrac{n(x)}{d(x)} = \dfrac{(2x + 3)(x - 1)}{(x - 1)^2} = \dfrac{2x + 3}{x - 1}$

The denominator is 0 at $x = 1$, the numerator is nonzero. Therefore, $x = 1$ is a vertical asymptote.

13. $f(x) = \dfrac{3x^2 + 2x + 5}{2x^2 + 3x - 20}$

Horizontal asymptote: $\dfrac{a_m x^m}{b_n x^n} = \dfrac{3x^2}{2x^2} = \dfrac{3}{2}$;

$y = \dfrac{3}{2}$ is a horizontal asymptote.

Vertical asymptotes: Let $n(x) = 3x^2 + 2x + 5$ and $d(x) = 2x^2 + 3x - 20 = (2x - 5)(x + 4)$. Since $d\left(\dfrac{5}{2}\right) = 0$ and $d(-4) = 0$, and $n\left(\dfrac{5}{2}\right) \neq 0$, $n(-4) \neq 0$, $x = \dfrac{5}{2}$ and $x = -4$ are vertical asymptotes.

15. Step 1. Analyze $f(x)$:

(A) Domain: All real numbers

(B) Intercepts: y-intercept: 0
$\qquad\qquad\quad$ x-intercepts: -4, 0, 4

(C) Asymptotes: Horizontal asymptote: $y = 2$

Step 2. Analyze $f'(x)$:

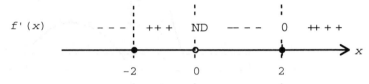

Step 3. Analyze $f''(x)$:

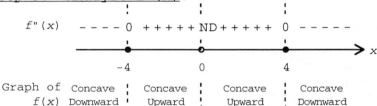

Step 4. Sketch the graph of f:

17. Step 1. Analyze $f(x)$:

(A) Domain: All real numbers except $x = -2$

(B) Intercepts: y-intercept: 0
$\qquad\qquad\quad$ x-intercepts: -4, 0

(C) Asymptotes: Horizontal asymptote: $y = 1$
$\qquad\qquad\qquad\quad$ Vertical asymptote: $x = -2$

Step 2. Analyze $f'(x)$:

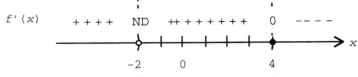

$f'(x)$ + + + +   ND   ++ + + + + +   0   - - - -

-2   0   4

$f(x)$ Increasing ┊   Increasing ┊ Decreasing

Local
maximum

Step 3. Analyze $f''(x)$:

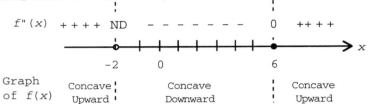

$f''(x)$ + + + +   ND   - - - - - - -   0   ++ + +

-2   0   6

Graph
of $f(x)$ Concave ┊   Concave   ┊ Concave
           Upward ┊   Downward   ┊ Upward

Step 4. Sketch the graph of f:

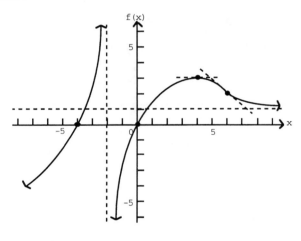

19. Step 1. Analyze $f(x)$:

(A) Domain: All real numbers except
$x = -1$

(B) Intercepts: y-intercept: -1
x-intercept: 1

(C) Asymptotes: Horizontal asymptote: $y = 1$
Vertical asymptote: $x = -1$

Step 2. Analyze $f'(x)$:

$f'(x)$ + + + + +   ND   + + + + + +

-1   0

$f(x)$ Increasing ┊ Increasing

Step 3. Analyze $f''(x)$:

$f''(x)$ + + + ND – – –

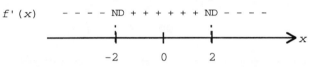

Graph of f −1   0

Concave   Concave
Upward   Downward

Step 4. Sketch the graph of f:

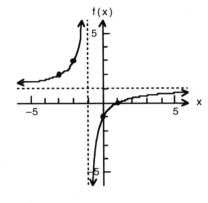

21. Step 1. Analyze $f(x)$:

(A) Domain: All real numbers except $x = -2$, $x = 2$

(B) Intercepts: y-intercept: 0
                 x-intercept: 0

(C) Asymptotes: Horizontal asymptote: $y = 0$
                      Vertical asymptotes: $x = -2$, $x = 2$

Step 2. Analyze $f'(x)$:

$f'(x)$ – – – – ND + + + + + + ND – – – –

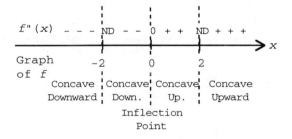

         −2   0   2

$f(x)$ Decreasing ¦ Increasing ¦ Decreasing

Step 3. Analyze $f''(x)$:

$f''(x)$ – – – ND – – 0 + + ND + + +

Graph of f −2   0   2

Concave ¦Concave¦ Concave¦ Concave
Downward¦ Down. ¦ Up. ¦ Upward

                 Inflection
                  Point

Step 4. Sketch the graph of f:

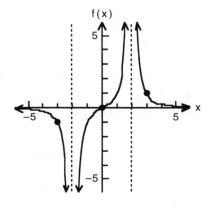

23. $f(x) = \dfrac{x + 3}{x - 3}$

Step 1. Analyze $f(x)$:

(A) Domain: All real numbers except $x = 3$.

(B) Intercepts: y-intercept: $f(0) = \dfrac{3}{-3} = -1$

$\qquad\qquad\qquad x$-intercepts: $\dfrac{x + 3}{x - 3} = 0$

$\qquad\qquad\qquad\qquad\qquad x + 3 = 0$

$\qquad\qquad\qquad\qquad\qquad\qquad x = -3$

(C) Asymptotes:

$\qquad$ Horizontal asymptote: $\lim\limits_{x \to \infty} \dfrac{x + 3}{x - 3} = \lim\limits_{x \to \infty} \dfrac{x\left(1 + \frac{3}{x}\right)}{x\left(1 - \frac{3}{x}\right)} = 1.$

$\qquad$ Thus, $y = 1$ is a horizontal asymptote.

$\qquad$ Vertical asymptote: The denominator is 0 at $x = 3$ and the numerator is not 0 at $x = 3$. Thus, $x = 3$ is a vertical asymptote.

Step 2. Analyze $f'(x)$:

$f'(x) = \dfrac{(x - 3)(1) - (x + 3)(1)}{(x - 3)^2} = \dfrac{-6}{(x - 3)^2} = -6(x - 3)^{-2}$

Critical values: None
Partition number: $x = 3$
Sign chart for f':

$f'(x)$	$-\ -\ -\ -\ -$ ND $-\ -\ -\ -$				Test Numbers

x	$f'(x)$
2	$-6 \ (-)$
4	$-6 \ (-)$

$f(x)$ 0 1 2 3 4   Decreasing ⋮ Decreasing

Thus, f is decreasing on $(-\infty, 3)$ and on $(3, \infty)$; there are no local extrema.

Step 3. Analyze $f''(x)$:

$f''(x) = 12(x - 3)^{-3} = \dfrac{12}{(x - 3)^3}$

Partition number for f'': $x = 3$
Sign chart for f'':

$f''(x)$	$-\ -\ -\ -\ -$ ND $+ + + +$

x	$f''(x)$
2	$-12 \ (-)$
4	$12 \ (+)$

Graph of f 0 1 2 3 4   Concave Downward ⋮ Concave Upward

Thus, the graph of f is concave downward on $(-\infty, 3)$ and concave upward on $(3, \infty)$.

Step 4. Sketch the graph of f:

x	$f(x)$
-3	0
0	-1
5	4

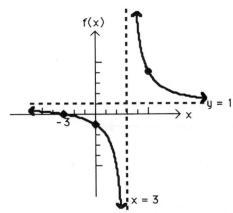

25. $f(x) = \dfrac{x}{x - 2}$

Step 1. Analyze $f(x)$:

(A) Domain: All real numbers except $x = 2$.

(B) Intercepts: y-intercept: $f(0) = \dfrac{0}{-2} = 0$

x-intercepts: $\dfrac{x}{x - 2} = 0$

$\qquad\qquad\qquad x = 0$

(C) Asymptotes:

<u>Horizontal asymptote</u>: $\lim\limits_{x \to \infty} \dfrac{x}{x - 2} = \lim\limits_{x \to \infty} \dfrac{x}{x\left(1 - \frac{2}{x}\right)} = 1$.

Thus, $y = 1$ is a horizontal asymptote.

<u>Vertical asymptote</u>: The denominator is 0 at $x = 2$ and the numerator is not 0 at $x = 2$. Thus, $x = 2$ is a vertical asymptote.

Step 2. Analyze $f'(x)$:

$f'(x) = \dfrac{(x - 2)(1) - x(1)}{(x - 2)^2} = \dfrac{-2}{(x - 2)^2} = -2(x - 2)^{-2}$

Critical values: None
Partition number: $x = 2$
Sign chart for f':

$f'(x)$ — — — — ND — — — —

Test Numbers	
x	$f'(x)$
0	$-\frac{1}{2}$ (−)
3	-2 (−)

$f(x)$ Decreasing ┊ Decreasing

Thus, f is decreasing on $(-\infty, 2)$ and on $(2, \infty)$; there are no local extrema.

Step 3. Analyze $f''(x)$:

$$f''(x) = 4(x - 2)^{-3} = \frac{4}{(x - 2)^3}$$

Partition number for f'': $x = 2$
Sign chart for f'':

$f''(x)$ $\quad$ $- - - -$ ND $+ + + +$

Graph of f

	0	1	2	3	
		Concave Downward		Concave Upward	

Test Numbers

x	$f''(x)$
0	$-\frac{1}{2}$ (−)
3	4 (+)

Thus, the graph of f is concave downward on $(-\infty, 2)$ and concave upward on $(2, \infty)$.

Step 4. Sketch the graph of f:

x	$f(x)$
0	0
4	2

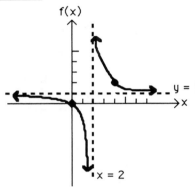

27. $f(x) = \dfrac{x}{x^2 - 4} = \dfrac{x}{(x - 2)(x + 2)}$

Step 1. Analyze $f(x)$:

(A) Domain: All real numbers except $x = 2$, $x = -2$.

(B) Intercepts: y-intercept: $f(0) = \dfrac{0}{-4} = 0$

$\qquad$ x-intercept: $\dfrac{x}{x^2 - 4} = 0$

$\qquad\qquad\qquad\qquad x = 0$

(C) Asymptotes:
$\quad$ Horizontal asymptote:

$$\lim_{x \to \infty} \frac{x}{x^2 - 4} = \lim_{x \to \infty} \frac{x}{x^2\left(1 - \frac{4}{x^2}\right)} = \lim_{x \to \infty} \frac{1}{x}\left(\frac{1}{1 - \frac{4}{x^2}}\right) = 0$$

Thus, $y = 0$ (the x axis) is a horizontal asymptote.

Vertical asymptotes: The denominator is 0 at $x = 2$ and $x = -2$. The numerator is nonzero at each of these points. Thus, $x = 2$ and $x = -2$ are vertical asymptotes.

Step 2. Analyze $f'(x)$:

$$f'(x) = \frac{(x^2 - 4)(1) - x(2x)}{(x^2 - 4)^2} = \frac{-(x^2 + 4)}{(x^2 - 4)^2}$$

Critical values: None ($x^2 + 4 \neq 0$ for all x)
Partition numbers: $x = 2$, $x = -2$
Sign chart for f':

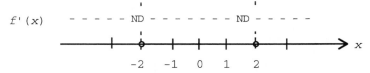

Thus, f is decreasing on $(-\infty, -2)$, on $(-2, 2)$, and on $(2, \infty)$; f has no local extrema.

Step 3. Analyze $f''(x)$:

$$f''(x) = \frac{(x^2 - 4)^2(-2x) - [-(x^2 + 4)](2)(x^2 - 4)(2x)}{(x^2 - 4)^4}$$

$$= \frac{(x^2 - 4)(-2x) + 4x(x^2 + 4)}{(x^2 - 4)^3} = \frac{2x^3 + 24x}{(x^2 - 4)^3} = \frac{2x(x^2 + 12)}{(x^2 - 4)^3}$$

Partition numbers for f'': $x = 0$, $x = 2$, $x = -2$
Sign chart for f'':

Test Numbers	
x	$f''(x)$
-3	$-\frac{126}{125}$ (–)
-1	$\frac{26}{27}$ (+)
1	$-\frac{26}{27}$ (–)
3	$\frac{126}{127}$ (+)

f''(x)   - - - - ND + + + + 0 - - - - - ND + + +

Graph of f: Concave Downward | Concave Upward | Concave Downward | Concave Upward

Inflection point

Thus, the graph of f is concave downward on $(-\infty, -2)$ and on $(0, 2)$; the graph of f is concave upward on $(-2, 0)$ and on $(2, \infty)$; the graph has an inflection point at $x = 0$.

Step 4. Sketch the graph of f:

x	$f(x)$
0	0
1	$-\frac{1}{3}$
-1	$\frac{1}{3}$
3	$\frac{3}{5}$
-3	$-\frac{3}{5}$

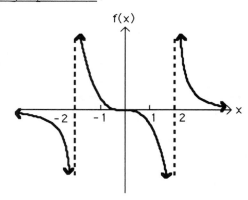

29. $f(x) = \dfrac{1}{1 + x^2}$

Step 1. Analyze $f(x)$:

(A) Domain: All real numbers ($1 + x^2 \neq 0$ for all x).

(B) Intercepts: y-intercept: $f(0) = 1$

$\qquad\qquad\qquad\quad x$-intercept: $\dfrac{1}{1 + x^2} \neq 0$ for all x; no x intercepts

(C) Asymptotes:

Horizontal asymptote: $\displaystyle\lim_{x \to \infty} \dfrac{1}{1 + x^2} = 0$

Thus, $y = 0$ (the x-axis) is a horizontal asymptote.

Vertical asymptotes: Since $1 + x^2 \neq 0$ for all x, there are no vertical asymptotes.

Step 2. Analyze $f'(x)$:

$f'(x) = \dfrac{(1 + x^2)(0) - 1(2x)}{(1 + x^2)^2} = \dfrac{-2x}{(1 + x^2)^2}$

Critical values: $x = 0$

Partition numbers: $x = 0$

Sign chart for f':

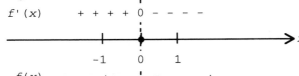

Test Numbers	
x	$f'(x)$
-1	$\frac{1}{2}$ (+)
1	$-\frac{1}{2}$ (−)

Thus, f is increasing on $(-\infty,\ 0)$; f is decreasing on $(0,\ \infty)$; f has a local maximum at $x = 0$.

Step 3. Analyze $f''(x)$:

$f''(x) = \dfrac{(1 + x^2)^2(-2) - (-2x)(2)(1 + x^2)2x}{(1 + x^2)^4} = \dfrac{(-2)(1 + x^2) + 8x^2}{(1 + x^2)^3}$

$\qquad = \dfrac{6x^2 - 2}{(1 + x^2)^3} = \dfrac{6\left(x + \frac{\sqrt{3}}{3}\right)\left(x - \frac{\sqrt{3}}{3}\right)}{(1 + x^2)^3}$

Partition numbers for f'': $x = -\dfrac{\sqrt{3}}{3},\ x = \dfrac{\sqrt{3}}{3}$

Sign chart for f'':

Test Numbers	
x	$f''(x)$
-1	$\frac{1}{2}$ (+)
0	-2 (−)
1	$\frac{1}{2}$ (+)

Thus, the graph of f is concave upward on $\left(-\infty, \frac{-\sqrt{3}}{3}\right)$ and on $\left(\frac{\sqrt{3}}{3}, \infty\right)$; the graph of f is concave downward on $\left(\frac{-\sqrt{3}}{3}, \frac{\sqrt{3}}{3}\right)$; the graph has inflection points at $x = \frac{-\sqrt{3}}{3}$ and $x = \frac{\sqrt{3}}{3}$.

Step 4. Sketch the graph of f:

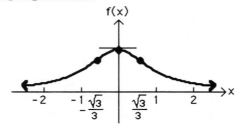

x	$f(x)$
$-\frac{\sqrt{3}}{3}$	$\frac{3}{4}$
0	1
$\frac{\sqrt{3}}{3}$	$\frac{3}{4}$

31. $f(x) = \dfrac{2x}{1 - x^2}$

Step 1. Analyze $f(x)$:

(A) Domain: All real numbers except $x = -1$ and $x = 1$.

(B) Intercepts: y-intercept: $f(0) = \dfrac{0}{1} = 0$

$\qquad$ x-intercepts: $\dfrac{2x}{1 - x^2} = 0$

$\qquad\qquad\qquad\qquad x = 0$

(C) Asymptotes:

$\qquad$ <u>Horizontal asymptote</u>: $\displaystyle\lim_{x\to\infty} \frac{2x}{1 - x^2} = \lim_{x\to\infty} \frac{\frac{2}{x}}{\frac{1}{x^2} - 1} = 0$. Thus, $y = 0$

$\qquad\qquad$ (the x-axis) is a horizontal asymptote.

$\qquad$ <u>Vertical asymptotes</u>: The denominator is 0 at $x = \pm 1$ and the numerator is not 0 at $x = \pm 1$. Thus, $x = -1$, $x = 1$ are vertical asymptotes.

Step 2. Analyze $f'(x)$:

$f'(x) = \dfrac{(1 - x^2)2 - 2x(-2x)}{(1 - x^2)^2} = \dfrac{4x^2 + 2}{(1 - x^2)^2}$

Critical values: none
Partition numbers: $x = -1$, $x = 1$
Sign chart for f':

```
          + + + ND + + ND + + +
  f'(x)  ──┼──┼──┼──┼──┼──→ x
  f(x)    -2  -1  0  1  2
         Increasing ¦ Incr. ¦ Increasing
```

Test Numbers	
x	$f'(x)$
-2	$2 (+)$
0	$2 (+)$
2	$2 (+)$

Thus, f is increasing on $(-\infty, -1)$, $(-1, 1)$, and $(1, \infty)$.

Step 3. Analyze $f''(x)$:

$$f''(x) = \frac{(1 - x^2)^2 8x - (4x^2 + 2)(2)(1 - x^2)(-2x)}{(1 - x^2)^4} = \frac{8x(x^2 + 2)}{(1 - x^2)^3}$$

Partition numbers for $f''(x)$: $x = -1$, $x = 0$, $x = 1$
Sign chart for f'':

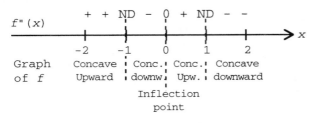

Test Numbers	
x	$f''(x)$
-2	$\frac{32}{3}$ (+)
$-\frac{1}{2}$	$-\frac{16}{3}$ (−)
$\frac{1}{2}$	$\frac{16}{3}$ (+)
2	$-\frac{32}{3}$ (−)

Thus, the graph of f is concave upward on $(-\infty, -1)$ and $(0, 1)$, concave downward on $(-1, 0)$ and $(1, \infty)$, and has an inflection point at $x = 0$.

Step 4. Sketch the graph of f:

x	$f(x)$
0	0

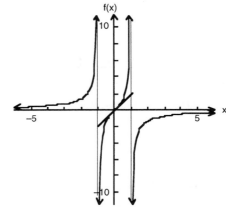

33. $f(x) = \dfrac{-5x}{(x - 1)^2} = \dfrac{-5x}{x^2 - 2x + 1}$

Step 1. Analyze $f(x)$:

(A) Domain: All real numbers except $x = 1$.

(B) Intercepts: y-intercept: $f(0) = 0$

   x-intercepts: $\dfrac{-5x}{(x - 1)^2} = 0$

   $x = 0$

(C) Asymptotes:

   Horizontal asymptote: $\lim\limits_{x \to \infty} \dfrac{-5x}{x^2 - 2x + 1} = \lim\limits_{x \to \infty} \dfrac{-\frac{5}{x}}{1 - \frac{2}{x} + \frac{1}{x^2}} = 0$. Thus,

   $y = 0$ (the x-axis) is a horizontal asymptote.

   Vertical asymptotes: The denominator is 0 at $x = 1$ and the numerator is not 0 at $x = 1$. Thus, $x = 1$ is a vertical asymptote.

Step 2. Analyze $f'(x)$:

$$f'(x) = \frac{(x - 1)^2(-5) + 5x(2)(x - 1)}{(x - 1)^4} = \frac{5(x + 1)}{(x - 1)^3}$$

Critical values: $x = -1$

Partition numbers: $x = -1$, $x = 1$

Sign chart for f':

$f'(x)$ $+ + + \ 0 - - - \ ND \ + + +$

$f(x)$ $\quad$ -2 -1 0 1 2

$\qquad$ Increasing ┊ Decr. ┊ Increasing

$\qquad\qquad$ Local
$\qquad\qquad$ maximum

Test Numbers

x	$f'(x)$
-2	$\frac{5}{27}$ (+)
0	-5 (−)
2	15 (+)

Thus, f is increasing on $(-\infty, -1)$, $(1, \infty)$, decreasing on $(-1, 1)$, and has a local maximum at $x = -1$.

Step 3. Analyze $f''(x)$:

$$f''(x) = \frac{(x-1)^3 5 - 5(x+1)(3)(x-1)^2}{(x-1)^6} = \frac{-10(x+2)}{(x-1)^4}$$

Partition numbers for $f''(x)$: $x = -2$, $x = 1$

Sign chart for f'':

$f''(x)$ $+ + 0 - - - - \ ND - -$

$\qquad\qquad$ -3 -2 -1 0 1 2

Graph   Concave ┊ Concave ┊ Concave
of f Upward ┊ downward ┊ downward

Test Numbers

x	$f''(x)$
-3	(+)
0	-10 (−)
2	-40 (−)

Thus, the graph of f is concave upward on $(-\infty, -2)$, concave downward on $(-2, 1)$ and $(1, \infty)$, and has an inflection point at $x = -2$.

Step 4. Sketch the graph of f:

x	$f(x)$
-2	$\frac{10}{9}$
-1	$\frac{5}{4}$
0	0

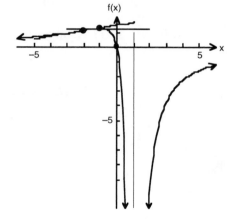

35. $f(x) = \dfrac{x^2 + 2}{x}$

Step 1. Analyze $f(x)$:

(A) Domain: All real numbers except $x = 0$.

(B) Intercepts: y-intercept: $f(0)$ not defined; no y-intercept

$\qquad\qquad$ x-intercepts: $\dfrac{x^2 + 2}{x} = 0$; no solutions; no x-intercepts

(C) Asymptotes:
$\qquad$ Horizontal asymptote: no horizontal asymptote.
$\qquad$ Vertical asymptotes: $x = 0$ (the y-axis)

Step 2. Analyze $f'(x)$:

$$f'(x) = \frac{x(2x) - (x^2 + 2)}{x^2} = \frac{x^2 - 2}{x^2} = 1 - \frac{2}{x^2}$$

Critical values: $x = -\sqrt{2}$, $x = \sqrt{2}$
Partition numbers: $x = -\sqrt{2}$, $x = 0$, $x = \sqrt{2}$
Sign chart for f':

Test Numbers	
x	$f'(x)$
-2	$2\,(+)$
-1	$-1\,(-)$
1	$1\,(-)$
2	$2\,(+)$

$f'(x)$ $+ + + 0 - - -$ ND $- - - 0 + + +$

$f(x)$ -2 $-\sqrt{2}$ -1 0 1 $\sqrt{2}$ 2

Incr. | Decr. | Decr. | Incr.
Local maximum   Local minimum

Thus, f is increasing on $(-\infty, -\sqrt{2})$ and $(\sqrt{2}, \infty)$, decreasing on $(-\sqrt{2}, 0)$ and $(0, \sqrt{2})$, and has a local maximum at $x = -\sqrt{2}$ and a local minimum at $x = \sqrt{2}$.

Step 3. Analyze $f''(x)$:

$$f''(x) = \frac{4}{x^3}$$

Partition numbers for $f''(x)$: $x = 0$
Sign chart for f'':

Test Numbers	
x	$f''(x)$
-1	$-4\,(-)$
1	$4\,(+)$

$f''(x)$ $- - - - -$ ND $+ + + +$

-1 0 1

Graph of f | Concave Downward | Concave Upward

The graph of f is concave upward on $(0, \infty)$ and concave downward on $(-\infty, 0)$.

Step 4. Sketch the graph of f:

x	$f(x)$
$-\sqrt{2}$	$-2\sqrt{2}$
$\sqrt{2}$	$2\sqrt{2}$

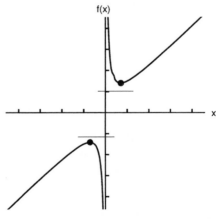

37. $f(x) = \dfrac{x^2 + x - 2}{x^2} = \dfrac{(x + 2)(x - 1)}{x^2}$

Step 1. Analyze $f(x)$:

(A) Domain: All real numbers except $x = 0$.

(B) Intercepts: y-intercept: $f(0)$ not defined; no y-intercept

x-intercepts: $\dfrac{(x + 2)(x - 1)}{x^2} = 0$

$$x = -2, \quad x = 1$$

(C) Asymptotes:

Horizontal asymptote: $\lim\limits_{x\to\infty} \dfrac{x^2 + x - 2}{x^2} = \lim\limits_{x\to\infty} \dfrac{1 + \frac{1}{x} - \frac{2}{x^2}}{1} = 1.$

Thus, $y = 1$ is a horizontal asymptote.

Vertical asymptotes: $x = 0$ (the x-axis)

Step 2. Analyze $f'(x)$:

$f'(x) = \dfrac{x^2(2x + 1) - (x^2 + x - 2)(2x)}{x^4} = \dfrac{4 - x}{x^3}$

Critical values: $x = 4$

Partition numbers: $x = 0$, $x = 4$

Sign chart for f':

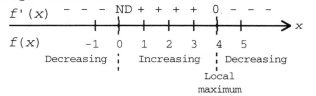

Test Numbers	
x	$f'(x)$
-1	-5 $(-)$
1	3 $(+)$
5	$(-)$

Thus, f is increasing on $(0, 4)$, decreasing on $(-\infty, 0)$ and $(4, \infty)$, and has a local maximum at $x = 4$.

Step 3. Analyze $f''(x)$:

$f''(x) = \dfrac{x^3(-1) - (4 - x)(3x^2)}{x^6} = \dfrac{2x - 12}{x^4} = \dfrac{2(x - 6)}{x^4}$

Partition numbers for $f''(x)$: $x = 0$, $x = 6$

Sign chart for f'':

```
f"(x)     - - ND - - - - - - - 0 + +
          +--+--+--+--+--+--+--+--+--+--> x
          -1 0  1              6
Graph
of f    Concave       Concave      Concave
        Downward      Downward     Upward
                               Inflection
                                 point
```

Test Numbers	
x	$f''(x)$
-1	-14 $(-)$
1	-10 $(-)$
7	$(+)$

Thus, the graph of f is concave upward on $(6, \infty)$, concave downward on $(-\infty, 0)$ and $(0, 6)$, and has an inflection point at $x = 6$.

Step 4. Sketch the graph of f:

x	$f(x)$
4	$\frac{9}{8}$
6	$\frac{10}{9}$

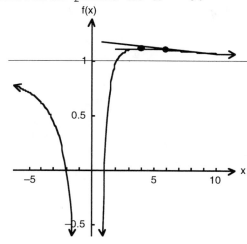

39. $f(x) = \dfrac{x^2}{x - 1}$

Step 1. Analyze $f(x)$:

(A) Domain: All real numbers except $x = 1$.

(B) Intercepts: y-intercept: $f(0) = 0$

x-intercepts: $\dfrac{x^2}{x - 1} = 0$

$x = 0$

(C) Asymptotes:

Horizontal asymptote: $\dfrac{x^2}{x} = x$; no horizontal asymptote

Vertical asymptote: $x = 1$

Step 2. Analyze $f'(x)$:

$f'(x) = \dfrac{(x - 1)(2x) - x^2}{(x - 1)^2} = \dfrac{x^2 - 2x}{(x - 1)^2} = \dfrac{x(x - 2)}{(x - 1)^2}$

Critical values: $x = 0$, $x = 2$

Partition numbers: $x = 0$, $x = 1$, $x = 2$

Sign chart for f':

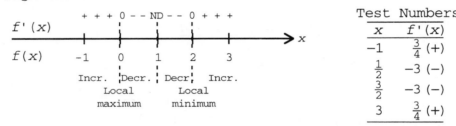

Test Numbers

x	$f'(x)$
-1	$\frac{3}{4}$ (+)
$\frac{1}{2}$	-3 (−)
$\frac{3}{2}$	-3 (−)
3	$\frac{3}{4}$ (+)

Thus, f is increasing on $(-\infty, 0)$ and $(2, \infty)$, decreasing on $(0, 1)$ and $(1, 2)$, and has a local maximum at $x = 0$ and a local minimum at $x = 2$.

Step 3. Analyze $f''(x)$:

$f''(x) = \dfrac{(x - 1)^2(2x - 2) - (x^2 - 2x)(2)(x - 1)}{(x - 1)^4} = \dfrac{2}{(x - 1)^3}$

Partition numbers for $f''(x)$: $x = 1$

Sign chart for f'':

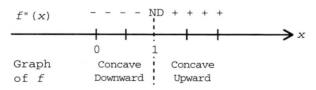

Thus, the graph of f is concave upward on $(1, \infty)$ and concave downward on $(-\infty, 1)$.

Step 4. Sketch the graph of f:

x	$f(x)$
0	0
2	4

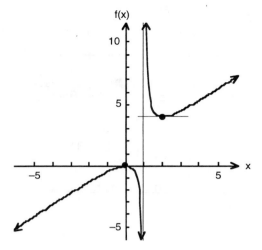

41. $f(x) = \dfrac{3x^2 + 2}{x^2 - 9}$

Step 1. Analyze $f(x)$:

(A) Domain: All real numbers except $x = -3$, $x = 3$.

(B) Intercepts: y-intercept: $f(0) = -\dfrac{2}{9}$

x-intercepts: $3x^2 + 2 \neq 0$ for all x; no x-intercepts

(C) Asymptotes:

Horizontal asymptote: $\dfrac{3x^2}{x^2} = 3$; $y = 3$ is a horizontal asymptote

Vertical asymptote: $x = -3$, $x = 3$

Step 2. Analyze $f'(x)$:

$f'(x) = \dfrac{(x^2 - 9)(6x) - (3x^2 + 2)(2x)}{(x^2 - 9)^2} = \dfrac{-58x}{(x^2 - 9)^2}$

Critical values: $x = 0$
Partition numbers: $x = -3$, $x = 0$, $x = 3$
Sign chart for f':

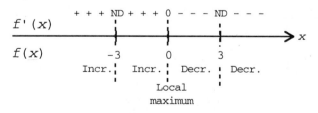

Test Numbers

x	$f'(x)$
-4	$(+)$
-2	$(+)$
2	$(-)$
4	$(-)$

Thus, f is increasing on $(-\infty, -3)$ and $(-3, 0)$, decreasing on $(0, 3)$ and $(3, \infty)$, and has a local maximum at $x = 0$.

Step 3. Analyze $f''(x)$:

$f''(x) = \dfrac{(x^2 - 9)^2(-58) + 58x(2)(x^2 - 9)(2x)}{(x^2 - 9)^4} = \dfrac{174(x^2 + 3)}{(x^2 - 9)^3}$

Partition numbers for $f''(x)$: $x = -3$, $x = 3$

Sign chart for f'':

$f''(x)$ $\quad$ + + + ND - - - - - - - ND + + +

Test Numbers

x	$f''(x)$
-4	$(+)$
0	$(-)$
4	$(+)$

	-3	0	3	
Graph of f	Concave Upward	Concave Downward	Concave Upward	

Thus, the graph of f is concave upward on $(-\infty, -3)$ and $(3, \infty)$, and concave downward on $(-3, 3)$.

Step 4. Sketch the graph of f:

x	$f(x)$
0	$-\frac{2}{9}$

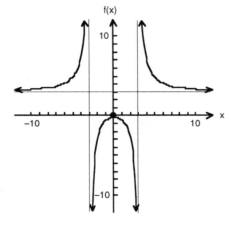

43. $f(x) = \dfrac{x^3}{x - 2}$

Step 1. Analyze $f(x)$:

(A) Domain: All real numbers except $x = 2$.

(B) Intercepts: y-intercept: $f(0) = 0$

$\qquad\qquad$ x-intercepts: $\dfrac{x^3}{x - 2} = 0$

$\qquad\qquad\qquad\qquad\qquad$ $x = 0$

(C) Asymptotes:

$\qquad$ Horizontal asymptote: $\dfrac{x^3}{x} = x^2$; no horizontal asymptote

$\qquad$ Vertical asymptote: $x = 2$

Step 2. Analyze $f'(x)$:

$f'(x) = \dfrac{(x - 2)(3x^2) - x^3}{(x - 2)^2} = \dfrac{2x^2(x - 3)}{(x - 2)^2}$

Critical values: $x = 0$, $x = 3$

Partition numbers: $x = 0$, $x = 2$, $x = 3$

Sign chart for f':

$f'(x)$ $\quad$ - - 0 - - - - ND - 0 + +

Test Numbers

x	$f'(x)$
-1	$-\frac{8}{9}$ $(-)$
1	-4 $(-)$
$\frac{5}{2}$	-25 $(-)$
4	8 $(+)$

$f(x)$	-1	0	1	2	3	4	
	Decreasing		Decr.		Dec.	Increasing	

Local minimum

Thus, f is increasing on $(3, \infty)$, decreasing on $(-\infty, 2)$ and $(2, 3)$, and has a local minimum at $x = 3$.

Step 3. Analyze $f''(x)$:

$$f''(x) = \frac{(x-2)^2[2x^2 + 4x(x-3)] - 2x^2(x-3)(2)(x-2)}{(x-2)^4} = \frac{2x(x^2 - 6x + 12)}{(x-2)^3}$$

Partition numbers for $f''(x)$: $x = 0$, $x = 2$ ($x^2 - 6x + 12$ has no real roots)

Sign chart for f'':

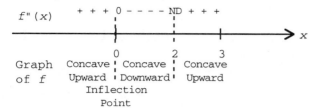

Test Numbers	
x	$f''(x)$
-1	$\frac{38}{9}$ (+)
1	-14 (−)
3	18 (+)

Thus, the graph of f is concave upward on $(-\infty, 0)$ and $(2, \infty)$, concave downward on $(0, 2)$, and has an inflection point at $x = 0$.

Step 4. Sketch the graph of f:

x	$f(x)$
0	0
3	27

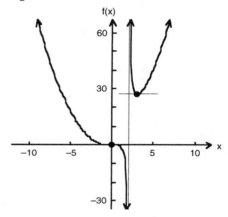

45. $f(x) = \dfrac{1}{x^2 + 2x - 8} = \dfrac{1}{(x+4)(x-2)}$

Step 1. Analyze $f(x)$:

(A) Domain: All real numbers except $x = -4$, $x = 2$.

(B) Intercepts: y-intercept: $f(0) = -\dfrac{1}{8}$

      x-intercepts: no x-intercept

(C) Asymptotes:

  Horizontal asymptote: $\dfrac{1}{x^2}$; $y = 0$ (the x-axis) is a horizontal asymptote

  Vertical asymptote: $x = -4$, $x = 2$

Step 2. Analyze $f'(x)$:

$$f'(x) = \frac{-(2x+2)}{(x^2 + 2x - 8)^2} = \frac{-2(x+1)}{(x^2 + 2x - 8)^2}$$

Critical values: $x = -1$

Partition numbers: $x = -4$, $x = -1$, $x = 2$

Sign chart for f':

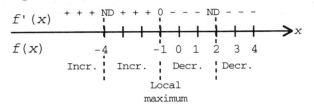

Test Numbers	
x	$f'(x)$
-5	$(+)$
-2	$(+)$
0	$-\frac{1}{32}$ $(-)$
3	$(-)$

Thus, f is increasing on $(-\infty, -4)$ and $(-4, -1)$, decreasing on $(-1, 2)$ and $(2, \infty)$, and has a local maximum at $x = -1$.

Step 3. Analyze $f''(x)$:

$$f''(x) = \frac{(x^2 + 2x - 8)^2(-2) + (2x + 2)(2)(x^2 + 2x - 8)(2x + 2)}{(x^2 + 2x - 8)^4} = \frac{6(x^2 + 2x + 4)}{(x^2 + 2x - 8)^3}$$

Partition numbers for $f''(x)$: $x = -4$, $x = 2$ ($x^2 + 2x + 4$ has no real roots)

Sign chart for f'':

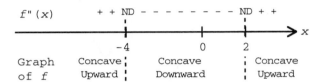

Test Numbers	
x	$f''(x)$
-5	$(+)$
0	$(-)$
3	$(+)$

Thus, the graph of f is concave upward on $(-\infty, -4)$ and $(2, \infty)$, and concave downward on $(-4, 2)$.

Step 4. Sketch the graph of f:

x	$f(x)$
-1	$-\frac{1}{9}$
0	$-\frac{1}{8}$

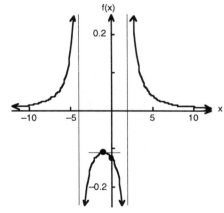

47. $f(x) = \dfrac{x}{x^2 - 4}$

Step 1. Analyze $f(x)$:

(A) Domain: All real numbers except $x = -2$, $x = 2$.

(B) Intercepts: y-intercept: $f(0) = 0$

x-intercepts: $\dfrac{x}{x^2 - 4} = 0$, $x = 0$

(C) Asymptotes:

Horizontal asymptotes: $\dfrac{x}{x^2} = \dfrac{1}{x}$; $y = 0$ (the x-axis) is a horizontal asymptote

Vertical asymptotes: $x = -2$, $x = 2$

$$f'(x) = \frac{(x^2 - 4)(1) - x(2x)}{(x^2 - 4)^2} = \frac{-x^2 - 4}{(x^2 - 4)^2} = -\frac{(x^2 + 4)}{(x^2 - 4)^2}$$

Critical values: No critical values
Partition numbers: $x = -2$, $x = 2$
Sign chart for f':

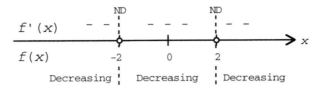

Thus, f is decreasing on $(-\infty, -2)$, $(-2, 2)$ and $(2, \infty)$.

Step 3. Analyze $f''(x)$:

$$f''(x) = \frac{(x^2 - 4)^2(-2x) + (x^2 + 4)2(x^2 - 4)2x}{(x^2 - 4)^4} = \frac{2x^3 + 16x}{(x^2 - 4)^3} = \frac{2x(x^2 + 8)}{(x^2 - 4)^3}$$

Partition numbers for $f''(x)$: $x = -2$, $x = 0$, $x = 2$
Sign chart for f'':

Test Numbers	
x	$f''(x)$
-3	$(-)$
-1	$(+)$
1	$(-)$
3	$(+)$

Thus, the graph of f is concave upward on $(-2, 0)$ and $(2, \infty)$, concave downward on $(-\infty, -2)$ and $(0, 2)$, and has an inflection point at $x = 0$.

Step 4. Sketch the graph of f:

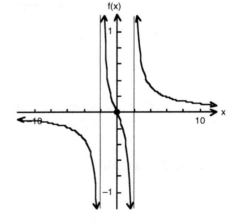

49. $f(x) = \dfrac{x^3}{(x - 4)^2}$

Step 1. Analyze $f(x)$:
(A) Domain: All real numbers except $x = 4$.
(B) Intercepts: y-intercept: $f(0) = 0$

$$x\text{-intercepts: } \frac{x^3}{(x - 4)^2} = 0, \; x = 0$$

(C) Asymptotes:

Horizontal asymptote: $\dfrac{x^3}{x^2} = x$; no horizontal asymptote

Vertical asymptote: $x = 4$

Step 2. Analyze $f'(x)$:

$$f'(x) = \frac{(x-4)^2(3x^2) - x^3(2)(x-4)}{(x-4)^4} = \frac{x^2(x-12)}{(x-4)^3}$$

Critical values: $x = 0$, $x = 12$
Partition numbers: $x = 0$, $x = 4$, $x = 12$
Sign chart for f':

Test Numbers	
x	$f'(x)$
-1	$(+)$
1	$(+)$
5	$(-)$
13	$(+)$

Thus, f is increasing on $(-\infty, 0)$, $(0, 4)$, and $(12, \infty)$, decreasing on $(4, 12)$, and has a local minimum at $x = 12$.

Step 3. Analyze $f''(x)$:

$$f''(x) = \frac{(x-4)^3(3x^2-24x) - x^2(x-12)(3)(x-4)^2}{(x-4)^6} = \frac{96x}{(x-4)^4}$$

Partition numbers for $f''(x)$: $x = 0$, $x = 4$
Sign chart for f'':

$f''(x)$	$-$ $-$ 0 $+$ $+$ $+$ $+$ ND $+$ $+$		
	-1 $\quad 0 \quad 1$ $\qquad 4 \quad 5$		
Graph of f	Concave Downward	Concave Upward	Concave Upward
	Inflection point		

Test Numbers	
x	$f''(x)$
-1	$(-)$
1	$(+)$
5	$(+)$

Thus, the graph of f is concave upward on $(0, 4)$ and $(4, \infty)$, concave downward on $(-\infty, 0)$, and has an inflection point at $x = 0$.

Step 4. Sketch the graph of f:

x	$f(x)$
0	0
12	27

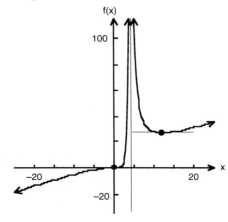

51. $f(x) = \dfrac{x^3}{3 - x^2}$

Step 1. Analyze $f(x)$:

(A) Domain: All real numbers except $x = -\sqrt{3}$, $x = \sqrt{3}$.

(B) Intercepts: y-intercept: $f(0) = 0$

$$x\text{-intercepts: } \frac{x^3}{3 - x^2} = 0, \; x = 0$$

(C) Asymptotes:

Horizontal asymptote: $\dfrac{x^3}{-x^2} = -x$; no horizontal asymptote

Vertical asymptote: $x = -\sqrt{3}$, $x = \sqrt{3}$

Step 2. Analyze $f'(x)$:

$$f'(x) = \frac{(3 - x^2)(3x^2) - x^3(-2x)}{(3 - x^2)^2} = \frac{x^2(9 - x^2)}{(3 - x^2)^2}$$

Critical values: $x = -3$, $x = 0$, $x = 3$

Partition numbers: $x = -3$, $x = -\sqrt{3}$, $x = 0$, $x = \sqrt{3}$, $x = 3$

Sign chart for f':

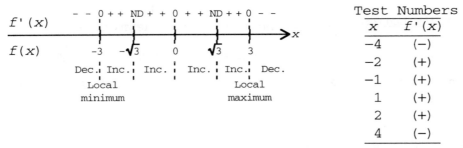

Test Numbers	
x	$f'(x)$
-4	$(-)$
-2	$(+)$
-1	$(+)$
1	$(+)$
2	$(+)$
4	$(-)$

Thus, f is increasing on $(-3, -\sqrt{3})$, $(-\sqrt{3}, \sqrt{3})$, $(\sqrt{3}, 3)$, decreasing on $(-\infty, -3)$ and $(3, \infty)$, and has a local minimum at $x = -3$ and a local maximum at $x = 3$.

Step 3. Analyze $f''(x)$:

$$f''(x) = \frac{(3 - x^2)^2(18x - 4x^3) - x^2(9 - x^2)2(3 - x^2)(-2x)}{(3 - x^2)^4} = \frac{6x(9 + x^2)}{(3 - x^2)^3}$$

Partition numbers for $f''(x)$: $x = -\sqrt{3}$, $x = 0$, $x = \sqrt{3}$

Sign chart for f'':

$f''(x) \quad + + \text{ND} - - - 0 + + + \text{ND} - - \longrightarrow x$

$\qquad\qquad -\sqrt{3} \qquad 0 \qquad \sqrt{3}$

Graph of f: Concave Upward | Concave Downward | Concave Upward | Concave Downward

Inflection point

Test Numbers	
x	$f''(x)$
-2	$(+)$
-1	$(-)$
1	$(+)$
2	$(-)$

Thus, the graph of f is concave upward on $(-\infty, -\sqrt{3})$ and $(0, \sqrt{3})$, concave downward on $(-\sqrt{3}, 0)$ and $(\sqrt{3}, \infty)$, and has an inflection point at $x = 0$.

Step 4. Sketch the graph of f:

x	$f(x)$
-3	$\frac{9}{2}$
0	0
3	$-\frac{9}{2}$

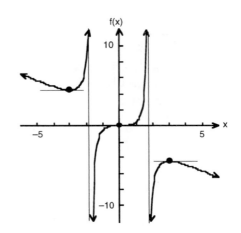

53. $f(x) = x + \dfrac{4}{x} = \dfrac{x^2 + 4}{x}$

Step 1. Analyze $f(x)$:

(A) Domain: All real numbers except $x = 0$.

(B) Intercepts: y-intercept: no y-intercept

x-intercepts: no x-intercepts

(C) Asymptotes:

Horizontal asymptote: $\dfrac{x^2}{x} = x$; no horizontal asymptote

Vertical asymptote: $x = 0$ (the y-axis) is a vertical asymptote

Oblique asymptote: $\lim\limits_{x \to \infty} \left(x + \dfrac{4}{x} \right) = x$; $y = x$ is an oblique asymptote.

Step 2. Analyze $f'(x)$:

$f'(x) = 1 - \dfrac{4}{x^2} = \dfrac{x^2 - 4}{x^2}$

Critical values: $x = -2$, $x = 2$

Partition numbers: $x = -2$, $x = 0$, $x = 2$

Sign chart for f':

```
f'(x)    + + + 0 - - ND - - 0 + +
      ─┼──┼──┼──┼──┼──┼──┼──→ x
f(x)     -3  -2    0    2  3

         Incr. Decr.  Decr.  Incr.
          Local          Local
         maximum        minimum
```

Test Numbers	
x	$f'(x)$
-3	$\frac{5}{9}$ (+)
-1	-3 (−)
1	-3 (−)
3	$\frac{5}{9}$ (+)

Thus, f is increasing on $(-\infty, -2)$ and $(2, \infty)$, decreasing on $(-2, 0)$ and $(0, 2)$, and has a local maximum at $x = -2$ and a local minimum at $x = 2$.

Step 3. Analyze $f''(x)$:

$f''(x) = \dfrac{8}{x^3}$

Partition numbers for $f''(x)$: $x = 0$

Sign chart for f'':

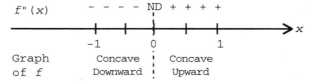

$f''(x)$ — — — — ND + + + +

-1   0   1

Graph   Concave   Concave
of f Downward   Upward

Thus, the graph of f is concave upward on $(0, \infty)$ and concave downward on $(-\infty, 0)$.

Step 4. Sketch the graph of f:

x	$f(x)$
-2	-4
2	4

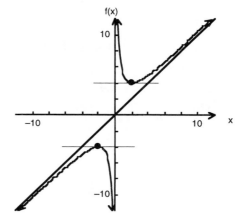

55. $f(x) = x - \dfrac{4}{x^2} = \dfrac{x^3 - 4}{x^2}$

Step 1. Analyze $f(x)$:

(A) Domain: All real numbers except $x = 0$.

(B) Intercepts: y-intercept: no y-intercept

x-intercepts: $\dfrac{x^3 - 4}{x} = 0$, $x = \sqrt[3]{4}$

(C) Asymptotes:

Horizontal asymptote: $\dfrac{x^3}{x^2} = x$; no horizontal asymptote

Vertical asymptote: $x = 0$ (the y-axis) is a vertical asymptote

Oblique asymptote: $\displaystyle\lim_{x \to \infty}\left(x - \dfrac{4}{x^2}\right) = x$; $y = x$ is an oblique asymptote

Step 2. Analyze $f'(x)$:

$f'(x) = 1 + \dfrac{8}{x^3} = \dfrac{x^3 + 8}{x^3}$

Critical values: $x = -2$
Partition numbers: $x = -2$, $x = 0$
Sign chart for f':

$f'(x)$ + + + 0 — — — ND + + +

$f(x)$ -2 0

Increasing ┊ Decr. ┊ Increasing
     Local
     maximum

Test Numbers	
x	$f'(x)$
-3	$\frac{19}{27}$ (+)
-1	-7 (−)
1	9 (+)

Thus, f is increasing on $(-\infty, -2)$ and $(0, \infty)$, decreasing on $(-2, 0)$; f has a local maximum at $x = -2$.

Step 3. Analyze $f''(x)$:

$f''(x) = -\dfrac{24}{x^4}$

Partition numbers for $f''(x)$: $x = 0$

Sign chart for f'':

Thus, the graph of f is concave downward on $(-\infty, 0)$ and $(0, \infty)$.

Step 4. Sketch the graph of f:

x	$f(x)$
-2	-3

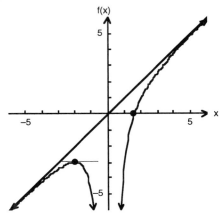

57. $f(x) = x - \dfrac{9}{x^3} = \dfrac{x^4 - 9}{x^3} = \dfrac{(x^2 - 3)(x^2 + 3)}{x^3}$

Step 1. Analyze $f(x)$:

(A) Domain: All real numbers except $x = 0$.

(B) Intercepts: y-intercept: no y-intercept
  x-intercepts: $x = -\sqrt{3}$, $x = \sqrt{3}$

(C) Asymptotes:

  <u>Horizontal asymptote</u>: $\dfrac{x^4}{x^3} = x$; no horizontal asymptote

  <u>Vertical asymptote</u>: $x = 0$ (the y-axis) is a vertical asymptote

  <u>Oblique asymptote</u>: $\lim\limits_{x \to \infty}\left(x + \dfrac{9}{x^3}\right) = x$; $y = x$ is an oblique asymptote

Step 2. Analyze $f'(x)$:

$f'(x) = 1 + \dfrac{27}{x^4} = \dfrac{x^4 + 27}{x^4}$

Critical values: none
Partition numbers: $x = 0$

Sign chart for f':

Thus, f is increasing on $(-\infty, 0)$ and $(0, \infty)$.

Step 3. Analyze $f''(x)$:

$$f''(x) = -\frac{108}{x^5}$$

Partition numbers for $f''(x)$: $x = 0$

Sign chart for f'':

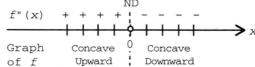

Thus, the graph of f is concave upward on $(-\infty, 0)$ and concave downward on $(0, \infty)$.

Step 4. Sketch the graph of f:

x	$f(x)$
$-\sqrt{3}$	0
$\sqrt{3}$	0

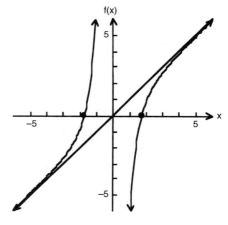

59. $f(x) = x + \dfrac{1}{x} + \dfrac{4}{x^3} = \dfrac{x^4 + x^2 + 4}{x^3}$

Step 1. Analyze $f(x)$:

(A) Domain: All real numbers except $x = 0$.

(B) Intercepts: y-intercept: no y-intercept
x-intercepts: no x-intercepts

(C) Asymptotes:

Horizontal asymptote: $\dfrac{x^4}{x^3} = x$; no horizontal asymptote

Vertical asymptote: $x = 0$ (the y-axis) is a vertical asymptote

Oblique asymptote: $\lim\limits_{x \to \infty}\left(x + \dfrac{1}{x} + \dfrac{4}{x^3}\right) = x$; $y = x$ is an oblique asymptote

Step 2. Analyze $f'(x)$:

$$f'(x) = 1 - \frac{1}{x^2} - \frac{12}{x^4} = \frac{x^4 - x^2 - 12}{x^4} = \frac{(x^2 - 4)(x^2 + 3)}{x^4}$$

Critical values: $x = -2$, $x = 2$

Partition numbers: $x = -2$, $x = 0$, $x = 2$

Sign chart for f':

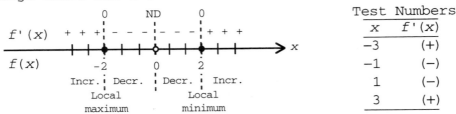

Test Numbers	
x	$f'(x)$
-3	$(+)$
-1	$(-)$
1	$(-)$
3	$(+)$

Thus, f is increasing on $(-\infty, -2)$ and $(2, \infty)$, decreasing on $(-2, 0)$ and $(0, 2)$; f has a local maximum at $x = -2$ and a local minimum at $x = 2$.

<u>Step 3. Analyze $f''(x)$</u>:

$$f''(x) = \frac{2}{x^3} + \frac{48}{x^5} = \frac{2x^2 + 48}{x^5}$$

Partition numbers for $f''(x)$: $x = 0$

Sign chart for f'':

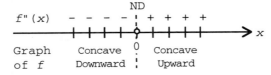

Thus, the graph of f is concave upward on $(0, \infty)$ and concave downward on $(-\infty, 0)$.

<u>Step 4. Sketch the graph of f</u>:

x	$f(x)$
-2	-3
2	3

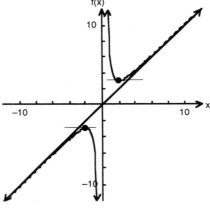

61. $f(x) = \dfrac{x^2 + x - 6}{x^2 - 6x + 8} = \dfrac{(x + 3)(x - 2)}{(x - 4)(x - 2)} = \dfrac{x + 3}{x - 4}, \quad x \neq 2$

<u>Step 1. Analyze $f(x)$</u>:

(A) Domain: All real numbers except $x = 2$, $x = 4$.

(B) Intercepts: y-intercept: $f(0) = -\dfrac{3}{4}$

x-intercepts: $x = -3$

(C) Asymptotes:

<u>Horizontal asymptote</u>: $\dfrac{x^2}{x^2} = 1$, $y = 1$ is a horizontal asymptote

<u>Vertical asymptote</u>: $x = 4$ is a vertical asymptote

Step 2. Analyze $f'(x)$:

$$f'(x) = \frac{x - 4 - (x + 3)}{(x - 4)^2} = -\frac{7}{(x - 4)^2}$$

Critical values: None

Partition numbers: $x = 4$

Sign chart for f':

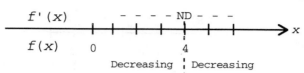

Thus, f is decreasing on $(-\infty, 4)$ and $(4, \infty)$.

Step 3. Analyze $f''(x)$:

$$f''(x) = \frac{14}{(x - 4)^3}$$

Partition numbers for $f''(x)$: $x = 4$

Sign chart for f'':

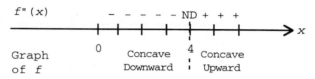

The graph of f is concave upward on $(4, \infty)$ and concave downward on $(-\infty, 4)$.

Step 4. Sketch the graph of f:

x	$f(x)$
-3	0
0	$-\frac{3}{4}$

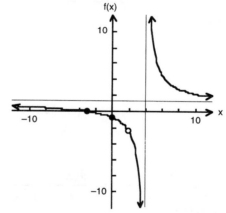

63. $f(x) = \dfrac{2x^2 + x - 15}{x^2 - 9} = \dfrac{(2x - 5)(x + 3)}{(x - 3)(x + 3)} = \dfrac{2x - 5}{x - 3}$, $x \neq -3$

Step 1. Analyze $f(x)$:

(A) Domain: All real numbers except $x = -3$, $x = 3$.

(B) Intercepts: y-intercept: $f(0) = \dfrac{5}{3}$

x-intercepts: $x = \dfrac{5}{2}$

(C) Asymptotes:

Horizontal asymptote: $\dfrac{2x^2}{x^2} = 2$, $y = 2$ is a horizontal asymptote

Vertical asymptote: $x = 3$ is a vertical asymptote

Step 2. Analyze $f'(x)$:

$$f'(x) = \frac{(x - 3)2 - (2x - 5)}{(x - 3)^2} = \frac{-1}{(x - 3)^2}$$

Critical values: None

Partition numbers: $x = 3$

Sign chart for f':

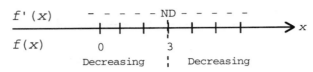

Thus, f is decreasing on $(-\infty, 3)$ and $(3, \infty)$.

Step 3. Analyze $f''(x)$:

$$f''(x) = \frac{2}{(x - 3)^3}$$

Partition numbers for $f''(x)$: $x = 3$

Sign chart for f'':

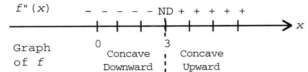

The graph of f is concave upward on $(3, \infty)$ and concave downward on $(-\infty, 3)$.

Step 4. Sketch the graph of f:

x	$f(x)$
$\frac{5}{2}$	0
0	$\frac{5}{3}$

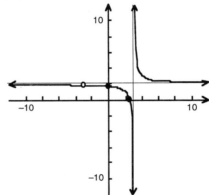

65. $f(x) = \dfrac{x^3 - 5x^2 + 6x}{x^2 - x - 2} = \dfrac{x(x - 3)(x - 2)}{(x - 2)(x + 1)} = \dfrac{x(x - 3)}{x + 1}, \quad x \neq 2$

Step 1. Analyze $f(x)$:

(A) Domain: All real numbers except $x = -1$, $x = 2$.

(B) Intercepts: y-intercept: $f(0) = 0$

x-intercepts: $x = 0$, $x = 3$

(C) Asymptotes:

Horizontal asymptote: $\dfrac{x^3}{x^2} = x$; no horizontal asymptote

Vertical asymptote: $x = -1$ is a vertical asymptote

Step 2. Analyze $f'(x)$:

$$f'(x) = \frac{(x + 1)(2x - 3) - (x^2 - 3x)}{(x + 1)^2} = \frac{x^2 + 2x - 3}{(x + 1)^2} = \frac{(x + 3)(x - 1)}{(x + 1)^2}$$

Critical values: $x = -3$, $x = 1$

Partition numbers: $x = -3$, $x = -1$, $x = 1$

Sign chart for f':

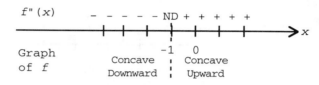

	Test Numbers	
	x	$f'(x)$
	-4	$\frac{5}{9}$ (+)
	-2	-3 (−)
	0	-3 (−)
	2	$\frac{5}{9}$ (+)

Thus, f is increasing on $(-\infty, -3)$ and $(1, \infty)$, f is decreasing on $(-3, -1)$ and $(-1, 1)$; f has a local maximum at $x = -3$ and a local minimum at $x = 1$.

Step 3. Analyze $f''(x)$:

$$f''(x) = \frac{(x + 1)^2(2x + 2) - (x^2 + 2x - 3)(2)(x + 1)}{(x + 1)^4} = \frac{8}{(x + 1)^3}$$

Partition numbers for $f''(x)$: $x = -1$

Sign chart for f'':

The graph of f is concave upward on $(-1, \infty)$ and concave downward on $(-\infty, -1)$.

Step 4. Sketch the graph of f:

x	$f(x)$
-3	-9
0	0
1	-1
3	0

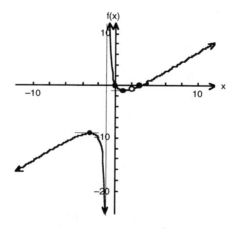

67. $f(x) = \dfrac{x^2 + x - 2}{x^2 - 2x + 1} = \dfrac{(x + 2)(x - 1)}{(x - 1)^2} = \dfrac{x + 2}{x - 1}, \ x \neq 1$

Step 1. Analyze $f(x)$:

(A) Domain: All real numbers except $x = 1$.

(B) Intercepts: y-intercept: $f(0) = -2$
   x-intercepts: $x = -2$

(C) Asymptotes:

   Horizontal asymptote: $\dfrac{x^2}{x^2} = 1$; $y = 1$ is a horizontal asymptote

   Vertical asymptote: $x = 1$ is a vertical asymptote

Step 2. Analyze $f'(x)$:

$$f'(x) = \frac{(x - 1) - (x + 2)}{(x - 1)^2} = \frac{-3}{(x - 1)^2}$$

Critical values: None

Partition numbers: $x = 1$

Sign chart for f':

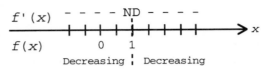

Thus, f is decreasing on $(-\infty, 1)$ and $(1, \infty)$.

Step 3. Analyze $f''(x)$:

$$f''(x) = \frac{6}{(x - 1)^3}$$

Partition numbers for $f''(x)$: $x = 1$

Sign chart for f'':

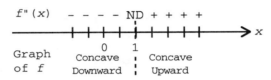

The graph of f is concave upward on $(1, \infty)$ and concave downward on $(-\infty, 1)$.

Step 4. Sketch the graph of f:

x	$f(x)$
-2	0
0	-2

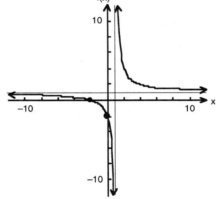

71. $P(x) = \dfrac{2x}{1 - x}$, $0 \le x < 1$

(A) $P'(x) = \dfrac{(1 - x)(2) - 2x(-1)}{(1 - x)^2} = \dfrac{2}{(1 - x)^2}$

$P'(x) > 0$ for $0 \le x < 1$. Thus, P is increasing on $(0, 1)$.

(B) From (A), $P'(x) = 2(1 - x)^{-2}$. Thus,

$P''(x) = -4(1 - x)^{-3}(-1) = \dfrac{4}{(1 - x)^3}$.

$P''(x) > 0$ for $0 \le x < 1$, and the graph of P is concave upward on $(0, 1)$.

(C) Since the domain of P is $[0, 1)$, there are no horizontal asymptotes. The denominator is 0 at $x = 1$ and the numerator is nonzero there. Thus, $x = 1$ is a vertical asymptote.

(D) $P(0) = \dfrac{2 \cdot 0}{1 - 0} = 0$.

Thus, the origin is both an x and a y intercept of the graph.

(E) The graph of P is:

x	$P(x)$
0	0
$\frac{1}{2}$	2
$\frac{3}{4}$	6

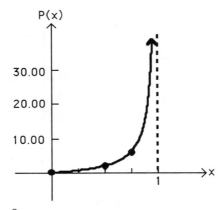

73. $C(n) = 3200 + 250n + 50n^2$, $0 < n < \infty$

(A) Average cost per year:
$$\overline{C}(n) = \frac{C(n)}{n} = \frac{3200}{n} + 250 + 50n, \quad 0 < n < \infty$$

(B) Graph $\overline{C}(n)$:

<u>Step 1. Analyze $\overline{C}(n)$:</u>

Domain: $0 < n < \infty$

Intercepts: C intercept: None ($n > 0$)

n intercepts: $\frac{3200}{n} + 250 + 50n > 0$ on $(0, \infty)$;

there are no n intercepts.

Asymptotes: For large n, $C(n) = \frac{3200}{n} + 250 + 50n \approx 250 + 50n$.

Thus, $y = 250 + 50n$ is an oblique asymptote. As $n \to 0$, $\overline{C}(n) \to \infty$; thus, $n = 0$ is a vertical asymptote.

<u>Step 2. Analyze $\overline{C}'(n)$:</u>

$$\overline{C}'(n) = -\frac{3200}{n^2} + 50 = \frac{50n^2 - 3200}{n^2} = \frac{50(n^2 - 64)}{n^2}$$
$$= \frac{50(n - 8)(n + 8)}{n^2}, \quad 0 < n < \infty$$

Critical value: $n = 8$

Sign chart for $\overline{C}'$:

$\overline{C}'(n)$ $- - - - \ 0 \ + + + +$

0   8 $\to n$

$C(n)$ Decreasing ⋮ Increasing

Local
minimum

Test Numbers	
n	$\overline{C}(n)$
7	$(-)$
9	$(+)$

Thus, $\overline{C}$ is decreasing on $(0, 8)$ and increasing on $(8, \infty)$; $n = 8$ is a local minimum.

<u>Step 3: Analyze $C''(n)$:</u>

$$\overline{C}''(n) = \frac{6400}{n^3}, \quad 0 < n < \infty$$

$\overline{C}''(n) > 0$ on $(0, \infty)$. Thus, the graph of $\overline{C}$ is concave upward on $(0, \infty)$.

Step 4. Sketch the graph of $\overline{C}$:

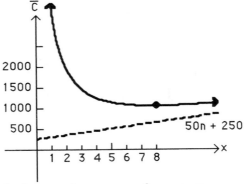

(C) The average cost per year is a minimum when $n = 8$ years.

75. $C(x) = 1000 + 5x + 0.1x^2$, $0 < x < \infty$.

(A) The average cost function is: $\overline{C}(x) = \dfrac{1000}{x} + 5 + 0.1x$.

Now, $\overline{C}'(x) = -\dfrac{1000}{x^2} + \dfrac{1}{10} = \dfrac{x^2 - 10,000}{10x^2} = \dfrac{(x + 100)(x - 100)}{10x^2}$

Sign chart for $\overline{C}'$:

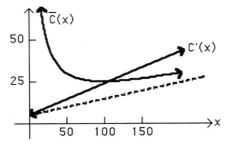

Test Numbers		
x		$\overline{C}'(x)$
1	$\approx$	$-1000 \; (-)$
101	$\approx$	$\dfrac{1}{500} \; (+)$

Thus, $\overline{C}$ is decreasing on $(0, 100)$ and increasing on $(100, \infty)$; $\overline{C}$ has a minimum at $x = 100$.

Since $\overline{C}''(x) = \dfrac{2000}{x^3} > 0$ for $0 < x < \infty$, the graph of $\overline{C}$ is concave upward on $(0, \infty)$. The line $x = 0$ is a vertical asymptote and the line $y = 5 + 0.1x$ is an oblique asymptote for the graph of $\overline{C}$.
The marginal cost function is $C'(x) = 5 + 0.2x$.
The graphs of $\overline{C}$ and C' are:

(B) The minimum average cost is:

$$\overline{C}(100) = \dfrac{1000}{100} + 5 + \dfrac{1}{10}(100) = 25$$

77. (A)

(B) The average cost function $\overline{y} = \dfrac{y(x)}{x}$ where

$y(x)$ is the regression equation found in part (A).

The minimum average cost is \$4.35 when 177 pizzas are produced.

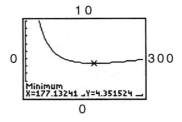

79. $C(t) = \dfrac{0.14t}{t^2 + 1}$

<u>Step 1. Analyze $C(t)$:</u>

Domain: $t \geq 0$, i.e., $[0, \infty)$

Intercepts: y intercept: $C(0) = 0$

$\qquad\qquad\quad$ t intercepts: $\dfrac{0.14t}{t^2 + 1} = 0$

$\qquad\qquad\qquad\qquad\qquad\qquad t = 0$

Asymptotes:

<u>Horizontal asymptote</u>: $\displaystyle\lim_{t\to\infty} \dfrac{0.14t}{t^2 + 1} = \lim_{t\to\infty} \dfrac{0.14t}{t^2\left(1 + \frac{1}{t^2}\right)} = \lim_{t\to\infty} \dfrac{0.14}{t\left(1 + \frac{1}{t^2}\right)} = 0$

Thus, $y = 0$ (the t axis) is a horizontal asymptote.

<u>Vertical asymptotes</u>: Since $t^2 + 1 > 0$ for all t, there are no vertical asymptotes.

<u>Step 2. Analyze $C'(t)$:</u>

$C'(t) = \dfrac{(t^2 + 1)(0.14) - 0.14t(2t)}{(t^2 + 1)^2} = \dfrac{0.14(1 - t^2)}{(t^2 + 1)^2} = \dfrac{0.14(1 - t)(1 + t)}{(t^2 + 1)^2}$

Critical values on $[0, \infty)$: $t = 1$

Sign chart for C':

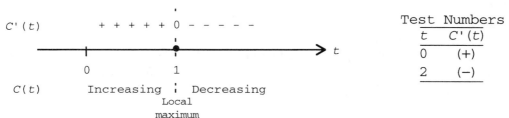

Test Numbers	
t	$C'(t)$
0	(+)
2	(−)

Thus, C is increasing on $(0, 1)$ and decreasing on $(1, \infty)$; C has a maximum value at $t = 1$.

$$C''(t) = \frac{(t^2 + 1)^2(-0.28t - 0.14(1 - t^2)(2)(t^2 + 1)(2t)}{(t^2 + 1)^4}$$

$$= \frac{(t^2 + 1)(-0.28t) - 0.56t(1 - t^2)}{(t^2 + 1)^3} = \frac{0.28t^3 - 0.84t}{(t^2 + 1)^3}$$

$$= \frac{0.28t(t^2 - 3)}{(t^2 + 1)^3} = \frac{0.28t(t - \sqrt{3})(t + \sqrt{3})}{(t^2 + 1)^3}, \quad 0 \le t < \infty$$

Partition numbers for C'' on $[0, \infty)$: $t = \sqrt{3}$

Sign chart for C'':

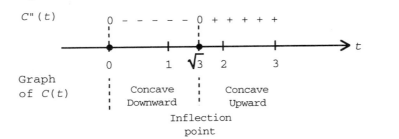

Test Numbers	
t	$C''(t)$
1	-0.07 $(-)$
2	≈ 0.005 $(+)$

Thus, the graph of C is concave downward on $(0, \sqrt{3})$ and concave upward on $(\sqrt{3}, \infty)$; the graph has an inflection point at $t = \sqrt{3}$.

Step 4. Sketch the graph of $C(t)$:

t	$C(t)$
0	0
1	0.07
$\sqrt{3}$	≈ 0.06

81. $N(t) = \dfrac{5t + 20}{t} = 5 + 20t^{-1}, \quad 1 \le t \le 30$

Step 1. Analyze $N(t)$:

Domain: $1 \le t \le 30$, or $[1, 30]$.

Intercepts: There are no t or N intercepts.

Asymptotes: Since N is defined only for $1 \le t \le 30$, there are no horizontal asymptotes. Also, since $t \ne 0$ on $[1, 30]$, there are no vertical asymptotes.

Step 2. Analyze $N'(t)$:

$N'(t) = -20t^{-2} = \dfrac{-20}{t^2}, \quad 1 \le t \le 30$

Since $N'(t) < 0$ for $1 \le t \le 30$, N is decreasing on $(1, 30)$; N has no local extrema.

Step 3. Analyze $N''(t)$:

$$N''(t) = \frac{40}{t^3}, \quad 1 \leq t \leq 30$$

Since $N''(t) > 0$ for $1 \leq t \leq 30$, the graph of N is concave upward on $(1, 30)$.

Step 4. Sketch the graph of N:

t	$N(t)$
1	25
5	9
10	7
30	5.67

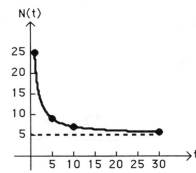

EXERCISE 4-4

Things to remember:

1. ABSOLUTE MAXIMA AND MINIMA

   If $f(c) \geq f(x)$ for all x in the domain of f, then $f(c)$ is called the ABSOLUTE MAXIMUM VALUE of f.

   If $f(c) \leq f(x)$ for all x in the domain of f, then $f(x)$ is called the ABSOLUTE MINIMUM VALUE of f.

2. A function f continuous on a closed interval $[a, b]$ has both an absolute maximum and an absolute minimum on that interval. Absolute extrema (if they exist) must always occur at critical values or at endpoints.

3. PROCEDURE FOR FINDING ABSOLUTE EXTREMA ON A CLOSED INTERVAL

   Step 1. Check to make certain that f is continuous over $[a, b]$.

   Step 2. Find the critical values in the interval (a, b).

   Step 3. Evaluate f at the endpoints a and b and at the critical values found in step 2.

   Step 4. The absolute maximum $f(x)$ on $[a, b]$ is the largest of the values found in step 3.

   Step 5. The absolute minimum $f(x)$ on $[a, b]$ is the smallest of the values found in step 3.

4. SECOND DERIVATIVE TEST

Let c be a critical value for $f(x)$.

$f'(c)$	$f''(c)$	GRAPH OF f IS:	$f(c)$	EXAMPLE
0	+	Concave upward	Local minimum	
0	−	Concave downward	Local maximum	
0	0	?	Test does not apply	

5. SECOND DERIVATIVE TEST FOR ABSOLUTE EXTREMUM

Let f be continuous on an interval I with only one critical value c on I:

If $f'(c) = 0$ and $f''(c) > 0$, then $f(c)$ is the absolute minimum of f on I.

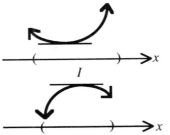

If $f'(c) = 0$ and $f''(c) < 0$, then $f(c)$ is the absolute maximum of f on I.

1. Interval $[0, 10]$; absolute minimum: $f(0) = 0$; absolute maximum: $f(10) = 14$

3. Interval $[0, 8]$; absolute minimum: $f(0) = 0$; absolute maximum: $f(3) = 9$

5. Interval $[1, 10]$; absolute minimum: $f(1) = f(7) = 5$; absolute maximum: $f(10) = 14$

7. Interval $[1, 9]$; absolute minimum: $f(1) = f(7) = 5$; absolute maximum: $f(4) = f(9) = 9$

9. Interval $[2, 5]$; absolute minimum: $f(5) = 7$; absolute maximum: $f(3) = 9$

11. $f(x) = x^2 - 2x + 3$, $I = (-\infty, \infty)$
$f'(x) = 2x - 2 = 2(x - 1)$
$f'(x) = 0$: $2(x - 1) = 0$
$\qquad\qquad x = 1$

$x = 1$ is the ONLY critical value on I, and $f(1) = 1^2 - 2(1) + 3 = 2$
$f''(x) = 2$ and $f''(1) = 2 > 0$. Therefore, $f(1) = 2$ is the absolute minimum. The function does not have an absolute maximum since $\lim\limits_{x \to \pm\infty} f(x) = \infty$.

13. $f(x) = -x^2 - 6x + 9$, $I = (-\infty, \infty)$
$f'(x) = -2x - 6 = -2(x + 3)$
$f'(x) = 0$: $-2(x + 3) = 0$
$\qquad\qquad x = -3$
$x = -3$ is the ONLY critical value on I, and
$f(-3) = -(-3)^2 - 6(-3) + 9 = 18$
$f''(x) = -2$ and $f''(-3) = -2 < 0$. Therefore, $f(-3) = 18$ is the absolute maximum. The function does not have an absolute minimum since $\lim\limits_{x \to \pm\infty} f(x) = -\infty$.

15. $f(x) = x^3 + x$, $I = (-\infty, \infty)$

$f'(x) = 3x^2 + 1 \geq 1$ on I; f is increasing on I and $\lim\limits_{x \to -\infty} f(x) = -\infty$,

$\lim\limits_{x \to \infty} f(x) = \infty$. Therefore, f does not have any absolute extrema.

17. $f(x) = 8x^3 - 2x^4$; domain: all real numbers

$f'(x) = 24x^2 - 8x^3 = 8x^2(3 - x)$

$f''(x) = 48x - 24x^2 = 24x(2 - x)$

Critical values: $x = 0$, $x = 3$

$f''(0) = 0$ (second derivative test fails)

$f''(3) = -72$ f has a local maximum at $x = 3$.

Sign chart for $f'(x) = 8x^2(3 - x)$
(0 and 3 are partition numbers)

From the sign chart, f does not
have a local extremum at $x = 0$;
f has a local maximum at $x = 3$
which must be an absolute maximum

```
              + + + 0 + + + + 0 - - -
f'(x)   ─────┼─┼─┼─┼─┼─┼─┼─┼─┼─┼─┼──→ x
f(x)          0         3
        Increasing  Increasing  Decreasing
                              Local
                              maximum
```

since f is increasing on $(-\infty, 3)$ and decreasing on $(3, \infty)$; $f(3) = 54$ is
the absolute maximum of f. f does not have an absolute minimum since
$\lim\limits_{x \to \infty} f(x) = \lim\limits_{x \to -\infty} f(x) = -\infty$.

19. $f(x) = x + \dfrac{16}{x}$; domain: all real numbers except $x = 0$.

$f'(x) = 1 - \dfrac{16}{x^2} = \dfrac{x^2 - 16}{x^2} = \dfrac{(x - 4)(x + 4)}{x^2}$

$f''(x) = \dfrac{32}{x^3}$

Critical values: $x = -4$, $x = 4$

$f''(-4) = -\dfrac{1}{2} < 0$; f has a local maximum at $x = -4$

$f''(4) = \dfrac{1}{2} > 0$; f has a local minimum at $x = 4$

$\lim\limits_{x \to \infty} f(x) = \lim\limits_{x \to \infty}\left(x + \dfrac{16}{x}\right) = \infty$; $\lim\limits_{x \to -\infty} f(x) = \lim\limits_{x \to -\infty}\left(x + \dfrac{16}{x}\right) = -\infty$;
f has no absolute extrema.

21. $f(x) = \dfrac{x^2}{x^2 + 1}$; domain: all real numbers

$f'(x) = \dfrac{(x^2 + 1)2x - x^2(2x)}{(x^2 + 1)^2} = \dfrac{2x}{(x^2 + 1)^2}$

$f''(x) = \dfrac{(x^2 + 1)^2(2) - 2x(2)(x^2 + 1)(2x)}{(x^2 + 1)^4} = \dfrac{2 - 6x^2}{(x^2 + 1)^3}$

Critical value: $x = 0$

Since f has only one critical value and $f''(0) = 2 > 0$, $f(0) = 0$ is the

absolute minimum of f. Since $\lim\limits_{x \to \infty} f(x) = \lim\limits_{x \to \infty} \dfrac{x^2}{x^2 + 1} = 1$, f has no

absolute maximum; $y = 1$ is a horizontal asymptote for the graph of f.

23. $f(x) = \dfrac{2x}{x^2 + 1}$; domain: all real numbers

$f'(x) = \dfrac{(x^2 + 1)2 - 2x(2x)}{(x^2 + 1)^2} = \dfrac{2 - 2x^2}{(x^2 + 1)^2} = \dfrac{2(1 - x^2)}{(x^2 + 1)^2}$

$f''(x) = \dfrac{(x^2 + 1)^2(-4x) - 2(1 - x^2)(2)(x^2 + 1)(2x)}{(x^2 + 1)^4} = \dfrac{4x(x^2 - 3)}{(x^2 + 1)^3}$

Critical values: $x = -1$, $x = 1$
$f''(-1) = 8 > 0$; f has a local minimum at $x = -1$
$f''(1) = -8 < 0$; f has a local maximum at $x = 1$

Sign chart for $f'(x)$
(partition numbers are -1 and 1)

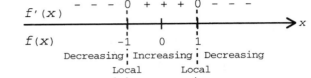

$\lim\limits_{x \to \pm\infty} f(x) = \lim\limits_{x \to \pm\infty} \dfrac{2x}{x^2 + 1} = 0$
(the x-axis is a horizontal asymptote)

We can now conclude that $f(1) = 1$ is the absolute maximum of f and $f(-1) = -1$ is the absolute minimum of f.

25. $f(x) = \dfrac{x^2 - 1}{x^2 + 1}$; domain: all real numbers

$f'(x) = \dfrac{(x^2 + 1)(2x) - (x^2 - 1)(2x)}{(x^2 + 1)^2} = \dfrac{4x}{(x^2 + 1)^2}$

$f''(x) = \dfrac{(x^2 + 1)^2(4) - 4x(2)(x^2 + 1)2x}{(x^2 + 1)^4} = \dfrac{4(3 - x^2)}{(x^2 + 1)^3}$

Critical value: $x = 0$
$f''(0) = 12 > 0$; f has a local minimum at $x = 0$

Sign chart for $f'(x) = \dfrac{4x}{(x^2 + 1)^2}$

(0 is the partition number)

$\lim\limits_{x \to \pm\infty} f(x) = \lim\limits_{x \to \pm\infty} \dfrac{x^2 - 1}{x^2 + 1} = 1$
($y = 1$ is a horizontal asymptote)

We can now conclude that $f(0) = -1$ is the absolute minimum and f does not have an absolute maximum.

27. $f(x) = 2x^2 - 8x + 6$ on $I = [0, \infty)$
$f'(x) = 4x - 8 = 4(x - 2)$
$f''(x) = 4$
Critical value: $x = 2$
$f''(2) = 4 > 0$; f has a local minimum at $x = 2$
Since $x = 2$ is the only critical value of f on I, $f(2) = -2$ is the absolute minimum of f on I.

29. $f(x) = 3x^2 - x^3$ on $I = [0, \infty)$

$f'(x) = 6x - 3x^2 = 3x(2 - x)$

$f''(x) = 6 - 6x$

Critical value (in $(0, \infty)$): $x = 2$

$f''(2) = -6 < 0$; f has a local maximum at $x = 2$

Since $f(0) = 0$ and $x = 2$ is the only critical value of f in $(0, \infty)$, $f(2) = 4$ is the absolute maximum value of f on I.

31. $f(x) = (x + 4)(x - 2)^2$ on $I = [0, \infty)$

$$
\begin{aligned}
f'(x) = (x + 4)(2)(x - 2) + (x - 2)^2 &= (x - 2)[2x + 8 + x - 2] \\
&= (x - 2)(3x + 6) \\
&= 3x^2 - 12
\end{aligned}
$$

$f''(x) = 6x$

Critical value in I: $x = 2$

$f''(2) = 12 > 0$; f has a local minimum at $x = 2$

Since $f(0) = 16$ and $x = 2$ is the only critical value of f in $(0, \infty)$, $f(2) = 0$ is the absolute minimum of f on I.

33. $f(x) = 2x^4 - 8x^3$ on $I = (0, \infty)$

Since $\lim\limits_{x \to \infty} f(x) = \lim\limits_{x \to \infty} (2x^4 - 8x^3) = \infty$, f does not have an absolute maximum on I.

35. $f(x) = 20 - 3x - \dfrac{12}{x}$, $x > 0$; $I = (0, \infty)$

$f'(x) = -3 + \dfrac{12}{x^2}$

$$
\begin{aligned}
f'(x) = 0: \quad -3 + \frac{12}{x^2} &= 0 \\
3x^2 &= 12 \\
x^2 &= 4 \\
x &= 2 \ (-2 \text{ is not in } I)
\end{aligned}
$$

$x = 2$ is the only critical value of f on I, and

$f(2) = 20 - 3(2) - \dfrac{12}{2} = 8$.

$f''(x) = -\dfrac{24}{x^2}$; $f''(2) = -\dfrac{24}{4} = -6 < 0$. Therefore, $f(2) = 8$ is the absolute maximum of f. The function does not have an absolute minimum since $\lim\limits_{x \to \infty} f(x) = -\infty$. (Also, $\lim\limits_{x \to 0^+} f(x) = -\infty$.)

37. $f(x) = 10 + 2x + \dfrac{64}{x^2}$, $x > 0$; $I = (0, \infty)$

$f'(x) = 2 - \dfrac{128}{x^3}$

$f'(x) = 0$: $2 - \dfrac{128}{x^3} = 0$

$\qquad\qquad 2x^3 = 128$

$\qquad\qquad\; x^3 = 64$

$\qquad\qquad\;\; x = 4$

$x = 4$ is the only critical value of f on I and

$f(4) = 10 + 2(4) + \dfrac{64}{4^2} = 22$

$f''(x) = \dfrac{384}{x^4}$; $f''(4) = \dfrac{384}{4^4} = \dfrac{3}{2} > 0$. Therefore, $f(4) = 22$ is the absolute minimum of f. The function does not have an absolute maximum since $\lim\limits_{x \to \infty} f(x) = \infty$. (Also, $\lim\limits_{x \to 0^+} f(x) = \infty$.)

39. $f(x) = x + \dfrac{1}{x} + \dfrac{30}{x^3}$ on $I = (0, \infty)$

$f'(x) = 1 - \dfrac{1}{x^2} - \dfrac{90}{x^4} = \dfrac{x^4 - x^2 - 90}{x^4} = \dfrac{(x^2 - 10)(x^2 + 9)}{x^4}$

$f''(x) = \dfrac{2}{x^3} + \dfrac{360}{x^5}$

Critical value (in $(0, \infty)$): $x = \sqrt{10}$

$f''(\sqrt{10}) = \dfrac{2}{(10)^{3/2}} + \dfrac{360}{(10)^{5/2}} > 0$; f has a local minimum at $x = \sqrt{10}$

Since $\sqrt{10}$ is the only critical value of f on I, $f(\sqrt{10}) = \dfrac{14}{\sqrt{10}}$ is the absolute minimum of f on I.

41. $f(x) = x^3 - 6x^2 + 9x - 6$

$f'(x) = 3x^2 - 12x + 9 = 3(x^2 - 4x + 3) = 3(x - 3)(x - 1)$

Critical values: $x = 1, 3$

(A) On the interval $[-1, 5]$: $f(-1) = -1 - 6 - 9 - 6 = -22$

$\qquad\qquad\qquad\qquad\qquad\; f(1) = 1 - 6 + 9 - 6 = -2$

$\qquad\qquad\qquad\qquad\qquad\; f(3) = 27 - 54 + 27 - 6 = -6$

$\qquad\qquad\qquad\qquad\qquad\; f(5) = 125 - 150 + 45 - 6 = 14$

Thus, the absolute maximum of f is $f(5) = 14$, and the absolute minimum of f is $f(-1) = -22$.

(B) On the interval $[-1, 3]$: $f(-1) = -22$

$\qquad\qquad\qquad\qquad\qquad\; f(1) = -2$

$\qquad\qquad\qquad\qquad\qquad\; f(3) = -6$

Absolute maximum of f: $f(1) = -2$

Absolute minimum of f: $f(-1) = -22$

(C) On the interval $[2, 5]$: $f(2) = 8 - 24 + 18 - 6 = -4$

$\qquad\qquad\qquad\qquad\qquad f(3) = -6$

$\qquad\qquad\qquad\qquad\qquad f(5) = 14$

Absolute maximum of f: $f(5) = 14$

Absolute minimum of f: $f(3) = -6$

43. $f(x) = (x - 1)(x - 5)^3 + 1$

$$f'(x) = (x - 1)3(x - 5)^2 + (x - 5)^3$$
$$= (x - 5)^2(3x - 3 + x - 5)$$
$$= (x - 5)^2(4x - 8)$$

Critical values: $x = 2, 5$

(A) Interval $[0, 3]$: $f(0) = (-1)(-5)^3 + 1 = 126$
$$f(2) = (2 - 1)(2 - 5)^3 + 1 = -26$$
$$f(3) = (3 - 1)(3 - 5)^3 + 1 = -15$$

Absolute maximum of f: $f(0) = 126$
Absolute minimum of f: $f(2) = -26$

(B) Interval $[1, 7]$: $f(1) = 1$
$$f(2) = -26$$
$$f(5) = 1$$
$$f(7) = (7 - 1)(7 - 5)^3 + 1 = 6 \cdot 8 + 1 = 49$$

Absolute maximum of f: $f(7) = 49$
Absolute minimum of f: $f(2) = -26$

(C) Interval $[3, 6]$: $f(3) = (3 - 1)(3 - 5)^3 + 1 = -15$
$$f(5) = 1$$
$$f(6) = (6 - 1)(6 - 5)^3 + 1 = 6$$

Absolute maximum of f: $f(6) = 6$
Absolute minimum of f: $f(3) = -15$

45. $f(x) = x^4 - 4x^3 + 5$

$f'(x) = 4x^3 - 12x^2 = 4x^2(x - 3)$
Critical values: $x = 0$, $x = 3$

(A) On the interval $[-1, 2]$: $f(-1) = 10$
$$f(0) = 5$$
$$f(2) = -11$$

Thus, the absolute maximum of f is $f(-1) = 10$; the absolute minimum of f is $f(2) = -11$.

(B) On the interval $[0, 4]$: $f(0) = 5$
$$f(3) = -22$$
$$f(4) = 5$$

Absolute maximum of f: $f(0) = f(4) = 5$
Absolute minimum of f: $f(3) = -22$

(C) On the interval $[-1, 1]$: $f(-1) = 10$
$$f(0) = 5$$
$$f(1) = 2$$

Absolute maximum of f: $f(-1) = 10$
Absolute minimum of f: $f(1) = 2$

47. f has a local minimum at $x = 2$.

49. Unable to determine from the given information ($f'(-3) = f''(-3) = 0$).

51. Neither a local maximum nor a local minimum at $x = 6$; $x = 6$ is not a critical value of f.

53. f has a local maximum at $x = 2$.

Things to remember:

STRATEGY FOR SOLVING OPTIMIZATION PROBLEMS

<u>Step 1</u>. Introduce variables, look for relationships among these variables, and construct a mathematical model of the form: Maximize (or minimize) $f(x)$ on the interval I

<u>Step 2</u>. Find the critical values of $f(x)$.

<u>Step 3</u>. Use the procedures developed in Section 4-4 to find the absolute maximum (or minimum) value of $f(x)$ on the interval I and the value(s) of x where this occurs.

<u>Step 4</u>. Use the solution to the mathematical model to answer all the questions asked in the problem.

1. Let one length = x and the other = $10 - x$.
Since neither length can be negative, we have $x \geq 0$ and $10 - x \geq 0$, or $x \leq 10$. We want the maximum value of the product $x(10 - x)$, where $0 \leq x \leq 10$.

Let $f(x) = x(10 - x) = 10x - x^2$; domain $I = [0, 10]$
$f'(x) = 10 - 2x$; $x = 5$ is the only critical value
$f''(x) = -2$
$f''(5) = -2 < 0$
Thus, $f(5) = 25$ is the absolute maximum; divide the line in half.

3. Let one number = x. Then the other number = $x + 30$.
$f(x) = x(x + 30) = x^2 + 30x$; domain $I = (-\infty, \infty)$
$f'(x) = 2x + 30$; $x = -15$ is the only critical value
$f''(x) = 2$
$f''(-15) = 2 > 0$
Thus, the absolute minimum of f occurs at $x = -15$. The numbers, then, are -15 and $-15 + 30 = 15$.

5. Let x = the length of the rectangle and y = the width of the rectangle.
Then, $2x + 2y = 100$
$\qquad x + y = 50$
$\qquad\quad y = 50 - x$

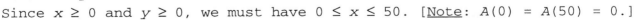

We want to find the maximum of the area:
$A(x) = x \cdot y = x(50 - x) = 50x - x^2$.
Since $x \geq 0$ and $y \geq 0$, we must have $0 \leq x \leq 50$. [<u>Note</u>: $A(0) = A(50) = 0.$]
$A'(x) = \dfrac{dA}{dx} = 50 - 2x$; $x = 25$ is the only critical value.
Now, $A'' = -2$ and $A''(25) = -2 < 0$. Thus, $A(25)$ is the absolute maximum.
The maximum area is $A(25) = 25(50 - 25) = 625$ cm^2, which means that the rectangle is actually a square with sides measuring 25 cm each.

7. Let the rectangle of fixed area A have dimensions x and y. Then $A = xy$ and $y = \dfrac{A}{x}$.

The cost of the fence is
$$C = 2Bx + 2By = 2Bx + \frac{2AB}{x}, \quad x > 0$$
Thus, we want to find the absolute minimum of
$$C(x) = 2Bx + \frac{2AB}{x}, \quad x > 0$$
Since $\lim\limits_{x \to 0} C(x) = \lim\limits_{x \to \infty} C(x) = \infty$, and $C(x) > 0$ for all $x > 0$, we can conclude that C has an absolute minimum on $(0, \infty)$. This agrees with our intuition that there should be a cheapest way to build the fence.

9. Let x and y be the dimensions of the rectangle and let C be the fixed amount which can be spent. Then
$$C = 2Bx + 2By \quad \text{and} \quad y = \frac{C - 2Bx}{2B}$$
The area enclosed by the fence is:
$$A = xy = x\left[\frac{C - 2Bx}{2B}\right]$$
Thus, we want to find the absolute maximum value of
$$A(x) = \frac{C}{2B}x - x^2, \quad 0 \le x \le \frac{C}{2B}$$
Since $A(x)$ is a continuous function on the closed interval $\left[0, \dfrac{C}{2B}\right]$, it has an absolute maximum value. This agrees with our intuition that there should be a largest rectangular area that can be enclosed with a fixed amount of fencing.

11. Price-demand: $p(x) = 500 - 0.5x$; cost: $C(x) = 20{,}000 + 135x$

   (A) Revenue: $R(x) = x \cdot p(x) = 500x - 0.5x^2$, $0 \le x < \infty$
      $R'(x) = 500 - x$
      $R'(x) = 500 - x = 0$ implies $x = 500$
      $R''(x) = -1$; $R''(500) = -1 < 0$
      R has an absolute maximum at $x = 500$.
      $p(500) = 500 - 0.5(500) = 250$; $R(500) = (500)^2 - 0.5(500)^2 = 125{,}000$
The company should produce 500 phones each week at a price of \$250 per phone to maximize their revenue. The maximum revenue is \$125,000

   (B) Profit: $P(x) = R(x) - C(x) = 500x - 0.5x^2 - (20{,}000 + 135x)$
$$= 365x - 0.5x^2 - 20{,}000$$
      $P'(x) = 365 - x$
      $P'(x) = 365 - x = 0$ implies $x = 365$
      $P''(x) = -1$; $P''(365) = -1 < 0$
      P has an absolute maximum at $x = 365$
      $p(365) = 500 - 0.5(365) = 317.50$;
      $P(365) = (365)^2 - 0.5(365)^2 - 20{,}000 = 46{,}612.50$
To maximize profit, the company should produce 365 phones each week at a price of \$317.50 per phone. The maximum profit is \$46,612.50.

13. **(A)** Revenue $R(x) = x \cdot p(x) = x\left(200 - \dfrac{x}{30}\right) = 200x - \dfrac{x^2}{30}$, $0 \leq x \leq 6{,}000$

$R'(x) = 200 - \dfrac{2x}{30} = 200 - \dfrac{x}{15}$

Now $R'(x) = 200 - \dfrac{x}{15} = 0$ implies $x = 3000$.

$R''(x) = -\dfrac{1}{15} < 0$.

Thus, $R''(3000) = -\dfrac{1}{15} < 0$ and we conclude that R has an absolute maximum at $x = 3000$. The maximum revenue is

$R(3000) = 200(3000) - \dfrac{(3000)^2}{30} = \$300{,}000$

(B) Profit $P(x) = R(x) - C(x) = 200x - \dfrac{x^2}{30} - (72{,}000 + 60x)$

$= 140x - \dfrac{x^2}{30} - 72{,}000$

$P'(x) = 140 - \dfrac{x}{15}$

Now $140 - \dfrac{x}{15} = 0$ implies $x = 2{,}100$.

$P''(x) = -\dfrac{1}{15}$ and $P''(2{,}100) = -\dfrac{1}{15} < 0$. Thus, the maximum profit occurs when 2,100 television sets are produced. The maximum profit is

$P(2{,}100) = 140(2{,}100) - \dfrac{(2{,}100)^2}{30} - 72{,}000 = \$75{,}000$

the price that the company should charge is

$p(2{,}100) = 200 - \dfrac{2{,}100}{30} = \$130$ for each set.

(C) If the government taxes the company \$5 for each set, then the profit $P(x)$ is given by

$P(x) = 200x - \dfrac{x^2}{30} - (72{,}000 + 60x) - 5x$

$= 135x - \dfrac{x^2}{30} - 72{,}000.$

$P'(x) = 135 - \dfrac{x}{15}.$

Now $135 - \dfrac{x}{15} = 0$ implies $x = 2{,}025$.

$P''(x) = -\dfrac{1}{15}$ and $P''(2{,}025) = -\dfrac{1}{15} < 0$. Thus, the maximum profit in this case occurs when 2,025 television sets are produced. The maximum profit is

$P(2{,}025) = 135(2{,}025) - \dfrac{(2{,}025)^2}{30} - 72{,}000 = \$64{,}687.50$

and the company should charge $p(2{,}025) = 200 - \dfrac{2{,}025}{30} = \$132.50/\text{set}$.

15. (A)
```
QuadReg
 y=ax²+bx+c
 a=-2.352941ᴇ-5
 b=-.0325964781
 c=288.9535407
```
(B)
```
LinReg
 y=ax+b
 a=53.50318471
 b=82245.22293
```

(C) The revenue at the demand level x is:
$$R(x) = xp(x)$$
where $p(x)$ is the quadratic regression equation in (A).

The cost at the demand level x is $C(x)$ given by the linear regression equation in (B). The profit $P(x) = R(x) - C(x)$.

The maximum profit is \$118,996 at the demand level $x = 1422$.

The price per saw at the demand level $x = 1422$ is \$195.

17. (A) Let x = number of 10¢ reductions in price. Then
$640 + 40x$ = number of sandwiches sold at x 10¢ reductions
$8 - 0.1x$ = price per sandwich $0 \leq x \leq 80$
Revenue: $R(x) = (640 + 40x)(8 - 0.1x)$
$$= 5120 + 256x - 4x^2, \ 0 \leq x \leq 80$$
$R'(x) = 256 - 8x$
$R'(x) = 256 - 8x = 0$ implies $x = 32$
$R(0) = 5120$, $R(32) = 9216$, $R(80) = 0$

Thus, the deli should charge $8 - 3.20 = \$4.80$ per sandwich to realize a maximum revenue of \$9216.

(B) Let x = number of 20¢ reductions in price. Then
$640 + 15x$ = number of sandwiches sold
$8 - 0.2x$ = price per sandwich $0 \leq x \leq 40$
Revenue: $R(x) = (640 + 15x)(8 - 0.2x)$
$$= 5120 - 8x - 3x^2, \ 0 \leq x \leq 40$$
$R'(x) = -8 - 6x$
$R'(x) = -8 - 6x = 0$ has no solutions in $(0, 40)$
Now, $R(0) = 640 \cdot 8 = \$5120$
$R(40) = 0$

Thus, the deli should charge \$8 per sandwich to maximize their revenue under these conditions.

19. Let x = number of dollar increases in the rate per day. Then
$200 - 5x$ = total number of cars rented and $30 + x$ = rate per day.
Total income = (total number of cars rented)(rate)
$$y(x) = (200 - 5x)(30 + x), \ 0 \leq x \leq 40$$
$$y'(x) = (200 - 5x)(1) + (30 + x)(-5)$$
$$= 200 - 5x - 150 - 5x$$
$$= 50 - 10x$$
$$= 10(5 - x)$$
Thus, $x = 5$ is the only critical value and
$y(5) = (200 - 25)(30 + 5) = 6125$.
$y''(x) = -10$
$y''(5) = -10 < 0$
Therefore, the absolute maximum income is $y(5) = \$6125$ when the rate is \$35 per day.

21. Let x = number of additional trees planted per acre. Then $30 + x$ = total number of trees per acre and $50 - x$ = yield per tree.
Yield per acre = (total number of trees per acre)(yield per tree)
$$y(x) = (30 + x)(50 - x), \quad 0 \le x \le 20$$
$$y'(x) = (30 + x)(-1) + (50 - x)$$
$$= 20 - 2x$$
$$= 2(10 - x)$$
The only critical value is $x = 10$, $y(10) = 40(40) = 1600$ pounds per acre.
$y''(x) = -2$
$y''(10) = -2 < 0$
Therefore, the absolute maximum yield is $y(10) = 1600$ pounds per acre when the number of trees per acre is 40.

23. Volume = $V(x) = (12 - 2x)(8 - 2x)x, \quad 0 \le x \le 4$
$$= 96x - 40x^2 + 4x^3$$
$$V'(x) = 96 - 80x + 12x^2$$
$$= 4(24 - 20x + 3x^2)$$

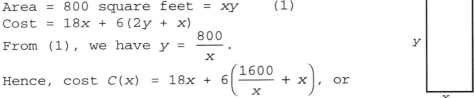

We solve $24 - 20x + 3x^2 = 0$ by using the quadratic formula:
$$x = \frac{20 \pm \sqrt{400 - 4 \cdot 24 \cdot 3}}{6} = \frac{10 \pm 2\sqrt{7}}{3}$$

Thus, $x = \dfrac{10 - 2\sqrt{7}}{3} \approx 1.57$ is the only critical value on the interval $[0, 4]$.
$V''(x) = -80 + 24x$
$V''(1.57) = -80 + 24(1.57) < 0$
Therefore, a square with a side of length $x = 1.57$ inches should be cut from each corner to obtain the maximum volume.

25. Area = 800 square feet = xy (1)
Cost = $18x + 6(2y + x)$
From (1), we have $y = \dfrac{800}{x}$.

Hence, cost $C(x) = 18x + 6\left(\dfrac{1600}{x} + x\right)$, or

$$C(x) = 24x + \frac{9600}{x}, \quad x > 0,$$

$$C'(x) = 24 - \frac{9600}{x^2} = \frac{24(x^2 - 400)}{x^2} = \frac{24(x - 20)(x + 20)}{x^2}.$$

Therefore, $x = 20$ is the only critical value.

$$C''(x) = \frac{19,200}{x^3}$$

$$C''(20) = \frac{19,200}{8000} > 0. \quad \text{Therefore, } x = 20 \text{ for the}$$

minimum cost.
The dimensions of the fence are shown in the diagram at the right.

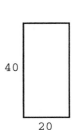

27. Let x = number of cans of paint produced in each production run. Then, number of production runs: $\dfrac{16,000}{x}$, $1 \le x \le 16,000$

Cost: $C(x)$ = cost of storage + cost of set up

$$= \dfrac{x}{2}(4) + \dfrac{16,000}{x}(500)$$

[Note: $\dfrac{x}{2}$ is the average number of cans of paint in storage per day.]

Thus,

$$C(x) = 2x + \dfrac{8,000,000}{x}, \quad 1 \le x \le 16,000$$

$$C'(x) = 2 - \dfrac{8,000,000}{x^2} = \dfrac{2x^2 - 8,000,000}{x^2} = \dfrac{2(x^2 - 4,000,000)}{x^2}$$

Critical value: $x = 2000$

$$C''(x) = \dfrac{16,000,000}{x^3}; \quad C''(2000) > 0$$

Thus, the minimum cost occurs when $x = 2000$ and the number of production runs is $\dfrac{16,000}{2,000} = 8$.

29. Let x = number of books produced each printing. Then, the number of printings = $\dfrac{50,000}{x}$.

Cost = $C(x)$ = cost of storage + cost of printing

$$= \dfrac{x}{2} + \dfrac{50,000}{x}(1000), \quad x > 0$$

[Note: $\dfrac{x}{2}$ is the average number in storage each day.]

$$C'(x) = \dfrac{1}{2} - \dfrac{50,000,000}{x^2} = \dfrac{x^2 - 100,000,000}{2x^2} = \dfrac{(x + 10,000)(x - 10,000)}{2x^2}$$

Critical value: $x = 10,000$

$$C''(x) = \dfrac{100,000,000}{x^3}$$

$$C''(10,000) = \dfrac{100,000,000}{(10,000)^3} > 0$$

Thus, the minimum cost occurs when $x = 10,000$ and the number of printings is $\dfrac{50,000}{10,000} = 5$.

31. (A) Let the cost to lay the pipe on the land be 1 unit; then the cost to lay the pipe in the lake is 1.4 units.

$$C(x) = \text{total cost} = (1.4)\sqrt{x^2 + 25} + (1)(10 - x), \quad 0 \le x \le 10$$

$$= (1.4)(x^2 + 25)^{1/2} + 10 - x$$

$$C'(x) = (1.4)\dfrac{1}{2}(x^2 + 25)^{-1/2}(2x) - 1$$

$$= (1.4)x(x^2 + 25)^{-1/2} - 1$$

$$= \dfrac{1.4x - \sqrt{x^2 + 25}}{\sqrt{x^2 + 25}}$$

$C'(x) = 0$ when $1.4x - \sqrt{x^2 + 25} = 0$ or $1.96x^2 = x^2 + 25$

$$.96x^2 = 25$$

$$x^2 = \frac{25}{.96} = 26.04$$

$$x = \pm 5.1$$

Thus, the critical value is $x = 5.1$.

$$C''(x) = (1.4)(x^2 + 25)^{-1/2} + (1.4)x\left(-\frac{1}{2}\right)(x^2 + 25)^{-3/2}2x$$

$$= \frac{1.4}{(x^2 + 25)^{1/2}} - \frac{(1.4)x^2}{(x^2 + 25)^{3/2}} = \frac{35}{(x^2 + 25)^{3/2}}$$

$$C''(5.1) = \frac{35}{[(5.1)^2 + 25]^{3/2}} > 0$$

Thus, the cost will be a minimum when $x = 5.1$.

Note that: $C(0) = (1.4)\sqrt{25} + 10 = 17$

$$C(5.1) = (1.4)\sqrt{51.01} + (10 - 5.1) = 14.9$$

$$C(10) = (1.4)\sqrt{125} = 15.65$$

Thus, the absolute minimum occurs when $x = 5.1$ miles.

(B) $C(x) = (1.1)\sqrt{x^2 + 25} + (1)(10 - x)$, $0 \le x \le 10$

$$C'(x) = \frac{(1.1)x - \sqrt{x^2 + 25}}{\sqrt{x^2 + 25}}$$

$C'(x) = 0$ when $1.1x - \sqrt{x^2 + 25} = 0$ or $(1.21)x^2 = x^2 + 25$

$$.21x^2 = 25$$

$$x^2 = \frac{25}{.21} = 119.05$$

$$x = \pm 10.91$$

Critical value: $x = 10.91 > 10$, i.e., there are no critical values on the interval $[0, 10]$. Now,

$$C(0) = (1.1)\sqrt{25} + 10 = 15.5,$$

$$C(10) = (1.1)\sqrt{125} \approx 12.30.$$

Therefore, the absolute minimum occurs when $x = 10$ miles.

33. $C(t) = 30t^2 - 240t + 500$, $0 \le t \le 8$
$C'(t) = 60t - 240$; $t = 4$ is the only critical value.
$C''(t) = 60$
$C''(4) = 60 > 0$
Now, $C(0) = 500$

$$C(4) = 30(4)^2 - 240(4) + 500 = 20,$$

$$C(8) = 30(8)^2 - 240(8) + 500 = 500.$$

Thus, 4 days after a treatment, the concentration will be minimum; the minimum concentration is 20 bacteria per cm^3.

35. Let x = the number of mice ordered in each order. Then the number of orders = $\dfrac{500}{x}$.

$C(x) = \text{Cost} = \dfrac{x}{2} \cdot 4 + \dfrac{500}{x}(10)$ [<u>Note</u>: Cost = cost of feeding + cost of order, $\dfrac{x}{2}$ is the average number of mice at any one time.]

$C(x) = 2x + \dfrac{5000}{x}, \quad 0 < x \le 500$

$C'(x) = 2 - \dfrac{5000}{x^2} = \dfrac{2x^2 - 5000}{x^2} = \dfrac{2(x^2 - 2500)}{x^2} = \dfrac{2(x + 50)(x - 50)}{x^2}$

Critical value: $x = 50$ (-50 is not a critical value, since the domain of C is $x > 0$.

$C''(x) = \dfrac{10{,}000}{x^3}$ and $C''(50) = \dfrac{10{,}000}{50^3} > 0$

Therefore, the minimum cost occurs when 50 mice are ordered each time. The total number of orders is $\dfrac{500}{50} = 10$.

37. $H(t) = 4t^{1/2} - 2t, \quad 0 \le t \le 2$

$H'(t) = 2t^{-1/2} - 2$

Thus, $t = 1$ is the only critical value.

Now, $H(0) = 4 \cdot 0^{1/2} - 2(0) = 0,$

$\quad\quad H(1) = 4 \cdot 1^{1/2} - 2(1) = 2,$

$\quad\quad H(2) = 4 \cdot 2^{1/2} - 4 \approx 1.66.$

Therefore, $H(1)$ is the absolute maximum, and after one month the maximum height will be 2 feet.

39. $N(t) = 30 + 12t^2 - t^3, \quad 0 \le t \le 8$

The rate of increase = $R(t) = N'(t) = 24t - 3t^2$, and

$R'(t) = N''(t) = 24 - 6t.$

Thus, $t = 4$ is the only critical value of $R(t)$.

Now, $R(0) = 0,$

$\quad\quad R(4) = 24 \cdot 4 - 3 \cdot 4^2 = 48,$

$\quad\quad R(8) = 24 \cdot 8 - 3 \cdot 8^2 = 0.$

Therefore, the absolute maximum value of R occurs when $t = 4$; the maximum rate of increase will occur four years from now.

CHAPTER 4 REVIEW

1. The function f is increasing on (a, c_1), (c_3, c_6).   (4-1, 4-2)

2. $f'(x) < 0$ on (c_1, c_3), (c_6, b).   (4-1, 4-2)

3. The graph of f is concave downward on (a, c_2), (c_4, c_5), (c_7, b).

     (4-1, 4-2)

4. A local minimum occurs at $x = c_3$.   (4-1)

5. The absolute maximum occurs at $x = c_6$.   (4-4)

6. $f'(x)$ appears to be zero at $x = c_1, c_3, c_5$.   (4-1)

7. $f'(x)$ does not exist at $x = c_6$. (4-1)

8. $x = c_2,\ c_4,\ c_5,\ c_7$ are inflection points. (4-2)

9.

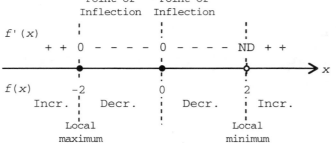

Using this information together with the points $(-3, 0)$, $(-2, 3)$, $(-1, 2)$, $(0, 0)$, $(2, -3)$, $(3, 0)$ on the graph, we have

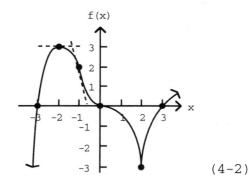

10. Domain: all real numbers
Intercepts: y-intercept: $f(0) = 0$
$\qquad\qquad$ x-intercepts: $x = 0$
Asymptotes: Horizontal asymptote: $y = 2$
$\qquad\qquad$ no vertical asymptotes
Critical values: $x = 0$

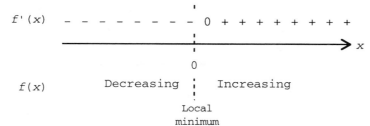

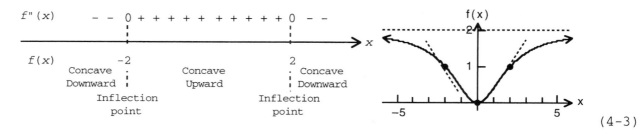

(4-2)

(4-3)

11. $f(x) = x^4 + 5x^3$

$f'(x) = 4x^3 + 15x^2$

$f''(x) = 12x^2 + 30x$ (4-2)

12. $y = 3x + \dfrac{4}{x}$

$y' = 3 - \dfrac{4}{x^2}$

$y'' = \dfrac{8}{x^3}$ (4-2)

13. $f(x) = x^3 - 18x^2 + 81x$

Step 1. Analyze $f(x)$:

Intercepts: y-intercept: $f(0) = 0^3 - 18(0)^2 + 81(0) = 0$

x-intercepts: $x^3 - 18x^2 + 81x = 0$

$x(x^2 - 18x + 81) = 0$

$x(x - 9)^2 = 0$

$x = 0,\ 9$

Step 2. Analyze $f'(x)$:

$f'(x) = 3x^2 - 36x + 81 = 3(x^2 - 12x + 27) = 3(x - 3)(x - 9)$

zeros of $f'(x)$: $x = 3$, $x = 9$

Sign chart for f':

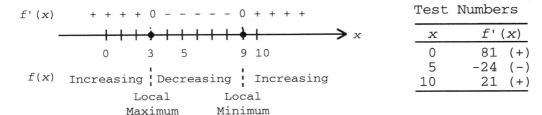

Test Numbers	
x	$f'(x)$
0	81 (+)
5	-24 (−)
10	21 (+)

Thus, f is increasing on $(-\infty, 3)$ and on $(9, \infty)$; f is decreasing on $(3, 9)$. There is a local maximum at $x = 3$ and a local minimum at $x = 9$.

Step 3. Analyze $f''(x)$:

$f''(x) = 6x - 36 = 6(x - 6)$

Thus, $x = 6$ is a partition number for f''.

Sign chart for f'':

Test Numbers	
x	$f''(x)$
0	-36 (−)
7	6 (+)

Thus, the graph of f is concave downward on $(-\infty, 6)$ and concave upward on $(6, \infty)$. The point $x = 6$ is an inflection point.

Step 4. Sketch the graph of f:

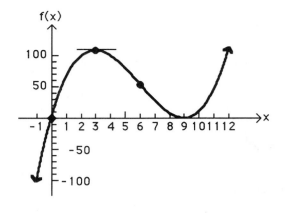

(4-2)

14. $f(x) = (x + 4)(x - 2)^2$

Step 1. Analyze $f(x)$:

(A) Domain: All real numbers, $(-\infty, \infty)$.

(B) Intercepts: y intercept: $f(0) = 4(-2)^2 = 16$

x intercepts: $(x + 4)(x - 2)^2 = 0$

$x = -4, 2$

(C) Asymptotes: Since f is a polynomial, there are no horizontal or vertical asymptotes.

Step 2. Analyze $f'(x)$:

$f'(x) = (x + 4)2(x - 2)(1) + (x - 2)^2(1)$

$= (x - 2)[2(x + 4) + (x - 2)]$

$= (x - 2)(3x + 6)$

$= 3(x - 2)(x + 2)$

Critical values: $x = -2$, $x = 2$

Partition numbers: $x = -2$, $x = 2$

Sign chart for f':

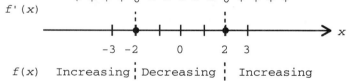

Test Numbers	
x	$f'(x)$
-3	15 (+)
0	-12 (-)
3	15 (+)

Thus, f is increasing on $(-\infty, -2)$ and on $(2, \infty)$; f is decreasing on $(-2, 2)$; f has a local maximum at $x = -2$ and a local minimum at $x = 2$.

Step 3. Analyze $f''(x)$:

$f''(x) = 3(x + 2)(1) + 3(x - 2)(1) = 6x$

Partition number for f'': $x = 0$

Sign chart for f'':

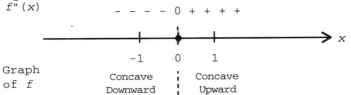

$f''(x)$ − − − − 0 + + + +

−1   0   1

Graph of f

Concave Downward   Concave Upward

Inflection Point

Test Numbers	
x	$f''(x)$
1	−6 (−)
1	6 (+)

Thus, the graph of f is concave downward on $(-\infty, 0)$ and concave upward on $(0, \infty)$; there is an inflection point at $x = 0$.

Step 4.   Sketch the graph of f:

x	$f(x)$
−2	32
0	16
2	0

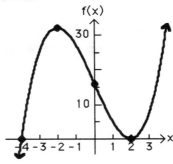

(4-2)

15. $f(x) = 8x^3 - 2x^4$

Step 1.   Analyze $f(x)$:

(A) Domain: All real numbers, $(-\infty, \infty)$.

(B) Intercepts: y intercept: $f(0) = 0$

               x intercepts: $8x^3 - 2x^4 = 0$

                            $2x^3(4 - x) = 0$

                                  $x = 0, 4$

(C) Asymptotes: No horizontal or vertical asymptotes.

Step 2.   Analyze $f'(x)$:

$f'(x) = 24x^2 - 8x^3 = 8x^2(3 - x)$

Critical values: $x = 0$, $x = 3$

Partition numbers: $x = 0$, $x = 3$

Sign chart for f':

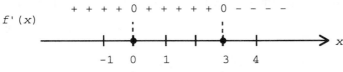

+ + + + 0 + + + + + 0 − − − −

$f'(x)$

−1   0   1   3   4

$f(x)$ Increasing ┊ Increasing ┊ Decreasing

Local Maximum

Test Numbers	
x	$f'(x)$
−1	32 (+)
1	16 (+)
4	−128 (−)

Thus, f is increasing on $(-\infty, 3)$ and decreasing on $(3, \infty)$; f has a local maximum at $x = 3$.

Step 3. Analyze $f''(x)$:

$f''(x) = 48x - 24x^2 = 24x(2 - x)$
Partition numbers for f'': $x = 0$, $x = 2$
Sign chart for f'':

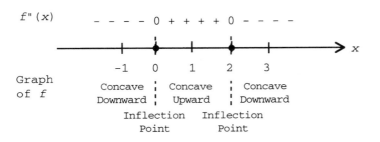

Test Numbers

x	$f''(x)$
-1	-72 $(-)$
1	24 $(+)$
3	-72 $(-)$

Thus, the graph of f is concave downward on $(-\infty, 0)$ and on $(2, \infty)$; the graph is concave upward on $(0, 2)$; there are inflection points at $x = 0$ and $x = 2$.

Step 4. Sketch the graph of f:

x	$f(x)$
0	0
2	32
3	54

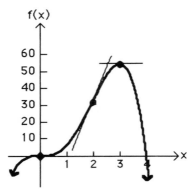

(4-2)

16. $f(x) = (x - 1)^3(x + 3)$

Step 1. Analyze $f(x)$:

(A) Domain: All real numbers.

(B) Intercepts: y intercept: $f(0) = (-1)^3(3) = -3$
$\quad\quad\quad\quad\quad\quad$ x intercepts: $(x - 1)^3(x + 3) = 0$
$\quad\quad\quad\quad\quad\quad\quad\quad\quad\quad\quad\quad\quad$ $x = 1, -3$

(C) Asymptotes: Since f is a polynomial (of degree 4), the graph of f has no asymptotes.

Step 2. Analyze $f'(x)$:

$f'(x) = (x - 1)^3(1) + (x + 3)(3)(x - 1)^2(1)$
$\quad\quad = (x - 1)^2[(x - 1) + 3(x + 3)]$
$\quad\quad = 4(x - 1)^2(x + 2)$
Critical values: $x = -2$, $x = 1$
Partition numbers: $x = -2$, $x = 1$

Sign chart for f':

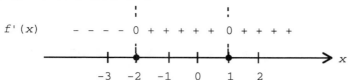

$f'(x)$	- - - - 0 + + + + + 0 + + + +

-3 -2 -1   0   1   2

$f(x)$ Decreasing ┆ Increasing ┆ Increasing

Test Numbers

x	$f'(x)$
-3	-64 (−)
0	8 (+)
2	16 (+)

Thus, f is decreasing on $(-\infty, -2)$; f is increasing on $(-2, 1)$ and $(1, \infty)$; f has a local minimum at $x = -2$.

Step 3. Analyze $f''(x)$:

$$f''(x) = 4(x - 1)^2(1) + 4(x + 2)(2)(x - 1)(1)$$
$$= 4(x - 1)[(x - 1) + 2(x + 2)]$$
$$= 12(x - 1)(x + 1)$$

Partition numbers for f'': $x = -1$, $x = 1$.
Sign chart for f'':

$f''(x)$	+ + + + 0 - - - - - 0 + + + +

-2 -1   0   1   2

Graph
of f Concave ┆ Concave ┆ Concave
         Upward ┆ Downward ┆ Upward

Test Numbers

x	$f''(x)$
-2	36 (+)
0	-12 (−)
2	36 (+)

Thus, the graph of f is concave upward on $(-\infty, -1)$ and on $(1, \infty)$; the graph of f is concave downward on $(-1, 1)$; the graph has inflection points at $x = -1$ and at $x = 1$.

Step 4. Sketch the graph of f:

x	$f(x)$
-2	-27
0	-3
1	0

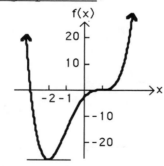

(4-2)

17. $f(x) = \dfrac{3x}{x + 2}$

Step 1. Analyze $f(x)$:
The domain of f is all real numbers except $x = -2$.

Intercepts: y-intercept: $f(0) = \dfrac{3(0)}{0 + 2} = 0$

x-intercepts: $\dfrac{3x}{x + 2} = 0$

$3x = 0$

$x = 0$

Asymptotes:
Horizontal asymptotes: $\dfrac{a_n x^n}{b_m x^m} = \dfrac{3x}{x} = 3$

Thus, the line $y = 3$ is a horizontal asymptote.

Vertical asymptote(s): The denominator is 0 at $x = -2$ and the numerator is nonzero at $x = -2$. Thus, the line $x = -2$ is a vertical asymptote.

Step 2. Analyze $f'(x)$:

$$f'(x) = \frac{(x + 2)(3) - 3x(1)}{(x + 2)^2} = \frac{6}{(x + 2)^2}$$

Critical values: $f'(x) = \dfrac{6}{(x + 2)^2} \neq 0$ for all x $(x \neq -2)$.

Thus, f does not have any critical values.
Partition numbers: $x = -2$ is a partition number for f'.
Sign chart for f':

	Test Numbers	
	x	$f'(x)$
	-3	$6\ (+)$
	0	$\frac{3}{2}\ (+)$

Thus, f is increasing on $(-\infty, -2)$ and on $(-2, \infty)$; f does not have any local extrema.

Step 3. Analyze $f''(x)$:

$$f''(x) = -12(x + 2)^{-3} = \frac{-12}{(x + 2)^3}$$

Partition numbers for f'': $x = -2$
Sign chart for f'':

	Test Numbers	
	x	$f''(x)$
	-3	$12\ (+)$
	0	$-\frac{3}{2}\ (-)$

The graph of f is concave upward on $(-\infty, -2)$ and concave downward on $(-2, \infty)$. The graph of f does not have any inflection points.

Step 4. Sketch the graph of f:

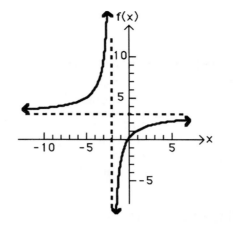

(4-3)

18. $f(x) = \dfrac{x^2}{x^2 + 27}$

Step 1. Analyze $f(x)$:

(A) Domain: All real numbers.

(B) Intercepts: y-intercepts: $f(0) = 0$

x-intercepts: $\dfrac{x^2}{x^2 + 27} = 0$, $x = 0$

(C) Asymptotes

Horizontal asymptote: $\dfrac{x^2}{x^2} = 1$; $y = 1$ is a horizontal asymptote

Vertical asymptote: no vertical asymptotes

Step 2. Analyze $f'(x)$:

$f'(x) = \dfrac{(x^2 + 27)(2x) - x^2(2x)}{(x^2 + 27)^2} = \dfrac{54x}{(x^2 + 27)^2}$

Critical values: $x = 0$
Partition numbers: $x = 0$

Sign chart for f':

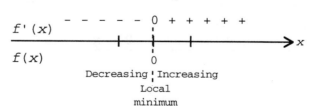

Thus, f is decreasing on $(-\infty, 0)$ and increasing on $(0, \infty)$; f has a local minimum at $x = 0$.

Step 3. Analyze $f''(x)$:

$f''(x) = \dfrac{(x^2 + 27)^2(54) - 54x(2)(x^2 + 27)2x}{(x^2 + 27)^4} = \dfrac{162(9 - x^2)}{(x^2 + 27)^3}$

Partition numbers for $f''(x)$: $x = -3$, $x = 3$

Sign chart for f'':

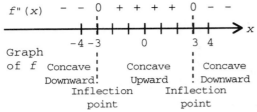

Test Numbers	
x	$f''(x)$
-4	$(-)$
0	$(+)$
4	$(-)$

The graph of f is concave upward on $(-3, 3)$ and concave downward on $(-\infty, -3)$ and $(3, \infty)$; the graph has inflection points at $x = -3$ and $x = 3$.

Step 4. Sketch the graph of f:

x	$f(x)$
-3	$\frac{1}{4}$
0	0
3	$\frac{1}{4}$

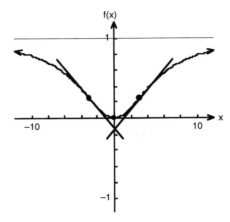

19. $f(x) = \dfrac{x}{(x + 2)^2}$

(4-3)

Step 1. Analyze $f(x)$:
(A) Domain: All real numbers except $x = -2$.
(B) Intercepts: y-intercepts: $f(0) = 0$
x-intercepts: $\dfrac{x}{(x + 2)^2} = 0$, $x = 0$

(C) Asymptotes

  Horizontal asymptote: $\dfrac{x}{x^2} = \dfrac{1}{x} = 1$; $y = 0$ (the x-axis) is a horizontal asymptote.

  Vertical asymptote: $x = -2$ is a vertical asymptote

Step 2. Analyze $f'(x)$:
$$f'(x) = \frac{(x + 2)^2 - x(2)(x + 2)}{(x + 2)^4} = \frac{2 - x}{(x + 2)^3}$$
Critical values: $x = 2$
Partition numbers: $x = -2$, $x = 2$
Sign chart for f':

Test Numbers	
x	$f'(x)$
-3	$-5\ (-)$
0	$\frac{1}{4}\ (+)$
3	$-\frac{1}{125}\ (-)$

Thus, f is increasing on $(-2, 2)$ and decreasing on $(-\infty, -2)$ and $(2, \infty)$; f has a local maximum at $x = 2$.

Step 3. Analyze $f''(x)$:

$$f''(x) = \frac{(x + 2)^3(-1) - (2 - x)(3)(x + 2)^2}{(x + 2)^6} = \frac{2(x - 4)}{(x + 2)^4}$$

Partition numbers for $f''(x)$: $x = -2$, $x = 4$
Sign chart for f'':

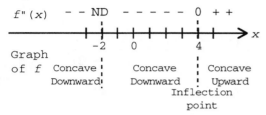

Test Numbers	
x	$f''(x)$
-3	-14 $(-)$
0	$-\frac{1}{2}$ $(-)$
5	$(+)$

The graph of f is concave upward on $(4, \infty)$ and concave downward on $(-\infty, -2)$ and $(-2, 4)$; the graph has an inflection point at $x = 4$.

Step 4. Sketch the graph of f:

x	$f(x)$
0	0
2	$\frac{1}{8}$
4	$\frac{1}{9}$

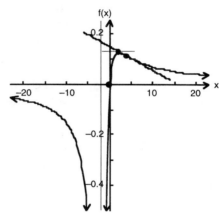

(4-3)

20. $f(x) = \dfrac{x^3}{x^2 + 3}$

Step 1. Analyze $f(x)$:

(A) Domain: All real numbers.

(B) Intercepts: y-intercepts: $f(0) = 0$

x-intercepts: $\dfrac{x^3}{x^2 + 3} = 0$, $x = 0$

(C) Asymptotes

Horizontal asymptote: $\dfrac{x^3}{x^2} = x$; no horizontal asymptote.

Vertical asymptote: no vertical asymptotes

Step 2. Analyze $f'(x)$:

$$f'(x) = \frac{(x^2 + 3)(3x^2) - x^3(2x)}{(x^2 + 3)^2} = \frac{x^2(x^2 + 9)}{(x^2 + 3)^2}$$

Critical values: $x = 0$
Partition numbers: $x = 0$

Sign chart for f':

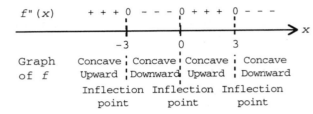

f is increasing on $(-\infty, \infty)$.

Step 3. Analyze $f''(x)$:

$$f''(x) = \frac{(x^2 + 3)(4x^3 + 18x) - x^2(x^2 + 9)(2)(x^2 + 3)2x}{(x^2 + 3)^4} = \frac{6x(9 - x^2)}{(x^2 + 3)^3}$$

Partition numbers for $f''(x)$: $x = -3$, $x = 0$, $x = 3$
Sign chart for f'':

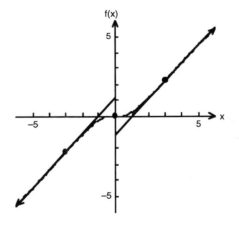

Test Numbers	
x	$f''(x)$
-4	$(+)$
-1	$(-)$
1	$(+)$
4	$(-)$

The graph of f is concave upward on $(-\infty, -3)$ and $(0, 3)$, and concave downward on $(-3, 0)$ and $(3, \infty)$; the graph has inflection points at $x = -3$, $x = 0$, $x = 3$.

Step 4. Sketch the graph of f:

x	$f(x)$
-3	$-\frac{9}{4}$
0	0
3	$\frac{9}{4}$

$(4-3)$

21.

x	$f'(x)$	$f(x)$
$-\infty < x < -2$	Negative and increasing	Decreasing and concave upward
$x = -2$	x-intercept	Local minimum
$-2 < x < -1$	Positive and increasing	Increasing and concave upward
$x = -1$	Local maximum	Inflection point
$-1 < x < 1$	Positive and decreasing	Increasing and concave downward
$x = 1$	Local minimum	Inflection point
$1 < x < \infty$	Positive and increasing	Increasing and concave upward

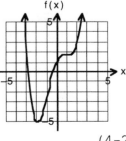

$(4-2)$

22. The graph in (C) could be the graph of $y = f''(x)$.

$(4-2)$

23. $f(x) = x^3 - 6x^2 - 15x + 12$

$f'(x) = 3x^2 - 12x - 15$

$3x^2 - 12x - 15 = 0$

$3(x^2 - 4x - 5) = 0$

$3(x - 5)(x + 1) = 0$

Thus, $x = -1$ and $x = 5$ are critical values of f.

$f''(x) = 6x - 12$

Now, $f''(-1) = 6(-1) - 12 = -18 < 0$.

Thus, f has a local maximum at $x = -1$.

Also, $f''(5) = 6(5) - 12 = 18 > 0$ and f has a local minimum at $x = 5$.

(4-2)

24. $y = f(x) = x^3 - 12x + 12$, $-3 \leq x \leq 5$

$f'(x) = 3x^2 - 12$

Critical values: f' is defined for all x:

$f'(x) = 3x^2 - 12 = 0$

$3(x^2 - 4) = 0$

$3(x - 2)(x + 2) = 0$

Thus, the critical values of f are: $x = -2$, $x = 2$.

$f(-3) = (-3)^3 - 12(-3) + 12 = 21$

$f(-2) = (-2)^3 - 12(-2) + 12 = 28$

$f(2) = 2^3 - 12(2) + 12 = -4$ Absolute minimum

$f(5) = 5^3 - 12(5) + 12 = 77$ Absolute maximum

(4-4)

25. $y = f(x) = x^2 + \dfrac{16}{x^2}$, $x > 0$

$f'(x) = 2x - \dfrac{32}{x^3} = \dfrac{2x^4 - 32}{x^3} = \dfrac{2(x^4 - 16)}{x^3} = \dfrac{2(x - 2)(x + 2)(x^2 + 4)}{x^3}$

$f''(x) = 2 + \dfrac{96}{x^4}$

The only critical value of f in the interval $(0, \infty)$ is $x = 2$. Since

$f''(2) = 2 + \dfrac{96}{2^4} = 8 > 0$,

$f(2) = 8$ is the absolute minimum of f on $(0, \infty)$.

(4-4)

26. Yes. Consider f on the interval $[a, b]$. Since f is a polynomial, f is continuous on $[a, b]$. Therefore, f has an absolute maximum on $[a, b]$. Since f has a local minimum at $x = a$ and $x = b$, the absolute maximum of f on $[a, b]$ must occur at some point c in (a, b); f has a local maximum at $x = c$.

(4-4)

27. No, increasing/decreasing properties are stated in terms of intervals in the domain of f. A correct statement is: $f(x)$ is decreasing on $(-\infty, 0)$ and $(0, \infty)$.

(4-1)

28. A critical value for $f(x)$ is a partition number for $f'(x)$ that is also in the domain of f. However, $f'(x)$ may have partition numbers that are not in the domain of f and hence are not critical values for $f(x)$. For example, let $f(x) = \dfrac{1}{x}$. Then $f'(x) = -\dfrac{1}{x^2}$ and 0 is a partition number for $f'(x)$, but 0 is NOT a critical value for $f(x)$ since it is not in the domain of f.

(4-1)

29. $f(x) = 6x^2 - x^3 + 8$, $0 \le x \le 4$
$f'(x) = 12x - 3x^2$
$f''(x) = 12 - 6x$

Now, $f''(x)$ is defined for all x and $f''(x) = 12 - 6x = 0$ implies $x = 2$. Thus, f' has a critical value at $x = 2$. Since this is the only critical value of f' and $(f'(x))'' = f'''(x) = -6$ so that $f'''(2) = -6 < 0$, it follows that $f'(2) = 12$ is the absolute maximum of f'. The graph is shown at the right.

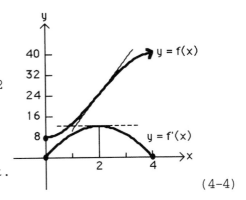

(4-4)

30. Let $x > 0$ be one of the numbers. Then $\dfrac{400}{x}$ is the other number. Now, we have:

$S(x) = x + \dfrac{400}{x}$, $x > 0$,

$S'(x) = 1 - \dfrac{400}{x^2} = \dfrac{x^2 - 400}{x^2} = \dfrac{(x - 20)(x + 20)}{x^2}$

Thus, $x = 20$ is the only critical value of S on $(0, \infty)$.

$S''(x) = \dfrac{800}{x^3}$ and $S''(20) = \dfrac{800}{8000} = \dfrac{1}{10} > 0$

Therefore, $S(20) = 20 + \dfrac{400}{20} = 40$ is the absolute minimum sum, and this occurs when each number is 20.

(4-4)

31. $f(x) = x^4 + x^3 + 4x^2 - 3x + 4$.
<u>Step 1. Analyze $f(x)$</u>:
(A) Domain: All real numbers (f is a polynomial function)
(B) Intercepts: y-intercept: $f(0) = 4$
    x-intercepts: $x \approx 0.79$, 1.64
(C) Asymptotes: Since f is a polynomial function (of degree 4), the graph of f has no asymptotes.

<u>Step 2. Analyze $f'(x)$</u>:
   $f'(x) = 4x^3 + 3x^2 - 8x - 3$
Critical values: $x \approx -1.68$, -0.35, 1.28;
f is increasing on $(-1.68, -0.35)$ and $(1.28, \infty)$; f is decreasing on $(-\infty, -1.68)$ and $(-0.35, 1.28)$. f has local minima at $x = -1.68$ and $x = 1.28$. f has a local maximum at $x = -0.35$.

Step 3. Analyze $f''(x)$:

$\quad f''(x) = 12x^2 + 6x - 8$

The graph of f is concave downward on $(-1.10, 0.60)$; the graph of f is concave upward on $(-\infty, -1.10)$ and $(0.60, \infty)$; the graph has inflection points at $x \approx -1.10$ and 0.60. (4-2)

32. $f(x) = 0.25x^4 - 5x^3 + 31x^2 - 70x$

Step 1. Analyze $f(x)$:

(A) Domain: all real numbers

(B) Intercepts: y-intercept: $f(0) = 0$
$\qquad\qquad\qquad x$-intercepts: $x = 0, 11.10$

(C) Asymptotes: since f is a polynomial function (of degree 4), the graph of f has no asymptotes; $\lim\limits_{x \to \pm\infty} f(x) = \infty$

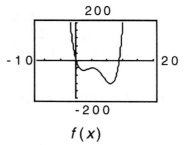

$f(x)$

Step 2. Analyze $f'(x)$:

$f'(x) = x^3 - 15x^2 + 62x - 70$

Critical values: $x \approx 1.87, 4.19, 8.94$

Sign chart for f':

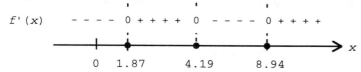

f is increasing on $(1.87, 4.19)$ and $(8.94, \infty)$;
f is decreasing on $(-\infty, 1.87)$ and $(4.19, 8.94)$;
f has local minima at $x = 1.87$ and $x = 8.94$;
f has a local maximum at $x = 4.19$

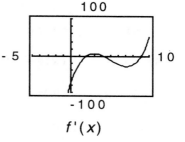

$f'(x)$

Step 3. Analyze f'':

$f''(x) = 3x^2 - 30x + 62$

Partition numbers for f'': $x \approx 2.92, 7.08$
Sign chart for f'':

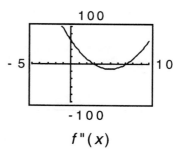

$f''(x)$

The graph of f is concave downward on $(2.92, 7.08)$ and concave upward on $(-\infty, 2.92)$ and $(7.08, \infty)$; the graph has inflection points at $x = 2.92$ and $x = 7.08$. (4-2)

33. (A) For the first 15 months, the price is increasing and concave down, with a local maximum at $t = 15$. For the next 15 months, the price is decreasing and concave down, with an inflection point at $t = 30$. For the next 15 months, the price is decreasing and concave up, with a local minimum at $t = 45$. For the remaining 15 months, the price is increasing and concave up.

(B)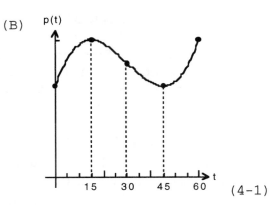

(4-1)

34. (A) $R(x) = xp(x) = 500x - 0.025x^2$, $0 \leq x \leq 20,000$
$R'(x) = 500 - 0.05x$; $500 - 0.05x = 0$
$$x = 10,000$$
Thus, $x = 10,000$ is a critical value.

Now, $R(0) = 0$
$R(10,000) = 2,500,000$
$R(20,000) = 0$

Thus, $R(10,000) = \$2,500,000$ is the absolute maximum of R.

(B) $P(x) = R(x) - C(x) = 500x - 0.025x^2 - (350x + 50,000)$
$$= 150x - 0.025x^2 - 50,000, \ 0 \leq x \leq 20,000$$
$P'(x) = 150 - 0.05x$; $150 - 0.05x = 0$
$$x = 3,000$$

Now, $P(0) = -50,000$
$P(3,000) = 175,000$
$P(20,000) = -7,050,000$

Thus, the maximum profit is $\$175,000$ when 3000 stoves are manufactured and sold at $p(3,000) = \$425$ each.

(C) If the government taxes the company $20 per stove, then the cost equation is:
$$C(x) = 370x + 50,000$$
and
$$P(x) = 500x - 0.025x^2 - (370x + 50,000)$$
$$= 130x - 0.025x^2 - 50,000, \ 0 \leq x \leq 20,000$$
$P'(x) = 130 - 0.05x$; $130 - 0.05x = 0$
$$x = 2,600$$

The maximum profit is $P(2,600) = \$119,000$ when 2,600 stoves are produced and sold for $p(2,600) = \$435$ each.

(4-5)

35.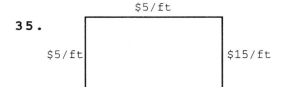

Let x be the length and y the width of the rectangle.

(A) $C(x, y) = 5x + 5x + 5y + 15y = 10x + 20y$

Also, Area $A = xy = 5000$, so $y = \dfrac{5000}{x}$

and $C(x) = 10x + \dfrac{100,000}{x}$, $x \geq 0$

Now, $C'(x) = 10 - \dfrac{100,000}{x^2}$ and

$10 - \dfrac{100,000}{x^2} = 0$ implies $10x^2 = 100,000$

$$x^2 = 10,000$$
$$x = \pm 100$$

Thus, $x = 100$ is the critical value.

Now, $C''(x) = \dfrac{200,000}{x^3}$ and $C''(100) = \dfrac{200,000}{1,000,000} = 0.2 > 0$

and the most economical (i.e. least cost) fence will have dimensions: length $x = 100$ feet and width $y = \dfrac{5000}{100} = 50$ feet.

(B) We want to maximize $A = xy$ subject to
$C(x, y) = 10x + 20y = 3000$ or $x = 300 - 2y$

Thus, $A = y(300 - 2y) = 300y - 2y^2$, $0 \leq y \leq 150$.

Now, $A'(y) = 300 - 4y$ and
$300 - 4y = 0$ implies $y = 75$.

Therefore, $y = 75$ is the critical value.

Now, $A''(y) = -4$ and $A''(75) = -4 < 0$. Thus, A has an absolute maximum when $y = 75$. Therefore the dimensions of the rectangle that will enclose maximum area are:
length $x = 300 - 2(75) = 150$ feet and width $y = 75$ feet. (4-5)

36. Let $x =$ the number of dollars increase in the nightly rate, $x \geq 0$. Then $200 - 4x$ rooms will be rented at $(40 + x)$ dollars per room. [Note: Since $200 - 4x \geq 0$, $x \leq 50$.] The cost of service for $200 - 4x$ rooms at \$8 per room is $8(200 - 4x)$. Thus:

Gross profit: $P(x) = (200 - 4x)(40 + x) - 8(200 - 4x)$
$= (200 - 4x)(32 + x)$
$= 6400 + 72x - 4x^2$, $0 \leq x \leq 50$

$P'(x) = 72 - 8x$
Critical value: $72 - 8x = 0$
$x = 9$

Now, $P(0) = 6400$
$P(9) = 6724$ Absolute maximum
$P(50) = 0$

Thus, the maximum gross profit is \$6724 and this occurs at $x = 9$, i.e., the rooms should be rented at \$49 per night. (4-5)

37. Let $x =$ number of times the company should order. Then, the number of disks per order $= \dfrac{7200}{x}$. The average number of unsold disks is given by:

$$\frac{7200}{2x} = \frac{3600}{x}$$

Total cost: $C(x) = 5x + 0.2\left(\dfrac{3600}{x}\right), \quad x > 0$

$$C(x) = 5x + \frac{720}{x}$$

$$C'(x) = 5 - \frac{720}{x^2} = \frac{5x^2 - 720}{x^2} = \frac{5(x^2 - 144)}{x^2}$$

$$= \frac{5(x + 12)(x - 12)}{x^2}$$

Critical value: $x = 12$ [Note: $x > 0$, so $x = -12$ is not a critical value.]

$C''(x) = \dfrac{1440}{x^3}$ and $C''(12) = \dfrac{1440}{12^3} > 0$

Therefore, $C(x)$ is a minimum when $x = 12$.   (4-5)

38. $C(x) = 4000 + 10x + 0.1x^2, \quad x > 0$

Average cost $= \overline{C}(x) = \dfrac{4000}{x} + 10 + 0.1x$

Marginal cost $= C'(x) = 10 + \dfrac{2}{10}x = 10 + 0.2x$

The graph of $C'(x)$ is a straight line with slope $\dfrac{1}{5}$ and y intercept 10.

$\overline{C}'(x) = \dfrac{-4000}{x^2} + \dfrac{1}{10} = \dfrac{-40,000 + x^2}{10x^2} = \dfrac{(x + 200)(x - 200)}{10x^2}$

Thus, $\overline{C}'(x) < 0$ on $(0, 200)$ and $\overline{C}'(x) > 0$ on $(200, \infty)$.   Therefore, $\overline{C}(x)$ is decreasing on $(0, 200)$, increasing on $(200, \infty)$, and a minimum occurs at $x = 200$.

Min $\overline{C}(x) = \overline{C}(200) = \dfrac{4000}{200} + 10 + \dfrac{1}{10}(200) = 50$

$\overline{C}''(x) = \dfrac{8000}{x^3} > 0$ on $(0, \infty)$.

Therefore, the graph of $\overline{C}(x)$ is concave upward on $(0, \infty)$.

Using this information and point-by-point plotting (use a calculator), the graphs of $C(x)$ and $\overline{C}(x)$ are as shown in the diagram at the right.
The line $y = 0.1x + 10$ is an oblique asymptote for $y = \overline{C}(x)$.

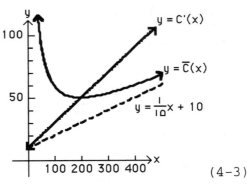

(4-3)

39. $N(x) = -0.25x^4 + 11x^3 - 108x^2 + 3,000, \quad 9 \le x \le 24$

$N'(x) = -x^3 + 33x^2 - 216x$

$N''(x) = -3x^2 + 66x - 216 = -3(x^2 - 22x + 72)$

$\qquad\qquad = -3(x - 4)(x - 18)$

Partition numbers for $N''(x)$: $x = 18$

Sign chart for $N''(x)$:

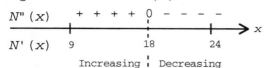

Thus, N' is increasing on (9, 18) and decreasing on (18, 24); the point of diminishing returns is $x = 18$; the maximum rate of change is $N'(18) = 972$.

Test Numbers

x	$N''(x)$
17	39 (+)
19	−45 (−)

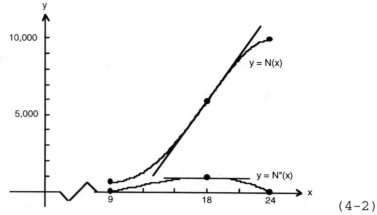

(4-2)

40. Let x be the length of the vertical portion of the chain. Then the length of each of the "arms" of the "Y" is $\sqrt{(10 - x)^2 + 36} = \sqrt{x^2 - 20x + 136}$. Thus, the total length is given by:

$$L(x) = x + 2\sqrt{x^2 - 20x + 136} \quad 0 \le x \le 10$$

Now,

$$L'(x) = 1 + 2\left(\frac{1}{2}\right)(x^2 - 20x + 136)^{-1/2}(2x - 20)$$

$$= 1 + \frac{2x - 20}{(x^2 - 20x + 136)^{1/2}}$$

$L'(x) = 0$:
$$1 + \frac{2x - 20}{(x^2 - 20x + 136)^{1/2}} = 0$$

$$(x^2 - 20x + 136)^{1/2} + 2x - 20 = 0$$

$$(x^2 - 20x + 136)^{1/2} = 2(10 - x)$$

$$x^2 - 20x + 136 = 4(100 - 20x + x^2)$$

$$-3x^2 + 60x - 264 = 0$$

$$x = \frac{20 \pm \sqrt{48}}{2} = 10 \pm 2\sqrt{3}$$

Critical value (in (0, 10)): $x = 10 - 2\sqrt{3} \approx 6.54$

Sign chart for $L'(x)$:

L'(x) – – – – 0 + + + + → x
L(x)   0   6.54   10
       Decreasing ┊ Increasing
            Local
           minimum

Test Numbers

x	$L'(x)$
0	(−)
10	1 (+)

Thus, to minimize the length of the chain, the vertical portion should be 6.54 feet long. The total length of the chain will be $L(6.54) = 20.39$ feet.

(4-5)

41. (A)

```
QuadReg
 y=ax²+bx+c
 a=.0061285714
 b=.1224285714
 c=102.2
```

(B) Let $C(x)$ be the regression equation from part (A). The average cost function $\overline{C}(x) = \dfrac{C(x)}{x}$.

Using the "find the minimum" routine on the graphing utility, we find that
$$\min \overline{C}(x) = \overline{C}(129) = 1.71$$

The minimum average cost is \$1.71 at a production level of 129 dozen cookies.   (4-5)

42. (A)

```
CubicReg
 y=ax³+bx²+cx+d
 a=-.01
 b=.83
 c=-2.3
 d=221
```

(B) The regression equation found in (A) is:
$$y(x) = -0.01x^3 + 0.83x^2 - 2.3x + 221$$

The rate of change of sales with respect to the number of ads is:

$$y'(x) = -0.03x^2 + 1.66x - 2.3$$
$$y''(x) = -0.06x + 1.66$$

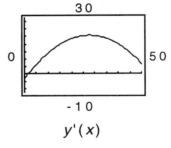

$y'(x)$

Critical value: $-0.06x + 1.66 = 0$
$$x \approx 27.667$$

From the graph, the absolute maximum of $y'(x)$ occurs at $x \approx 27.667$. Thus, 28 ads should be placed each month. The expected number of sales is: $y(28) \approx 588$ (4-5)

43. $C(t) = 20t^2 - 120t + 800, \ 0 \le t \le 9$

$C'(t) = 40t - 120 = 40(t - 3)$

Critical value: $t = 3$

$C''(t) = 40 \quad$ and $\quad C''(3) = 40 > 0$

Therefore, a local minimum occurs at $t = 3$.

$C(3) = 20(3^2) - 120(3) + 800 = 620 \quad$ Absolute minimum

$C(0) = 800$

$C(9) = 20(81) - 120(9) + 800 = 1340$

Therefore, the bacteria count will be at a minimum three days after a treatment.   (4-5)

44. $N = 10 + 6t^2 - t^3$, $0 \le t \le 5$

$\dfrac{dN}{dt} = 12t - 3t^2$

Now, find the critical values of the rate function $R(t)$:

$R(t) = \dfrac{dN}{dt} = 12t - 3t^2$

$R'(t) = \dfrac{dR}{dt} = \dfrac{d^2N}{dt^2} = 12 - 6t$

Critical value: $t = 2$

$R''(t) = -6$ and $R''(2) = -6 < 0$

$R(0) = 0$

$R(2) = 12$ Absolute maximum

$R(5) = -15$

Therefore, $R(t)$ has an absolute maximum at $t = 2$. The rate of increase will be a maximum after two years. (4-4)

5 ADDITIONAL DERIVATIVE TOPICS

Things to remember:

1. THE NUMBER e

   The irrational number e is defined by
   $$e = \lim_{n \to \infty} \left(1 + \frac{1}{n}\right)^n$$
   or alternatively,
   $$e = \lim_{s \to 0} (1 + s)^{1/s}$$
   $$e = 2.7182818\ldots$$

2. CONTINUOUS COMPOUND INTEREST

   $A = Pe^{rt}$
   where P = Principal
   r = Annual nominal interest rate compounded continuously
   t = Time in years
   A = Amount at time t

---

1. $A = \$1000e^{0.1t}$
   When $t = 2$, $A = \$1000e^{(0.1)2} = \$1000e^{0.2} = \$1221.40$.
   When $t = 5$, $A = \$1000e^{(0.1)5} = \$1000e^{0.5} = \$1628.72$.
   When $t = 8$, $A = \$1000e^{(0.1)8} = \$1000e^{0.8} = \$2225.54$

3.

   $A = 6{,}000\ e^{0.1\,t}$

5. $2 = e^{0.06t}$
   Take the natural log of both sides of this equation
   $$\ln(e^{0.06t}) = \ln 2$$
   $$0.06t \ln e = \ln 2$$
   $$0.06t = \ln 2 \quad (\ln e = 1)$$
   $$t = \frac{\ln 2}{0.06} \approx 11.55$$

7. $3 = e^{0.1t}$
   $$\ln(e^{0.1t}) = \ln 3$$
   $$0.1t = \ln 3$$
   $$t = \frac{\ln 3}{0.1} \approx 10.99$$

9. $2 = e^{5r}$
   $$\ln(e^{5r}) = \ln 2$$
   $$5r = \ln 2$$
   $$r = \frac{\ln 2}{5} \approx 0.14$$

11.

n	$\left(1 + \dfrac{1}{n}\right)^n$
10	2.59374
100	2.70481
1000	2.71692
10,000	2.71815
100,000	2.71827
1,000,000	2.71828
10,000,000	2.71828
↓	↓
∞	$e = 2.7182818...$

13.

n	4	16	64	256	1024	4096
$(1 + n)^{1/n}$	1.495349	1.193722	1.067399	1.021913	1.006793	1.002033

$\lim\limits_{n \to \infty} (1 + n)^{1/n} = 1$

15. The graphs of $y_1 = \left(1 + \dfrac{1}{n}\right)^n$,

$y_2 = 2.718281828 \approx e$, and

$y_3 = \left(1 + \dfrac{1}{n}\right)^{n+1}$ for $0 \le n \le 20$

are given at the right.

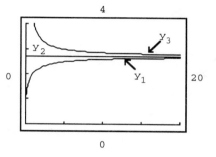

17. (A) $A = Pe^{rt}$; $P = \$10{,}000$, $r = 5.51\% = 0.0551$, $t = 10$:

$A = 10{,}000e^{(0.0551)10} = 10{,}000e^{0.551} = \$17{,}349.87$

(B) $A = \$15{,}000$, $P = \$10{,}000$, $r = 0.0551$:

$15{,}000 = 10{,}000e^{0.0551t}$

$e^{0.0551t} = 1.5$

$0.0551t = \ln(1.5)$

$t = \dfrac{\ln(1.5)}{0.0551} \approx 7.36$ years

19. $A = Pe^{rt}$; $A = \$20{,}000$, $r = 0.052$, $t = 10$:

$20{,}000 = Pe^{(0.052)10} = Pe^{0.52}$

$P = \dfrac{20{,}000}{e^{0.52}} = 20{,}000e^{-0.52} \approx \$11{,}890.41$

21. $30{,}000 = 20{,}000e^{5r}$

$e^{5r} = 1.5$

$5r = \ln(1.5)$

$r = \dfrac{\ln(1.5)}{5} \approx 0.0811$ or 8.11%

23. $P = 10,000e^{-0.08t}, \; 0 \leq t \leq 50$

(A)

t	0	10	20	30	40	50
P	10,000	4493.30	2019	907.18	407.62	183.16

The graph of P is shown at the right.

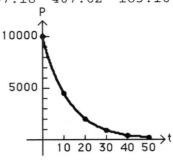

(B) $\displaystyle\lim_{t \to \infty} 10,000e^{-0.08t} = 0$

25.
$$2P = Pe^{0.07t}$$
$$e^{0.07t} = 2$$
$$0.07t = \ln 2$$
$$t = \frac{\ln 2}{0.07} \approx 9.9 \text{ years}$$

27.
$$2P = Pe^{r(8)}$$
$$e^{8r} = 2$$
$$8r = \ln 2$$
$$r = \frac{\ln 2}{8} \approx 0.0866 \text{ or } 8.66\%$$

29. The total investment in the two accounts is given by
$$A = 10,000e^{0.072t} + 10,000(1 + 0.084)^t$$
$$= 10,000[e^{0.072t} + (1.084)^t]$$

On a graphing utility, locate the intersection point of
$$y_1 = 10,000[e^{0.072x} + (1.084)^x]$$
and $y_2 = 35,000$.

The result is: $x = t \approx 7.3$ years.

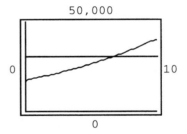

31. (A) $A = Pe^{rt}$; set $A = 2P$

(B)
$$2P = Pe^{rt}$$
$$e^{rt} = 2$$
$$rt = \ln 2$$
$$t = \frac{\ln 2}{r}$$

In theory, r could be any positive number. However, the restrictions on r are reasonable in the sense that most investments would be expected to earn between 2% and 30%.

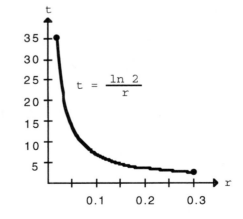

(C) $r = 5\%$; $t = \dfrac{\ln 2}{0.05} \approx 13.86$ years

$\quad r = 10\%$; $t = \dfrac{\ln 2}{0.10} \approx 6.93$ years

$\quad r = 15\%$; $t = \dfrac{\ln 2}{0.15} \approx 4.62$ years

$\quad r = 20\%$; $t = \dfrac{\ln 2}{0.20} \approx 3.47$ years

$\quad r = 25\%$; $t = \dfrac{\ln 2}{0.25} \approx 2.77$ years

$\quad r = 30\%$; $t = \dfrac{\ln 2}{0.30} \approx 2.31$ years

33.
$$Q = Q_0 e^{-0.0004332t}$$
$$\tfrac{1}{2}Q_0 = Q_0 e^{-0.0004332t}$$
$$e^{-0.0004332t} = \tfrac{1}{2}$$
$$\ln(e^{-0.0004332t}) = \ln\left(\tfrac{1}{2}\right) = \ln 1 - \ln 2$$
$$-0.0004332t = -\ln 2 \quad (\ln 1 = 0)$$
$$t = \dfrac{\ln 2}{0.0004332}$$
$$\approx \dfrac{0.6931}{0.0004332} \approx 1599.95$$

Thus, the half-life of radium is approximately 1600 years.

35.
$$Q = Q_0 e^{rt} \quad (r < 0)$$
$$\tfrac{1}{2}Q_0 = Q_0 e^{r(30)}$$
$$e^{30r} = \tfrac{1}{2}$$
$$\ln(e^{30r}) = \ln\left(\tfrac{1}{2}\right) = \ln 1 - \ln 2$$
$$30r = -\ln 2 \quad (\ln 1 = 0)$$
$$r = \dfrac{-\ln 2}{30} \approx \dfrac{-0.6931}{30}$$
$$\approx -0.0231$$

Thus, the continuous compound rate of decay of the cesium isotope is approximately -0.0231.

37. $2P_0 = P_0 e^{0.013t}$

$\quad e^{0.013t} = 2$

$\quad 0.013t = \ln 2$

$\quad\quad t = \dfrac{\ln 2}{0.013} \approx 53.3$

It will take approximately 53.3 years.

39. $2P_0 = P_0 e^{r(50)}$

$\quad e^{50r} = 2$

$\quad 50r = \ln 2$

$\quad\quad r = \dfrac{\ln 2}{50} \approx 0.0139$

$\quad\quad\quad$ or 1.39%

Things to remember:

1. COMPOSITE FUNCTIONS

   A function m is a COMPOSITE of functions f and g if
   $$m(x) = f[g(x)]$$
   The domain of m is the set of all numbers x such that x is in the domain of g and $g(x)$ is in the domain of f.

2. EXPONENTIAL DERIVATIVE FORMULAS

   (a) $\dfrac{d}{dx}e^x = e^x$

   (b) If $u = u(x)$ is a differentiable function of x, then
   $$\frac{d}{dx}e^u = e^u \frac{d}{dx}u = e^{u(x)}u'(x)$$

---

1. $f(u) = u^3$, $g(x) = 3x^2 + 2$
   $f[g(x)] = (3x^2 + 2)^3$

3. $f(u) = e^u$, $g(x) = -x^2$
   $f[g(x)] = e^{-x^2}$

5. Let $u = g(x) = 3x^2 - x + 5$ and $f(u) = u^4$. Then $y = f(u) = u^4$.

7. Let $u = g(x) = 1 + x + x^2$ and $f(u) = e^u$. Then $y = f(u) = e^u$.

9. $f(x) = 4x^3 + 5e^x$
   $f'(x) = 12x^2 + 5e^x$

11. $y = 4e^x - 3x^e$
   $\dfrac{dy}{dx} = 4e^x - 3ex^{e-1}$
   [Note: e is a constant so we use the power rule on the second term.]

13. $y = -3e^{-x} + 2e^x$
   $y' = -3e^{-x}(-1) + 2e^x = 3e^{-x} + 2e^x$

15. $f(x) = x^3 e^x$
   $f'(x) = x^3 \dfrac{d}{dx}e^x + e^x \dfrac{d}{dx}x^3$ (Product rule)
   $= x^3 e^x + e^x 3x^2 = x^2 e^x(x + 3)$

17. $f(x) = 3e^{2x}$
   $f'(x) = 3e^{2x}(2) = 6e^{2x}$

19. $f(x) = 5e^{-3x}$
   $f'(x) = 5e^{-3x}(-3) = -15e^{-3x}$

21. $f(x) = 200e^{-0.5x}$

$f'(x) = 200e^{-0.5x}(-0.5)$

$\quad\quad = -100e^{-0.5x}$

23. $f(x) = xe^{-2x}$

$f'(x) = x\dfrac{d}{dx}e^{-2x} + e^{-2x}\dfrac{d}{dx}x$

$\quad\quad = xe^{-2x}(-2) + e^{-2x}(1)$

$\quad\quad = -2xe^{-2x} + e^{-2x} = e^{-2x}(1 - 2x)$

25. $f(x) = \dfrac{e^x}{x^2 + 9}$

$f'(x) = \dfrac{(x^2 + 9)\dfrac{d}{dx}e^x - e^x\dfrac{d}{dx}(x^2 + 9)}{(x^2 + 9)^2}$ (Quotient rule)

$\quad\quad = \dfrac{(x^2 + 9)e^x - e^x(2x)}{(x^2 + 9)^2} = \dfrac{e^x(x^2 - 2x + 9)}{(x^2 + 9)^2}$

27. $\dfrac{d}{dx}e^{3x^2-2x} = e^{3x^2-2x}(6x - 2) = (6x - 2)e^{3x^2-2x}$

29. $\dfrac{d}{dx}(e^{2x} - 1)^4 = 4(e^{2x} - 1)^3[e^{2x}(2)] = 8e^{2x}(e^{2x} - 1)^3$

31. $f(x) = \dfrac{x^2 + 1}{e^x}$

$f'(x) = \dfrac{e^x\dfrac{d}{dx}(x^2 + 1) - (x^2 + 1)\dfrac{d}{dx}e^x}{(e^x)^2} = \dfrac{e^x(2x) - (x^2 + 1)e^x}{e^{2x}} = \dfrac{2x - x^2 - 1}{e^x}$

33. $\dfrac{d}{dx}(x^2 + 1)e^{-x} = (x^2 + 1)\dfrac{d}{dx}e^{-x} + e^{-x}\dfrac{d}{dx}(x^2 + 1)$

$\quad\quad = (x^2 + 1)e^{-x}(-1) + e^{-x}(2x) = e^{-x}(2x - x^2 - 1)$

35. $f(x) = xe^x - e^x$

$f'(x) = x\dfrac{d}{dx}e^x + e^x\dfrac{d}{dx}x - \dfrac{d}{dx}e^x = xe^x + e^x - e^x = xe^x$

37. An equation for the tangent line to the graph of $f(x) = e^x$ at the point $(3, f(3)) = (3, e^3)$ is:

$\quad\quad y - e^3 = e^3(x - 3)$

$\quad$ or $\quad y = xe^3 - 2e^3 = e^3(x - 2)$

Clearly, $y = 0$ when $x = 2$, that is the tangent line passes through the point $(2, 0)$.

In general, an equation for the tangent line to the graph of $f(x) = e^x$ at the point $(c, f(c)) = (c, e^c)$ is:

$\quad\quad y - e^c = e^c(x - c)$

$\quad$ or $\quad y = e^c(x - [c - 1])$

Thus, the tangent line at the point (c, e^c) passes through $(c - 1, 0)$; then tangent line at the point $(4, e^4)$ passes through $(3, 0)$.

39. $f(x) = \dfrac{e^x}{x^2}$, $x > 0$

$$f'(x) = \frac{x^2 \dfrac{d}{dx} e^x - e^x \dfrac{d}{dx} x^2}{x^4} = \frac{x^2 e^x - 2x e^x}{x^4} = \frac{x e^x(x - 2)}{x^4} = \frac{e^x(x - 2)}{x^3}$$

Critical values: $f'(x) = \dfrac{e^x(x - 2)}{x^3} = 0$

$$e^x(x - 2) = 0$$

$$x = 2 \quad [\underline{\text{Note}}: e^x \neq 0 \text{ for all } x.]$$

Thus, $x = 2$ is the only critical value of f on $(0, \infty)$.
Sign chart for f' [$\underline{\text{Note}}$: This approach is a little easier than calculating $f''(x)$]:

Test Numbers	
x	$f'(x)$
1	$-e$ $(-)$
3	$\dfrac{e^3}{27}$ $(+)$

By the first derivative test, f has a minimum value at $x = 2$;

$f(2) = \dfrac{e^2}{2^2} = \dfrac{e^2}{4} \approx 1.847$ is the absolute minimum value of f.

41. $f(x) = \dfrac{x^3}{e^x}$

$$f'(x) = \frac{\left(\dfrac{d}{dx} x^3\right) e^x - \left(\dfrac{d}{dx} e^x\right) x^3}{(e^x)^2}$$

$$= \frac{3x^2 e^x - x^3 e^x}{e^{2x}} = \frac{x^2(3 - x) e^x}{e^{2x}} = \frac{x^2(3 - x)}{e^x}$$

Critical values: $f'(x) = \dfrac{x^2(3 - x)}{e^x} = 0$

$$x^2(3 - x) = 0$$

$$x = 0 \text{ and } x = 3$$

Sign chart for f' [$\underline{\text{Note}}$: This approach is a little easier than calculating $f''(x)$]:

Test Numbers	
x	$f'(x)$
-1	$\dfrac{4}{e^{-1}}$ $(+)$
1	$\dfrac{2}{e}$ $(+)$
4	$-\dfrac{16}{e^4}$ $(-)$

By the first derivative test, f has a maximum value at $x = 3$;

$f(3) = \dfrac{27}{e^3} \approx 1.344$ is the absolute maximum value of f.

43. $f(x) = 1 - e^{-x}$

Step 1. Analyze $f(x)$:

(A) Domain: All real numbers, $(-\infty, \infty)$.

(B) Intercepts: y-intercept: $f(0) = 1 - e^{-0} = 0$

x-intercept: $1 - e^{-x} = 0$

$$e^{-x} = 1$$

$$x = 0$$

(C) Asymptotes:

Horizontal asymptote: $\lim\limits_{x \to \infty} (1 - e^{-x}) = \lim\limits_{x \to \infty} \left(1 - \dfrac{1}{e^x}\right) = 1$

$\lim\limits_{x \to \infty} (1 - e^{-x})$ does not exist.

$y = 1$ is a horizontal asymptote.

Vertical asymptotes: There are no vertical asymptotes.

Step 2. Analyze $f'(x)$:

$f'(x) = -e^{-x}(-1) = e^{-x}$

Since $e^{-x} > 0$ for all x, f is increasing on $(-\infty, \infty)$; there are no local extrema.

Step 3. Analyze $f''(x)$:

$f''(x) = e^{-x}(-1) = -e^{-x}$

Since $-e^{-x} < 0$ for all x, the graph of f is concave downward on $(-\infty, \infty)$.

Step 4. Sketch the graph of f:

x	$f(x)$
0	0
−1	≈ −1.72
1	≈ 0.63

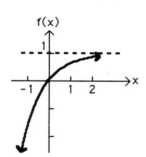

45. $f(x) = 5 + 5e^{-0.1x}$

Step 1. Analyze $f(x)$:

(A) Domain: All real numbers.

(B) Intercepts: y-intercept: $f(0) = 5 + 5e^{0} = 10$

x-intercept: $5 + 5e^{-0.1x} = 0$

$$e^{-0.1x} = -1; \text{ no solutions}$$

$$e^{-0.1x} > 0 \text{ for all } x$$

(C) Asymptotes:

Vertical asymptotes: None

Horizontal asymptotes: $\lim\limits_{x \to \infty} (5 + 5e^{-0.1x}) = \lim\limits_{x \to \infty} \left(5 + \dfrac{5}{e^{0.1x}}\right) = 5$

$\lim\limits_{x \to -\infty} (5 + 5e^{-0.1x})$ does not exist

$y = 5$ is a horizontal asymptote.

Step 2. Analyze $f'(x)$:

$f'(x) = 5e^{-0.1x}(-0.1) = -0.5e^{-0.1x}$

Critical values: None

Partition numbers: None

Sign chart for f':

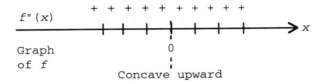

Thus, f decreases on $(-\infty, \infty)$.

Step 3. Analyze $f''(x)$:

$f''(x) = -0.5e^{-0.1x}(-0.1) = 0.05e^{-0.1x}$

Partition numbers for $f''(x)$: None

Sign chart for f':

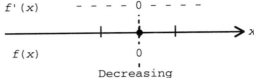

Thus, the graph of f is concave upward on $(-\infty, \infty)$.

Step 4. Sketch the graph of f:

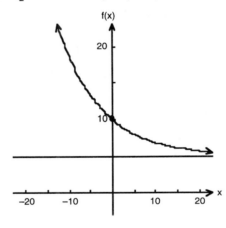

47. $f(x) = 5xe^{-0.2x}$

Step 1. Analyze $f(x)$:

(A) Domain: All real numbers.

(B) Intercepts: y-intercept: $f(0) = 5(0)e^0 = 0$

                  x-intercept: $5xe^{-0.2x} = 0$

                              $x = 0$

(C) Asymptotes:

    Vertical asymptotes: None

    Horizontal asymptotes:

x	10	20	30	40 $\to \infty$
$f(x)$	6.77	1.83	0.37	0.067 $\to$ 0

x	-10	-20	$\to -\infty$
$f(x)$	-369.45	-5458.01	$\to -\infty$

    $y = 0$ is a horizontal asymptote

Step 2. Analyze $f'(x)$:

$f'(x) = 5xe^{-0.2x}(-0.2) + e^{-0.2x}5 = 5e^{-0.2x}[1 - 0.2x]$

Critical values: $x = 5$

Partition numbers: $x = 5$

Sign chart for f':

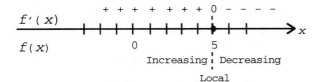

Test Numbers	
x	$f'(x)$
0	5 (+)
6	$-e^{-1.2}$ (−)

Thus, $f(x)$ increases on $(-\infty, 5)$, has a local maximum at $x = 5$, and decreases on $(5, \infty)$.

Step 3. Analyze $f''(x)$:

$f''(x) = 5e^{-0.2x}(-0.2) + [1 - 0.2x]5e^{-0.2x}(-0.2)$

$\qquad = -e^{-0.2x}[2 - 0.2x]$

Partition numbers for $f''(x)$: $x = 10$

Sign chart for f'':

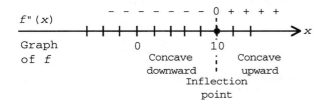

Test Numbers	
x	$f''(x)$
0	−2 (−)
20	$2e^{-4}$ (+)

Step 4. Sketch the graph of f:

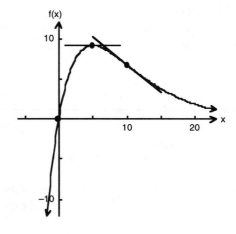

49. $f(x) = (3 - x)e^x$

Step 1. Analyze $f(x)$:

(A) Domain: All real numbers, $(-\infty, \infty)$.

(B) Intercepts: y-intercept: $f(0) = (3 - 0)e^0 = 3$

$\qquad\qquad\qquad x$-intercept: $(3 - x)e^x = 0$

$\qquad\qquad\qquad\qquad\qquad 3 - x = 0$

$\qquad\qquad\qquad\qquad\qquad\qquad x = 3$

(C) Asymptotes:

<u>Horizontal asymptote</u>: Consider the behavior of f as $x \to \infty$ and as $x \to -\infty$.

Using the following tables,

x	-1	-10	-20
$f(x)$	1.47	0.00059	0.000000047

x	5	10
$f(x)$	-296.83	-154,185.26

we conclude that $\lim\limits_{x \to -\infty} f(x) = 0$ and $\lim\limits_{x \to \infty} f(x)$ does not exist. Because of the first limit, $y = 0$ is a horizontal asymptote.

<u>Vertical asymptotes</u>: There are no vertical asymptotes.

<u>Step 2.</u> <u>Analyze $f'(x)$</u>:

$f'(x) = (3 - x)e^x + e^x(-1) = (2 - x)e^x$

Critical values: $(2 - x)e^x = 0$

$$x = 2 \quad [\underline{\text{Note}}: e^x > 0]$$

Partition numbers: $x = 2$

Sign chart for f':

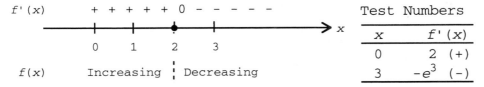

x	$f'(x)$
0	2 (+)
3	$-e^3$ (-)

Thus, f is increasing on $(-\infty, 2)$ and decreasing on $(2, \infty)$; f has a local maximum at $x = 2$.

<u>Step 3.</u> <u>Analyze $f''(x)$</u>:

$f''(x) = (2 - x)e^x + e^x(-1) = (1 - x)e^x$

Partition number for f'': $x = 1$

Sign chart for f'':

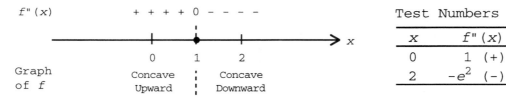

x	$f''(x)$
0	1 (+)
2	$-e^2$ (-)

Thus, the graph of f is concave upward on $(-\infty, 1)$ and concave downward on $(1, \infty)$; the graph has an inflection point at $x = 1$.

<u>Step 4.</u> <u>Sketch the graph of f</u>:

x	$f(x)$
0	3
2	$e^2 \approx 7.4$
3	0

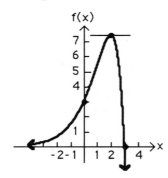

51. $f(x) = e^{-(1/2)x^2}$

Step 1. Analyze $f(x)$:

(A) Domain: All real numbers, $(-\infty, \infty)$.

(B) Intercepts: y-intercept: $f(0) = e^{-(1/2)0} = e^0 = 1$

x-intercepts: Since $e^{-(1/2)x^2} \neq 0$ for all x, there are no x-intercepts.

(C) Asymptotes: $\lim\limits_{x \to \infty} f(x) = \lim\limits_{x \to \infty} e^{-(1/2)x^2} = \lim\limits_{x \to \infty} \dfrac{1}{e^{(1/2)x^2}} = 0$

$\lim\limits_{x \to -\infty} f(x) = \lim\limits_{x \to -\infty} e^{-(1/2)x^2} = \lim\limits_{x \to -\infty} \dfrac{1}{e^{(1/2)x^2}} = 0$

Thus, $y = 0$ is a horizontal asymptote.

Since $f(x) = e^{-(1/2)x^2} = \dfrac{1}{e^{(1/2)x^2}}$ and $g(x) = e^{(1/2)x^2} \neq 0$ for all x,

there are no vertical asymptotes.

Step 2. Analyze $f'(x)$:

$f'(x) = e^{-(1/2)x^2}(-x) = -xe^{-(1/2)x^2}$

Critical values: $-xe^{-(1/2)x^2} = 0$

$x = 0$

Partition numbers: $x = 0$

Sign chart for f':

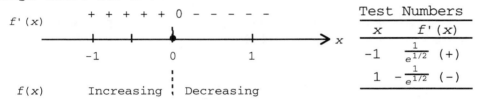

x	f'(x)
-1	$\frac{1}{e^{1/2}}$ (+)
1	$-\frac{1}{e^{1/2}}$ (-)

Test Numbers

Thus, f is increasing on $(-\infty, 0)$ and decreasing on $(0, \infty)$; f has a local maximum at $x = 0$.

Step 3. Analyze $f''(x)$:

$f''(x) = -xe^{-(1/2)x^2}(-x) - e^{-(1/2)x^2}$

$= e^{-(1/2)x^2}(x^2 - 1) = e^{-(1/2)x^2}(x - 1)(x + 1)$

Partition numbers for f'': $e^{-(1/2)x^2}(x - 1)(x + 1) = 0$

$(x - 1)(x + 1) = 0$

$x = -1, 1$

Sign chart for f'':

x	f''(x)
-2	$\frac{3}{e^2}$ (+)
0	-1 (-)
2	$\frac{3}{e^2}$ (+)

Test Numbers

Thus, the graph of f is concave upward on $(-\infty, -1)$ and on $(1, \infty)$; the graph of f is concave downward on $(-1, 1)$; the graph has inflection points at $x = -1$ and at $x = 1$.

Step 4. Sketch the graph of f:

x	$f(x)$
0	1
-1	≈ 0.61
1	≈ 0.61

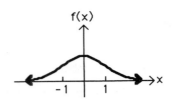

53. $f(x) = e^x - 2x^2 \qquad -\infty < x < \infty$

$f'(x) = e^x - 4x$

Critical values:

Solve $f'(x) = e^x - 4x = 0$

To two decimal places, $x = 0.36$ and $x = 2.15$

Increasing/Decreasing: $f(x)$ is increasing on $(-\infty, 0.36)$ and on $(2.15, \infty)$; $f(x)$ is decreasing on $(0.36, 2.15)$

Local extrema: $f(x)$ has a local maximum at $x = 0.36$ and a local minimum at $x = 2.15$

55. On a graphing utility, graph $y_1 = e^x$ and $y_2 = x^4$. Rounded off to two decimal places, the points of intersection are: $(-0.82, 0.44)$, $(1.43, 4.18)$, $(8.61, 5503.66)$.

57. Demand: $p = 10e^{-x}$, $0 \leq x \leq 2$

(A) $p'(x) = -10e^{-x}$; $p'(0.8) = -10e^{-0.8} \approx -4.49$

At the demand level of 800 ($= 0.8$ thousand) lipsticks per week, the price is DECREASING at the rate of $4.49.

(B) The sign chart for R' is:

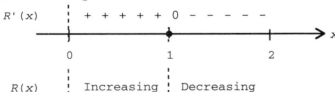

Test Numbers	
x	$f'(x)$
0	10 (+)
2	$-\dfrac{10}{e^2}$ (−)

Thus, R is increasing on $(0, 1)$ and decreasing on $(1, 2)$; the maximum value of R occurs at $x = 1$, as noted in (A).

$R''(x) = 10e^{-x}(x - 2) < 0$ on $(0, 2)$
Thus, the graph of R is concave downward on $(0, 2)$. The graph is shown at the right.

x	$R(x)$
0	0
1	3.68
2	2.71

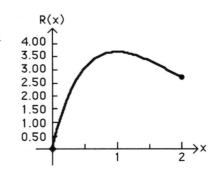

59. Price: $p = 100e^{-0.05x}$, $x \geq 0$

Revenue: $R(x) = xp = 100xe^{-0.05x}$

$R'(x) = 100xe^{-0.05x}(-0.05) + 100e^{-0.05x}$

$= 100e^{-0.05x}(1 - 0.05x)$

Critical value(s): $R'(x) = 100e^{-0.05x}(1 - 0.05x) = 0$

$1 - 0.05x = 0$

$x = 20$

$R''(x) = 100e^{-0.05x}(-0.05) + (1 - 0.05x)100e^{-0.05x}(-0.05)$

$= 100e^{-0.05x}(0.0025x - 0.1)$

$R''(20) = -100e^{-1}(0.05) = \dfrac{-5}{e} < 0$

Since $x = 20$ is the only critical value and $R''(20) < 0$, the production level that maximizes the revenue is 20 units. The maximum revenue is $R(20) = 20(36.79) = 735.80$ or \$735.80, and the price is $p(20) = 36.79$ or \$36.79 each.

61. The cost function $C(x)$ is given by

$C(x) = 400 + 6x$

and the revenue function $R(x)$ is

$R(x) = xp = 100xe^{-0.05x}$

The profit function $P(x)$ is

$P(x) = R(x) - C(x)$

$= 100xe^{-0.05x} - 400 - 6x$

and $P'(x) = 100e^{-0.05x} - 5xe^{-0.05x} - 6$

We graph $y = P(x)$ and $y = P'(x)$ in the viewing rectangle $0 \leq x \leq 50$, $-400 \leq y \leq 300$

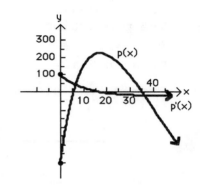

Critical value: Solve $P'(x) = (100 - 5x)e^{-0.05x} - 6 = 0$

To the nearest integer, $x = 17$.

$P(x)$ is increasing on $(0, 17)$ and decreasing on $(17, \infty)$; $P(x)$ has a maximum at $x = 17$. Thus, the maximum profit $P(17) = \$224.61$ is realized at a production level of 17 units at a price of \$42.74 per unit.

63. $S(t) = 300{,}000e^{-0.1t}$, $t \geq 0$

$S'(t) = 300{,}000e^{-0.1t}(-0.1) = -30{,}000e^{-0.1t}$

The rate of depreciation after one year is:

$S'(1) = -30{,}000e^{-0.1} \approx -\$27{,}145.12$ per year.

The rate of depreciation after five years is:

$S'(5) = -30{,}000e^{-0.5} \approx -\$18{,}195.92$ per year.

The rate of depreciation after ten years is:

$S'(10) = -30{,}000e^{-1} \approx -\$11{,}036.38$ per year.

65. Revenue: $R(t) = 200,000(1 - e^{-0.03t})$, $t \geq 0$

Cost: $C(t) = 4000 + 3000t$, $t \geq 0$

Profit: $P(t) = R(t) - C(t) = 200,000(1 - e^{-0.03t}) - (4000 + 3000t)$

$$= 200,000(1 - e^{-0.03t}) - 3000t - 4000$$

(A) $P'(t) = -200,000e^{-0.03t}(-0.03) - 3000 = 6000e^{-0.03t} - 3000$

Critical value(s): $P'(t) = 6000e^{-0.03t} - 3000 = 0$

$$e^{-0.03t} = \frac{1}{2}$$

$$-0.03t = \ln\left(\frac{1}{2}\right) = -\ln 2$$

$$t = \frac{\ln 2}{0.03} \approx 23$$

$$P''(t) = 6000e^{-0.03t}(-0.03) = -180e^{-0.03t}$$

$$P''(23) = -180e^{-0.69} < 0$$

Since $t = 23$ is the only critical value and $P''(23) < 0$, 23 days of TV promotion should be used to maximize profits. The maximum profit is: $P(23) = 200,000(1 - e^{-0.03(23)}) - 3000(23) - 4000 \approx \$26,685$
The proportion of people buying the disk after t days is:

$$p(t) = 1 - e^{-0.03t}$$

Thus, $p(23) = 1 - e^{-0.03(23)} \approx 0.50$ or approximately 50%.

(B) From A, the sign chart for P' is:

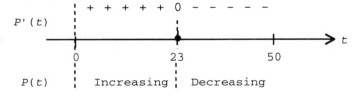

Test Numbers	
t	$P'(t)$
0	3000 (+)
50	-1661.22 (-)

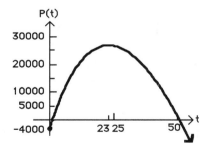

Thus, P is increasing on $(0, 23)$ and decreasing on $(23, \infty)$; P has a maximum at $t = 23$.
Since $P''(t) = -180e^{-0.03t} < 0$ on $(0, \infty)$, the graph of P is concave downward on $(0, \infty)$;
$P(0) = -4000$ and $P(50) \approx 0$.
The graph of P is shown at the right.

67. $C(t) = 4.35e^{-t} = \dfrac{4.35}{e^t}$, $0 \leq t \leq 5$

(A) $C'(t) = \dfrac{-4.35e^t}{e^{2t}} = \dfrac{-4.35}{e^t} = -4.35e^{-t}$

$C'(1) = -4.35e^{-1} \approx -1.60$

$C'(4) = -4.35e^{-4} \approx -0.08$

Thus, after one hour, the concentration is decreasing at the rate of 1.60 mg/ml per hour; after four hours, the concentration is decreasing at the rate of 0.08 mg/ml per hour.

(B) $C'(t) = -4.35e^{-t} < 0$ on $(0, 5)$
Thus, C is decreasing on $(0, 5)$; there are no local extrema.

$$C''(t) = \frac{4.35e^t}{e^{2t}} = \frac{4.35}{e^t} = 4.35e^{-t} > 0 \text{ on } (0, 5)$$

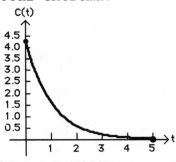

Thus, the graph of C is concave upward on $(0, 5)$. The graph of C is shown at the right.

t	$C(t)$
0	4.35
1	1.60
4	0.08
5	0.03

69. $N(n) = 1{,}000{,}000e^{-0.09(n-1)}$, $1 \le n \le 20$
There are no asymptotes and no intercepts.
Using the first derivative:
$$N'(n) = 1{,}000{,}000e^{-0.09(n-1)}(-0.09)$$
$$= -90{,}000e^{-0.09(n-1)} < 0, \ 1 \le n \le 20$$
Thus, N is decreasing on $(0, 20)$.
Using the second derivative:
$$N''(n) = -90{,}000e^{-0.09(n-1)}(-0.09)$$
$$= 8100e^{-0.09(n-1)} > 0, \ 1 \le n \le 20$$
Thus, the graph of N is concave upward on $(0, 20)$.

The graph of N is:

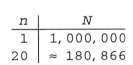

n	N
1	1,000,000
20	$\approx 180{,}866$

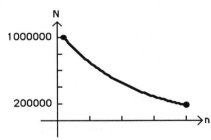

EXERCISE 5-3

Things to remember:

1. LOGARITHMIC FUNCTIONS

   The inverse of an exponential function is called a LOGARITHMIC FUNCTION. For $b > 0$, $b \ne 1$,

Logarithmic form	Exponential form
$y = \log_b x$ is equivalent to	$x = b^y$

   Domain: $(0, \infty)$ Domain: $(-\infty, \infty)$
   Range: $(-\infty, \infty)$ Range: $(0, \infty)$

   The graphs of $y = \log_b x$ and $y = b^x$ are symmetric with respect to the line $y = x$.

2. DERIVATIVE FORMULAS FOR LOGARITHMIC FUNCTIONS

(a) $\dfrac{d}{dx}\ln x = \dfrac{1}{x}$

(b) If $u = u(x)$ is a differentiable function of x, then
$$\dfrac{d}{dx}\ln u = \dfrac{1}{u}\dfrac{d}{dx}u = \dfrac{1}{u(x)}\cdot u'(x) = \dfrac{u'(x)}{u(x)}$$

(c) Other bases: For $b > 0$, $b \neq 1$,
$$\dfrac{d}{dx}\log_b x = \dfrac{1}{\ln b}\cdot\dfrac{1}{x} \quad\text{and}\quad \dfrac{d}{dx}b^x = b^x \ln b$$

---

1. $\dfrac{d}{dx}\ln(x - 3) = \dfrac{1}{x - 3}(1)$ (using **3b**)

$\qquad\qquad\quad = \dfrac{1}{x - 3}$

3. $\dfrac{d}{dt}\ln(3 - 2t) = \dfrac{1}{3 - 2t}(-2)$ (using **3b**)

$\qquad\qquad\quad = \dfrac{-2}{3 - 2t}$

5. $y = \ln x^3 \qquad\qquad$ or $\quad y = \ln x^3 = 3\ln x$ [Using logarithm properties]

$\quad y' = \dfrac{1}{x^3}\cdot 3x^2 = \dfrac{3}{x} \qquad\quad y' = \dfrac{3}{x}$

7. $\dfrac{d}{dx}(\ln x)^6 = 6(\ln x)^5\cdot\dfrac{1}{x} = \dfrac{6(\ln x)^5}{x}$

9. $f(x) = x^4\ln x$

$\quad f'(x) = x^4\dfrac{d}{dx}\ln x + \ln x\dfrac{d}{dx}x^4$ (Product rule)

$\qquad\quad = x^4\left(\dfrac{1}{x}\right) + (\ln x)4x^3 = x^3 + 4x^3\ln x = x^3(1 + 4\ln x)$

11. $\dfrac{d}{dx}\ln(x + 1)^4 = \dfrac{d}{dx}4\ln(x + 1) = 4\dfrac{d}{dx}\ln(x + 1) = 4\dfrac{1}{x + 1}(1) = \dfrac{4}{x + 1}$

13. $f(x) = \dfrac{\ln x}{x^4}$

$\quad f'(x) = \dfrac{x^4\dfrac{d}{dx}\ln x - \ln x\dfrac{d}{dx}x^4}{(x^4)^2}$ (Quotient rule)

$\qquad\quad = \dfrac{x^4\left(\dfrac{1}{x}\right) - (\ln x)4x^3}{x^8} = \dfrac{x^3 - 4x^3\ln x}{x^8} = \dfrac{1 - 4\ln x}{x^5}$

15. $f(x) = (x + 2)^3 \ln x$

$f'(x) = (x + 2)^3 \dfrac{d}{dx} \ln x + (\ln x) \dfrac{d}{dx} (x + 2)^3$

$= (x + 2)^3 \left(\dfrac{1}{x}\right) + (\ln x) [3(x + 2)^2 (1)]$

$= 3(x + 2)^2 \ln x + \dfrac{(x + 2)^3}{x} = (x + 2)^2 \left[3 \ln x + \dfrac{x + 2}{x}\right]$

17. $f(x) = \ln(x^2 + 1)$

$f'(x) = \dfrac{1}{x^2 + 1} \dfrac{d}{dx} (x^2 + 1) = \dfrac{2x}{x^2 + 1}$

19. $\dfrac{d}{dx} \ln(x^2 + 1)^{1/2} = \dfrac{d}{dx} \dfrac{1}{2} \ln(x^2 + 1) = \dfrac{1}{2} \dfrac{d}{dx} \ln(x^2 + 1)$

$= \dfrac{1}{2} \left(\dfrac{1}{x^2 + 1}\right)(2x) = \dfrac{x}{x^2 + 1}$

21. $f(x) = [\ln(x^2 + 1)]^{1/2}$

$f'(x) = \dfrac{1}{2} [\ln(x^2 + 1)]^{-1/2} \dfrac{d}{dx} [\ln(x^2 + 1)] = \dfrac{1}{2} [\ln(x^2 + 1)^{-1/2} \dfrac{2x}{x^2 + 1}$

$= \dfrac{x}{(x^2 + 1)[\ln(x^2 + 1)]^{1/2}}$

23. $f(x) = x(\ln x)^3$

$f'(x) = x \dfrac{d}{dx} (\ln x)^3 + (\ln x)^3 \dfrac{d}{dx} x$

$= x(3)(\ln x)^2 \left(\dfrac{1}{x}\right) + (\ln x)^3 (1) = (\ln x)^2 [3 + \ln x]$

25. $f(x) = \sqrt{1 + \ln x} = (1 + \ln x)^{1/2}$

$f'(x) = \dfrac{1}{2} (1 + \ln x)^{-1/2} \left(\dfrac{1}{x}\right)$

$= \dfrac{1}{2x(1 + \ln x)^{1/2}} = \dfrac{1}{2x\sqrt{1 + \ln x}}$

27. $f(x) = 2x^2 \ln x - x^2$

$f'(x) = 2x^2 \dfrac{d}{dx} \ln x + \ln x \dfrac{d}{dx} 2x^2 - \dfrac{d}{dx} x^2 = 2x^2 \left(\dfrac{1}{x}\right) + 4x \ln x - 2x$

$= 4x \ln x$

29. $\dfrac{d}{dx} e^{-x} \ln x = e^{-x} \dfrac{d}{dx} \ln x + \ln x \dfrac{d}{dx} e^{-x} = e^{-x} \left(\dfrac{1}{x}\right) + (\ln x)(e^{-x})(-1)$

$= \dfrac{e^{-x}}{x} - e^{-x} \ln x = \dfrac{e^{-x}[1 - x \ln x]}{x}$

31. $\dfrac{d}{dx} \dfrac{1}{\ln(1 + x^2)} = \dfrac{d}{dx} [\ln(1 + x^2)]^{-1} = -1[\ln(1 + x^2)]^{-2} \dfrac{d}{dx} \ln(1 + x^2)$

$= -[\ln(1 + x^2)]^{-2} \dfrac{1}{1 + x^2} (2x) = \dfrac{-2x}{(1 + x^2)[\ln(1 + x^2)]^2}$

33. $\dfrac{d}{dx}\sqrt[3]{\ln(1-x^2)} = \dfrac{d}{dx}[\ln(1-x^2)]^{1/3} = \dfrac{1}{3}[\ln(1-x^2)]^{-2/3}\dfrac{d}{dx}\ln(1-x^2)$

$$= \dfrac{1}{3}[\ln(1-x^2)]^{-2/3}\dfrac{1}{1-x^2}(-2x) = \dfrac{-2x}{3(1-x^2)[\ln(1-x^2)]^{2/3}}$$

35. $f(x) = \ln x$

$f'(x) = \dfrac{d}{dx}(\ln x) = \dfrac{1}{x}$

The tangent line at $x = e$ has an equation of the form
$y - y_1 = m(x - x_1)$

where $x_1 = e$, $y_1 = f(e) = \ln e = 1$, and $m = f'(e) = \dfrac{1}{e}$.   Thus, we have:

$y - 1 = \dfrac{1}{e}(x - e)$ or $y = \dfrac{1}{e}x$

37. $f(x) = \ln(2 - x^2)$

$f'(x) = \dfrac{1}{(2-x^2)}\dfrac{d}{dx}(2 - x^2) = \dfrac{-2x}{2-x^2}$

The tangent line at $x = 1$ has an equation of the form
$y - y_1 = m(x - x_1)$

where $x_1 = 1$, $y_1 = f(1) = \ln(1) = 0$ and $m = f'(1) = -2$

Thus, we have $y = -2(x - 1)$ or $y = -2x + 2$.

39. An equation for the tangent line to the graph of $g(x) = \ln x$ at the
point $(3, g(3)) = (3, \ln 3)$ is:
$$y - \ln 3 = m(x - 3) \text{ where } m = g'(3)$$
$g'(x) = \dfrac{d}{dx}\ln x = \dfrac{1}{x}$; $g'(3) = \dfrac{1}{3}$. Thus,

$y - \ln 3 = \dfrac{1}{3}(x - 3)$

For $x = 0$, $y = \ln 3 - 1$, so this tangent line does not pass through the
origin. In fact, for any real number c, the tangent line to $g(x) = \ln x$
at the point $(c, \ln c)$ has equation $y - \ln c = \dfrac{1}{c}(x - c)$, and thus the
only tangent line which passes through the origin is the tangent line at
$(e, 1)$.

41. $f(x) = \ln(1 - x)$

Step 1. Analyze $f(x)$:
(A) Domain: All real numbers x such that $1 - x > 0$, i.e., $x < 1$
             or $(-\infty, 1)$.

(B) Intercepts: y-intercept: $f(0) = \ln(1 - 0) = \ln 1 = 0$
                 x-intercepts: $\ln(1 - x) = 0$
                                  $1 - x = 1$
                                      $x = 0$

(C) Asymptotes:
     Horizontal asymptote: $\lim\limits_{x \to -\infty} f(x) = \lim\limits_{x \to -\infty} \ln(1 - x)$ does not exist.
                           Thus, there are no horizontal asymptotes.
     Vertical asymptote: From the table,

x	0.9	0.99	0.99999	0.9999999	$\to 1$
$f(x)$	-2.30	-4.61	-11.51	-16.12	$\to -\infty$

We conclude that $x = 1$ is a vertical asymptote.

Step 2. Analyze $f'(x)$:

$$f'(x) = \frac{1}{1-x}(-1), \quad x < 1$$

$$= \frac{1}{x-1}$$

Now, $f'(x) = \frac{1}{x-1} < 0$ on $(-\infty, 1)$.

Thus, f is decreasing on $(-\infty, 1)$; there are no critical values and no local extrema.

Step 3. Analyze $f''(x)$:

$$f'(x) = (x-1)^{-1}$$

$$f''(x) = -1(x-1)^{-2} = \frac{-1}{(x-1)^2}$$

Since $f''(x) = \frac{-1}{(1-x)^2} < 0$ on $(-\infty, 1)$, the graph of f is concave

downward on $(-\infty, 1)$; there are no inflection points.

Step 4. Sketch the graph of f:

x	$f(x)$
0	0
-2	≈ 1.10
.9	≈ -2.30

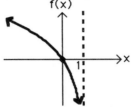

43. $f(x) = x - \ln x$

Step 1. Analyze $f(x)$:

(A) Domain: All positive real numbers, $(0, \infty)$.
   [Note: $\ln x$ is defined only for positive numbers.]

(B) Intercepts: y-intercept: There is no y intercept; $f(0) = 0 - \ln(0)$
   is not defined.
   x-intercept: $x - \ln x = 0$
   $\ln x = x$
   Since the graph of $y = \ln x$ is below the graph of $y = x$, there are
   no solutions to this equation; there are no x-intercepts.

(C) Asymptotes:

   Horizontal asymptote: None

   Vertical asymptotes: Since $\lim\limits_{x \to 0^+} \ln x = -\infty$, $\lim\limits_{x \to 0^+}(x - \ln x) = \infty$.
   Thus, $x = 0$ is a vertical asymptote for
   $f(x) = x - \ln x$.

Step 2. Analyze $f'(x)$:

$$f'(x) = 1 - \frac{1}{x} = \frac{x-1}{x}, \quad x > 0$$

Critical values: $\frac{x-1}{x} = 0$

$$x = 1$$

Partition numbers: $x = 1$

Sign chart for $f'(x) = \dfrac{x-1}{x}$:

$f'(x)$ — — — — — — 0 + + + + +   → x

0    $\frac{1}{2}$ 1   2

$f(x)$ Decreasing   Increasing

Test Numbers	
x	$f'(x)$
$\frac{1}{2}$	-1 $(-)$
2	$\frac{1}{2}$ $(+)$

Thus, f is decreasing on $(0, 1)$ and increasing on $(1, \infty)$; f has a local minimum at $x = 1$.

Step 3. Analyze $f''(x)$:

$f''(x) = \dfrac{1}{x^2}$, $x > 0$

Thus, $f''(x) > 0$ and the graph of f is concave upward on $(0, \infty)$.

Step 4. Sketch the graph of f:

x	$f(x)$
0.1	≈ 2.4
1	1
10	≈ 7.7

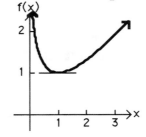

45. $f(x) = x^2 \ln x$.

Step 1. Analyze $f(x)$:

(A) Domain: All positive numbers, $(0, \infty)$.

(B) Intercepts: y-intercept: There is no y intercept.

                 x-intercept: $x^2 \ln x = 0$

                           $\ln x = 0$

                                $x = 1$

(C) Asymptotes: Consider the behavior of f as $x \to \infty$ and as $x \to 0$. It is clear that $\lim\limits_{x \to \infty} f(x)$ does not exist; f is unbounded as x approaches ∞.

The following table indicates that f approaches 0 as x approaches 0.

x	1	0.1	0.01	0.001
$f(x)$	0	-0.023	-0.00046	-0.000007

Thus, there are no vertical or horizontal asymptotes.

Step 2. Analyze $f'(x)$:

$f'(x) = x^2\left(\dfrac{1}{x}\right) + (\ln x)(2x) = x(1 + 2 \ln x)$

Critical values: $x(1 + 2 \ln x) = 0$

                  $1 + 2 \ln x = 0$ [Note: $x > 0$]

                       $\ln x = -\dfrac{1}{2}$

                             $x = e^{-1/2} = \dfrac{1}{\sqrt{e}} \approx 0.6065$

Partition number: $x = \dfrac{1}{\sqrt{e}} \approx 0.6065$

Sign chart for f':

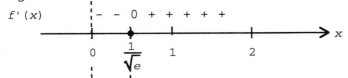

Test Numbers	
x	$f'(x)$
$\frac{1}{2}$	$\approx$ -0.19 $(-)$
1	1 $(+)$

Thus, f is decreasing on $(0, e^{-1/2})$ and increasing on $(e^{-1/2}, \infty)$; f has a local minimum at $x = e^{-1/2}$.

Step 3. Analyze $f''(x)$:

$$f''(x) = x\left(\frac{2}{x}\right) + (1 + 2 \ln x) = 3 + 2 \ln x$$

Partition number for f'': $3 + 2 \ln x = 0$

$$\ln x = -\frac{3}{2}$$

$$x = e^{-3/2} \approx 0.2231$$

Sign chart for f'':

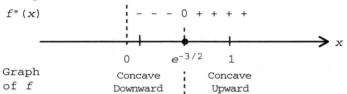

Test Numbers	
x	$f''(x)$
$\frac{1}{10}$	$\approx$ -1.61 $(-)$
1	3 $(+)$

Thus, the graph of f is concave downward on $(0, e^{-3/2})$ and concave upward on $(e^{-3/2}, \infty)$; the graph has an inflection point at $x = e^{-3/2}$.

Step 4. Sketch the graph of f:

x	$f(x)$
$e^{-3/2}$	≈ -0.075
$e^{-1/2}$	≈ -0.18
1	0

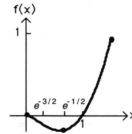

47. $f(x) = (\ln x)^2$

Step 1. Analyze $f(x)$:

(A) Domain: All positive numbers, $(0, \infty)$.

(B) Intercepts: y-intercept: There is no y-intercept.

$$x\text{-intercept: } (\ln x)^2 = 0$$
$$\ln x = 0$$
$$x = 1$$

(C) Asymptotes:

Vertical asymptotes: Consider the behavior of f as $x \to \infty$ and as $x \to 0$. It is clear that $\lim_{x \to \infty} f(x)$ does not exist; $f(x) \to \infty$ as $x \to \infty$. Thus, there is no horizontal asymptote.

The following table indicates that $f(x) \to \infty$ as $x \to 0$.

$x = 0$ (the y-axis) is a vertical asymptote.

x	1	0.01	0.0001	0.000001
$f(x)$	0	21.21	84.83	190.89

Step 2. Analyze $f(x)$:

$$f'(x) = 2(\ln x)\frac{d}{dx}\ln x = \frac{2\ln x}{x}$$

Critical values: $\dfrac{2\ln x}{x} = 0$

$$\ln x = 0$$
$$x = 1$$

Partition numbers: $x = 1$
Sign chart for f':

	Test Numbers

$f'(x)$ $\quad$ $- - - - 0\ + + + +$

$f(x)$ $\qquad$ 0 $\quad$ 1
$\qquad\qquad$ Decreasing $\vdots$ Increasing

$\qquad\qquad\qquad$ Local
$\qquad\qquad\qquad$ minimum

Test Numbers	
x	$f'(x)$
0.5	$-2.77\ (-)$
2	$2.77\ (+)$

Thus, f is decreasing on $(0, 1)$ and increasing on $(1, \infty)$; f has a local minimum at $x = 1$.

Step 3. Analyze $f''(x)$:

$$f''(x) = \frac{x\left(\frac{2}{x}\right) - 2\ln x}{x^2} = \frac{2(1 - \ln x)}{x^2}$$

Partition numbers for $f''(x)$: $\dfrac{2(1 - \ln x)}{x^2} = 0$

$$\ln x = 1$$
$$x = e$$

Sign chart for f'':

$f''(x)$ $\quad$ $+ + + + + + + 0 - - - -$

Graph $\qquad$ 0 $\quad$ 1 $\quad$ 2 $\ e\ $ 3
of f $\qquad\quad$ Concave $\qquad$ Concave
$\qquad\qquad$ upward $\quad\vdots\quad$ downward

$\qquad\qquad\qquad$ Inflection
$\qquad\qquad\qquad$ point

Test Numbers	
x	$f''(x)$
1	$2\ (+)$
4	$-0.48\ (-)$

Thus, the graph of f is concave upward on $(0, e)$ and concave downward on (e, ∞); the graph has an inflection point at $x = e$.

Step 4. Sketch the graph of f:

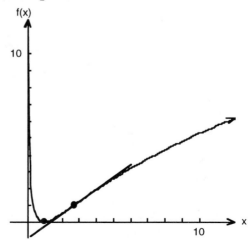

49. $f(x) = 5x - 2x \ln x, \quad x > 0$

$f'(x) = 5 - 2x\dfrac{d}{dx}(\ln x) - \ln x \dfrac{d}{dx}(2x)$

$\qquad = 5 - 2x\left(\dfrac{1}{x}\right) - 2 \ln x = 3 - 2 \ln x, \quad x > 0$

Critical values: $f'(x) = 3 - 2 \ln x = 0$

$$\ln x = \frac{3}{2} = 1.5; \quad x = e^{1.5}$$

Thus, $x = e^{1.5}$ is the only critical value of f on $(0, \infty)$.

Now, $f''(x) = \dfrac{d}{dx}(3 - 2 \ln x) = -\dfrac{2}{x}$

and $f''(e^{1.5}) = -\dfrac{2}{e^{1.5}} < 0$.

Therefore, f has a maximum value at $x = e^{1.5}$, and
$f(e^{1.5}) = 5e^{1.5} - 2e^{1.5} \ln(e^{1.5}) = 5e^{1.5} - 2(1.5)e^{1.5} = 2e^{1.5}$
is the absolute maximum of f.

51. $f(x) = x^2(3 - \ln x), \quad x > 0$

$f'(x) = x^2 \dfrac{d}{dx}(3 - \ln x) + (3 - \ln x)\dfrac{d}{dx}x^2$

$\qquad = x^2\left(-\dfrac{1}{x}\right) + (3 - \ln x)2x = -x + 6x - 2x \ln x = 5x - 2x \ln x$

Critical values: $f'(x) = 5x - 2x \ln x = 0$

$$x(5 - 2 \ln x) = 0$$
$$5 - 2 \ln x = 0$$
$$\ln x = \frac{5}{2} = 2.5$$
$$x = e^{2.5} \quad [\text{Note: } x \neq 0 \text{ on } (0, \infty)]$$

Now $\quad f''(x) = 5 - 2x\left(\dfrac{1}{x}\right) - 2 \ln x$

$\qquad\qquad = 3 - 2 \ln x$

and $f''(e^{2.5}) = 3 - 2\cdot\ln(e^{2.5}) = 3 - 2(2.5) = 3 - 5 = -2 < 0$

Therefore, f has a maximum value at $x = e^{2.5}$ and

$f(e^{2.5}) = (e^{2.5})^2(3 - \ln e^{2.5}) = e^5(3 - 2.5) = \dfrac{e^5}{2} \approx 74.207$

is the absolute maximum value of f.

53. $f(x) = \ln(xe^{-x}), \quad x > 0$

$f'(x) = \dfrac{1}{xe^{-x}}\dfrac{d}{dx}(xe^{-x}) = \dfrac{1}{xe^{-x}}[e^{-x} - xe^{-x}] = \dfrac{1 - x}{x}$

Critical values: $f'(x) = \dfrac{1 - x}{x} = 0; \quad x = 1$

Sign chart for $f'(x)$:

Test Numbers	
x	$f(x)$
$\frac{1}{2}$	$1 \; (+)$
2	$-\frac{1}{2} \; (-)$

By the first derivative test, f has a maximum value at $x = 1$;
$f(1) = \ln(e^{-1}) = -1$ is the absolute maximum value of f.

55. $\dfrac{d}{dx}\log_2(3x^2 - 1) = \dfrac{1}{\ln 2} \cdot \dfrac{1}{3x^2 - 1} \cdot 6x = \dfrac{1}{\ln 2} \cdot \dfrac{6x}{3x^2 - 1}$

57. $\dfrac{d}{dx}10^{x^2+x} = 10^{x^2+x}(\ln 10)(2x + 1) = (2x + 1)10^{x^2+x}\ln 10$

59. $\dfrac{d}{dx}\log_3(4x^3 + 5x + 7) = \dfrac{1}{\ln 3} \cdot \dfrac{1}{4x^3 + 5x + 7}(12x^2 + 5)$

$$= \dfrac{12x^2 + 5}{\ln 3(4x^3 + 5x + 7)}$$

61. $\dfrac{d}{dx}2^{x^3 - x^2 + 4x + 1} = 2^{x^3 - x^2 + 4x + 1}\ln 2(3x^2 - 2x + 4)$

$$= \ln 2(3x^2 - 2x + 4)2^{x^3 - x^2 + 4x + 1}$$

63. On a graphing utility, graph $y_1 = (\ln x)^2$ and $y_2(x) = x$. The curves intersect at $(0.49, 0.49)$ (two decimal places).

65. On a graphing utility, graph $y_1 = \ln x$ and $y_2 = x^{1/5}$. There is a point of intersection at $(3.65, 1.30)$ (two decimal places). Using the hint that $\ln x < x^{1/5}$ for large x, we find a second point of intersection at $(332,105.11, 12.71)$ (two decimal places).

67. $f'(x) = \dfrac{1}{5(x^2 + 3)^4}[20(x^2 + 3)^3](2x) = \dfrac{8x}{x^2 + 3}$

$g'(x) = 4 \cdot \dfrac{1}{x^2 + 3}(2x) = \dfrac{8x}{x^2 + 3}$

For another way to see this, recall the properties of logarithms discussed in Section 2-3:

$f(x) = \ln[5(x^2 + 3)^4] = \ln 5 + \ln(x^2 + 3)^4 = \ln 5 + 4\ln(x^2 + 3)$
$$= \ln 5 + g(x)$$

Now $\dfrac{d}{dx}f(x) = \dfrac{d}{dx}\ln 5 + \dfrac{d}{dx}g(x) = 0 + \dfrac{d}{dx}g(x) = \dfrac{d}{dx}g(x)$

Conclusion: $f'(x)$ and $g'(x)$ ARE the same function.

69. Demand: $p = 5 - \ln x$, $5 \le x \le 50$

Revenue: $R = xp = x(5 - \ln x) = 5x - x \ln x$

Cost: $C = x(1) = x$

Profit = Revenue - Cost: $P = 5x - x \ln x - x$

$$\text{or} \quad P(x) = 4x - x \ln x$$

$$P'(x) = 4 - x\left(\frac{1}{x}\right) - \ln x$$

$$= 3 - \ln x$$

Critical value(s): $P'(x) = 3 - \ln x = 0$

$$\ln x = 3$$

$$x = e^3$$

$P''(x) = -\dfrac{1}{x}$ and $P''(e^3) = -\dfrac{1}{e^3} < 0$.

Since $x = e^3$ is the only critical value and $P''(e^3) < 0$, the maximum weekly profit occurs when $x = e^3 \approx 20.09$ and the price $p = 5 - \ln(e^3) = 2$. Thus, the hot dogs should be sold at $2.

71. Cost: $C(x) = 600 + 100x - 100 \ln x$, $x \ge 1$

Average cost: $\overline{C}(x) = \dfrac{600}{x} + 100 - \dfrac{100}{x}\ln x$

$$\overline{C}'(x) = \frac{-600}{x^2} - \frac{100}{x^2} + \frac{100 \ln x}{x^2} = \frac{-700 + 100 \ln x}{x^2}, \quad x \ge 1$$

Critical value(s): $\overline{C}'(x) = \dfrac{-700 + 100 \ln x}{x^2} = 0$

$$-700 + 100 \ln x = 0$$

$$\ln x = 7$$

$$x = e^7$$

$$\overline{C}''(x) = \frac{x^2 \frac{100}{x} - (-700 + 100 \ln x)(2x)}{x^4}$$

$$= \frac{100x + 1400x - 200x \ln x}{x^4} = \frac{1500 - 200 \ln x}{x^3}$$

$$\overline{C}''(e^7) = \frac{1500 - 200 \ln(e^7)}{e^{21}} = \frac{100}{e^{21}} > 0$$

Since $x = e^7$ is the only critical value and $\overline{C}''(e^7) > 0$, the minimum average cost is

$$\overline{C}(e^7) = \frac{600}{e^7} + 100 - \frac{100}{e^7}\ln(e^7) = \frac{600}{e^7} + 100 - \frac{700}{e^7} = 100 - \frac{100}{e^7} \approx 99.91$$

Thus, the minimal average cost is approximately $99.91.

73. Let x = the number of jeans sold. Then

$C(x) = 20x$

The logarithmic regression equation for the price p is:

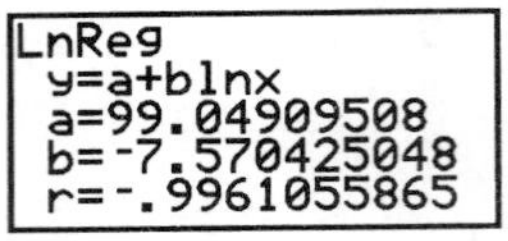
LnReg
y=a+blnx
a=99.04909508
b=-7.570425048
r=-.9961055865

and revenue $R(x) = xp(x) = x(99.04909508 - 7.570425048 \ln x)$

$$= 99.04909508x - 7.570425048x \ln x.$$

$$\text{Profit } P(x) = 99.04909508x - 7.570425048x \ln x - 20x$$
$$= 79.04909508x - 7.570425048x \ln x$$

$$P'(x) = 79.04909508 - 7.570425048 - 7.570425048 \ln x$$
$$= 71.47867003 - 7.570425048 \ln x$$

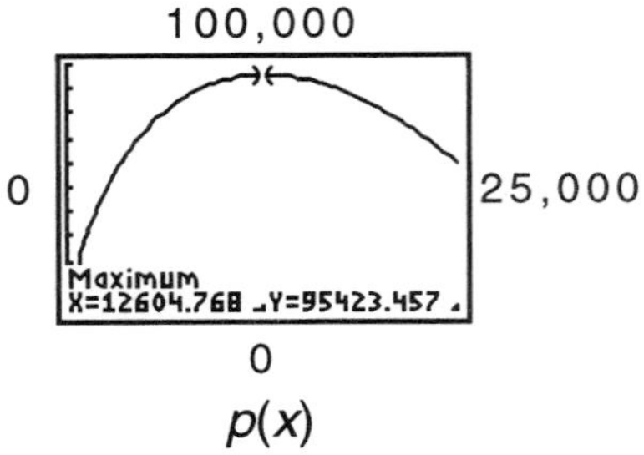
100,000
0
25,000
Maximum
X=12604.768 Y=95423.457
0
p(x)

Critical value: $71.47867003 - 7.570425048 \ln x = 0$

$$\ln x \approx \frac{71.47867003}{7.570425048} \approx 9.441830489$$

$$x = e^{9.441830489} \approx 12,605$$

The maximum profit occurs when $x = 12,605$ jeans are sold at the price $p = \$27.57$.

75. Let x = the number of modems per week. The weekly cost is $C(x) = 100x$. The weekly revenue is $R(x) = xp(x)$, where $p(x) = ab^x$ is the exponential regression model for the given data.

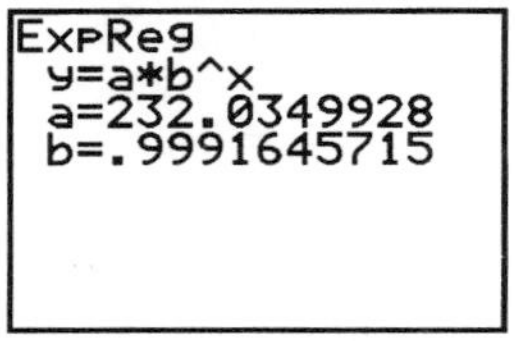
ExpReg
y=a*b^x
a=232.0349928
b=.9991645715

The weekly profit is $P(x) = R(x) - C(x)$. Using a graphing utility we find that the maximum profit is achieved at the demand level $x = 447$. The price that will maximize the profit is $p(447) = \$159.70$ (to the nearest cent).

77. $P(x) = 17.5(1 + \ln x)$, $10 \le x \le 100$

$$P'(x) = \frac{17.5}{x}$$

$$P'(40) = \frac{17.5}{40} \approx 0.44$$

$$P'(90) = \frac{17.5}{90} \approx 0.19$$

Thus, at the 40 pound weight level, blood pressure would increase at the rate of 0.44 mm of mercury per pound of weight gain; at the 90 pound weight level, blood pressure would increase at the rate of 0.19 mm of mercury per pound of weight gain.

79. $P(x) = 40 + 25 \ln(x + 1) \quad 0 \le x \le 65$

$P'(x) = 25\left(\dfrac{1}{x + 1}\right)(1) = \dfrac{25}{x + 1}$

$P'(10) = \dfrac{25}{11} \approx 2.27$

$P'(30) = \dfrac{25}{31} \approx 0.81$

$P'(60) = \dfrac{25}{61} \approx 0.41$

Thus, the rate of change of pressure at the end of 10 years is 2.27 millimeters of mercury per year; at the end of 30 years the rate of change is 0.81 millimeters of mercury per year; at the end of 60 years the rate of change is 0.41 millimeters of mercury per year.

81. $A(t) = 5000 \cdot 2^{2t}$

$A'(t) = 5000 \cdot 2^{2t}(2)(\ln 2) = 10{,}000 \cdot 2^{2t}(\ln 2)$

$A'(1) = 10{,}000 \cdot 2^{2}(\ln 2) = 40{,}000 \ln 2$

$\qquad \approx 27{,}726$ rate of change of bacteria at the end of the first hour.

$A'(5) = 10{,}000 \cdot 2^{2 \cdot 5}(\ln 2) = 10{,}000 \cdot 2^{10}(\ln 2)$

$\qquad \approx 7{,}097{,}827$ rate of change of bacteria at the end of the fifth hour.

83. $R = k \ln(S/S_0)$

$\quad = k[\ln S - \ln S_0]$

$\dfrac{dR}{dS} = \dfrac{k}{S}$

EXERCISE 5-4
_____

Things to remember:

    <u>1</u>. THE CHAIN RULE: GENERAL FORM

        If $y = f(u)$ and $u = g(x)$ define the composite function
          $y = m(x) = f[g(x)]$,

        then

            $\dfrac{dy}{dx} = \dfrac{dy}{du}\dfrac{du}{dx}$ provided that $\dfrac{dy}{du}$ and $\dfrac{du}{dx}$ exist.

        Or, equivalently,
          $m'(x) = f'[g(x)]g'(x)$ provided that $f'[g(x)]$ and $g'(x)$ exist.

    <u>2</u>.   GENERAL DERIVATIVE RULES

        (a) $\dfrac{d}{dx}[f(x)]^n = n[f(x)]^{n-1}f'(x)$

        (b) $\dfrac{d}{dx}\ln[f(x)] = \dfrac{1}{f(x)}f'(x)$

        (c) $\dfrac{d}{dx}e^{f(x)} = e^{f(x)}f'(x)$

3\. RELATIVE AND PERCENTAGE RATES OF CHANGE

The RELATIVE RATE OF CHANGE of a function $f(x)$ is $\dfrac{f'(x)}{f(x)}$.

The PERCENTAGE RATE OF CHANGE is $100 \times \dfrac{f'(x)}{f(x)}$.

4\. ELASTICITY OF DEMAND

If price and demand are related by $x = f(p)$, then the ELASTICITY OF DEMAND is given by

$$E(p) = -\frac{pf'(p)}{f(p)}$$

5\. INTERPRETATION OF ELASTICITY OF DEMAND

$E(p)$	Demand	Interpretation
$0 < E(p) < 1$	Inelastic	Demand is not sensitive to changes in price. A change in price produces a smaller change in demand.
$E(p) > 1$	Elastic	Demand is sensitive to changes in price. A change in price produces a larger change in demand.
$E(p) = 1$	Unit	A change in price produces the same change in demand.

6\. REVENUE AND ELASTICITY OF DEMAND

If $R(p) = pf(p)$ is the revenue function, then $R'(p)$ and $[1 - E(p)]$ always have the same sign.

Demand is inelastic $[E(p) < 1, R'(p) > 0]$:

A price increase will increase revenue.

A price decrease will decrease revenue.

Demand is elastic $[E(p) > 1, R'(p) < 0]$:

A price increase will decrease revenue.

A price decrease will increase revenue.

---

1. $y = u^2;\ u = 2 + e^x$

$$\frac{dy}{du} = 2u,\quad \frac{du}{dx} = e^x;\quad \frac{dy}{dx} = \frac{dy}{du} \cdot \frac{du}{dx} = 2ue^x$$
$$= 2(2 + e^x)e^x$$

3. $y = e^u;\ u = 2 - x^4$

$$\frac{dy}{du} = e^u,\quad \frac{du}{dx} = -4x^3;\quad \frac{dy}{dx} = \frac{dy}{du} \cdot \frac{du}{dx} = e^u(-4x^3)$$
$$= e^{(2-x^4)}(-4x^3)$$
$$= -4x^3 e^{(2-x^4)}$$

8

5. $y = \ln u;\ u = 4x^5 - 7$

$$\frac{dy}{du} = \frac{1}{u},\ \frac{du}{dx} = 20x^4;\ \frac{dy}{dx} = \frac{dy}{du} \cdot \frac{du}{dx} = \frac{1}{u}(20x^4)$$

$$= \frac{20x^4}{4x^5 - 7}$$

7. $y = 1 + w^2;\ w = \ln u;\ u = 2 + e^x$

$$\frac{dy}{dw} = 2w,\ \frac{dw}{du} = \frac{1}{u},\ \frac{du}{dx} = e^x;$$

$$\frac{dy}{dx} = \frac{dy}{dw} \cdot \frac{dw}{du} \cdot \frac{du}{dx} = 2w\left(\frac{1}{u}\right)e^x = 2\ \ln u\left(\frac{1}{2 + e^x}\right)e^x$$

$$= \frac{2e^x \ln(2 + e^x)}{2 + e^x}$$

9. $y = \ln w;\ w = u^2 + 1;\ u = e^x$

$$\frac{dy}{dw} = \frac{1}{w},\ \frac{dw}{du} = 2u,\ \frac{du}{dx} = e^x;$$

$$\frac{dy}{dx} = \frac{dy}{dw} \cdot \frac{dw}{du} \cdot \frac{du}{dx} = \frac{1}{w}(2u)e^x = \frac{1}{u^2 + 1}(2e^x)e^x$$

$$= \frac{2e^{2x}}{e^{2x} + 1}$$

11. $y = (w + 4)^2;\ w = \ln u;\ u = e^x$

$$\frac{dy}{dw} = 2(w + 4),\ \frac{dw}{du} = \frac{1}{u},\ \frac{du}{dx} = e^x$$

$$\frac{dy}{dx} = \frac{dy}{dw} \cdot \frac{dw}{du} \cdot \frac{du}{dx} = 2(w + 4)\left(\frac{1}{u}\right)e^x = 2(\ln u + 4)\frac{1}{e^x}e^x$$

$$= 2(\ln e^x + 4)$$

$$= 2(x + 4)$$

13. $f(x) = 10x + 500$

$f'(x) = 10$

Relative rate of change of f: $\dfrac{f'(x)}{f(x)} = \dfrac{10}{10x + 500} = \dfrac{1}{x + 50}$

15. $f(x) = 100x - 0.5x^2$

$f'(x) = 100 - x$

Relative rate of change of f: $\dfrac{f'(x)}{f(x)} = \dfrac{100 - x}{100x - 0.5x^2}$

17. $f(x) = 4 + 2e^{-2x}$

$f'(x) = -4e^{-2x}$

Relative rate of change of f: $\dfrac{f'(x)}{f(x)} = \dfrac{-4e^{-2x}}{4 + 2e^{-2x}}$

$$= -\frac{2e^{-2x}}{2 + e^{-2x}} \cdot \frac{e^{2x}}{e^{2x}} = -\frac{2}{1 + 2e^{2x}}$$

19. $f(x) = 25x + 3x \ln x$

$f'(x) = 25 + 3 \ln x + 3 = 28 + 3 \ln x$

Relative rate of change of f: $\dfrac{f'(x)}{f(x)} = \dfrac{28 + 3 \ln x}{25x + 3x \ln x}$

21. $x = f(p) = 12{,}000 - 10p^2$

$f'(p) = -20p$

Elasticity of demand: $E(p) = \dfrac{-pf'(p)}{f(p)} = \dfrac{20p^2}{12{,}000 - 10p^2}$

(A) At $p = 10$: $E(10) = \dfrac{2000}{12{,}000 - 1000} = \dfrac{2000}{11{,}000} = \dfrac{2}{11}$

Demand is inelastic.

(B) At $p = 20$: $E(20) = \dfrac{8000}{12{,}000 - 4000} = \dfrac{8000}{8000} = 1$; unit elasticity.

(C) At $p = 30$: $E(30) = \dfrac{18{,}000}{12{,}000 - 9{,}000} = \dfrac{18{,}000}{3{,}000} = 6$

Demand is elastic.

23. $x = f(p) = 950 - 2p - 0.1p^2$

$f'(p) = -2 - 0.2p$

Elasticity of demand: $E(p) = \dfrac{-pf'(p)}{f(p)} = \dfrac{2p + 0.2p^2}{950 - 2p - 0.1p^2}$

(A) At $p = 30$: $E(30) = \dfrac{60 + 180}{950 - 60 - 90} = \dfrac{240}{800} = \dfrac{3}{10}$

Demand is inelastic.

(B) At $p = 50$: $E(50) = \dfrac{100 + 500}{950 - 100 - 250} = \dfrac{600}{600} = 1$; unit elasticity.

(C) At $p = 70$: $E(70) = \dfrac{140 + 980}{950 - 140 - 490} = \dfrac{1120}{320} = 3.5$

Demand is elastic.

25. $p + 0.005x = 30$

(A) $x = \dfrac{30 - p}{0.005} = 6000 - 200p, \ 0 \le p \le 30$

(B) $f(p) = 6000 - 200p$

$f'(p) = -200$

Elasticity of demand: $E(p) = \dfrac{-pf'(p)}{f(p)} = \dfrac{200p}{6000 - 200p}$

$= \dfrac{p}{30 - p}$

(C) At $p = 10$: $E(10) = \dfrac{10}{30 - 10} = \dfrac{1}{2} = 0.5$

If the price increases by 10%, the demand will decrease by approximately $0.5(10\%) = 5\%$.

(D) At $p = 25$: $E(25) = \dfrac{25}{30 - 25} = 5$

If the price increases by 10%, the demand will decrease by approximately $5(10\%) = 50\%$.

(E) At $p = 15$: $E(15) = \dfrac{15}{30 - 15} = 1$

If the price increases by 10%, the demand will decrease by approximately 10%.

27. $0.02x + p = 60$

(A) $x = \dfrac{60 - p}{0.02} = 3000 - 50p$, $\ 0 \le p \le 60$

(B) $R(p) = p(3000 - 50p) = 3000p - 50p^2$

(C) $f(p) = 3000 - 50p$
$f'(p) = -50$

Elasticity of demand: $E(p) = \dfrac{-pf'(p)}{f(p)} = \dfrac{50p}{3000 - 50p}$

$$= \dfrac{p}{60 - p}$$

(D) Elastic: $E(p) = \dfrac{p}{60 - p} > 1$

$p > 60 - p$
$p > 30, \qquad 30 < p < 60$

Inelastic: $E(p) = \dfrac{p}{60 - p} < 1$

$p < 60 - p$
$p < 30, \qquad 0 < p < 30$

(E) $R'(p) = f(p)[1 - E(p)]$ (equation (9))
$R'(p) > 0$ if $E(p) < 1$; $R'(p) < 0$ if $E(p) > 1$
Therefore, revenue is increasing for $0 < p < 30$ and decreasing for $30 < p < 60$.

(F) If $p = \$10$ and the price is decreased, revenue will also decrease.

(G) If $p = \$40$ and the price is decreased, revenue will increase.

29. $x = f(p) = 10(p - 30)^2$, $0 \le p \le 30$

$\quad\quad f'(p) = 20(p - 30)$

Elasticity of demand: $E(p) = \dfrac{-p[20(p - 30)]}{10(p - 30)^2} = \dfrac{-2p}{p - 30}$

Elastic: $E(p) = -\dfrac{2p}{p - 30} > 1$

$\quad\quad\quad\quad -2p < p - 30$ ($p - 30 < 0$ reverses inequality)
$\quad\quad\quad\quad -3p < -30$
$\quad\quad\quad\quad p > 10;$ $\quad\quad 10 < p < 30$

Inelastic: $E(p) = -\dfrac{2p}{p - 30} < 1$

$\quad\quad\quad\quad -2p > p - 30$ ($p - 30 < 0$ reverses inequality)
$\quad\quad\quad\quad -3p > -30$
$\quad\quad\quad\quad p < 10;$ $\quad\quad 0 < p < 10$

31. $x = f(p) = \sqrt{144 - 2p}$, $0 \le p \le 72$

$\quad\quad f'(p) = \dfrac{1}{2}(144 - 2p)^{-1/2}(-2) = \dfrac{-1}{\sqrt{144 - 2p}}$

Elasticity of demand: $E(p) = \dfrac{p}{144 - 2p}$

Elastic: $E(p) = \dfrac{p}{144 - 2p} > 1$

$\quad\quad\quad\quad p > 144 - 2p$
$\quad\quad\quad\quad 3p > 144$
$\quad\quad\quad\quad p > 48,$ $\quad 48 < p < 72$

Inelastic: $E(p) = \dfrac{p}{144 - 2p} < 1$

$\quad\quad\quad\quad p < 144 - 2p$
$\quad\quad\quad\quad 3p < 144$
$\quad\quad\quad\quad p < 48,$ $\quad 0 < p < 48$

33. $x = f(p) = \sqrt{2,500 - 2p^2}$ $\quad 0 \le p \le 25\sqrt{2}$

$\quad\quad f'(p) = \dfrac{1}{2}(2,500 - 2p^2)^{-1/2}(-4p) = \dfrac{-2p}{(2,500 - 2p^2)^{1/2}}$

Elasticity of demand: $E(p) = \dfrac{2p^2}{2,500 - 2p^2} = \dfrac{p^2}{1,250 - p^2}$

Elastic: $E(p) = \dfrac{p^2}{1,250 - p^2} > 1$

$\quad\quad\quad\quad p^2 > 1,250 - p^2$
$\quad\quad\quad\quad 2p^2 > 1,250$
$\quad\quad\quad\quad p^2 > 625$
$\quad\quad\quad\quad p > 25,$ $\quad 25 < p < 25\sqrt{2}$

Inelastic: $E(p) = \dfrac{p^2}{1,250 - p^2} < 1$

$$p^2 < 1,250 - p^2$$
$$2p^2 < 1,250$$
$$p^2 < 625$$
$$p < 25, \quad 0 < p < 25$$

35. $x = f(p) = 20(10 - p) \quad 0 \le p \le 10$

$R(p) = pf(p) = 20p(10 - p) = 200p - 20p^2$
$R'(p) = 200 - 40p$
Critical value: $R'(p) = 200 - 40p = 0; \quad p = 5$
Sign chart for $R'(p)$:

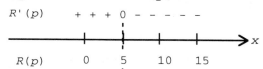

Test Numbers	
p	$R'(p)$
0	200 (+)
10	−200 (−)

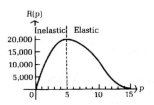

37. $x = f(p) = 40(p - 15)^2 \quad 0 \le p \le 15$

$R(p) = pf(p) = 40p(p - 15)^2$
$R'(p) = 40(p - 15)^2 + 40p(2)(p - 15)$
$\quad = 40(p - 15)[p - 15 + 2p]$
$\quad = 40(p - 15)(3p - 15)$
$\quad = 120(p - 15)(p - 5)$
Critical values [in $(0, 15)$]: $p = 5$

Sign chart for $R'(p)$:

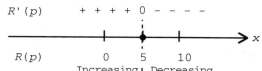

Test Numbers	
p	$R'(p)$
0	(+)
10	(−)

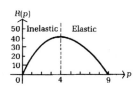

39. $x = f(p) = 30 - 10\sqrt{p} \quad 0 \le p \le 9$

$R(p) = pf(p) = 30p - 10p\sqrt{p}$
$R'(p) = 30 - 10\sqrt{p} - 10p \cdot \dfrac{1}{2}p^{-1/2}$

$\quad = 30 - 10\sqrt{p} - \dfrac{5p}{\sqrt{p}} = 30 - 15\sqrt{p}$

Critical values: $R'(p) = 30 - 15\sqrt{p} = 0$
$$\sqrt{p} = 2; \quad p = 4$$

Sign chart for $R'(p)$:

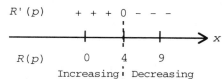

Test Numbers	
p	$R'(p)$
0	30 (+)
5	(−)

41. $p = g(x) = 50 - 0.1x$

$\quad g'(x) = -0.1$

$\quad E(x) = -\dfrac{g(x)}{xg'(x)} = -\dfrac{50 - 0.1x}{-0.1x} = \dfrac{500}{x} - 1$

$\quad E(200) = \dfrac{500}{200} - 1 = \dfrac{3}{2}$

43. $p = g(x) = 50 - 2\sqrt{x}$

$\quad g'(x) = -\dfrac{1}{\sqrt{x}}$

$\quad E(x) = -\dfrac{g(x)}{xg'(x)} = -\dfrac{50 - 2\sqrt{x}}{x\left(-\dfrac{1}{\sqrt{x}}\right)} = \dfrac{50}{\sqrt{x}} - 2$

$\quad E(400) = \dfrac{50}{20} - 2 = \dfrac{1}{2}$

45. $x = f(p) = Ap^{-k}$, A, k positive constants

$\quad f'(p) = -Akp^{-k-1}$

$\quad E(p) = \dfrac{-pf'(p)}{f(p)} = \dfrac{Akp^{-k}}{Ap^{-k}} = k$

47. The company's daily cost is increasing by
1.25(20) = \$25 per day.

49. $x + 400p = 2,000$

$\quad x = f(p) = 2,000 - 400p$

$\quad\quad f'(p) = -400$

$\quad$ Elasticity of demand: $E(p) = \dfrac{400p}{2,000 - 400p} = \dfrac{p}{5 - p}$

$\quad E(2) = \dfrac{2}{3} < 1$

$\quad$ The demand is inelastic; a price increase will increase revenue.

51. $x + 1,000p = 800$

$\quad x = f(p) = 800 - 1,000p$

$\quad\quad f'(p) = -1,000$

$\quad$ Elasticity of demand: $E(p) = \dfrac{1,000p}{800 - 1,000p} = \dfrac{5p}{4 - 5p}$

$\quad E(0.30) = \dfrac{1.5}{4 - 1.5} = \dfrac{1.5}{2.5} = \dfrac{3}{5} < 1$

$\quad$ The demand is inelastic; a price decrease will decrease revenue.

53. From Problem 49, $R(p) = pf(p) = 2,000p - 400p^2$

$\quad R'(p) = 2,000 - 800p$

$\quad$ Critical values: $R'(p) = 2,000 - 800p = 0$

$\quad\quad\quad\quad\quad\quad\quad\quad\quad\quad 800p = 2000$

$\quad\quad\quad\quad\quad\quad\quad\quad\quad\quad\quad p = 2.50$

$\quad R''(p) = -800$

$\quad$ Since $p = 2.50$ is the only critical value and $R''(2.50) = -800 < 0$, the
maximum revenue occurs when the price $p = \$2.50$.

55. $f(t) = 0.34t + 14.6, \ 0 \leq t \leq 50$

$f'(t) = 0.34$

Percentage rate of change:

$$100 \frac{f'(t)}{f(t)} = \frac{34}{0.34t + 14.6}$$

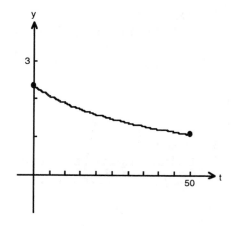

57. $r(t) = 11.3 - 3.6 \ln t$

$r'(t) = -\dfrac{3.6}{t}$

Relative rate of change of $f(t)$: $\dfrac{f'(t)}{f(t)} = \dfrac{\frac{-3.6}{t}}{11.3 - 3.6 \ln t}$

$$= \frac{-3.6}{11.3t - 3.6 \, t \ln t} = C(t)$$

Relative rate of change in 2002: $C(12) = \dfrac{-3.6}{11.3(12) - 3.6(12) \ln(12)} \approx -0.13$

The relative rate of change for robberies annually per 1,000 population age 12 and over is approximately -0.13.

EXERCISE 5-5

Things to remember:

1. Let $y = y(x)$. Then

(a) $\dfrac{d}{dx} y^n = n y^{n-1} y'$ (General Power Rule)

(b) $\dfrac{d}{dx} \ln y = \dfrac{1}{y} \cdot y' = \dfrac{y'}{y}$

(c) $\dfrac{d}{dx} e^y = e^y \cdot y' = y' e^y$

1. $3x + 5y + 9 = 0$

(A) Implicit differentiation:

$$\frac{d}{dx}(3x) + \frac{d}{dx}(5y) + \frac{d}{dx}(9) = \frac{d}{dx}(0)$$

$$3 + 5y' + 0 = 0$$

$$y' = -\frac{3}{5}$$

(B) Solve for y:

$$5y = -9 - 3x$$

$$y = -\frac{9}{5} - \frac{3}{5}x$$

$$y' = -\frac{3}{5}$$

3. $3x^2 - 4y - 18 = 0$

    (A) Implicit differentiation:

$$\frac{d}{dx}(3x^2) - \frac{d}{dx}(4y) - \frac{d}{dx}(18) = \frac{d}{dx}(0)$$

$$6x - 4y' - 0 = 0$$

$$y' = \frac{6}{4}x = \frac{3}{2}x$$

    (B) Solve for y:

$$-4y = 18 - 3x^2$$

$$y = \frac{3}{4}x^2 - \frac{9}{2}$$

$$y' = \frac{6}{4}x = \frac{3}{2}x$$

5. $y - 5x^2 + 3 = 0$; $(1, 2)$

    Using implicit differentiation:

$$\frac{d}{dx}(y) - \frac{d}{dx}(5x^2) + \frac{d}{dx}(3) = \frac{d}{dx}(0)$$

$$y' - 10x = 0$$

$$y' = 10x$$

$$y'\Big|_{(1,2)} = 10(1) = 10$$

7. $x^2 - y^3 - 3 = 0$; $(2, 1)$

$$\frac{d}{dx}(x^2) - \frac{d}{dx}(y^3) - \frac{d}{dx}(3) = \frac{d}{dx}(0)$$

$$2x - 3y^2y' = 0$$

$$3y^2y' = 2x$$

$$y' = \frac{2x}{3y^2}$$

$$y'\Big|_{(2,1)} = \frac{4}{3}$$

9. $y^2 + 2y + 3x = 0$; $(-1, 1)$

$$\frac{d}{dx}(y^2) + \frac{d}{dx}(2y) + \frac{d}{dx}(3x) = \frac{d}{dx}(0)$$

$$2yy' + 2y' + 3 = 0$$

$$2y'(y + 1) = -3$$

$$y' = -\frac{3}{2(y + 1)}$$

$$y'\Big|_{(-1,1)} = \frac{-3}{2(2)} = -\frac{3}{4}$$

11. $xy - 6 = 0$

$$\frac{d}{dx}xy - \frac{d}{dx}6 = \frac{d}{dx}(0)$$

$$xy' + y - 0 = 0$$

$$xy' = -y$$

$$y' = -\frac{y}{x}$$

$$y' \text{ at } (2, 3) = -\frac{3}{2}$$

13. $2xy + y + 2 = 0$

$$2\frac{d}{dx}xy + \frac{d}{dx}y + \frac{d}{dx}2 = \frac{d}{dx}(0)$$

$$2xy' + 2y + y' + 0 = 0$$

$$y'(2x + 1) = -2y$$

$$y' = \frac{-2y}{2x + 1}$$

$$y' \text{ at } (-1, 2) = \frac{-2(2)}{2(-1) + 1} = 4$$

15. $x^2y - 3x^2 - 4 = 0$

$$\frac{d}{dx}x^2y - \frac{d}{dx}3x^2 - \frac{d}{dx}4 = \frac{d}{dx}(0)$$

$$x^2y' + y\frac{d}{dx}(x^2) - 6x - 0 = 0$$

$$x^2y' + y2x - 6x = 0$$

$$x^2y' = 6x - 2yx$$

$$y' = \frac{6x - 2yx}{x^2} \text{ or } \frac{6 - 2y}{x}$$

$$y'\Big|_{(2,4)} = \frac{6 \cdot 2 - 2 \cdot 4 \cdot 2}{2^2} = \frac{12 - 16}{4} = -1$$

17. $e^y = x^2 + y^2$

$$\frac{d}{dx}e^y = \frac{d}{dx}x^2 + \frac{d}{dx}y^2$$

$$e^y y' = 2x + 2yy'$$

$$y'(e^y - 2y) = 2x$$

$$y' = \frac{2x}{e^y - 2y}$$

$$y'\Big|_{(1,\,0)} = \frac{2 \cdot 1}{e^0 - 2 \cdot 0} = \frac{2}{1} = 2$$

19. $x^3 - y = \ln y$

$$\frac{d}{dx}x^3 - \frac{d}{dx}y = \frac{d}{dx}\ln y$$

$$3x^2 - y' = \frac{y'}{y}$$

$$3x^2 = \left(1 + \frac{1}{y}\right)y'$$

$$3x^2 = \frac{y + 1}{y}y'$$

$$y' = \frac{3x^2 y}{y + 1}$$

$$y'\Big|_{(1,\,1)} = \frac{3 \cdot 1^2 \cdot 1}{1 + 1} = \frac{3}{2}$$

21. $x \ln y + 2y = 2x^3$

$$\frac{d}{dx}[x \ln y] + \frac{d}{dx}2y = \frac{d}{dx}2x^3$$

$$\ln y \cdot \frac{d}{dx}x + x\frac{d}{dx}\ln y + 2y' = 6x^2$$

$$\ln y \cdot 1 + x \cdot \frac{y'}{y} + 2y' = 6x^2$$

$$y'\left(\frac{x}{y} + 2\right) = 6x^2 - \ln y$$

$$y' = \frac{6x^2 y - y \ln y}{x + 2y}$$

$$y'\Big|_{(1,\,1)} = \frac{6 \cdot 1^2 \cdot 1 - 1 \cdot \ln 1}{1 + 2 \cdot 1} = \frac{6}{3} = 2$$

23. $x^2 - t^2 x + t^3 + 11 = 0$

$$\frac{d}{dt}x^2 - \frac{d}{dt}(t^2 x) + \frac{d}{dt}t^3 + \frac{d}{dt}11 = \frac{d}{dt}0$$

$$2xx' - [t^2 x' + x(2t)] + 3t^2 + 0 = 0$$

$$2xx' - t^2 x' - 2tx + 3t^2 = 0$$

$$x'(2x - t^2) = 2tx - 3t^2$$

$$x' = \frac{2tx - 3t^2}{2x - t^2}$$

$$x'\Big|_{(-2,\,1)} = \frac{2(-2)(1) - 3(-2)^2}{2(1) - (-2)^2}$$

$$= \frac{-4 - 12}{2 - 4} = \frac{-16}{-2} = 8$$

25. $(x - 1)^2 + (y - 1)^2 = 1$.

Differentiating implicitly, we have:

$$\frac{d}{dx}(x - 1)^2 + \frac{d}{dx}(y - 1)^2 = \frac{d}{dx}(1)$$
$$2(x - 1) + 2(y - 1)y' = 0$$
$$y' = -\frac{(x - 1)}{(y - 1)}$$

To find the points on the graph where $x = 1.6$, we solve the given equation for y:

$$(y - 1)^2 = 1 - (x - 1)^2$$
$$y - 1 = \pm\sqrt{1 - (x - 1)^2}$$
$$y = 1 \pm \sqrt{1 - (x - 1)^2}$$

Now, when $x = 1.6$, $y = 1 + \sqrt{1 - 0.36} = 1 + \sqrt{0.64} = 1.8$ and $y = 1 - \sqrt{0.64} = 0.2$. Thus, the points are $(1.6, 1.8)$ and $(1.6, 0.2)$. These values can be verified on the graph.

$$y'\Big|_{(1.6,\,1.8)} = -\frac{(1.6 - 1)}{(1.8 - 1)} = -\frac{0.6}{0.8} = -\frac{3}{4}$$
$$y'\Big|_{(1.6,\,0.2)} = -\frac{(1.6 - 1)}{(0.2 - 1)} = -\frac{0.6}{(-0.8)} = \frac{3}{4}$$

27. $xy - x - 4 = 0$

When $x = 2$, $2y - 2 - 4 = 0$, so $y = 3$. Thus, we want to find the equation of the tangent line at $(2, 3)$.

First, find y'.

$$\frac{d}{dx}xy - \frac{d}{dx}x - \frac{d}{dx}4 = \frac{d}{dx}0$$
$$xy' + y - 1 - 0 = 0$$
$$xy' = 1 - y$$
$$y' = \frac{1 - y}{x}$$
$$y'\Big|_{(2,\,3)} = \frac{1 - 3}{2} = -1$$

Thus, the slope of the tangent line at $(2, 3)$ is $m = -1$. The equation of the line through $(2, 3)$ with slope $m = -1$ is:

$$(y - 3) = -1(x - 2)$$
$$y - 3 = -x + 2$$
$$y = -x + 5$$

29. $y^2 - xy - 6 = 0$

When $x = 1$,

$$y^2 - y - 6 = 0$$
$$(y - 3)(y + 2) = 0$$
$$y = 3 \quad \text{or} \quad -2.$$

Thus, we want to find the equations of the tangent lines at $(1, 3)$ and $(1, -2)$. First, find y'.

$$\frac{d}{dx}y^2 - \frac{d}{dx}xy - \frac{d}{dx}6 = \frac{d}{dx}0$$
$$2yy' - xy' - y - 0 = 0$$
$$y'(2y - x) = y$$
$$y' = \frac{y}{2y - x}$$

$$y'\Big|_{(1,\,3)} = \frac{3}{2(3) - 1} = \frac{3}{5} \qquad \text{[Slope at } (1, \; 3)\text{]}$$

The equation of the tangent line at $(1, 3)$ with $m = \dfrac{3}{5}$ is:

$$(y - 3) = \frac{3}{5}(x - 1)$$
$$y - 3 = \frac{3}{5}x - \frac{3}{5}$$
$$y = \frac{3}{5}x + \frac{12}{5}$$

$$y'\Big|_{(1,\,-2)} = \frac{-2}{2(-2) - 1} = \frac{2}{5} \qquad \text{[Slope at } (1, \; -2)\text{]}$$

Thus, the equation of the tangent line at $(1, -2)$ with $m = \dfrac{2}{5}$ is:

$$(y + 2) = \frac{2}{5}(x - 1)$$
$$y + 2 = \frac{2}{5}x - \frac{2}{5}$$
$$y = \frac{2}{5}x - \frac{12}{5}$$

31. $xe^y = 1$

Implicit differentiation: $x \cdot \dfrac{d}{dx}e^y + e^y\dfrac{d}{dx}x = \dfrac{d}{dx}1$

$$xe^y y' + e^y = 0$$
$$y' = -\frac{e^y}{xe^y} = -\frac{1}{x}$$

Solve for y: $e^y = \dfrac{1}{x}$

$$y = \ln\left(\frac{1}{x}\right) = -\ln x \quad \text{(see Section 2-3)}$$
$$y' = -\frac{1}{x}$$

In this case, solving for y first and then differentiating is a little easier than differentiating implicitly.

33. $(1 + y)^3 + y = x + 7$

$\dfrac{d}{dx}(1 + y)^3 + \dfrac{d}{dx}y = \dfrac{d}{dx}x + \dfrac{d}{dx}7$

$3(1 + y)^2 y' + y' = 1$

$y'[3(1 + y)^2 + 1] = 1$

$y' = \dfrac{1}{3(1 + y)^2 + 1}$

$y'\Big|_{(2,\,1)} = \dfrac{1}{3(1 + 1)^2 + 1} = \dfrac{1}{13}$

35. $(x - 2y)^3 = 2y^2 - 3$

$\dfrac{d}{dx}(x - 2y)^3 = \dfrac{d}{dx}(2y^2) - \dfrac{d}{dx}(3)$

$3(x - 2y)^2(1 - 2y') = 4yy' - 0$ [Note: The chain rule is applied to the left-hand side.]

$3(x - 2y)^2 - 6(x - 2y)^2 y' = 4yy'$

$-6(x - 2y)^2 y' - 4yy' = -3(x - 2y)^2$

$-y'[6(x - 2y)^2 + 4y] = -3(x - 2y)^2$

$y' = \dfrac{3(x - 2y)^2}{6(x - 2y)^2 + 4y}$

$y'\Big|_{(1,\,1)} = \dfrac{3(1 - 2 \cdot 1)^2}{6(1 - 2)^2 + 4} = \dfrac{3}{10}$

37. $\sqrt{7 + y^2} - x^3 + 4 = 0$ or $(7 + y^2)^{1/2} - x^3 + 4 = 0$

$\dfrac{d}{dx}(7 + y^2)^{1/2} - \dfrac{d}{dx}x^3 + \dfrac{d}{dx}4 = \dfrac{d}{dx}0$

$\dfrac{1}{2}(7 + y^2)^{-1/2}\dfrac{d}{dx}(7 + y^2) - 3x^2 + 0 = 0$

$\dfrac{1}{2}(7 + y^2)^{-1/2}2yy' - 3x^2 = 0$

$\dfrac{yy'}{(7 + y^2)^{1/2}} = 3x^2$

$y' = \dfrac{3x^2(7 + y^2)^{1/2}}{y}$

$y'\Big|_{(2,\,3)} = \dfrac{3 \cdot 2^2(7 + 3^2)^{1/2}}{3} = \dfrac{12(16)^{1/2}}{3} = 16$

39. $\ln(xy) = y^2 - 1$

$$\frac{d}{dx}[\ln(xy)] = \frac{d}{dx}y^2 - \frac{d}{dx}1$$

$$\frac{1}{xy} \cdot \frac{d}{dx}(xy) = 2yy'$$

$$\frac{1}{xy}(x \cdot y' + y) = 2yy'$$

$$\frac{1}{y} \cdot y' - 2yy' + \frac{1}{x} = 0$$

$$xy' - 2xy^2y' + y = 0$$

$$y'(x - 2xy^2) = -y$$

$$y' = \frac{-y}{x - 2xy^2} = \frac{y}{2xy^2 - x}$$

$$y'\Big|_{(1,1)} = \frac{1}{2 \cdot 1 \cdot 1^2 - 1} = 1$$

41. First find point(s) on the graph of the equation with abscissa $x = 1$: Setting $x = 1$, we have

$$y^3 - y - 1 = 2 \quad \text{or} \quad y^3 - y - 3 = 0$$

Graphing this equation on a graphing utility, we get $y \approx 1.67$.

Now, differentiate implicitly to find the slope of the tangent line at the point $(1, 1.67)$: $\frac{d}{dx}y^3 + x\frac{d}{dx}y + y\frac{d}{dx}x - \frac{d}{dx}x^3 = \frac{d}{dx}2$

$$3y^2y' - xy' - y - 3x^2 = 0$$

$$(3y^2 - x)y' = 3x^2 + y$$

$$y' = \frac{3x^2 + y}{3y^2 - x};$$

$$y'\Big|_{(1,1.67)} = \frac{3 + 1.67}{3(1.67)^2 - 1} = \frac{4.67}{7.37} \approx 0.63$$

Tangent line: $y - 1.67 = 0.63(x - 1)$ or $y = 0.63x + 1.04$

43. $x = p^2 - 2p + 1000$

$$\frac{d(x)}{dx} = \frac{d(p^2)}{dx} - \frac{d(2p)}{dx} + \frac{d(1000)}{dx}$$

$$1 = 2p\frac{dp}{dx} - 2\frac{dp}{dx} + 0$$

$$1 = (2p - 2)\frac{dp}{dx}$$

Thus, $\dfrac{dp}{dx} = p' = \dfrac{1}{2p - 2}$.

45. $x = \sqrt{10,000 - p^2} = (10,000 - p^2)^{1/2}$

$\dfrac{d}{dx}x = \dfrac{d}{dx}(10,000 - p^2)^{1/2}$

$1 = \dfrac{1}{2}(10,000 - p^2)^{-1/2}\dfrac{d}{dx}[10,000 - p^2]$

$1 = \dfrac{1}{2(10,000 - p^2)^{1/2}} \cdot (-2pp')$

$1 = \dfrac{-pp'}{\sqrt{10,000 - p^2}}$

$p' = \dfrac{-\sqrt{10,000 - p^2}}{p}$

EXERCISE 5-6

Things to remember:

<u>1</u>. SUGGESTIONS FOR SOLVING RELATED RATE PROBLEMS

<u>Step 1</u>. Sketch a figure.

<u>Step 2</u>. Identify all relevant variables, including those whose rates are given and those whose rates are to be found.

<u>Step 3</u>. Express all given rates and rates to be found as derivatives.

<u>Step 4</u>. Find an equation connecting the variables in step 2.

<u>Step 5</u>. Implicitly differentiate the equation found in step 4, using the chain rule where appropriate, and substitute in all given values.

<u>Step 6</u>. Solve for the derivative that will give the unknown rate.

1. $y = x^2 + 2$

Differentiating with respect to t:

$\dfrac{dy}{dt} = 2x\dfrac{dx}{dt}$; $\dfrac{dy}{dt} = 2(5)(3) = 30$ when $x = 5$, $\dfrac{dx}{dt} = 3$

3. $x^2 + y^2 = 1$

Differentiating with respect to t:

$2x\dfrac{dx}{dt} + 2y\dfrac{dy}{dt} = 0$

$2x\dfrac{dx}{dt} = -2y\dfrac{dy}{dt}$

$\dfrac{dx}{dt} = -\dfrac{y}{x}\dfrac{dy}{dt}$; $\dfrac{dx}{dt} = -\dfrac{0.8}{(-0.6)}(-4) = -\dfrac{16}{3}$,

when $x = -0.6$, $y = 0.8$, $\dfrac{dy}{dt} = -4$

5. $x^2 + 3xy + y^2 = 11$

Differentiating with respect to t:

$$2x\frac{dx}{dt} + 2x\frac{dy}{dt} + 3y\frac{dx}{dt} + 2y\frac{dy}{dt} = 0$$

$$(3x + 2y)\frac{dy}{dt} = -(2x + 3y)\frac{dx}{dt}$$

$$\frac{dy}{dt} = -\frac{(2x + 3y)}{3x + 2y}\frac{dx}{dt}; \quad \frac{dy}{dt} = -\frac{(2 \cdot 1 + 3 \cdot 2)}{(3 \cdot 1 + 2 \cdot 2)}2 = -\frac{16}{7}$$

when $x = 1$, $y = 2$, $\frac{dx}{dt} = 2$

7. $xy = 36$

Differentiate with respect to t:

$$\frac{d(xy)}{dt} = \frac{d(36)}{dt}$$

$$x\frac{dy}{dt} + y\frac{dx}{dt} = 0$$

Given: $\frac{dx}{dt} = 4$ when $x = 4$ and $y = 9$. Therefore,

$$4\frac{dy}{dt} + 9(4) = 0$$

$$4\frac{dy}{dt} = -36$$

and $\frac{dy}{dt} = -9$.

The y coordinate is decreasing at 9 units per second.

9.

From the triangle,
$$x^2 + y^2 = z^2$$
or $x^2 + 16 = z^2$, since $y = 4$.

Differentiate with respect to t:

$$2x\frac{dx}{dt} = 2z\frac{dz}{dt}$$

or $$x\frac{dx}{dt} = z\frac{dz}{dt}$$

Given: $\frac{dz}{dt} = -3$. Also, when $x = 30$, $900 + 16 = z^2$ or $z = \sqrt{916}$.

Therefore,

$$30\frac{dx}{dt} = \sqrt{916}\,(-3) \quad \text{and} \quad \frac{dx}{dt} = \frac{-3\sqrt{916}}{30} = \frac{-\sqrt{916}}{10} \approx \frac{-30.27}{10}$$

$$\approx -3.03 \text{ feet per second.}$$

[Note: The negative sign indicates that the distance between the boat and the dock is decreasing.]

11. Area: $A = \pi R^2$

$$\frac{dA}{dt} = \frac{d\pi R^2}{dt} = \pi \cdot 2R\frac{dR}{dt}$$

Given: $\dfrac{dR}{dt} = 2$ ft/sec

$$\frac{dA}{dt} = 2\pi R \cdot 2 = 4\pi R$$

$$\left.\frac{dA}{dt}\right|_{R=10 \text{ ft}} = 4\pi(10) = 40\pi \text{ ft}^2/\text{sec}$$
$$\approx 126 \text{ ft}^2/\text{sec}$$

13. $V = \dfrac{4}{3}\pi R^3$

$$\frac{dV}{dt} = \frac{4}{3}\pi 3R^2\frac{dR}{dt} = 4\pi R^2\frac{dR}{dt}$$

Given: $\dfrac{dR}{dt} = 3$ cm/min

$$\frac{dV}{dt} = 4\pi R^2 3 = 12\pi R^2$$

$$\left.\frac{dV}{dt}\right|_{R=10 \text{ cm}} = 12\pi(10)^2 = 1200\pi$$
$$\approx 3768 \text{ cm}^3/\text{min}$$

15. $\dfrac{P}{T} = k \qquad\qquad (1)$

$P = kT$

Differentiate with respect to t:

$$\frac{dP}{dt} = k\frac{dT}{dt}$$

Given: $\dfrac{dT}{dt} = 3$ degrees per hour, $T = 250°$, $P = 500$ pounds per square inch.

From (1), for $T = 250$ and $P = 500$,

$k = \dfrac{500}{250} = 2$.

Thus, we have

$$\frac{dP}{dt} = 2\frac{dT}{dt}$$
$$\frac{dP}{dt} = 2(3) = 6$$

Pressure increases at 6 pounds per square inch per hour.

17. By the Pythagorean theorem,

$$x^2 + y^2 = 10^2$$

or $\quad x^2 + y^2 = 100 \qquad\qquad (1)$

Differentiate with respect to t:

$$2x\frac{dx}{dt} + 2y\frac{dy}{dt} = 0$$

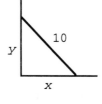

Therefore, $\dfrac{dy}{dt} = -\dfrac{x}{y}\dfrac{dx}{dt}$. Given: $\dfrac{dx}{dt} = 3$. Thus, $\dfrac{dy}{dt} = \dfrac{-3x}{y}$.

From (1), $y^2 = 100 - x^2$ and, when $x = 6$,

$y^2 = 100 - 6^2$
$\quad = 100 - 36 = 64$.

Thus, $y = 8$ when $x = 6$, and

$$\left.\frac{dy}{dt}\right|_{(6, 8)} = \frac{-3(6)}{8} = \frac{-18}{8} = \frac{-9}{4}\text{ft/sec}.$$

19. y = length of shadow
x = distance of man from light
z = distance of tip of shadow from light

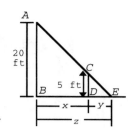

We want to compute $\dfrac{dz}{dt}$. Triangles *ABE* and *CDE* are similar

triangles; thus, the ratios of corresponding sides are equal.

Therefore, $\dfrac{z}{20} = \dfrac{y}{5} = \dfrac{z-x}{5}$ [<u>Note</u>: $y = z - x$.]

or $\qquad \dfrac{z}{20} = \dfrac{z-x}{5}$

$$z = 4(z - x)$$
$$z = 4z - 4x$$
$$4x = 3z$$

Differentiate with respect to t:

$$4\frac{dx}{dt} = 3\frac{dz}{dt}$$
$$\frac{dz}{dt} = \frac{4}{3}\frac{dx}{dt}$$

Given: $\dfrac{dx}{dt} = 5$.   Thus, $\dfrac{dz}{dt} = \dfrac{4}{3}(5) = \dfrac{20}{3}$ ft/sec.

21. $V = \dfrac{4}{3}\pi r^3$ (1)

Differentiate with respect to t:

$$\frac{dV}{dt} = 4\pi r^2 \frac{dr}{dt} \quad \text{and} \quad \frac{dr}{dt} = \frac{1}{4\pi r^2} \cdot \frac{dV}{dt}$$

Since $\dfrac{dV}{dt} = 4$ cu ft/sec,

$$\frac{dr}{dt} = \frac{1}{4\pi r^2}(4) = \frac{1}{\pi r^2}\,\text{ft/sec} \quad (2)$$

At $t = 1$ minute $= 60$ seconds,

$V = 4(60) = 240$ cu ft and, from (1),

$$r^3 = \frac{3V}{4\pi} = \frac{3(240)}{4\pi} = \frac{180}{\pi}; \quad r = \left(\frac{180}{\pi}\right)^{1/3} \approx 3.855.$$

From (2)

$$\frac{dr}{dt} = \frac{1}{\pi(3.855)^2} \approx 0.0214 \text{ ft/sec}$$

At $t = 2$ minutes $= 120$ seconds,

$V = 4(120) = 480$ cu ft and

$$r^3 = \frac{3V}{4\pi} = \frac{3(480)}{4\pi} = \frac{360}{\pi}; \quad r = \left(\frac{360}{\pi}\right)^{1/3} \approx 4.857$$

From (2),

$$\frac{dr}{dt} = \frac{1}{\pi(4.857)^2} \approx 0.0135 \text{ ft/sec}$$

To find the time at which $\frac{dr}{dt} = 100$ ft/sec, solve

$$\frac{1}{\pi r^2} = 100$$

$$r^2 = \frac{1}{100\pi}$$

$$r = \frac{1}{\sqrt{100\pi}} = \frac{1}{10\sqrt{\pi}}$$

Now, when $r = \frac{1}{10\sqrt{\pi}}$,

$$V = \frac{4}{3}\pi\left(\frac{1}{10\sqrt{\pi}}\right)^3$$

$$= \frac{4}{3} \cdot \frac{1}{1000\sqrt{\pi}}$$

$$= \frac{1}{750\sqrt{\pi}}$$

Since the volume at time t is $4t$, we have

$$4t = \frac{1}{750\sqrt{\pi}} \text{ and}$$

$$t = \frac{1}{3000\sqrt{\pi}} \approx 0.00019 \text{ secs.}$$

23. $y = e^x + x + 1$; $\frac{dx}{dt} = 3$.

Differentiate with respect to t:

$$\frac{dy}{dt} = e^x\frac{dx}{dt} + \frac{dx}{dt} = e^x(3) + 3 = 3(e^x + 1)$$

To find where the point crosses the x axis, use a graphing utility to solve

$$e^x + x + 1 = 0$$

The result is $x \approx -1.278$.

Now, at $x = -1.278$,

$$\frac{dy}{dt} = 3(e^{-1.278} + 1) \approx 3.835 \text{ units/sec.}$$

25. $C = 90,000 + 30x$ (1)

$$R = 300x - \frac{x^2}{30} \qquad (2)$$

$P = R - C$ (3)

(A) Differentiating (1) with respect to t:

$$\frac{dC}{dt} = \frac{d(90,000)}{dt} + \frac{d(30x)}{dt}$$

$$\frac{dC}{dt} = 30\frac{dx}{dt}$$

Thus, $\dfrac{dC}{dt} = 30(500)$ $\left(\dfrac{dx}{dt} = 500\right)$

$$= \$15,000 \text{ per week.}$$

Costs are increasing at $15,000 per week at this production level.

(B) Differentiating (2) with respect to t:

$$\frac{dR}{dt} = \frac{d(300x)}{dt} - \frac{d\frac{x^2}{30}}{dt}$$

$$= 300\frac{dx}{dt} - \frac{2x}{30}\frac{dx}{dt}$$

$$= \left(300 - \frac{x}{15}\right)\frac{dx}{dt}$$

Thus, $\dfrac{dR}{dt} = \left(300 - \dfrac{6000}{15}\right)(500)$ $\left(x = 6000, \dfrac{dx}{dt} = 500\right)$

$$= (-100)500$$

$$= -\$50,000 \text{ per week.}$$

Revenue is decreasing at $50,000 per week at this production level.

(C) Differentiating (3) with respect to t:

$$\frac{dP}{dt} = \frac{dR}{dt} - \frac{dC}{dt}$$

Thus, from parts (A) and (B), we have:

$$\frac{dP}{dt} = -50,000 - 15,000 = -\$65,000$$

Profits are decreasing at $65,000 per week at this production level.

27. $S = 60,000 - 40,000e^{-0.0005x}$

Differentiating implicitly with respect to t, we have

$$\frac{ds}{dt} = -40,000(-0.0005)e^{-0.0005x}\frac{dx}{dt} \text{ and } \frac{ds}{dt} = 20e^{-0.0005x}\frac{dx}{dt}$$

Now, for $x = 2000$ and $\dfrac{dx}{dt} = 300$, we have

$$\frac{ds}{dt} = 20(300)e^{-0.0005(2000)}$$

$$= 6000e^{-1} = 2,207$$

Thus, sales are increasing at the rate of $2,207 per week.

29. Price p and demand x are related by the equation
$$2x^2 + 5xp + 50p^2 = 80,000 \qquad (1)$$
Differentiating implicitly with respect to t, we have
$$4x\frac{dx}{dt} + 5x\frac{dp}{dt} + 5p\frac{dx}{dt} + 100p\frac{dp}{dt} = 0 \qquad (2)$$

(A) From (2), $\dfrac{dx}{dt} = \dfrac{-(5x + 100p)\dfrac{dp}{dt}}{4x + 5p}$

Setting $p = 30$ in (1), we get
$$2x^2 + 150x + 45,000 = 80,000$$
or $\quad x^2 + 75x - 17,500 = 0$

Thus, $x = \dfrac{-75 \pm \sqrt{(75)^2 + 70,000}}{2} = \dfrac{-75 \pm 275}{2} = 100, -175$

Since $x \geq 0$, $x = 100$

Now, for $x = 100$, $p = 30$ and $\dfrac{dp}{dt} = 2$, we have
$$\frac{dx}{dt} = \frac{-[5(100) + 100(30)] \cdot 2}{4(100) + 5(30)} = -\frac{7000}{550} \text{ and } \frac{dx}{dt} = -12.73$$
The demand is decreasing at the rate of -12.73 units/month.

(B) From (2), $\dfrac{dp}{dt} = \dfrac{-(4x + 5p)\dfrac{dx}{dt}}{(5x + 100p)}$

Setting $x = 150$ in (1), we get
$$45,000 + 750p + 50p^2 = 80,000$$
or $\qquad p^2 + 15p - 700 = 0$

and $p = \dfrac{-15 \pm \sqrt{225 + 2800}}{2} = \dfrac{-15 \pm 55}{2} = -35, 20$

Since $p \geq 0$, $p = 20$.

Now, for $x = 150$, $p = 20$ and $\dfrac{dx}{dt} = -6$, we have
$$\frac{dp}{dt} = -\frac{[4(150) + 5(20)](-6)}{5(150) + 100(20)} = \frac{4200}{2750} \approx 1.53$$
Thus, the price is increasing at the rate of $1.53 per month.

31. Volume $V = \pi R^2 h$, where h = thickness of the circular oil slick.
Since $h = 0.1 = \dfrac{1}{10}$, we have:

$$V = \frac{\pi}{10}R^2$$
Differentiating with respect to t:

$$\frac{dV}{dt} = \frac{d\left(\dfrac{\pi}{10}R^2\right)}{dt} = \frac{\pi}{10}2R\frac{dR}{dt} = \frac{\pi}{5}R\frac{dR}{dt}$$

Given: $\dfrac{dR}{dt} = 0.32$ when $R = 500$. Therefore,

$$\frac{dV}{dt} = \frac{\pi}{5}(500)(0.32) = 100\pi(0.32) \approx 100.48 \text{ cubic feet per minute.}$$

1. $A(t) = 2000e^{0.09t}$

$A(5) = 2000e^{0.09(5)} = 2000e^{0.45} \approx 3136.62$ or   \$3136.62

$A(10) = 2000e^{0.09(10)} = 2000e^{0.9} \approx 4919.21$ or   \$4919.21

$A(20) = 2000e^{0.09(20)} = 2000e^{1.8} \approx 12,099.29$ or   \$12,099.29   (5-1)

2. $\dfrac{d}{dx}(2 \ln x + 3e^x) = 2\dfrac{d}{dx}\ln x + 3\dfrac{d}{dx}e^x = \dfrac{2}{x} + 3e^x$ (5-2)

3. $\dfrac{d}{dx}e^{2x-3} = e^{2x-3}\dfrac{d}{dx}(2x - 3)$ (by the chain rule)

$\qquad = 2e^{2x-3}$ (5-2)

4. $y = \ln(2x + 7)$

$y' = \dfrac{1}{2x + 7}(2)$ (by the chain rule)

$\quad = \dfrac{2}{2x + 7}$ (5-2)

5. $y = \ln u$, where $u = 3 + e^x$.

(A) $y = \ln[3 + e^x]$

(B) $\dfrac{dy}{dx} = \dfrac{dy}{du} \cdot \dfrac{du}{dx} = \dfrac{1}{u}(e^x) = \dfrac{1}{3 + e^x}(e^x) = \dfrac{e^x}{3 + e^x}$ (5-3)

6. $\dfrac{d}{dx}2y^2 - \dfrac{d}{dx}3x^3 - \dfrac{d}{dx}5 = \dfrac{d}{dx}(0)$

$\qquad\qquad 4yy' - 9x^2 - 0 = 0$

$\qquad\qquad\qquad y' = \dfrac{9x^2}{4y}$

$\qquad\qquad \dfrac{dy}{dx}\Big|_{(1,\, 2)} = \dfrac{9 \cdot 1^2}{4 \cdot 2} = \dfrac{9}{8}$

$\qquad\qquad\qquad\qquad (5-4)$

7. $y = 3x^2 - 5$

$\dfrac{dy}{dt} = \dfrac{d(3x^2)}{dt} - \dfrac{d(5)}{dt}$

$\dfrac{dy}{dt} = 6x\dfrac{dx}{dt}$

$x = 12; \quad \dfrac{dx}{dt} = 3$

$\dfrac{dy}{dt} = 6 \cdot 12 \cdot 3 = 216$ (5-4)

8. $25p + x = 1,000$

(A) $x = 1,000 - 25p$

(B) $x = f(p) = 1,000 - 25p$

$\qquad f'(p) = -25$

$\qquad E(p) = -\dfrac{pf'(p)}{f(p)} = \dfrac{25p}{1,000 - 25p} = \dfrac{p}{40 - p}$

(C) $E(15) = \dfrac{15}{40 - 15} = \dfrac{15}{25} = \dfrac{3}{5} = 0.6$

    Demand is inelastic and insensitive to small changes in price.

(D) Revenue: $R(p) = pf(p) = 1,000p - 25p^2$

(E) From (B), $E(25) = \dfrac{25}{40 - 25} = \dfrac{25}{15} = \dfrac{5}{3} = 1.6$

    Demand is elastic; a price cut will increase revenue.   (5-4)

9. $y = 100e^{-0.1x}$

Step 1. Analyze $f(x)$:

(A) Domain: All real numbers, $(-\infty, \infty)$.

(B) Intercepts: y-intercept: $f(0) = 100e^{-0.1(0)} = 100$

x-intercept: Since $100e^{-0.1x} \neq 0$ for all x, there are no x-intercepts.

(C) Asymptotes:

$$\lim_{x \to \infty} 100e^{-0.1x} = \lim_{x \to \infty} \frac{100}{e^{0.1x}} = 0$$

$\lim_{x \to -\infty} 100e^{-0.1x}$ does not exist.

Thus, $y = 0$ is a horizontal asymptote. There are no vertical asymptotes.

Step 2. Analyze $f'(x)$:

$y' = 100e^{-0.1x}(-0.1)$

$\quad = -10e^{-0.1x} < 0$ on $(-\infty, \infty)$

Thus, y is decreasing on $(-\infty, \infty)$; there are no local extrema.

Step 3. Analyze $f''(x)$:

$y'' = -10e^{-0.1x}(-0.1)$

$\quad = e^{-0.1x} > 0$ on $(-\infty, \infty)$

Thus, the graph of f is concave upward on $(-\infty, \infty)$; there are no inflection points.

Step 4. Sketch the graph of f:

x	y
0	100
-1	≈ 110
10	≈ 37

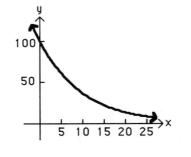

(5-2)

10.

n	1000	100,000	10,000,000	100,000,000
$\left(1 + \dfrac{2}{n}\right)^n$	7.374312	7.388908	7.389055	7.389056

$$\lim_{n \to \infty} \left(1 + \frac{2}{n}\right)^n \approx 7.38906 \text{ (5 decimal places)};$$

$$\lim_{n \to \infty} \left(1 + \frac{2}{n}\right)^n = e^2$$

(5-1)

11. $\dfrac{d}{dz}[(\ln z)^7 + \ln z^7] = \dfrac{d}{dz}[\ln z]^7 + \dfrac{d}{dz}7 \ln z$

$$= 7[\ln z]^6 \dfrac{d}{dz}\ln z + 7\dfrac{d}{dz}\ln z$$

$$= 7[\ln z]^6 \dfrac{1}{z} + \dfrac{7}{z}$$

$$= \dfrac{7(\ln z)^6 + 7}{z} = \dfrac{7[(\ln z)^6 + 1]}{z} \qquad (5\text{-}3)$$

12. $\dfrac{d}{dx}x^6 \ln x = x^6 \dfrac{d}{dx}\ln x + (\ln x)\dfrac{d}{dx}x^6$

$$= x^6\left(\dfrac{1}{x}\right) + (\ln x)6x^5 = x^5(1 + 6 \ln x) \qquad (5\text{-}2)$$

13. $\dfrac{d}{dx}\left(\dfrac{e^x}{x^6}\right) = \dfrac{x^6 \dfrac{d}{dx}e^x - e^x \dfrac{d}{dx}x^6}{(x^6)^2} = \dfrac{x^6 e^x - 6x^5 e^x}{x^{12}} = \dfrac{xe^x - 6e^x}{x^7} = \dfrac{e^x(x-6)}{x^7}$

$$\qquad (5\text{-}2)$$

14. $y = \ln(2x^3 - 3x)$

$$y' = \dfrac{1}{2x^3 - 3x}(6x^2 - 3) = \dfrac{6x^2 - 3}{2x^3 - 3x}$$

$$(5\text{-}3)$$

15. $f(x) = e^{x^3 - x^2}$

$$f'(x) = e^{x^3 - x^2}(3x^2 - 2x)$$

$$= (3x^2 - 2x)e^{x^3 - x^2} \qquad (5\text{-}3)$$

16. $y = e^{-2x}\ln 5x$

$$\dfrac{dy}{dx} = e^{-2x}\left(\dfrac{1}{5x}\right)(5) + (\ln 5x)(e^{-2x})(-2)$$

$$= e^{-2x}\left(\dfrac{1}{x} - 2 \ln 5x\right) = \dfrac{1 - 2x \ln 5x}{xe^{2x}} \qquad (5\text{-}3)$$

17. $f(x) = 1 + e^{-x}$

$$f'(x) = e^{-x}(-1) = -e^{-x}$$

An equation for the tangent line to the graph of f at $x = 0$ is:

$y - y_1 = m(x - x_1)$,

where $x_1 = 0$, $y_1 = f(0) = 1 + e^0 = 2$, and $m = f'(0) = -e^0 = -1$.

Thus, $y - 2 = -1(x - 0)$ or $y = -x + 2$.

An equation for the tangent line to the graph of f at $x = -1$ is

$y - y_1 = m(x - x_1)$,

where $x_1 = -1$, $y_1 = f(-1) = 1 + e$, and $m = f'(-1) = -e$. Thus,

$y - (1 + e) = -e[x - (-1)]$ or $y - 1 - e = -ex - e$ and $y = -ex + 1$.

$$(5\text{-}2)$$

18. $x^2 - 3xy + 4y^2 = 23$

Differentiate implicitly:

$2x - 3(xy' + y \cdot 1) + 8yy' = 0$

$2x - 3xy' - 3y + 8yy' = 0$

$8yy' - 3xy' = 3y - 2x$

$(8y - 3x)y' = 3y - 2x$

$y' = \dfrac{3y - 2x}{8y - 3x}$

$y'\Big|_{(-1,\,2)} = \dfrac{3 \cdot 2 - 2(-1)}{8 \cdot 2 - 3(-1)} = \dfrac{8}{19}$ [Slope at (-1, 2)]   (5-4)

19.

$x^3 - 2t^2x + 8 = 0$

$3x^2x' - (2t^2x' + x \cdot 4t) + 0 = 0$

$3x^2x' - 2t^2x' - 4xt = 0$

$(3x^2 - 2t^2)x' = 4xt$

$x' = \dfrac{4xt}{3x^2 - 2t^2}$

$x'\Big|_{(-2,\,2)} = \dfrac{4 \cdot 2 \cdot (-2)}{3(2^2) - 2(-2)^2} = \dfrac{-16}{12 - 8} = \dfrac{-16}{4} = -4$ (5-4)

20. $x - y^2 = e^y$

Differentiate implicitly:

$1 - 2yy' = e^y y'$

$1 = e^y y' + 2yy'$

$1 = y'(e^y + 2y)$

$y' = \dfrac{1}{e^y + 2y}$

$y'\Big|_{(1,\,0)} = \dfrac{1}{e^0 + 2 \cdot 0} = 1$

(5-4)

21. $\ln y = x^2 - y^2$

Differentiate implicitly:

$\dfrac{y'}{y} = 2x - 2yy'$

$y'\left(\dfrac{1}{y} + 2y\right) = 2x$

$y'\left(\dfrac{1 + 2y^2}{y}\right) = 2x$

$y' = \dfrac{2xy}{1 + 2y^2}$

$y'\Big|_{(1,\,1)} = \dfrac{2 \cdot 1 \cdot 1}{1 + 2(1)^2} = \dfrac{2}{3}$ (5-4)

22. $y^2 - 4x^2 = 12$

Differentiate with respect to t:

$2y\dfrac{dy}{dt} - 8x\dfrac{dx}{dt} = 0$

Given: $\dfrac{dx}{dt} = -2$ when $x = 1$ and $y = 4$. Therefore,

$2 \cdot 4\dfrac{dy}{dt} - 8 \cdot 1 \cdot (-2) = 0$

$8\dfrac{dy}{dt} + 16 = 0$

$\dfrac{dy}{dt} = -2.$

The y coordinate is decreasing at 2 units per second.   (5-6)

23. From the figure, $x^2 + y^2 = 17^2$.

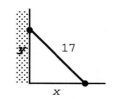

Differentiate with respect to t:

$$2x\frac{dx}{dt} + 2y\frac{dy}{dt} = 0 \quad \text{or} \quad x\frac{dx}{dt} + y\frac{dy}{dt} = 0$$

We are given $\frac{dx}{dt} = -0.5$ feet per second. Therefore,

$$x(-0.5) + y\frac{dy}{dt} = 0 \quad \text{or} \quad \frac{dy}{dt} = \frac{0.5x}{y} = \frac{x}{2y}$$

Now, when $x = 8$, we have: $8^2 + y^2 = 17^2$
$$y^2 = 289 - 64 = 225$$
$$y = 15$$

Therefore, $\left.\frac{dy}{dt}\right|_{(8,\,15)} = \frac{8}{2(15)} = \frac{4}{15} \approx 0.27$ ft/sec.   (5-6)

24. $A = \pi R^2$. Given: $\frac{dA}{dt} = 24$ square inches per minute.

Differentiate with respect to t:

$$\frac{dA}{dt} = 2\pi R\frac{dR}{dt}$$
$$24 = 2\pi R\frac{dR}{dt}$$

Therefore, $\frac{dR}{dt} = \frac{24}{2\pi R} = \frac{12}{\pi R}$.

$$\left.\frac{dR}{dt}\right|_{R=12} = \frac{12}{\pi \cdot 12} = \frac{1}{\pi} \approx 0.318 \text{ inches per minute}$$ (5-6)

25. $x = f(p) = 20(p - 15)^2 \qquad 0 \le p \le 15$
$$f'(p) = 40(p - 15)$$

$$E(p) = -\frac{pf'(p)}{f(p)} = \frac{-40p(p - 15)}{20(p - 15)^2} = \frac{-2p}{p - 15}$$

Elastic: $E(p) = \dfrac{-2p}{p - 15} > 1$

$$-2p < p - 15 \qquad (p - 15 < 0 \text{ reverses inequality})$$
$$-3p < -15$$
$$p > 5; \qquad 5 < p < 15$$

Inelastic: $E(p) = \dfrac{-2p}{p - 15} < 1$

$$-2p > p - 15 \qquad (p - 15 < 0 \text{ reverses inequality})$$
$$-3p > -15$$
$$p < 5; \qquad 0 < p < 5$$ (5-4)

26. $x = f(p) = 5(20 - p)$ $0 \le p \le 20$

$R(p) = pf(p) = 5p(20 - p) = 100p - 5p^2$

$R'(p) = 100 - 10p = 10(10 - p)$

Critical values: $p = 10$

Sign chart for $R'(p)$:

R'(p)   + + + 0 - - -

R(p)   0   10   20

Increasing ┊ Decreasing

Demand: Inelastic ┊ Elastic

Test Numbers	
p	$R'(p)$
5	50 (+)
15	−50 (−)

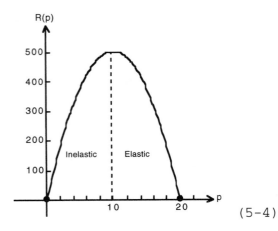

(5-4)

27. $f(x) = 11x - 2x \ln x$, $x > 0$

$f'(x) = 11 - 2x\left(\dfrac{1}{x}\right) - (\ln x)(2)$

$\qquad = 11 - 2 - 2 \ln x = 9 - 2 \ln x$, $x > 0$

Critical value(s): $f'(x) = 9 - 2 \ln x = 0$

$\qquad\qquad\qquad\qquad\qquad\qquad 2 \ln x = 9$

$\qquad\qquad\qquad\qquad\qquad\qquad \ln x = \dfrac{9}{2}$

$\qquad\qquad\qquad\qquad\qquad\qquad x = e^{9/2}$

$f''(x) = -\dfrac{2}{x}$ and $f''(e^{9/2}) = -\dfrac{2}{e^{9/2}} < 0$

Since $x = e^{9/2}$ is the only critical value, and $f''(e^{9/2}) < 0$, f has an absolute maximum at $x = e^{9/2}$. The absolute maximum is:

$f(e^{9/2}) = 11e^{9/2} - 2e^{9/2}\ln(e^{9/2})$

$\qquad\quad\; = 11e^{9/2} - 9e^{9/2}$

$\qquad\quad\; = 2e^{9/2} \approx 180.03$

(5-2)

28. $f(x) = 10xe^{-2x}$, $x > 0$

$f'(x) = 10xe^{-2x}(-2) + 10e^{-2x}(1) = 10e^{-2x}(1 - 2x)$, $x > 0$

Critical value(s): $f'(x) = 10e^{-2x}(1 - 2x) = 0$

$\qquad\qquad\qquad\qquad\qquad\qquad 1 - 2x = 0$

$\qquad\qquad\qquad\qquad\qquad\qquad x = \dfrac{1}{2}$

$f''(x) = 10e^{-2x}(-2) + 10(1 - 2x)e^{-2x}(-2)$

$\qquad\quad = -20e^{-2x}(1 + 1 - 2x)$

$\qquad\quad = -40e^{-2x}(1 - x)$

$f''\left(\dfrac{1}{2}\right) = -20e^{-1} < 0$

Since $x = \dfrac{1}{2}$ is the only critical value, and $f''\left(\dfrac{1}{2}\right) = -20e^{-1} < 0$,

f has an absolute maximum at $x = \dfrac{1}{2}$. The absolute maximum of f is:

$$f\left(\dfrac{1}{2}\right) = 10\left(\dfrac{1}{2}\right)e^{-2(1/2)}$$
$$= 5e^{-1} \approx 1.84$$

(5-3)

29. $f(x) = 3x - x^2 + e^{-x}, \; x > 0$
$f'(x) = 3 - 2x - e^{-x}, \; x > 0$
Critical value(s): $f'(x) = 3 - 2x - e^{-x} = 0$
$$x \approx 1.373$$
$f''(x) = -2 + e^{-x}$ and $f''(1.373) = -2 + e^{-1.373} < 0$

Since $x \approx 1.373$ is the only critical value, and $f''(1.373) < 0$, f has an absolute maximum at $x = 1.373$. The absolute maximum of f is:

$$f(1.373) = 3(1.373) - (1.373)^2 + e^{-1.373}$$
$$\approx 2.487$$

(5-2)

30. $f(x) = \dfrac{\ln x}{e^x}, \; x > 0$

$$f'(x) = \dfrac{e^x\left(\dfrac{1}{x}\right) - (\ln x)e^x}{(e^x)^2} = \dfrac{e^x\left(\dfrac{1}{x} - \ln x\right)}{e^{2x}}$$
$$= \dfrac{1 - x \ln x}{xe^x}, \; x > 0$$

Critical value(s): $f'(x) = \dfrac{1 - x \ln x}{xe^x} = 0$
$$1 - x \ln x = 0$$
$$x \ln x = 1$$
$$x \approx 1.763$$

$$f''(x) = \dfrac{xe^x[-1 - \ln x] - (1 - x \ln x)(xe^x + e^x)}{x^2 e^{2x}}$$
$$= \dfrac{-x(1 + \ln x) - (x + 1)(1 - x \ln x)}{x^2 e^x};$$
$$f''(1.763) \approx \dfrac{-1.763(1.567) - (2.763)(0.000349)}{(1.763)^2 e^{1.763}} < 0$$

Since $x = 1.763$ is the only critical value, and $f''(1.763) < 0$, f has an absolute maximum at $x = 1.763$. The absolute maximum of f is:

$$f(1.763) = \dfrac{\ln(1.763)}{e^{1.763}} \approx 0.097$$

(5-2)

31. $f(x) = 5 - 5e^{-x}$

Step 1. Analyze $f(x)$:
(A) Domain: All real numbers, $(-\infty, \infty)$.

(B) Intercepts: y intercept: $f(0) = 5 - 5e^{-0} = 0$
$\qquad$ x intercepts: $5 - 5e^{-x} = 0$
$$e^{-x} = 1$$
$$x = 0$$

(C) Asymptotes:
$$\lim_{x \to \infty} (5 - 5e^{-x}) = \lim_{x \to \infty} \left(5 - \frac{5}{e^x} \right) = 5$$
$$\lim_{x \to -\infty} (5 - 5e^{-x}) \text{ does not exist.}$$
Thus, $y = 5$ is a horizontal asymptote.

Since $f(x) = 5 - \dfrac{5}{e^x} = \dfrac{5e^x - 5}{e^x}$ and $e^x \neq 0$ for all x, there are no vertical asymptotes.

Step 2. Analyze $f'(x)$:
$f'(x) = -5e^{-x}(-1) = 5e^{-x} > 0$ on $(-\infty, \infty)$
Thus, f is increasing on $(-\infty, \infty)$; there are no local extrema.

Step 3. Analyze $f''(x)$:
$f''(x) = -5e^{-x} < 0$ on $(-\infty, \infty)$.
Thus, the graph of f is concave downward on $(-\infty, \infty)$; there are no inflection points.

Step 4. Sketch the graph of f:

x	$f(x)$
0	0
-1	-8.59
2	4.32

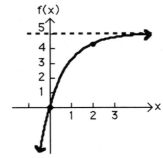

(5-2)

32. $f(x) = x^3 \ln x$

Step 1. Analyze $f(x)$:

(A) Domain: all positive real numbers, $(0, \infty)$.

(B) Intercepts: y-intercept: Since $x = 0$ is not in the domain, there is no y-intercept.
$\qquad$ x-intercepts: $x^3 \ln x = 0$
$$\ln x = 0$$
$$x = 1$$

(C) Asymptotes:

$\lim\limits_{x\to\infty} (x^3 \ln x)$ does not exist.

It can be shown that $\lim\limits_{x\to 0^+} (x^3 \ln x) = 0$. Thus, there are no horizontal or vertical asymptotes.

Step 2. Analyze $f'(x)$:

$f'(x) = x^3\left(\dfrac{1}{x}\right) + (\ln x)3x^2$

$\qquad = x^2[1 + 3\ln x],\ x > 0$

Critical values: $x^2[1 + 3\ln x] = 0$

$\qquad\qquad\qquad\qquad 1 + 3\ln x = 0$ (since $x > 0$)

$\qquad\qquad\qquad\qquad\qquad \ln x = -\dfrac{1}{3}$

$\qquad\qquad\qquad\qquad\qquad\quad x = e^{-1/3} \approx 0.72$

Partition numbers: $x = e^{-1/3}$

Sign chart for f':

Test Numbers	
x	$f'(x)$
0.5	-0.27 (−)
1	1 (+)

f'(x) − − − − − − 0 + + + + + → x

0        $e^{-1/3}$ 1   2

f(x)   Decreasing | Increasing

Thus, f is decreasing on $(0, e^{-1/3})$ and increasing on $(e^{-1/3}, \infty)$; f has a local minimum at $x = e^{-1/3}$.

Step 3. Analyze $f''(x)$:

$f''(x) = x^2\left(\dfrac{3}{x}\right) + (1 + 3\ln x)2x$

$\qquad = x(5 + 6\ln x),\ x > 0$

Partition numbers: $x(5 + 6\ln x) = 0$

$\qquad\qquad\qquad\qquad 5 + 6\ln x = 0$

$\qquad\qquad\qquad\qquad\qquad \ln x = -\dfrac{5}{6}$

$\qquad\qquad\qquad\qquad\qquad\quad x = e^{-5/6} \approx 0.43$

Sign chart for f'':

Test Numbers	
x	$f''(x)$
.2	-0.93 (−)
1	5 (+)

f''(x) − − − − − − 0 + + + + + → x

0        $e^{-5/6}$ .5   1

Graph   Concave | Concave
of f Downward | Upward

Thus, the graph of f is concave downward on $(0, e^{-5/6})$ and concave upward on $(e^{-5/6}, \infty)$; the graph has an inflection point at $x = e^{-5/6}$.

Step 4. Sketch the graph of f:

x	$f(x)$
$e^{-5/6}$	-0.07
$e^{-1/3}$	-0.12
1	0

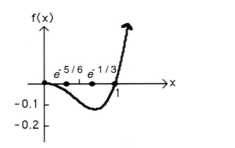

(5-2)

33. $y = w^3$, $w = \ln u$, $u = 4 - e^x$

(A) $y = [\ln(4 - e^x)]^3$

(B) $\dfrac{dy}{dx} = \dfrac{dy}{dw} \cdot \dfrac{dw}{du} \cdot \dfrac{du}{dx}$

$\qquad = 3w^2 \cdot \dfrac{1}{u} \cdot (-e^x) = 3[\ln(4 - e^x)]^2\left(\dfrac{1}{4 - e^x}\right)(-e^x)$

$\qquad\qquad = \dfrac{-3e^x[\ln(4 - e^x)]^2}{4 - e^x}$

(5-3)

34. $y = 5^{x^2-1}$

$y' = 5^{x^2-1}(\ln 5)(2x) = 2x5^{x^2-1}(\ln 5)$

(5-3)

35. $\dfrac{d}{dx}\log_5(x^2 - x) = \dfrac{1}{x^2 - x} \cdot \dfrac{1}{\ln 5} \cdot \dfrac{d}{dx}(x^2 - x) = \dfrac{1}{\ln 5} \cdot \dfrac{2x - 1}{x^2 - x}$

(5-3)

36. $\dfrac{d}{dx}\sqrt{\ln(x^2 + x)} = \dfrac{d}{dx}[\ln(x^2 + x)]^{1/2} = \dfrac{1}{2}[\ln(x^2 + x)]^{-1/2}\dfrac{d}{dx}\ln(x^2 + x)$

$\qquad = \dfrac{1}{2}[\ln(x^2 + x)]^{-1/2}\dfrac{1}{x^2 + x}\dfrac{d}{dx}(x^2 + x)$

$\qquad = \dfrac{1}{2}[\ln(x^2 + x)]^{-1/2} \cdot \dfrac{2x + 1}{x^2 + x} = \dfrac{2x + 1}{2(x^2 + x)[\ln(x^2 + x)]^{1/2}}$

(5-3)

37. $e^{xy} = x^2 + y + 1$

Differentiate implicitly:

$\qquad \dfrac{d}{dx}e^{xy} = \dfrac{d}{dx}x^2 + \dfrac{d}{dx}y + \dfrac{d}{dx}1$

$e^{xy}(xy' + y) = 2x + y'$

$xe^{xy}y' - y' = 2x - ye^{xy}$

$\qquad\qquad y' = \dfrac{2x - ye^{xy}}{xe^{xy} - 1}$

$\qquad y'\Big|_{(0,\,0)} = \dfrac{2 \cdot 0 - 0 \cdot e^0}{0 \cdot e^0 - 1} = 0$

(5-4)

38. $A = \pi r^2$, $r \geq 0$

Differentiate with respect to t:

$\qquad \dfrac{dA}{dt} = 2\pi r\dfrac{dr}{dt} = 6\pi r$ since $\dfrac{dr}{dt} = 3$

The area increases at the rate $6\pi r$. This is smallest when $r = 0$; there is no largest value.

(5-6)

39. $y = x^3$

Differentiate with respect to t:

$$\frac{dy}{dt} = 3x^2 \frac{dx}{dt}$$

Solving for $\frac{dx}{dt}$, we get

$$\frac{dx}{dt} = \frac{1}{3x^2} \cdot \frac{dy}{dt} = \frac{5}{3x^2} \quad \text{since} \quad \frac{dy}{dt} = 5$$

To find where $\frac{dx}{dt} > \frac{dy}{dt}$, solve the inequality

$$\frac{5}{3x^2} > 5$$

$$\frac{1}{3x^2} > 1$$

$$3x^2 < 1$$

$$-\frac{1}{\sqrt{3}} < x < \frac{1}{\sqrt{3}} \quad \text{or} \quad \frac{-\sqrt{3}}{3} < x < \frac{\sqrt{3}}{3} \qquad (5\text{-}6)$$

40. (A) The compound interest formula is: $A = P(1 + r)^t$. Thus, the time for P to double when $r = 0.05$ and interest is compounded annually can be found by solving

$$2P = P(1 + 0.05)^t \quad \text{or} \quad 2 = (1.05)^t \quad \text{for } t.$$
$$\ln(1.05)^t = \ln 2$$
$$t \ln(1.05) = \ln 2$$
$$t = \frac{\ln 2}{\ln(1.05)} \approx 14.2 \text{ years}$$

(B) The continuous compound interest formula is: $A = Pe^{rt}$. Proceeding as above, we have

$$2P = Pe^{0.05t} \quad \text{or} \quad e^{0.05t} = 2.$$
Therefore, $0.05t = \ln 2$ and
$$t = \frac{\ln 2}{.05} \approx 13.9 \text{ years} \qquad (5\text{-}1)$$

41. $A(t) = 100e^{0.1t}$
$A'(t) = 100(0.1)e^{0.1t} = 10e^{0.1t}$
$A'(1) = 11.05 \quad \text{or} \quad \$11.05 \text{ per year}$
$A'(10) = 27.18 \quad \text{or} \quad \$27.18 \text{ per year} \qquad (5\text{-}1)$

42. $R(x) = xp(x) = 1000xe^{-0.02x}$
$R'(x) = 1000[xD_x e^{-0.02x} + e^{-0.02x}D_x x]$
$\quad\quad = 1000[x(-0.02)e^{-0.02x} + e^{-0.02x}]$
$\quad\quad = (1000 - 20x)e^{-0.02x} \qquad (5\text{-}3)$

43. From Problem 42,

$R'(x) = (1000 - 20x)e^{-0.02x}$

Critical value(3s): $R'(x) = (1000 - 20x)e^{-0.02x} = 0$

$1000 - 20x = 0$

$x = 50$

$R''(x) = (1000 - 20x)e^{-0.02x}(-0.02) + e^{-0.02x}(-20)$

$= e^{-0.02x}[0.4x - 20 - 20]$

$= e^{-0.02x}(0.4x - 40)$

$R''(50) = e^{-0.02(50)}[0.4(50) - 40] = -20e^{-1} < 0$

Since $x = 50$ is the only critical value and $R''(50) < 0$, R has an absolute maximum at a production level of 50 units. The maximum revenue is $R(50) = 1000(50)e^{-0.02(50)} = 50{,}000e^{-1} \approx 18{,}394$ or $18,394.
The price per unit at the production level of 50 units is
$p(50) = 1000e^{-0.02(50)} = 1000e^{-1} \approx 367.88$ or $367.88. (5-3)

44. $R(x) = 1000xe^{-0.02x}$, $0 \le x \le 100$

<u>Step 1. Analyze $R(x)$</u>:

(A) Domain: $0 \le x \le 100$ or $[0, 100]$

(B) Intercepts: y-intercept: $R(0) = 0$

x-intercepts: $100xe^{-0.02x} = 0$

$x = 0$

(C) Asymptotes: There are no horizontal or vertical asymptotes.

<u>Step 2. Analyze $R'(x)$</u>:

From Problems 47 and 48, $R'(x) = (1000 - 20x)e^{-0.02x}$ and $x = 50$ is a critical value.

Sign chart for R':

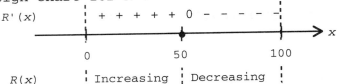

Test Numbers	
x	$R'(x)$
0	$1000\ (+)$
60	$\approx -60.24\ (-)$

Thus, R is increasing on $(0, 50)$ and decreasing on $(50, 100)$; R has a maximum at $x = 50$.

<u>Step 3. Analyze $R''(x)$</u>:

$R''(x) = (0.4x - 40)e^{-0.02x} < 0$ on $(0, 100)$
Thus, the graph of R is concave downward on $(0, 100)$.

<u>Step 4. Sketch the graph of R:</u>

x	$R(x)$
0	0
50	18,394
100	13,533

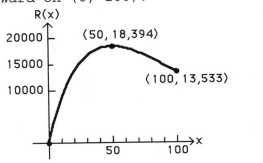

(5-3)

45. Cost: $C(x) = 220x$

Price-demand equation: $p(x) = 1{,}000e^{-0.02x}$

Revenue: $R(x) = xp(x) = 1{,}000xe^{-0.02x}$

Profit: $P(x) = R(x) - C(x) = 1{,}000xe^{-0.02x} - 220x$

On a graphing utility, graph $P(x)$ and calculate its maximum value. The maximum value is \$9,864 at a demand level of 29.969082 ($\approx$ 30). The price at this demand level is: $p = \$549.15$. (5-3)

46. Let x = the number of cream puffs.

Daily cost: $C(x) = x$ (dollars)

Daily revenue: $R(x) = xp(x)$, where

$p(x) = a + b \ln x$ is the logarithmic regression model for the given data.

```
LnReg
 y=a+blnx
 a=6.224213011
 b=-.5238332169
```

Profit: $P(x) = R(x) - C(x)$

Using a graphing utility, we find that the maximum profit is achieved at the demand level $x \approx 7887$. The price at this demand level is: $p(7887) = \$1.52$ (to the nearest cent). (5-2)

47. Cost: $C(x) = 200 + 50x - 50 \ln x$, $x \geq 1$

Average cost: $\overline{C} = \dfrac{C(x)}{x} = \dfrac{200}{x} + 50 - \dfrac{50}{x}\ln x$, $x \geq 1$

$\overline{C}'(x) = \dfrac{-200}{x^2} - \dfrac{50}{x}\left(\dfrac{1}{x}\right) + (\ln x)\dfrac{50}{x^2} = \dfrac{50(\ln x - 5)}{x^2}$, $x \geq 1$

Critical value(s): $\overline{C}'(x) = \dfrac{50(\ln x - 5)}{x^2} = 0$

$\ln x = 5$

$x = e^5$

Sign chart for $\overline{C}'$:

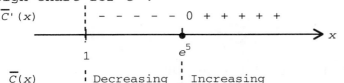

Test Numbers	
x	$\overline{C}'(x)$
1	-250 $(-)$
e^6	$\dfrac{50}{e^{12}}$ $(+)$

$\overline{C}'(x)$ $\quad$ $- - - - - - 0 + + + + + +$

$\overline{C}(x)$ $\quad$ Decreasing $\vdots$ Increasing

By the first derivative test, $\overline{C}$ has a local minimum at $x = e^5$. Since this is the only critical value of $\overline{C}$, $\overline{C}$ has as absolute minimum at $x = e^5$. Thus, the minimal average cost is:

$\overline{C}(e^5) = \dfrac{200}{e^5} + 50 - \dfrac{50}{e^5}\ln(e^5)$

$= 50 - \dfrac{50}{e^5} \approx 49.66$ or \$49.66 (5-2)

48. $x = \sqrt{5000 - 2p^3} = (5000 - 2p^3)^{1/2}$

Differentiate implicitly with respect to x:

$$1 = \frac{1}{2}(5000 - 2p^3)^{-1/2}(-6p^2)\frac{dp}{dx}$$

$$1 = \frac{-3p^2}{(5000 - 2p^3)^{1/2}}\frac{dp}{dx}$$

$$\frac{dp}{dx} = \frac{-(5000 - 2p^3)^{1/2}}{3p^2} \hspace{4cm} (5\text{-}3)$$

49. Given: $R(x) = 36x - \dfrac{x^2}{20}$ and $\dfrac{dx}{dt} = 10$ when $x = 250$.

Differentiate with respect to t:

$$\frac{dR}{dt} = 36\frac{dx}{dt} - \frac{1}{20}(2x)\frac{dx}{dt} = 36\frac{dx}{dt} - \frac{x}{10}\frac{dx}{dt}$$

Thus, $\left.\dfrac{dR}{dt}\right|_{x=250 \text{ and } \frac{dx}{dt}=10} = 36(10) - \dfrac{250}{10}(10)$

$$= \$110 \text{ per day} \hspace{3cm} (5\text{-}6)$$

50. $p = 16.8 - 0.002x$

$$x = f(p) = \frac{16.8}{0.002} - \frac{1}{0.002}p = 8,400 - 500p$$

$$f'(p) = -500$$

Elasticity of demand: $E(p) = \dfrac{-pf'(p)}{f(p)} = \dfrac{500p}{8,400 - 500p} = \dfrac{5p}{84 - 5p}$

$$E(8) = \frac{40}{84 - 40} = \frac{40}{44} = \frac{10}{11} < 1$$

Demand is inelastic, a (small) price increase will increase revenue.

$$\hspace{12cm} (5\text{-}4)$$

51. $f(t) = 1,700t + 20,500$

$f'(t) = 1,700$

Relative rate of change: $\dfrac{f'(t)}{f(t)} = \dfrac{1,700}{1,700t + 20,500}$

Relative rate of change at $t = 30$: $\dfrac{1,700}{1,700(30) + 20,500} \approx 0.02378 \hspace{1cm} (5\text{-}4)$

52. $C(t) = 5e^{-0.3t}$

$C'(t) = 5e^{-0.3t}(-0.3) = -1.5e^{-0.3t}$

After one hour, the rate of change of concentration is

$C'(1) = -1.5e^{-0.3(1)} = -1.5e^{-0.3} \approx -1.111$ mg/ml per hour.

After five hours, the rate of change of concentration is

$C'(5) = -1.5e^{-0.3(5)} = -1.5e^{-1.5} \approx -0.335$ mg/ml per hour. $\hspace{1cm} (5\text{-}3)$

53. Given: $A = \pi R^2$ and $\dfrac{dA}{dt} = -45$ mm² per day (negative because the area is decreasing).

Differentiate with respect to t:

$$\frac{dA}{dt} = \pi 2R\frac{dR}{dt}$$

$$-45 = 2\pi R\frac{dR}{dt}$$

$$\frac{dR}{dt} = -\frac{45}{2\pi R}$$

$$\left.\frac{dR}{dt}\right|_{R=15} = \frac{-45}{2\pi \cdot 15} = \frac{-3}{2\pi} \approx -0.477 \text{ mm per day} \tag{5-6}$$

54. $N(t) = 10(1 - e^{-0.4t})$

(A) $N'(t) = -10e^{-0.4t}(-0.4) = 4e^{-0.4t}$

$N'(1) = 4e^{-0.4(1)} = 4e^{-0.4} \approx 2.68$.

Thus, learning is increasing at the rate of 2.68 units per day after 1 day.

$N'(5) = 4e^{-0.4(5)} = 4e^{-2} \approx 0.54$

Thus, learning is increasing at the rate of 0.54 units per day after 5 days.

(B) From (A), $N'(t) = 4e^{-0.4t} > 0$ on $(0, 10)$. Thus, N is increasing on $(0, 10)$.

$N''(t) = 4e^{-0.4t}(-0.4) = -1.6e^{-0.4t} < 0$ on $(0, 10)$.

Thus, the graph of N is concave downward on $(0, 10)$. The graph of N is:

t	$N(t)$
0	0
5	8.65
10	9.82

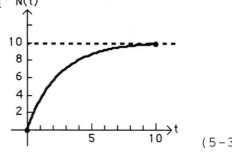

$(5-3)$

55. Given: $T = 2\left(1 + \dfrac{1}{x^{3/2}}\right) = 2 + 2x^{-3/2}$, and $\dfrac{dx}{dt} = 3$ when $x = 9$.

Differentiate with respect to t:

$$\frac{dT}{dt} = 0 + 2\left(-\frac{3}{2}x^{-5/2}\right)\frac{dx}{dt} = -3x^{-5/2}\frac{dx}{dt}$$

$$\left.\frac{dT}{dt}\right|_{x=9 \text{ and } \frac{dx}{dt}=3} = -3(9)^{-5/2}(3) = -3 \cdot 3^{-5} \cdot 3 = -3^{-3} = \frac{-1}{27}$$

$$\approx -0.037 \text{ minutes per operation per hour}$$

$(5-6)$

6 INTEGRATION

Things to remember:

1. A function $F(x)$ is an ANTIDERIVATIVE of $f(x)$ if $F'(x) = f(x)$.

2. THEOREM ON ANTIDERIVATIVES

    If the derivatives of two functions are equal on an open interval (a, b), then the functions can differ by at most a constant. Symbolically: If F and G are differentiable functions on the interval (a, b) and $F'(x) = G'(x)$ for all x in (a, b), then $F(x) = G(x) + k$ for some constant k.

3. The INDEFINITE INTEGRAL of $f(x)$, denoted

    $$\int f(x)dx,$$

    represents all antiderivatives of $f(x)$ and is given by

    $$\int f(x)dx = F(x) + C$$

    where $F(x)$ is any antiderivative of $f(x)$ and C is an arbitrary constant. The symbol $\int$ is called an INTEGRAL SIGN, the function $f(x)$ is called the INTEGRAND, and C is called the CONSTANT OF INTEGRATION.

4. Indefinite integration and differentiation are reverse operations (except for the addition of the constant of integration). This is expressed symbolically by:

    (a) $\dfrac{d}{dx}\left(\int f(x)dx \right) = f(x)$

    (b) $\int F'(x)dx = F(x) + C$

5. INDEFINITE INTEGRAL FORMULAS:

    (a) $\int x^n\, dx = \dfrac{x^{n+1}}{n+1} + C, \ n \neq -1$

    (b) $\int e^x\, dx = e^x + C$

    (c) $\int \dfrac{dx}{x} = \ln|x| + C, \ x \neq 0$

6. INDEFINITE INTEGRATION PROPERTIES:

    (a) $\int kf(x)dx = k \int f(x)dx, \ k$ constant

    (b) $\int [f(x) \pm g(x)]dx = \int f(x)dx \pm \int g(x)dx$

1. $\int x^2 \, dx = \dfrac{1}{3}x^3 + C$ [Formula 5a]

Check: $\dfrac{d}{dx}\left(\dfrac{1}{3}x^3 + C\right) = x^2$

3. $\int x^7 \, dx = \dfrac{1}{8}x^8 + C$ [Formula 5a]

Check: $\dfrac{d}{dx}\left(\dfrac{1}{8}x^8 + C\right) = x^7$

5. $\int 2 \, dx = 2\int dx = 2[x + C] = 2x + C$

Check: $\dfrac{d}{dx}(2x + C) = 2$

[Formula 5a, Property 6a, $x^0 = 1$, replace $2C$ by C]

7. $\int 5t^{-3} \, dt = 5\int t^{-3} \, dt = 5\dfrac{t^{-2}}{-2} + C = -\dfrac{5}{2}t^{-2} + C$ [Formula 5a, Property 6a]

Check: $\dfrac{d}{dt}\left(-\dfrac{5}{2}t^{-2} + C\right) = 5t^{-3}$

9. $\int \pi^2 \, dx = \pi^2\int dx = \pi^2 x + C$ [Formula 5a, Property 6a]

Check: $\dfrac{d}{dx}(\pi^2 x + C) = \pi^2$

11. $\int (6t + 3) \, dt = 6\int t \, dt + 3\int dt = 6\dfrac{t^2}{2} + 3t + C = 3t^2 + 3t + C$

Check: $\dfrac{d}{dt}(3t^2 + 3t + C) = 6t + 3$ [Formula 5a, Properties 6a, b]

13. $\int 3e^t \, dt = 3\int e^t \, dt = 3e^t + C$ [Formula 5b, Property 6a]

Check: $\dfrac{d}{dt}(3e^t + C) = 3e^t$

15. $\int \dfrac{6}{x} \, dx = 6\int \dfrac{1}{x} \, dx = 6 \ln|x| + C$

Check: $\dfrac{d}{dx}(\ln|x| + C) = \dfrac{1}{x}$ [Formula 5c, Property 6a]

17. $\int 15x^{1/2} \, dx = 15\int x^{1/2} \, dx = 15\dfrac{x^{1/2+1}}{1/2 + 1} + C = 15\dfrac{x^{3/2}}{3/2} + C = 10x^{3/2} + C$

Check: $\dfrac{d}{dx}(10x^{3/2} + C) = 15x^{1/2}$ [Formula 5a, Property 6a]

19. $\int 7t^{-4/3} \, dt = 7\int t^{-4/3} \, dt = 7\dfrac{t^{-4/3+1}}{-4/3 + 1} + C = 7\dfrac{t^{-1/3}}{-1/3} + C = -21t^{-1/3} + C$

Check: $\dfrac{d}{dt}(-21t^{-1/3} + C) = 7t^{-4/3}$ [Formula 5a, Property 6a]

21. $\int (x - \sqrt{x}) \, dx = \int x \, dx - \int x^{1/2} \, dx = \dfrac{1}{2}x^2 - \dfrac{x^{3/2}}{3/2} + C = \dfrac{1}{2}x^2 - \dfrac{2}{3}x^{3/2} + C$

Check: $\dfrac{d}{dx}\left(\dfrac{1}{2}x^2 - \dfrac{2}{3}x^{3/2} + C\right) = x - x^{1/2}$ [Formula 5a, Property 6b]

$= x - \sqrt{x}$

23. $\dfrac{dy}{dx} = 200x^4$

$$y = \int 200x^4\,dx = 200\int x^4\,dx = 200\,\frac{x^5}{5} + C = 40x^5 + C$$

25. $\dfrac{dP}{dx} = 24 - 6x$

$$P = \int (24 - 6x)\,dx = \int 24\ dx - \int 6x\ dx = \int 24\ dx - 6\int x\ dx$$

$$= 24x - \frac{6x^2}{2} + C = 24x - 3x^2 + C$$

27. $\dfrac{dy}{du} = 2u^5 - 3u^2 - 1$

$$y = \int (2u^5 - 3u^2 - 1)\,du = \int 2u^5\,du - \int 3u^2\,du - \int 1\ du$$

$$= 2\int u^5\,du - 3\int u^2\,du - \int du$$

$$= \frac{2u^6}{6} - \frac{3u^3}{3} - u + C = \frac{u^6}{3} - u^3 - u + C$$

29. $\dfrac{dy}{dx} = e^x + 3$

$$y = \int (e^x + 3)\,dx = \int e^x\,dx + \int 3\ dx = e^x + 3x + C$$

31. $\dfrac{dx}{dt} = 5t^{-1} + 1$

$$x = \int (5t^{-1} + 1)\,dt = \int 5t^{-1}\,dt + \int 1\ dt = 5\int \frac{1}{t}\,dt + \int dt$$

$$= 5\ \ln|t| + t + C$$

33. (A) False; x^{-1} does not have an antiderivative of the form $\dfrac{x^{n+1}}{n+1}$.

(B) True; $\dfrac{d}{dx}\,(\pi) = 0$ since π is a constant.

35. The graphs in this set ARE NOT graphs from a family of antiderivative functions since the graphs are not vertical translations of each other.

37. The graphs in this set could be graphs from a family of antiderivative functions since they appear to be vertical translations of each other.

39. $\displaystyle\int 5x(1 - x)\,dx = 5\int x(1 - x)\,dx = 5\int (x - x^2)\,dx$

$$= 5\int x\ dx - 5\int x^2\ dx = \frac{5x^2}{2} - \frac{5x^3}{3} + C$$

<u>Check</u>: $\left(\dfrac{5x^2}{2} - \dfrac{5x^3}{3} + C\right)' = 5x - 5x^2 = 5x(1 - x)$

41. $\int (2 + x^2)(3 + x^2)\,dx = \int (6 + 5x^2 + x^4)\,dx = 6\int dx + 5\int x^2\,dx + \int x^4\,dx$

$$= 6x + \frac{5x^3}{3} + \frac{x^5}{5} + C = 6x + \frac{5x^3}{3} + \frac{x^5}{5} + C$$

Check: $\left(6x + \dfrac{5x^3}{3} + \dfrac{x^5}{5} + C\right)' = 6 + 5x^2 + x^4 = (2 + x^2)(3 + x^2)$

43. $\int \dfrac{du}{\sqrt{u}} = \int \dfrac{du}{u^{1/2}} = \int u^{-1/2}\,du = \dfrac{u^{(-1/2)+1}}{-1/2 + 1} + C = \dfrac{u^{1/2}}{1/2} + C$

$$= 2u^{1/2} + C \text{ or } 2\sqrt{u} + C$$

Check: $(2u^{1/2} + C)' = 2\left(\dfrac{1}{2}\right)u^{-1/2} = \dfrac{1}{u^{1/2}} = \dfrac{1}{\sqrt{u}}$

45. $\int \dfrac{dx}{4x^3} = \dfrac{1}{4}\int x^{-3}\,dx = \dfrac{1}{4} \cdot \dfrac{x^{-2}}{-2} + C = \dfrac{-x^{-2}}{8} + C$

Check: $\left(\dfrac{-x^{-2}}{8} + C\right)' = \dfrac{1}{8}(-2)(-x^{-3}) = \dfrac{1}{4}x^{-3} = \dfrac{1}{4x^3}$

47. $\int \dfrac{4 + u}{u}\,du = \int \left(\dfrac{4}{u} + 1\right)du = 4\int \dfrac{1}{u}\,du + \int 1\,du$

$$= 4\ln|u| + u + C$$

Check: $\dfrac{d}{du}(4\ln|u| + u + C) = \dfrac{4}{u} + 1 = \dfrac{4 + u}{u}$

49. $\int (5e^z + 4)\,dz = 5\int e^z\,dz + 4\int dz = 5e^z + 4z + C$

Check: $(5e^z + 4z + C)' = 5e^z + 4$

51. $\int \left(3x^2 - \dfrac{2}{x^2}\right)dx = \int 3x^2\,dx - \int \dfrac{2}{x^2}\,dx$

$$= 3\int x^2\,dx - 2\int x^{-2}\,dx = 3 \cdot \dfrac{x^3}{3} - \dfrac{2x^{-1}}{-1} + C = x^3 + 2x^{-1} + C$$

Check: $(x^3 + 2x^{-1} + C)' = 3x^2 - 2x^{-2} = 3x^2 - \dfrac{2}{x^2}$

53. $\int \left(10x^4 - \dfrac{8}{x^5} - 2\right)dx = \int 10x^4\,dx - \int 8x^{-5}\,dx - \int 2\,dx$

$$= 10\int x^4\,dx - 8\int x^{-5}\,dx - \int 2\,dx$$

$$= \dfrac{10x^5}{5} - \dfrac{8x^{-4}}{-4} - 2x + C = 2x^5 + 2x^{-4} - 2x + C$$

Check: $(2x^5 + 2x^{-4} - 2x + C)' = 10x^4 - 8x^{-5} - 2 = 10x^4 - \dfrac{8}{x^5} - 2$

55. $\int \left(3\sqrt{x} + \dfrac{2}{\sqrt{x}} \right) dx = 3\int x^{1/2} dx + 2\int x^{-1/2} dx$

$$= \frac{3x^{3/2}}{3/2} + \frac{2x^{1/2}}{1/2} + C = 2x^{3/2} + 4x^{1/2} + C$$

Check: $(2x^{3/2} + 4x^{1/2} + C)' = 2\left(\dfrac{3}{2}\right)x^{1/2} + 4\left(\dfrac{1}{2}\right)x^{-1/2}$

$$= 3x^{1/2} + 2x^{-1/2} = 3\sqrt{x} + \frac{2}{\sqrt{x}}$$

57. $\int \left(\sqrt[3]{x^2} - \dfrac{4}{x^3} \right) dx = \int x^{2/3} dx - 4\int x^{-3} dx = \dfrac{x^{5/3}}{5/3} - \dfrac{4x^{-2}}{-2} + C$

$$= \frac{3x^{5/3}}{5} + 2x^{-2} + C$$

Check: $\left(\dfrac{3}{5} x^{5/3} + 2x^{-2} + C \right)' = \dfrac{3}{5}\left(\dfrac{5}{3}\right)x^{2/3} + 2(-2)x^{-3}$

$$= x^{2/3} - 4x^{-3} = \sqrt[3]{x^2} - \frac{4}{x^3}$$

59. $\int \dfrac{e^x - 3x}{4} dx = \int \left(\dfrac{e^x}{4} - \dfrac{3x}{4} \right) dx = \dfrac{1}{4}\int e^x dx - \dfrac{3}{4}\int x \, dx$

$$= \frac{1}{4}e^x - \frac{3}{4} \cdot \frac{x^2}{2} + C = \frac{1}{4}e^x - \frac{3x^2}{8} + C$$

Check: $\left(\dfrac{1}{4} e^x - \dfrac{3x^2}{8} + C \right)' = \dfrac{1}{4}e^x - \dfrac{6x}{8} = \dfrac{1}{4}e^x - \dfrac{3}{4}x$

61. $\int \dfrac{12 + 5z - 3z^3}{z^4} dz = \int \left(\dfrac{12}{z^4} + \dfrac{5}{z^3} - \dfrac{3}{z} \right) dz$

$$= 12\int z^{-4} dz + 5\int z^{-3} dz - 3\int \frac{1}{z} dz$$

$$= 12 \cdot \frac{z^{-3}}{-3} + 5 \cdot \frac{z^{-2}}{-2} - 3 \ln|z| + C$$

$$= -4z^{-3} - \frac{5}{2}z^{-2} - 3 \ln|z| + C$$

Check: $\dfrac{d}{dz}\left(-4z^{-3} - \dfrac{5}{2}z^{-2} - 3\ln|z| + C \right) = 12z^{-4} + 5z^{-3} - \dfrac{3}{z} = \dfrac{12 + 5z - 3z^3}{z^4}$

63. $\int \left(\dfrac{6x^2}{5} - \dfrac{2}{3x} \right) dx = \dfrac{6}{5}\int x^2 \, dx - \dfrac{2}{3}\int \dfrac{1}{x} dx$

$$= \frac{6}{5} \cdot \frac{x^3}{3} - \frac{2}{3} \ln|x| + C = \frac{2x^3}{5} - \frac{2}{3} \ln|x| + C$$

Check: $\left(\dfrac{2x^3}{5} - \dfrac{2}{3}\ln|x| + C \right)' = \dfrac{6}{5}x^2 - \dfrac{2}{3} \cdot \dfrac{1}{x} = \dfrac{6x^2}{5} - \dfrac{2}{3x}$

65. $\dfrac{dy}{dx} = 2x - 3$

$y = \int (2x - 3)\,dx = 2\int x\,dx - \int 3\,dx = \dfrac{2x^2}{2} - 3x + C = x^2 - 3x + C$

Given $y(0) = 5$: $5 = 0^2 - 3(0) + C$. Hence, $C = 5$ and $y = x^2 - 3x + 5$.

67. $C'(x) = 6x^2 - 4x$

$C(x) = \int (6x^2 - 4x)\,dx = 6\int x^2 dx - 4\int x\,dx = \dfrac{6x^3}{3} - \dfrac{4x^2}{2} + C = 2x^3 - 2x^2 + C$

Given $C(0) = 3000$: $3000 = 2(0^3) - 2(0^2) + C$. Hence, $C = 3000$ and
$C(x) = 2x^3 - 2x^2 + 3000$.

69. $\dfrac{dx}{dt} = \dfrac{20}{\sqrt{t}}$

$x = \int \dfrac{20}{\sqrt{t}}\,dt = 20\int t^{-1/2}dt = 20\dfrac{t^{1/2}}{1/2} + C = 40\sqrt{t} + C$

Given $x(1) = 40$: $40 = 40\sqrt{1} + C$ or $40 = 40 + C$. Hence, $C = 0$ and
$x = 40\sqrt{t}$.

71. $\dfrac{dy}{dx} = 2x^{-2} + 3x^{-1} - 1$

$y = \int (2x^{-2} + 3x^{-1} - 1)\,dx = 2\int x^{-2}dx + 3\int x^{-1}dx - dx$

$= \dfrac{2x^{-1}}{-1} + 3\ln|x| - x + C = \dfrac{-2}{x} + 3\ln|x| - x + C$

Given $y(1) = 0$: $0 = -\dfrac{2}{1} + 3\ln|1| - 1 + C$. Hence, $C = 3$ and

$y = -\dfrac{2}{x} + 3\ln|x| - x + 3$.

73. $\dfrac{dx}{dt} = 4e^t - 2$

$x = \int (4e^t - 2)\,dt = 4\int e^t dt - \int 2\,dt = 4e^t - 2t + C$

Given $x(0) = 1$: $1 = 4e^0 - 2(0) + C = 4 + C$. Hence, $C = -3$ and
$x = 4e^t - 2t - 3$.

75. $\dfrac{dy}{dx} = 4x - 3$

$y = \int (4x - 3)\,dx = 4\int x\,dx - \int 3\,dx = \dfrac{4x^2}{2} - 3x + C = 2x^2 - 3x + C$

Given $y(2) = 3$: $3 = 2 \cdot 2^2 - 3 \cdot 2 + C$. Hence, $C = 1$ and $y = 2x^2 - 3x + 1$.

77. $\displaystyle\int\frac{2x^4-x}{x^3}dx = \int\left(\frac{2x^4}{x^3}-\frac{x}{x^3}\right)dx$

$\displaystyle = 2\int x\,dx - \int x^{-2}dx = \frac{2x^2}{2} - \frac{x^{-1}}{-1} + C = x^2 + x^{-1} + C$

79. $\displaystyle\int\frac{x^5-2x}{x^4}dx = \int\left(\frac{x^5}{x^4}-\frac{2x}{x^4}\right)dx$

$\displaystyle = \int x\,dx - 2\int x^{-3}dx = \frac{x^2}{2} - \frac{2x^{-2}}{-2} + C = \frac{x^2}{2} + x^{-2} + C$

81. $\displaystyle\int\frac{x^2e^x-2x}{x^2}dx = \int\left(\frac{x^2e^x}{x^2}-\frac{2x}{x^2}\right)dx = \int e^x dx - 2\int x^{-1}dx = e^x - 2\ln|x| + C$

83. $\displaystyle\frac{dM}{dt} = \frac{t^2-1}{t^2}$

$\displaystyle M = \int\frac{t^2-1}{t^2}dt = \int\left(\frac{t^2}{t^2}-\frac{1}{t^2}\right)dt = \int dt - \int t^{-2}dt = t - \frac{t^{-1}}{-1} + C = t + \frac{1}{t} + C$

Given $M(4) = 5$: $5 = 4 + \dfrac{1}{4} + C$ or $C = 5 - \dfrac{17}{4} = \dfrac{3}{4}$.

Hence, $M = t + \dfrac{1}{t} + \dfrac{3}{4}$.

85. $\displaystyle\frac{dy}{dx} = \frac{5x+2}{\sqrt[3]{x}}$

$\displaystyle y = \int\frac{5x+2}{\sqrt[3]{x}}dx = \int\left(\frac{5x}{x^{1/3}}-\frac{2}{x^{1/3}}\right) = 5\int x^{2/3}dx + 2\int x^{-1/3}dx$

$\displaystyle = \frac{5x^{5/3}}{5/3} + \frac{2x^{2/3}}{2/3} + C = 3x^{5/3} + 3x^{2/3} + C$

Given $y(1) = 0$: $0 = 3\cdot1^{5/3} + 3\cdot1^{2/3} + C$. Hence, $C = -6$ and
$y = 3x^{5/3} + 3x^{2/3} - 6$.

87. $\displaystyle p'(x) = -\frac{10}{x^2}$

$\displaystyle p(x) = \int\frac{10}{x^2}dx = -10\int x^{-2}dx = \frac{-10x^{-1}}{-1} + C = \frac{10}{x} + C$

Given $p(1) = 20$: $20 = \dfrac{10}{1} + C = 10 + C$. Hence, $C = 10$ and
$p(x) = \dfrac{10}{x} + 10$.

89. $\displaystyle\frac{d}{dx}\left[\int x^3dx\right] = x^3$ [by <u>4</u>(a)]

91. $\int \frac{d}{dx} [x^4 + 3x^2 + 1]\, dx = x^4 + 3x^2 + 1 + C = x^4 + 3x^2 + C_1$ [by $\underline{4}$(b)]

    $(C_1 = 1 + C$ is an arbitrary constant since C is arbitrary)

93. $\frac{d}{dx}\left(\frac{x^{n+1}}{n+1} + C\right) = x^n$

95. Assume $x > 0$. Then $|x| = x$ and $\ln|x| = \ln x$.

    Therefore, $\frac{d}{dx}(\ln|x| + C) = \frac{d}{dx}(\ln x + C) = \frac{1}{x}$.

97. Assume $\int f(x)\, dx = F(x) + C_1$ and $\int g(x)\, dx = G(x) + C_2$.

    Then, $\frac{d}{dx}(F(x) + C_1) = f(x)$, $\frac{d}{dx}(G(x) + C_2) = g(x)$, and

$$\frac{d}{dx}(F(x) + C_1 + G(x) + C_2) = \frac{d}{dx}(F(x) + C_1) + \frac{d}{dx}(G(x) + C_2)$$

$$= f(x) + g(x).$$

99. $\overline{C}'(x) = -\frac{1,000}{x^2}$

$$\overline{C}(x) = \int \overline{C}'(x)\, dx = \int -\frac{1,000}{x^2}\, dx = -1,000\int x^{-2}\, dx$$

$$= -1,000\frac{x^{-1}}{-1} + C$$

$$= \frac{1,000}{x} + C$$

    Given $\overline{C}(100) = 25$: $\frac{1,000}{100} + C = 25$

$$C = 15$$

    Thus, $\overline{C}(x) = \frac{1,000}{x} + 15$.

    Cost function: $C(x) = x\overline{C}(x) = 15x + 1,000$
    Fixed costs: $C(0) = \$1,000$

101. (A) The cost function increases from 0 to 8. The graph is concave downward from 0 to 4 and concave upward from 4 to 8. There is an inflection point at $x = 4$.

    (B) $C(x) = \int C'(x)\, dx = \int (3x^2 - 24x + 53)\, dx$

$$= 3\int x^2\, dx - 24\int x\, dx + \int 53\, dx$$

$$= x^3 - 12x^2 + 53x + K$$

    Since $C(0) = 30$, we have $K = 30$ and

$$C(x) = x^3 - 12x^2 + 53x + 30.$$

$$C(4) = 4^3 - 12(4)^2 + 53(4) + 30 = \$114 \text{ thousand}$$
$$C(8) = 8^3 - 12(8)^2 + 53(8) + 30 = \$198 \text{ thousand}$$

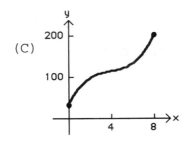

(C)

(D) Manufacturing plants are often inefficient at low and high levels of production.

103. $S'(t) = -25t^{2/3}$

$$S(t) = \int S'(t)\,dt = \int -25t^{2/3}\,dt = -25\int t^{2/3}\,dt = -25\frac{t^{5/3}}{5/3} + C = -15t^{5/3} + C$$

Given $S(0) = 2000$: $-15(0)^{5/3} + C = 2000$. Hence, $C = 2000$ and $S(t) = -15t^{5/3} + 2000$. Now, we want to find t such that $S(t) = 800$, that is: $-15t^{5/3} + 2000 = 800$

$$-15t^{5/3} = -1200$$
$$t^{5/3} = 80$$

and $t = 80^{3/5} \approx 14$

Thus, the company should manufacture the computer for 14 months.

105. $S'(t) = -25t^{2/3} - 70$

$$S(t) = \int S'(t)\,dt \quad = \int (-25t^{2/3} - 70)\,dt$$
$$= -25\int t^{2/3}\,dt - \int 70\,dt$$
$$= -25\frac{t^{5/3}}{5/3} - 70t + C$$
$$= -15t^{5/3} - 70t + C$$

Given $S(0) = 2,000$ implies $C = 2,000$ and
$$S(t) = 2,000 - 15t^{5/3} - 70t$$

Graphing $y_1 = 2,000 - 15t^{5/3} - 70t$, $y_2 = 800$ on $0 \le x \le 10$, $0 \le y \le 1000$, we see that the point of intersection is $x \approx 8.92066$, $y = 800$. So we get $t \approx 8.92$ months.

107. $L'(x) = g(x) = 2400x^{-1/2}$

$$L(x) = \int g(x)\,dx = \int 2400x^{-1/2}\,dx = 2400\int x^{-1/2}\,dx = 2400\,\frac{x^{1/2}}{1/2} + C$$

$$= 4800\,x^{1/2} + C$$

Given $L(16) = 19,200$: $19,200 = 4800(16)^{1/2} + C = 19,200 + C$. Hence, $C = 0$ and $L(x) = 4800x^{1/2}$.
$L(25) = 4800(25)^{1/2} = 4800(5) = 24,000$ labor hours.

109. $\dfrac{dW}{dh} = 0.0015h^2$

$$W = \int 0.0015h^2\,dh = 0.0015\int h^2\,dh = 0.0015\dfrac{h^3}{3} + C = 0.0005h^3 + C$$

Given $W(60) = 108$: $108 = 0.0005(60)^3 + C$ or $108 = 108 + C$.
Hence, $C = 0$ and $W(h) = 0.0005h^3$. Now $5'10" = 70"$ and
$W(70) = 0.0005(70)^3 = 171.5$ lb.

111. $\dfrac{dN}{dt} = 400 + 600\sqrt{t}, \quad 0 \le t \le 9$

$$N = \int(400 + 600\sqrt{t})\,dt = \int 400\,dt + 600\int t^{1/2}\,dt$$

$$= 400t + 600\dfrac{t^{3/2}}{3/2} + C = 400t + 400t^{3/2} + C$$

Given $N(0) = 5000$: $5000 = 400(0) + 400(0)^{3/2} + C$. Hence, $C = 5000$ and
$N(t) = 400t + 400t^{3/2} + 5000$.
$N(9) = 400(9) + 400(9)^{3/2} + 5000 = 3600 + 10,800 + 5000 = 19,400$

EXERCISE 6-2

Things to remember:

1. REVERSING THE CHAIN RULE

   The chain rule formula for differentiating a composite
   function:
   $$\dfrac{d}{dx}f[g(x)] = f'[g(x)]g'(x),$$
   yields the integral formula
   $$\int f'[g(x)]g'(x)\,dx = f[g(x)] + C$$

2. GENERAL INDEFINITE INTEGRAL FORMULAS (Version 1)

   (a) $\displaystyle\int [f(x)]^n f'(x)\,dx = \dfrac{[f(x)]^{n+1}}{n+1} + C, \ n \ne -1$

   (b) $\displaystyle\int e^{f(x)} f'(x)\,dx = e^{f(x)} + C$

   (c) $\displaystyle\int \dfrac{1}{f(x)} f'(x)\,dx = \ln|f(x)| + C$

3. DIFFERENTIALS

   If $y = f(x)$ defines a differentiable function, then:

   (a) The DIFFERENTIAL dx of the independent variable x is an
   arbitrary real number.

   (b) The DIFFERENTIAL dy of the dependent variable y is defined
   as the product of $f'(x)$ and dx; that is: $dy = f'(x)\,dx$.

<u>4</u>. GENERAL INDEFINITE INTEGRAL FORMULAS (Version 2)

(a) $\int u^n du = \dfrac{u^{n+1}}{n+1} + C,\ n \ne -1$

(b) $\int e^u du = e^u + C$

(c) $\int \dfrac{1}{u} du = \ln|u| + C$

<u>5</u>. INTEGRATION BY SUBSTITUTION

<u>Step 1</u>. Select a substitution that appears to simplify the integrand. In particular, try to select u so that du is a factor in the integrand.

<u>Step 2</u>. Express the integrand entirely in terms of u and du, completely eliminating the original variable and its differential.

<u>Step 3</u>. Evaluate the new integral, if possible.

<u>Step 4</u>. Express the antiderivative found in Step 3 in terms of the original variable.

1. $\int (3x + 5)^2 (3)\,dx = \int u^2 du = \dfrac{1}{3}u^3 + C = \dfrac{1}{3}(3x + 5)^3 + C$ [Formula <u>4</u>a]

Let $u = 3x + 5$
Then $du = 3\,dx$

<u>Check</u>: $\dfrac{d}{dx}\left[\dfrac{1}{3}(3x + 5)^3 + C\right] = \dfrac{1}{3} \cdot 3(3x + 5)^2 \dfrac{d}{dx}(3x + 5)$

$= (3x + 5)^2(3)$

3. $\int (x^2 - 1)^5 (2x)\,dx = \int u^5 du = \dfrac{1}{6}u^6 + C = \dfrac{1}{6}(x^2 - 1)^6 + C$ [Formula <u>4</u>a]

Let $u = x^2 - 1$
Then $du = 2x\,dx$

<u>Check</u>: $\dfrac{d}{dx}\left[\dfrac{1}{6}(x^2 - 1)^6 + C\right] = \dfrac{1}{6} \cdot 6(x^2 - 1)^5 \dfrac{d}{dx}(x^2 - 1)$

$= (x^2 - 1)^5(2x)$

5. $\int (5x^3 + 1)^{-3} (15x^2)\,dx = \int u^{-3} du = \dfrac{u^{-2}}{-2} + C = -\dfrac{1}{2}(5x^3 + 1)^{-2} + C$

Let $u = 5x^3 + 1$ [Formula <u>4</u>a]
Then $du = 15x^2\,dx$

<u>Check</u>: $\dfrac{d}{dx}\left[-\dfrac{1}{2}(5x^3 + 1)^{-2} + C\right] = -\dfrac{1}{2}(-2)(5x^3 + 1)^{-3} \dfrac{d}{dx}(5x^3 + 1)$

$= (5x^3 + 1)^{-3}(15x^2)$

7. $\int e^{5x}(5)\,dx = \int e^u du = e^u + C = e^{5x} + C$ [Formula <u>4</u>b]

Let $u = 5x$
Then $du = 5\,dx$

<u>Check</u>: $\dfrac{d}{dx}(e^{5x} + C) = e^{5x} \dfrac{d}{dx}(5x) = e^{5x}(5)$

9. $\int \dfrac{1}{1 + x^2}(2x)\,dx = \int \dfrac{1}{u}\,du = \ln|u| + C = \ln|1 + x^2| + C$

    Let $u = 1 + x^2$ $= \ln(1 + x^2) + C$ $(1 + x^2 > 0)$ [Formula <u>4</u>c]

    Then $du = 2x\,dx$

    <u>Check</u>: $\dfrac{d}{dx}(\ln(1 + x^2) + C) = \dfrac{1}{1 + x^2}\dfrac{d}{dx}(1 + x^2) = \dfrac{1}{1 + x^2}(2x)$

11. $\int \sqrt{1 + x^4}\,(4x^3)\,dx = \int \sqrt{u}\,du = u^{1/2}\,du = \dfrac{u^{3/2}}{3/2} + C$

    Let $u = 1 + x^4$ $= \dfrac{2}{3}u^{3/2} + C$

    Then $du = 4x^3\,dx$ $= \dfrac{2}{3}(1 + x^4)^{3/2} + C$

    <u>Check</u>: $\dfrac{d}{dx}\left[\dfrac{2}{3}(1 + x^4)^{3/2} + C\right] = \dfrac{3}{2}\cdot\dfrac{2}{3}(1 + x^4)^{1/2}\dfrac{d}{dx}(1 + x^4)$

                                    $= (1 + x^4)^{1/2}(4x^3) = \sqrt{1 + x^4}\,(4x^3)$

13. $\int (x + 3)^{10}\,dx = \int u^{10}\,du = \dfrac{1}{11}u^{11} + C = \dfrac{1}{11}(x + 3)^{11} + C$

    Let $u = x + 3$

    Then $du = dx$

    <u>Check</u>: $\dfrac{d}{dx}\left[\dfrac{1}{11}(x + 3)^{11} + C\right] = \dfrac{1}{11}\cdot 11(x + 3)^{10}\dfrac{d}{dx}(x + 3) = (x + 3)^{10}$

15. $\int (6t - 7)^{-2}\,dt = \int (6t - 7)^{-2}\dfrac{6}{6}\,dt = \dfrac{1}{6}\int (6t - 7)^{-2}(6)\,dt$

    Let $u = 6t - 7$ $= \dfrac{1}{6}\int u^{-2}\,du$

    Then $du = 6\,dt$

                                   $= \dfrac{1}{6}\cdot\dfrac{u^{-1}}{-1} + C$

                                   $= -\dfrac{1}{6}(6t - 7)^{-1} + C$

    <u>Check</u>: $\dfrac{d}{dt}\left[-\dfrac{1}{6}(6t - 7)^{-1} + C\right] = -\dfrac{1}{6}(-1)(6t - 7)^{-2}\dfrac{d}{dt}(6t - 7)$

                                $= \dfrac{1}{6}(6t - 7)^{-2}(6) = (6t - 7)^{-2}$

17. $\int (t^2 + 1)^5 t\,dt = \int (t^2 + 1)^5\dfrac{2}{2}t\,dt = \dfrac{1}{2}\int (t^2 + 1)^5 2t\,dt$

    Let $u = t^2 + 1$ $= \dfrac{1}{2}\int u^5\,du$

    Then $du = 2t\,dt$

                                   $= \dfrac{1}{2}\cdot\dfrac{1}{6}u^6 + C$

                                   $= \dfrac{1}{12}(t^2 + 1)^6 + C$

    <u>Check</u>: $\dfrac{d}{dt}\left[\dfrac{1}{12}(t^2 + 1)^6 + C\right] = \dfrac{1}{12}\cdot 6(t^2 + 1)^5\dfrac{d}{dt}(t^2 + 1)$

                                $= \dfrac{1}{2}(t^2 + 1)^5(2t) = (t^2 + 1)^5 t$

19. $\int xe^{x^2}dx = \int e^{x^2}\dfrac{2}{2}x\,dx = \dfrac{1}{2}\int e^{x^2}(2x)\,dx$

Let $u = x^2$ $\qquad = \dfrac{1}{2}\int e^u du = \dfrac{1}{2}e^u + C$

Then $du = 2x\,dx$

$\qquad\qquad\qquad\qquad = \dfrac{1}{2}e^{x^2} + C$

Check: $\dfrac{d}{dx}\left(\dfrac{1}{2}e^{x^2} + C\right) = \dfrac{1}{2}e^{x^2}\dfrac{d}{dx}(x^2) = \dfrac{1}{2}e^{x^2}(2x) = xe^{x^2}$

21. $\int\dfrac{1}{5x+4}dx = \int\dfrac{1}{5x+4}\cdot\dfrac{5}{5}dx = \dfrac{1}{5}\int\dfrac{1}{5x+4}5\,dx$

Let $u = 5x + 4$ $\qquad = \dfrac{1}{5}\int\dfrac{1}{u}\,du = \dfrac{1}{5}\ln|5x+4| + C$

Then $du = 5\,dx$

Check: $\dfrac{d}{dx}\left[\dfrac{1}{5}\ln|5x+4| + C\right] = \dfrac{1}{5}\cdot\dfrac{1}{5x+4}\dfrac{d}{dx}(5x+4)$

$\qquad\qquad\qquad\qquad = \dfrac{1}{5}\cdot\dfrac{1}{5x+4}\cdot 5 = \dfrac{1}{5x+4}$

23. $\int e^{1-t}dt = \int e^{1-t}\left(\dfrac{-1}{-1}\right)dt = \dfrac{1}{-1}\int e^{1-t}(-1)\,dt$

Let $u = 1 - t$ $\qquad = -\int e^u du = -e^u + C$

Then $du = -dt$ $\qquad = -e^{1-t} + C$

Check: $\dfrac{d}{dt}[-e^{1-t} + C] = -e^{1-t}\dfrac{d}{dt}(1-t) = -e^{1-t}(-1) = e^{1-t}$

25. Let $u = 3t^2 + 1$, then $du = 6t\,dt$.

$\int\dfrac{t}{(3t^2+1)^4}dt = \int(3t^2+1)^{-4}t\,dt = \int(3t^2+1)^{-4}\dfrac{6}{6}t\,dt$

$\qquad = \dfrac{1}{6}\int(3t^2+1)^{-4}6t\,dt = \dfrac{1}{6}\int u^{-4}du$

$\qquad = \dfrac{1}{6}\cdot\dfrac{u^{-3}}{-3} + C = \dfrac{-1}{18}(3t^2+1)^{-3} + C$

Check: $\dfrac{d}{dt}\left[\dfrac{-1}{18}(3t^2+1)^{-3} + C\right] = \left(\dfrac{-1}{18}\right)(-3)(3t^2+1)^{-4}(6t) = \dfrac{t}{(3t^2+1)^4}$

27. Let $u = 4 - x^3$, then $du = -3x^2dx$.

$\int\dfrac{x^2}{(4-x^3)^2}dx = \int(4-x^3)^{-2}x^2dx = \int(4-x^3)^{-2}\left(\dfrac{-3}{-3}\right)x^2dx$

$\qquad = \dfrac{-1}{3}\int(4-x^3)^{-2}(-3x^2)\,dx = \dfrac{-1}{3}\int u^{-2}du = \dfrac{-1}{3}\cdot\dfrac{u^{-1}}{-1} + C$

$\qquad = \dfrac{1}{3}(4-x^3)^{-1} + C$

Check: $\dfrac{d}{dx}\left[\dfrac{1}{3}(4-x^3)^{-1} + C\right] = \dfrac{1}{3}(-1)(4-x^3)^{-2}(-3x^2) = \dfrac{x^2}{(4-x^3)^2}$

29. $\int x\sqrt{x + 4}\,dx$

Let $u = x + 4$, then $du = dx$ and $x = u - 4$.

$\int x\sqrt{x + 4}\,dx = \int (u - 4)u^{1/2}\,du = \int (u^{3/2} - 4u^{1/2})\,du$

$= \dfrac{u^{5/2}}{5/2} - \dfrac{4u^{3/2}}{3/2} + C = \dfrac{2}{5}u^{5/2} - \dfrac{8}{3}u^{3/2} + C$

$= \dfrac{2}{5}(x + 4)^{5/2} - \dfrac{8}{3}(x + 4)^{3/2} + C$ (since $u = x + 4$)

Check: $\dfrac{d}{dx}\left[\dfrac{2}{5}(x + 4)^{5/2} - \dfrac{8}{3}(x + 4)^{3/2} + C\right]$

$= \dfrac{2}{5}\left(\dfrac{5}{2}\right)(x + 4)^{3/2}(1) - \dfrac{8}{3}\left(\dfrac{3}{2}\right)(x + 4)^{1/2}(1)$

$= (x + 4)^{3/2} - 4(x + 4)^{1/2} = (x + 4)^{1/2}[(x + 4) - 4] = x\sqrt{x + 4}$

31. $\int \dfrac{x}{\sqrt{x - 3}}\,dx$

Let $u = x - 3$, then $du = dx$ and $x = u + 3$.

$\int \dfrac{x}{\sqrt{x - 3}}\,dx = \int \dfrac{u + 3}{u^{1/2}}\,du = \int (u^{1/2} + 3u^{-1/2})\,du = \dfrac{u^{3/2}}{3/2} + \dfrac{3u^{1/2}}{1/2} + C$

$= \dfrac{2}{3}u^{3/2} + 6u^{1/2} + C = \dfrac{2}{3}(x - 3)^{3/2} + 6(x - 3)^{1/2} + C$

(since $u = x - 3$)

Check: $\dfrac{d}{dx}\left[\dfrac{2}{3}(x - 3)^{3/2/} + 6(x - 3)^{1/2} + C\right]$

$= \dfrac{2}{3}\left(\dfrac{3}{2}\right)(x - 3)^{1/2}(1) + 6\left(\dfrac{1}{2}\right)(x - 3)^{-1/2}(1)$

$= (x - 3)^{1/2} + \dfrac{3}{(x - 3)^{1/2}} = \dfrac{x - 3 + 3}{(x - 3)^{1/2}} = \dfrac{x}{\sqrt{x - 3}}$

33. $\int x(x - 4)^9\,dx$

Let $u = x - 4$, then $du = dx$ and $x = u + 4$.

$\int x(x - 4)^9\,dx = \int (u + 4)u^9\,du = \int (u^{10} + 4u^9)\,du$

$= \dfrac{u^{11}}{11} + \dfrac{4u^{10}}{10} + C = \dfrac{(x - 4)^{11}}{11} + \dfrac{2}{5}(x - 4)^{10} + C$

Check: $\dfrac{d}{dx}\left[\dfrac{(x - 4)^{11}}{11} + \dfrac{2}{5}(x - 4)^{10} + C\right]$

$= \dfrac{1}{11}(11)(x - 4)^{10}(1) + \dfrac{2}{5}(10)(x - 4)^9(1)$

$= (x - 4)^9[(x - 4) + 4] = x(x - 4)^9$

35. Let $u = 1 + e^{2x}$, then $du = 2e^{2x}dx$.

$$\int e^{2x}(1 + e^{2x})^3 dx = \int (1 + e^{2x})^3 \frac{2}{2} e^{2x} dx = \frac{1}{2}\int (1 + e^{2x})^3 2e^{2x} dx$$

$$= \frac{1}{2}\int u^3 du = \frac{1}{2} \cdot \frac{u^4}{4} + C = \frac{1}{2}(1 + e^{2x})^4 + C$$

Check: $\dfrac{d}{dx}\left[\dfrac{1}{8}(1 + e^{2x})^4 + C\right] = \left(\dfrac{1}{8}\right)(4)(1 + e^{2x})^3 e^{2x}(2) = e^{2x}(1 + e^{2x})^3$

37. Let $u = 4 + 2x + x^2$, then $du = (2 + 2x)dx = 2(1 + x)dx$.

$$\int \frac{1 + x}{4 + 2x + x^2} dx = \int \frac{1 + x}{4 + 2x + x^2} \cdot \frac{2(1 + x)}{2} dx = \frac{1}{2}\int \frac{1 + x}{4 + 2x + x^2} 2(2 + x)dx$$

$$= \frac{1}{2}\int \frac{1}{u}du = \frac{1}{2}\ln|u| + C = \frac{1}{2}\ln|4 + 2x + x^2| + C$$

Check: $\dfrac{d}{dx}\left[\dfrac{1}{2}\ln|4 + 2x + x^2| + C\right] = \left(\dfrac{1}{2}\right)\dfrac{1}{4 + 2x + x^2}(2 + 2x) = \dfrac{1 + x}{4 + 2x + x^2}$

39. Let $u = x^4 + 2x^2 + 1$, then $du = (4x^3 + 4x)dx = 4(x^3 + x)dx$.

$$\int \frac{x^3 + x}{(x^4 + 2x^2 + 1)^4} dx = \int (x^4 + 2x^2 + 1)^{-4} \frac{4}{4}(x^3 + x)dx$$

$$= \frac{1}{4}\int (x^4 + 2x^2 + 1)^{-4} 4(x^3 + x)dx$$

$$= \frac{1}{4}\int u^{-4}du = \frac{1}{4} \cdot \frac{u^{-3}}{-3} + C = \frac{-u^{-3}}{12} + C$$

$$= \frac{-(x^4 + 2x^2 + 1)^{-3}}{12} + C$$

Check: $\dfrac{d}{dx}\left[-\dfrac{1}{12}(x^4 + 2x^2 + 1)^{-3} + C\right] = \left(-\dfrac{1}{12}\right)(-3)(x^4 + 2x^2 + 1)^{-4}(4x^3 + 4x)$

$$= (x^4 + 2x^2 + 1)^{-4}(x^3 + x)$$

41. (A) Differentiate $F(x) = \ln|2x - 3| + C$ to see if you get the integrand
$$f(x) = \frac{1}{2x - 3}$$

(B) Wrong; $\dfrac{d}{dx}[\ln|2x - 3| + C] = \dfrac{1}{2x - 3}(2) = \dfrac{2}{2x - 3} \neq \dfrac{1}{2x - 3}$

(C) Let $u = 2x - 3$, then $du = 2\,dx$

$$\int \frac{1}{2x - 3}dx = \int \frac{1}{2x - 3} \cdot \frac{2}{2}dx = \frac{1}{2}\int \frac{1}{2x - 3}2\,dx$$

$$= \frac{1}{2}\int \frac{1}{u}du$$

$$= \frac{1}{2}\ln|u| + C$$

$$= \frac{1}{2}\ln|2x - 3| + C$$

Check: $\dfrac{d}{dx}\left[\dfrac{1}{2}\ln|2x - 3| + C\right] = \dfrac{1}{2} \cdot \dfrac{1}{2x - 3} \cdot 2 = \dfrac{1}{2x - 3}$

43. (A) Differentiate $F(x) = e^{x^4} + C$ to see if you get the integrand $f(x) = x^3 e^{x^4}$.

(B) Wrong; $\dfrac{d}{dx}[e^{x^4} + c] = e^{x^4}(4x^3) = 4x^3 e^{x^4} \neq x^3 e^{x^4}$

(C) Let $u = x^4$, then $du = 4x^3 dx$

$$\int x^3 e^{x^4} dx = \int \frac{4}{4} x^3 e^{x^4} dx = \frac{1}{4}\int 4x^3 e^{x^4} dx$$

$$= \frac{1}{4}\int e^u du$$

$$= \frac{1}{4} e^u + C$$

$$= \frac{1}{4} e^{x^4} + C$$

Check: $\dfrac{d}{dx}\left[\dfrac{1}{4} e^{x^4} + C\right] = \dfrac{1}{4} e^{x^4}(4x^3) = x^3 e^{x^4}$

45. (A) Differentiate $F(x) = \dfrac{(x^2 - 2)^2}{3x} + C$ to see if you get the integrand

$f(x) = 2(x^2 - 2)^2$

(B) Wrong; $\dfrac{d}{dx}\left[\dfrac{(x^2 - 2)^2}{3x} + C\right] = \dfrac{3x \cdot 2(x^2 - 2)(2x) - (x^2 - 2)^2 \cdot 3}{9x^2}$

$$= \frac{(x^2 - 2)[9x^2 + 6]}{9x^2} = \frac{9x^4 - 12x^2 - 12}{9x^2}$$

$$= \frac{3x^4 - 4x^2 - 4}{3x^2}$$

$$\neq 2(x^2 - 2)^2$$

(C) $\int 2(x^2 - 2)^2 dx = 2\int(x^4 - 4x^2 + 4) dx$

$$= 2 \cdot \left[\frac{1}{5} x^5 - \frac{4}{3} x^3 + 4x\right] + C$$

$$= \frac{2}{5} x^5 - \frac{8}{3} x^3 + 8x + C$$

Check: $\dfrac{d}{dx}\left[\dfrac{2}{5} x^5 - \dfrac{8}{3} x^3 + 8x + C\right] = 2x^4 - 8x^2 + 8 = 2[x^4 - 4x^2 + 4]$

$$= 2(x^2 - 2)^2$$

47. Let $u = 3x^2 + 7$, then $du = 6x\, dx$.

$$\int x\sqrt{3x^2 + 7}\, dx = \int(3x^2 + 7)^{1/2} x\, dx = \int(3x^2 + 7)^{1/2} \frac{6}{6} x\, dx$$

$$= \frac{1}{6}\int u^{1/2} du = \frac{1}{6} \cdot \frac{u^{3/2}}{3/2} + C = \frac{1}{9}(3x^2 + 7)^{3/2} + C$$

Check: $\dfrac{d}{dx}\left[\dfrac{1}{9}(3x^2 + 7)^{3/2} + C\right] = \dfrac{1}{9}\left(\dfrac{3}{2}\right)(3x^2 + 7)^{1/2}(6x) = x(3x^2 + 7)^{1/2}$

49. $\int x(x^3 + 2)^2 dx = \int x(x^6 + 4x^3 + 4) dx = \int (x^7 + 4x^4 + 4x) dx$

$$= \frac{x^8}{8} + \frac{4}{5}x^5 + 2x^2 + C$$

Check: $\frac{d}{dx}\left[\frac{x^8}{8} + \frac{4}{5}x^5 + 2x^2 + C\right] = x^7 + 4x^4 + 4x$

$$= x(x^6 + 4x^3 + 4) = x(x^3 + 2)^2$$

51. $\int x^2(x^3 + 2)^2 dx$

Let $u = x^3 + 2$, then $du = 3x^2 dx$.

$\int x^2(x^3 + 2)^2 dx = \int x^2(x^3 + 2)^2 \frac{3x^2}{3} dx = \frac{1}{3}\int (x^3 + 2)^2 3x^2 dx$

$$= \frac{1}{3}\int u^2 du = \frac{1}{3} \cdot \frac{u^3}{3} + C = \frac{1}{9}u^3 + C = \frac{1}{9}(x^3 + 2)^3 + C$$

Check: $\frac{d}{dx}\left[\frac{1}{9}(x^3 + 2)^3 + C\right] = \frac{1}{9}(3)(x^3 + 2)^2(3x^2) = x^2(x^3 + 2)^2$

53. Let $u = 2x^4 + 3$, then $du = 8x^3 dx$.

$\int \frac{x^3}{\sqrt{2x^4 + 3}} dx = \int (2x^4 + 3)^{-1/2} x^3 dx = \int (2x^4 + 3)^{-1/2} \frac{8}{8}x^3 dx$

$$= \frac{1}{8}\int u^{-1/2} du = \frac{1}{8} \cdot \frac{u^{1/2}}{1/2} + C = \frac{1}{4}(2x^4 + 3)^{1/2} + C$$

Check: $\frac{d}{dx}\left[\frac{1}{4}(2x^4 + 3)^{1/2} + C\right] = \frac{1}{4}\left(\frac{1}{2}\right)(2x^4 + 3)^{-1/2}(8x^3) = \frac{x^3}{(2x^4 + 3)^{1/2}}$

55. Let $u = \ln x$, then $du = \frac{1}{x} dx$.

$\int \frac{(\ln x)^3}{x} dx = \int u^3 du = \frac{u^4}{4} + C = \frac{(\ln x)^4}{4} + C$

Check: $\frac{d}{dx}\left[\frac{(\ln x)^4}{4} + C\right] = \frac{1}{4}(4)(\ln x)^3 \cdot \frac{1}{x} = \frac{(\ln x)^3}{x}$

57. Let $u = \frac{-1}{x} = -x^{-1}$, then $du = \frac{1}{x^2} dx$.

$\int \frac{1}{x^2} e^{-1/x} dx = \int e^u du = e^u + C = e^{-1/x} + C$

Check: $\frac{d}{dx}[e^{-1/x} + C] = e^{-1/x}\left(\frac{1}{x^2}\right) = \frac{1}{x^2}e^{-1/x}$

59. $\frac{dx}{dt} = 7t^2(t^3 + 5)^6$

Let $u = t^3 + 5$, then $du = 3t^2 dt$.

$x = \int 7t^2(t^3 + 5)^6 dt = 7\int t^2(t^3 + 5)^6 dt = 7\int (t^3 + 5)^6 \frac{3}{3}t^2 dt$

$$= \frac{7}{3}\int u^6 du = \frac{7}{3} \cdot \frac{u^7}{7} + C = \frac{1}{3}(t^3 + 5)^7 + C$$

61. $\dfrac{dy}{dt} = \dfrac{3t}{\sqrt{t^2 - 4}}$

Let $u = t^2 - 4$, then $du = 2t\ dt$.

$y = \displaystyle\int \dfrac{3t}{(t^2 - 4)^{1/2}}dt = 3\int (t^2 - 4)^{-1/2}t\ dt = 3\int (t^2 - 4)^{-1/2}\dfrac{2}{2}t\ dt$

$\qquad = \dfrac{3}{2}u^{-1/2}du = \dfrac{3}{2} \cdot \dfrac{u^{1/2}}{1/2} + C = 3(t^2 - 4)^{1/2} + C$

63. $\dfrac{dp}{dx} = \dfrac{e^x + e^{-x}}{(e^x - e^{-x})^2}$

Let $u = e^x - e^{-x}$, then $du = (e^x + e^{-x})\,dx$.

$p = \displaystyle\int \dfrac{e^x + e^{-x}}{(e^x - e^{-x})^2}dx = \int (e^x - e^{-x})^{-2}(e^x + e^{-x})\,dx = \int u^{-2}du$

$\qquad = \dfrac{u^{-1}}{-1} + C = -(e^x - e^{-x})^{-1} + C$

65. Let $v = au$, then $dv = a\ du$.

$\displaystyle\int e^{au}du = \int e^{au}\dfrac{a}{a}du = \dfrac{1}{a}\int e^{au}a\ du = \dfrac{1}{a}\int e^v dv = \dfrac{1}{a}e^v + C = \dfrac{1}{a}e^{au} + C$

Check: $\dfrac{d}{du}\left[\dfrac{1}{a}e^{au} + C\right] + \dfrac{1}{a}e^{au}(a) = e^{au}$

67. $p'(x) = \dfrac{-6000}{(3x + 50)^2}$

Let $u = 3x + 50$, then $du = 3\ dx$.

$p(x) = \displaystyle\int \dfrac{-6000}{(3x + 50)^2}dx = -6000\int (3x + 50)^{-2}dx = -6000\int (3x + 50)^{-2}\dfrac{3}{3}dx$

$\qquad = -2000\displaystyle\int u^{-2}du = -2000 \cdot \dfrac{u^{-1}}{-1} + C = \dfrac{2000}{3x + 50} + C$

Given $p(150) = 4$:

$4 = \dfrac{2000}{(3 \cdot 150 + 50)} + C$

$4 = \dfrac{2000}{500} + C$

$C = 0$

Thus, $p(x) = \dfrac{2000}{3x + 50}$.

Now, $2.50 = \dfrac{2000}{3x + 50}$

$2.50(3x + 50) = 2000$

$7.5x + 125 = 2000$

$7.5x = 1875$

$x = 250$

Thus, the demand is 250 bottles when the price is \$2.50.

69. $C'(x) = 12 + \dfrac{500}{x + 1}$, $x > 0$

$C(x) = \int\left(12 + \dfrac{500}{x + 1}\right)dx = \int 12\ dx + 500\int\dfrac{1}{x + 1}dx$ $(u = x = 1,\ du = dx)$

$= 12x + 500\ \ln(x + 1) + C$

Now, $C(0) = 2000$. Thus, $C(x) = 12x + 500\ \ln(x + 1) + 2000$. The average cost is:

$\overline{C}(x) = 12 + \dfrac{500}{x}\ln(x + 1) + \dfrac{2000}{x}$

and

$\overline{C}(1000) = 12 + \dfrac{500}{1000}\ln(1001) + \dfrac{2000}{1000} = 12 + \dfrac{1}{2}\ln(1001) + 2$

≈ 17.45 or \$17.45 per pair of shoes

71. $S'(t) = 10 - 10e^{-0.1t}$, $0 \le t \le 24$

(A) $S(t) = \int(10 - 10e^{-0.1t})\,dt = \int 10\ dt - 10\int e^{-0.1t}\ dt$

$= 10t - \dfrac{10}{-0.1}e^{-0.1t} + C = 10t + 100e^{-0.1t} + C$

Given $S(0) = 0$: $0 + 100e^0 + C = 0$

$100 + C = 0$

$C = -100$

Total sales at time t:

$S(t) = 10t + 100e^{-0.1t} - 100$

(B) $S(12) = 10(12) + 100e^{-0.1(12)} - 100$

$= 20 + 100e^{-1.2} \approx 50$

Total estimated sales for the first twelve months: \$50 million.

(C) On a graphing utility, solve

$10t + 100e^{-0.1t} - 100 = 100$

or $10t + 100e^{-0.1t} = 200$

The result is: $t \approx 18.41$ months.

73. $Q(t) = \int R(t)\,dt = \int\left(\dfrac{100}{t + 1} + 5\right)dt = 100\int\dfrac{1}{t + 1}\,dt + \int 5\,dt$

$= 100\ \ln(t + 1) + 5t + C$

Given $Q(0) = 0$:

$0 = 100\ \ln(1) + 0 + C$

Thus, $C = 0$ and $Q(t) = 100\ \ln(t + 1) + 5t$, $0 \le t \le 20$.

$Q(9) = 100\ \ln(9 + 1) + 5(9) = 100\ \ln 10 + 45 \approx 275$ thousand barrels.

75. $W(t) = \int W(t)\, dt = \int 0.2 e^{0.1t}\, dt = \dfrac{0.2}{0.1} \int e^{0.1t}(0.1)\, dt = 2 e^{0.1t} + C$

Given $W(0) = 2$:

$2 = 2 e^0 + C.$

Thus, $C = 0$ and $W(t) = 2 e^{0.1t}$.

The weight of the culture after 8 hours is given by:

$W(8) = 2 e^{0.1(8)} = 2 e^{0.8} \approx 4.45$ grams.

77. $\dfrac{dN}{dt} = -\dfrac{2000t}{1 + t^2}$, $0 \le t \le 10$

(A) To find the minimum value of $\dfrac{dN}{dt}$, calculate

$$\dfrac{d}{dt}\left(\dfrac{dN}{dt}\right) = \dfrac{d^2N}{dt^2} = -\dfrac{(1 + t^2)(2000) - 2000t(2t)}{(1 + t^2)^2}$$

$$= -\dfrac{2000[1 - t^2]}{(1 + t^2)^2} = \dfrac{-2000(1 - t)(1 + t)}{(1 + t^2)^2}$$

critical value: $t = 1$

Now $\dfrac{dN}{dt}\Big|_{t=0} = 0$

$\dfrac{dN}{dt}\Big|_{t=1} = -1{,}000$

$\dfrac{dN}{dt}\Big|_{t=10} = \dfrac{-20{,}000}{101} \approx -198.02$

Thus, the minimum value of $\dfrac{dN}{dt}$ is $-1{,}000$ bacteria/ml per day.

(B) $N = \int \dfrac{-2{,}000t}{1 + t^2}\, dt$

Let $u = 1 + t^2$, then $du = 2t\, dt$

$N = \int \dfrac{-2{,}000t}{1 + t^2}\, dt = -1{,}000 \int \dfrac{2t\, dt}{1 + t^2} = -1{,}000 \int \dfrac{1}{u}\, du$

$= -1{,}000 \ln|u| + C$

$= -1{,}000 \ln(1 + t^2) + C$

Given $N(0) = 5{,}000$:

$5{,}000 = -1{,}000 \ln(1) + C = C$ ($\ln 1 = 0$)

Thus, $C = 5{,}000$ and $N(t) = 5{,}000 - 1{,}000 \ln(1 + t^2)$

Now, $N(10) = 5{,}000 - 1{,}000 \ln(1 + 10^2)$

$= 5{,}000 - 1{,}000 \ln(101)$

≈ 385 bacteria/ml

(C) Set $N(t) = 1{,}000$ and solve for t:

$1{,}000 = 5{,}000 - 1{,}000 \ln(1 + t^2)$

$\ln(1 + t^2) = 4$

$1 + t^2 = e^4$

$t^2 = e^4 - 1$

$t = \sqrt{e^4 - 1} \approx 7.32$ days

79. $N'(t) = 6e^{-0.1t}, \ 0 \le t \le 15$

$N(t) = \int N(t)\,dt = \int 6e^{-0.1t}\,dt = 6\int e^{-0.1t}\,dt$

$$= \frac{6}{-0.1}\int e^{-0.1t}(-0.1)\,dt = -60e^{-0.1t} + C$$

Given $N(0) = 40$:

$40 = -60e^0 + C$

Hence, $C = 100$ and $N(t) = 100 - 60e^{-0.1t}, \ 0 \le t \le 15$.
The number of words per minute after completing the course is:

$N(15) = 100 - 60e^{-0.1(15)} = 100 - 60e^{-1.5} \approx 87$ words per minute.

81. $\dfrac{dE}{dt} = 5000(t + 1)^{-3/2}, \ t \ge 0$

Let $u = t + 1$, then $du = dt$

$E = \int 5000(t + 1)^{-3/2}\,dt = 5000\int (t + 1)^{-3/2}\,dt = 5000\int u^{-3/2}\,du$

$$= 5000\frac{u^{-1/2}}{-1/2} + C = -10,000(t + 1)^{-1/2} + C$$

$$= \frac{-10,000}{\sqrt{t + 1}} + C$$

Given $E(0) = 2000$:

$2000 = \dfrac{-10,000}{\sqrt{1}} + C$

Hence, $C = 12,000$ and $E(t) = 12,000 - \dfrac{10,000}{\sqrt{t + 1}}$.

The projected enrollment 15 years from now is:

$E(15) = 12,000 - \dfrac{10,000}{\sqrt{15 + 1}} = 12,000 - \dfrac{10,000}{\sqrt{16}} = 12,000 - \dfrac{10,000}{4}$

$$= 9500 \text{ students}$$

EXERCISE 6-3

Things to remember:

1. A DIFFERENTIAL EQUATION is an equation that involves an unknown function and one or more of its derivatives. The ORDER of a differential equation is the order of the highest derivative of the unknown function.

2. A SLOPE FIELD for a first-order differential equation is obtained by drawing tangent line segments determined by the equation at each point in a grid.

EXPONENTIAL GROWTH LAW

If $\dfrac{dQ}{dt} = rQ$ and $Q(0) = Q_0$, then $Q(t) = Q_0 e^{rt}$, where

$Q_0 =$ Amount at $t = 0$

$r =$ Continuous compound growth rate (expressed as a decimal)

$t =$ Time

$Q =$ Quantity at time t

4. COMPARISON OF EXPONENTIAL GROWTH PHENOMENA

DESCRIPTION	MODEL	SOLUTION	GRAPH	USES
Unlimited growth: Rate of growth is proportional to the amount present	$\dfrac{dy}{dt} = ky$ $k,\ t > 0$ $y(0) = c$	$y = ce^{kt}$		• Short-term population growth (people, bacteria, etc.) • Growth of money at continuous compound interest • Price-supply curves • Depletion of natural resources
Exponential decay: Rate of growth is proportional to the amount present	$\dfrac{dy}{dt} = -ky$ $k,\ t > 0$ $y(0) = c$	$y = ce^{-kt}$		• Radioactive decay • Light absorption in water • Price-demand curves • Atmospheric pressure (t is altitude)
Limited growth: Rate of growth is proportional to the difference between the amount present and a fixed limit	$\dfrac{dy}{dt} = k(M - y)$ $k,\ t > 0$ $y(0) = 0$	$y = M(1 - e^{-kt})$		• Sales fads (e.g., skateboards) • Depreciation of equipment • Company growth • Learning
Logistic growth: Rate of growth is proportional to the amount present and to the difference between the amount present and a fixed limit	$\dfrac{dy}{dt} = ky(M - y)$ $k,\ t > 0$ $y(0) = \dfrac{M}{1 + c}$	$y = \dfrac{M}{1 - ce^{-kMt}}$		• Long-term population growth • Epidemics • Sales of new products • Rumor spread • Company growth

1. $\dfrac{dy}{dx} = 6x$

$\displaystyle\int \dfrac{dy}{dx}\, dx = \int 6x\, dx = 6\int x\, dx$

$\displaystyle\int dy = 6\int x\, dx$

$y = 6 \cdot \dfrac{x^2}{2} + C = 3x^2 + C$

General solution: $y = 3x^2 + C$

3. $\dfrac{dy}{dx} = \dfrac{7}{x}$

$\displaystyle\int \dfrac{dy}{dx}\, dx = 7\int \dfrac{1}{x}\, dx$

$\displaystyle\int dy = 7\int \dfrac{1}{x}\, dx$

General solution: $y = 7 \cdot \ln|x| + C$

5. $\dfrac{dy}{dx} = e^{0.02x}$

$\displaystyle\int \dfrac{dy}{dx}\,dx = \int e^{0.02x}\,dx$

$\displaystyle\int dy = \int e^{0.02x}\,dx \qquad (u = 0.02x,\ du = 0.02dx)$

$y = \displaystyle\int e^u\,\dfrac{1}{0.02}\,du = \dfrac{1}{0.02}\int e^u\,du = \dfrac{1}{0.02}e^u + C = 50e^{0.02x} + C$

General solution: $y = 50e^{0.02x} + C$

7. $\dfrac{dy}{dx} = x^2 - x;\ y(0) = 0$

$\displaystyle\int \dfrac{dy}{dx}\,dx = \dfrac{dy}{dx}(x^2 - x)\,dx$

$y = \dfrac{1}{3}x^3 - \dfrac{1}{2}x^2 + C$

Given $y(0) = 0$: $\dfrac{1}{3}(0)^3 - \dfrac{1}{2}(0)^2 + C = 0$

$C = 0$

Particular solution: $y = \dfrac{1}{3}x^3 - \dfrac{1}{2}x^2$

9. $\dfrac{dy}{dx} = -2xe^{-x^2};\ y(0) = 3$

$\displaystyle\int \dfrac{dy}{dx}\,dx = \int -2xe^{-x^2}\,dx$

$y = \displaystyle\int -2xe^{-x^2}\,dx$

Let $u = -x^2$, then $du = -2x\,dx$ and

$\displaystyle\int -2xe^{-x^2}\,dx = \int e^u\,du = e^u + c = e^{-x^2} + c$

Thus, $y = e^{-x^2} + c$

Given $y(0) = 3$: $3 = e^0 + c$

$3 = 1 + c$

$c = 2$

Particular solution: $y = e^{-x^2} + 2$

11. $\dfrac{dy}{dx} = \dfrac{2}{1 + x};\ y(0) = 5$

$\displaystyle\int \dfrac{dy}{dx}\,dx = \int \dfrac{2}{1 + x}\,dx = 2\int \dfrac{1}{1 + x}\,dx$

$\displaystyle\int dy = 2\int \dfrac{1}{1 + x}\,dx \qquad (u = 1 + x,\ du = dx)$

$y = 2\displaystyle\int \dfrac{1}{u}\,du = 2\,\ln|u| + C = 2\,\ln|1 + x| + C$

Given $y(0) = 5$: $5 = 2\,\ln 1 + C$

$5 = C$

Particular solution: $y = 2\,\ln|1 + x| + 5$

13. Figure (b). When $x = 1$, $\frac{dy}{dx} = 1 - 1 = 0$ for any y. When $x = 0$, $\frac{dy}{dx} = 0 - 1 = -1$ for any y. When $x = 2$, $\frac{dy}{dx} = 2 - 1 = 1$ for any y; and so on. These facts are consistent with the slope-field in Figure (b); they are not consistent with the slope-field in Figure (a).

15. $\frac{dy}{dx} = x - 1$

$\int \frac{dy}{dx} = \int (x - 1) \, dx$

General solution: $y = \frac{1}{2}x^2 - x + c$

Given $y(0) = -2$: $\frac{1}{2}(0)^2 - 0 + c = -2$

$\qquad\qquad\qquad\qquad c = -2$

Particular solution: $y = \frac{1}{2}x^2 - x - 2$

17.

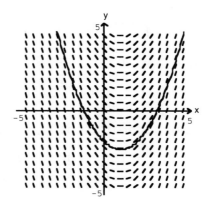

19. $\frac{dy}{dt} = 2y$

$\frac{1}{y}\frac{dy}{dt} = 2$

$\int \frac{1}{y}\frac{dy}{dt} \, dt = \int 2 \, dt$

$\qquad \int \frac{1}{u} \, du = \int 2 \, dt \quad [u = y, \ du = dy = \frac{dy}{dt} \cdot dt]$

$\quad \ln |u| = 2t + K \quad [K \text{ an arbitrary constant}]$

$\qquad |u| = e^{2t+K} = e^K e^{2t}$

$\qquad |u| = Ce^{2t} \qquad [C = e^K, \ C > 0]$

so $\quad |y| = Ce^{2t}$

Now, if we set $y(t) = Ce^{2t}$, C ANY constant, then

$\qquad y'(t) = 2Ce^{2t} = 2y(t),$

So $\quad y = Ce^{2t}$ satisfies the differential equation where C is any constant. This is the general solution. Note, the differential equation is the model for exponential growth with growth rate 2.

21. $\dfrac{dy}{dx} = -0.5y, \ y(0) = 100$

$\dfrac{1}{y}\dfrac{dy}{dx} = -0.5$

$\displaystyle\int \dfrac{1}{y}\dfrac{dy}{dx}\,dx = \int -0.5\,dx$

$\displaystyle\int \dfrac{1}{u}\,du = \int -0.5\,dx \qquad [u = y, \ du = dy = \dfrac{dy}{dx}\,dx]$

$\ln|u| = -0.5x + K$

$\quad |u| = e^{-0.5x+K} = e^K e^{-0.5x}$

$\quad |y| = Ce^{-0.5x}, \ C = e^K > 0.$

So, general solution: $y = Ce^{-0.5x}, \ C$ any constant.

Given $y(0) = 100$: $100 = Ce^0 = C$;

$\quad$ particular solution: $y = 100e^{-0.5x}$

23. $\dfrac{dx}{dt} = -5x$

$\dfrac{1}{x}\dfrac{dx}{dt} = -5$

$\displaystyle\int \dfrac{1}{x}\dfrac{dx}{dt}\,dt = \int -5\,dt$

$\displaystyle\int \dfrac{1}{x}\,dx = -5\int dt$

$\ln|x| = -5t + K$

$\quad |x| = e^{-5t+K} = e^K e^{-5t} = Ce^{-5t}, \ C = e^K > 0.$

General solution: $x = Ce^{-5t}, \ C$ any constant.

25. $\dfrac{dx}{dt} = -5t$

$\displaystyle\int \dfrac{dx}{dt}\,dt = \int -5t\,dt = -5\int t\,dt$

General solution: $x = -\dfrac{5t^2}{2} + C$

27. Figure (c). When $y = 1$, $\dfrac{dy}{dx} = 1 - 1 = 0$ for any x.

When $y = 2$, $\dfrac{dy}{dx} = 1 - 2 = -1$ for any x; and so on. This is consistent with the slope-field in Figure (c); it is not consistent with the slope-field in Figure (d).

29. $y = 1 - Ce^{-x}$

$$\frac{dy}{dx} = \frac{d}{dx}[1 - Ce^{-x}] = Ce^{-x}$$

From the original equation, $Ce^{-x} = 1 - y$

Thus, we have

$$\frac{dy}{dx} = 1 - y$$

and $y = 1 - Ce^{-x}$ is a solution of the differential equation for any number c.

Given $y(0) = 0$: $0 = 1 - Ce^0 = 1 - c$

$$c = 1$$

Particular solution: $y = 1 - e^{-x}$

31.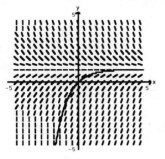

33.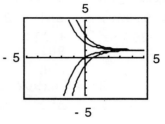

35. $y = 1,000e^{0.08t}$
$0 \le t \le 15,$
$0 \le y \le 3,500$

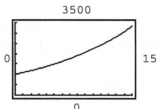

37. $p = 100e^{-0.05x}$
$0 \le x \le 30,$
$0 \le p \le 100$

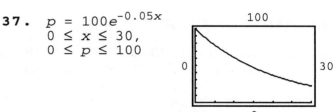

39. $N = 100(1 - e^{-0.05t})$
$0 \le t \le 100, \; 0 \le N \le 100$

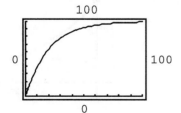

41. $N = \dfrac{1,000}{1 + 999e^{-0.4t}}$

$0 \le t \le 40, \; 0 \le N \le 1,000$

43. $\dfrac{dy}{dt} = ky(M - y)$, k, M positive constants. Set $f(y) = ky(M - y) = kMy - ky^2$.

This is a quadratic function which opens downward; it has a maximum value. Now

$$f'(y) = kM - 2ky$$

Critical value: $kM - 2ky = 0$

$$y = \frac{M}{2}$$

$$f''(y) = -2k < 0.$$

Thus, f has a maximum value at $y = \dfrac{M}{2}$.

45. In 1967: $\dfrac{dQ}{dt} = 3.5e^{0.02} \approx 3.571$

In 1999: $\dfrac{dQ}{dt} = 6e^{0.013} \approx 6.079$

The rate of growth in 1999 is almost twice the rate of growth in 1967.

47. $\dfrac{dA}{dt} = 0.08A$ and $A(0) = 1{,}000$ is an unlimited growth model. From $\underline{4}$,

the amount in the account after t years is: $A(t) = 1000e^{0.08t}$.

49. $\dfrac{dA}{dt} = rA$, $A(0) = 8{,}000$

is an unlimited growth model. From $\underline{4}$, $A(t) = 8{,}000e^{rt}$.

Since $A(2) = 9{,}020$, we solve $8{,}000e^{2r} = 9{,}020$ for r.

$$8000e^{2r} = 9{,}020$$
$$e^{2r} = \frac{902}{800}$$
$$2r = \ln(902/800)$$
$$r = \frac{\ln(902/800)}{2} \approx 0.06$$

Thus, $A(t) = 8{,}000e^{0.06t}$.

51. (A) $\dfrac{dp}{dx} = rp$, $p(0) = 100$

This is an UNLIMITED GROWTH MODEL. From $\underline{4}$, $p(x) = 100e^{rx}$.
Since $p(5) = 77.88$, we have
$$77.88 = 100e^{5r}$$
$$e^{5r} = 0.7788$$
$$5r = \ln(0.7788)$$
$$r = \frac{\ln(0.7788)}{5} \approx -0.05$$
Thus, $p(x) = 100e^{-0.05x}$.

(B) $p(10) = 100e^{-0.05(10)} = 100e^{-0.5}$
$$\approx \$60.65 \text{ per unit}$$

(C)

53. (A) $\dfrac{dN}{dt} = k(L - N)$; $N(0) = 0$

This is a LIMITED GROWTH MODEL. From $\underline{4}$, $N(t) = L(1 - e^{-kt})$.
Since $N(10) = 0.4L$, we have
$$0.4L = L(1 - e^{-10k})$$
$$1 - e^{-10k} = 0.4$$
$$e^{-10k} = 0.6$$
$$-10k = \ln(0.6)$$
$$k = \frac{\ln(0.6)}{-10} \approx 0.051$$
Thus, $N(t) = L(1 - e^{-0.051t})$.

(B) $N(5) = L[1 - e^{-0.051(5)}] = L[1 - e^{-0.255}] \approx 0.225L$

Approximately 22.5% of the possible viewers will have been exposed after 5 days.

(C) Solve $L(1 - e^{-0.051t}) = 0.8L$ for t:

$$1 - e^{-0.051t} = 0.8$$
$$e^{-0.051t} = 0.2$$
$$-0.051t = \ln(0.2)$$
$$t = \frac{\ln(0.2)}{-0.051} \approx 31.56$$

It will take 32 days for 80% of the possible viewers to be exposed.

(D)

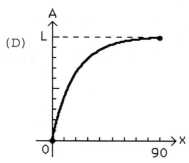

55. $\dfrac{dI}{dx} = -kI, \quad I(0) = I_0$

This is an exponential decay model. From $\underline{4}$, $I(x) = I_0 e^{-kx}$ with $k = 0.00942$, we have

$$I(x) = I_0 e^{-0.00942x}$$

To find the depth at which the light is reduced to half of that at the surface, solve,

$$I_0 e^{-0.00942x} = \frac{1}{2} I_0$$

for x:

$$e^{-0.00942x} = 0.5$$
$$-0.00942x = \ln(0.5)$$
$$x = \frac{\ln(0.5)}{-0.00942} \approx 74 \text{ feet}$$

57. $\dfrac{dQ}{dt} = -0.04Q, \quad Q(0) = Q_0.$

(A) This is a model for exponential decay. From 4,

$$Q(t) = Q_0 e^{-0.04t}$$

With $Q_0 = 3$, we have

$$Q(t) = 3e^{-0.04t}$$

(B) $Q(10) = 3e^{-0.04(10)} = 3e^{-0.4} \approx 2.01.$

There are approximately 2.01 milliliters in the body after 10 hours.

(C) $3e^{-0.04t} = 1$

$e^{-0.04t} = \dfrac{1}{3}$

$-0.04t = \ln(1/3)$

$t = \dfrac{\ln(1/3)}{-0.04} \approx 27.47$

(D)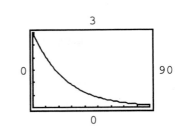

It will take approximately 27.47 hours for Q to decrease to 1 milliliter.

59. Using the exponential decay model, we have $\dfrac{dy}{dt} = -ky,\ y(0) = 100,\ k > 0$

where $y = y(t)$ is the amount of cesium-137 present at time t. From 4,

$y(t) = 100e^{-kt}$

Since $y(3) = 93.3$, we solve $93.3 = 100e^{-3k}$ for k to find the continuous compound decay rate:

$$93.3 = 100e^{-3k}$$

$$e^{-3k} = 0.933$$

$$-3k = \ln(0.933)$$

$$k = \dfrac{\ln(0.933)}{-3} \approx 0.023117$$

61. From Example 3: $Q = Q_0 e^{-0.0001238t}$

Now, the amount of radioactive carbon-14 present is 5% of the original amount. Thus, $0.05Q_0 = Q_0 e^{-0.0001238t}$ or $e^{-0.0001238t} = 0.05$.

Therefore, $-0.0001238t = \ln(0.05) \approx -2.9957$ and $t \approx 24{,}200$ years.

63. $N(k) = 180e^{-0.11(k-1)},\ 1 \le k \le 10$

Thus, $N(6) = 180e^{-0.11(6-1)} = 180e^{-0.55} \approx 104$ times

and $N(10) = 180e^{-0.11(10-1)} = 180e^{-0.99} \approx 67$ times.

65. (A) $x(t) = \dfrac{400}{1 + 399e^{-0.4t}}$

$x(5) = \dfrac{400}{1 + 399e^{(-0.4)5}} = \dfrac{400}{1 + 399e^{-2}} \approx \dfrac{400}{55} \approx 7$ people

$x(20) = \dfrac{400}{1 + 399e^{(-0.4)20}} = \dfrac{400}{1 + 399e^{-8}} \approx 353$ people

(B) $\lim_{t \to \infty} x(t) = 400.$

(C)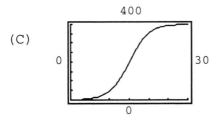

Things to remember:

<u>1</u>. APPROXIMATING AREAS BY LEFT AND RIGHT SUMS

Let $f(x)$ be defined and positive on the interval $[a, b]$. Divide the interval into n subintervals of equal length $\Delta x = \dfrac{b - a}{n}$, with endpoints $a = x_0 < x_1 < x_2 < \ldots < x_{n-1} < x_n = b$.

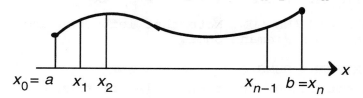

Then
$$L_n = f(x_0)\Delta x + f(x_1)\Delta x + f(x_2)\Delta x + \ldots + f(x_{n-1})\Delta x$$
is called a LEFT SUM;
$$R_n = f(x_1)\Delta x + f(x_2)\Delta x + \ldots + f(x_{n-1})\Delta x + f(x_n)\Delta x$$
is called a RIGHT SUM.

Left and right sums are approximations of the area between the graph of f and the x-axis from $x = a$ to $x = b$.

<u>2</u>. ERROR IN AN APPROXIMATION

The ERROR IN AN APPROXIMATION is the absolute value of the difference between the approximation and the actual value.

<u>3</u>. ERROR BOUNDS FOR APPROXIMATIONS OF AREA BY LEFT AND RIGHT SUMS

If $f(x) > 0$ and is either increasing on $[a, b]$ or decreasing on $[a, b]$, then
$$|f(b) - f(a)| \cdot \frac{b - a}{n}$$
is an error bound for the approximation of the area under the graph of f.

<u>4</u>. LIMITS OF LEFT AND RIGHT SUMS

If $f(x) > 0$ and is either increasing on $[a, b]$ or decreasing on $[a, b]$, then its left and right sums approach the same real number I as $n \to \infty$. This number is the area between the graph of f and the x-axis from $x = a$ to $x = b$.

5. RIEMANN SUMS

Let f be defined on the interval $[a, b]$. Divide the interval into n subintervals of equal length $\Delta x = \dfrac{b - a}{n}$ with endpoints $a = x_0 < x_1 < x_2 < \ldots < x_{n-1} < x_n = b$.

Choose a point $c_1 \in [x_0, x_1]$, a point $c_2 \in [x_1, x_2]$, ..., and a point $c_n \in [x_{n-1}, x_n]$. Then

$$S_n = f(c_1)\Delta x + f(c_2)\Delta x + \ldots + f(c_n)\Delta x$$

is called a RIEMANN SUM. Note that left sums and right sums are special cases of Riemann Sums.

6. LIMIT OF RIEMANN SUMS

If f is a continuous function on $[a, b]$ then the Riemann sums for f on $[a, b]$ approach a real number I as $n \to \infty$.

7. DEFINITE INTEGRAL

Let f be a continuous function on $[a, b]$. The limit I of Riemann sums for f on $[a, b]$ is called the DEFINITE INTEGRAL of f from a to b, denoted

$$\int_a^b f(x)dx$$

The INTEGRAND is $f(x)$, the LOWER LIMIT OF INTEGRATION is a, and the UPPER LIMIT OF INTEGRATION is b.

8. GEOMETRIC INTERPRETATION OF THE DEFINITE INTEGRAL

If $f(x)$ is positive for some value of x on $[a, b]$ and negative for others, then the DEFINITE INTEGRAL SYMBOL

$$\int_a^b f(x)dx$$

represents the cumulative sum of the signed areas between the curve $y = f(x)$ and the x-axis where the areas above the x-axis are counted positively and the areas below the x-axis are counted negatively (see the figure where A and B are actual areas of the indicated regions).

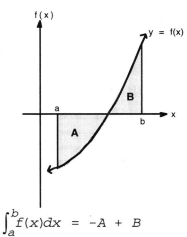

$$\int_a^b f(x)dx = {}^-A + B$$

<u>9</u>. PROPERTIES OF DEFINITE INTEGRALS

(a) $\int_a^a f(x)dx = 0$

(b) $\int_a^b f(x)dx = -\int_b^a f(x)dx$

(c) $\int_a^b Kf(x)dx = K\int_a^b f(x)dx$ K is a constant

(d) $\int_a^b [f(x) \pm g(x)]dx = \int_a^b f(x)dx \pm \int_a^b g(x)dx$

(e) $\int_a^b f(x)dx = \int_a^c f(x)dx + \int_c^b f(x)dx$

1.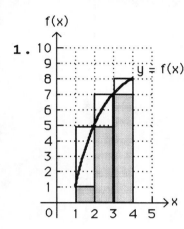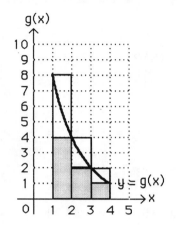

3. For Figure (A):

    $L_3 = f(1)\cdot 1 + f(2)\cdot 1 + f(3)\cdot 1$

      $= 1 + 5 + 7 = 13$

    $R_3 = f(2)\cdot 1 + f(3)\cdot 1 + f(4)\cdot 1$

      $= 5 + 7 + 8 = 20$

For Figure (B):

    $L_3 = g(1)\cdot 1 + g(2)\cdot 1 + g(3)\cdot 1$

      $= 8 + 4 + 2 = 14$

    $R_3 = g(2)\cdot 1 + g(3)\cdot 1 + g(4)\cdot 1$

      $= 4 + 2 + 1 = 7$

5. $L_3 \le \int_1^4 f(x)dx \le R_3$, $R_3 \le \int_1^4 g(x)dx \le L_3$; since f is increasing on $[1, 4]$, L_3 underestimates the area and R_3 overestimates the area; since g is decreasing on $[1, 4]$, L_3 overestimates the area and R_3 underestimates the area.

7. For Figure (A).

Error bound for L_3 and R_3:

$$\text{Error} \leq |f(4) - f(1)| \left(\frac{4-1}{3}\right) = |8 - 1| = 7$$

For Figure (B).

Error bound for L_3 and R_3:

$$\text{Error} \leq |f(4) - f(1)| \left(\frac{4-1}{3}\right) = |1 - 8| = |-7| = 7$$

9. $f(x) = 25 - 3x^2$ on $[-2, 8]$

$\Delta x = \dfrac{8 - (-2)}{5} = \dfrac{10}{5} = 2$; $x_0 = -2$, $x_1 = 0$, $x_2 = 2$, ..., $x_5 = 8$

$c_i = \dfrac{x_{i-1} + x_i}{2}$; $c_1 = -1$, $c_2 = 1$, $c_3 = 3$, $c_4 = 5$, $c_5 = 7$

$S_5 = f(-1)2 + f(1)2 + f(3)2 + f(5)2 + f(7)2$

$\quad = [22 + 22 - 2 - 50 - 122]2 = (-130)2 = -260$

11. $f(x) = 25 - 3x^2$ on $[0, 12]$

$\Delta x = \dfrac{12 - 0}{4} = 3$; $x_0 = 0$, $x_1 = 3$, $x_2 = 6$, $x_3 = 9$, $x_4 = 12$

$c_i = \dfrac{2x_{i-1} + x_i}{3}$; $c_1 = 1$, $c_2 = 4$, $c_3 = 7$, $c_4 = 10$

$S_4 = f(1)3 + f(4)3 + f(7)3 + f(10)3$

$\quad = [22 - 23 - 122 - 275]3 = (-398)3 = -1194$

13. $f(x) = x^2 - 5x - 6$

$\Delta x = \dfrac{3 - 0}{3} = 1$; $x_0 = 0$, $x_1 = 1$, $x_2 = 2$, $x_3 = 3$

$S_3 = f(0.7)1 + f(1.8)1 + f(2.4)1$

$\quad = -9.01 - 11.76 - 12.24 = -33.01$

15. $f(x) = x^2 - 5x - 6$

$\Delta x = \dfrac{7 - 1}{6} = 1$; $x_0 = 1$, $x_1 = 2$, $x_3 = 3$, ..., $x_6 = 7$

$S_6 = f(1)1 + f(3)1 + f(3)1 + f(5)1 + f(5)1 + f(7)1$

$\quad = -10 - 12 - 12 - 6 - 6 + 8 = -38$

17. $\displaystyle\int_b^0 f(x)\,dx = -\text{area } B = -2.475$

19. $\displaystyle\int_a^c f(x)\,dx = \text{area } A - \text{area } B + \text{area } C = 1.408 - 2.475 + 5.333 = 4.266$

21. $\displaystyle\int_a^d f(x)\,dx = \text{area } A - \text{area } B + \text{area } C - \text{area } D$

$\quad\quad\quad = 1.408 - 2.475 + 5.333 - 1.792 = 2.474$

23. $\displaystyle\int_c^0 f(x)\,dx = -\int_0^c f(x)\,dx = -\text{area } C = -5.333$

25. $\int_0^a f(x)\,dx = -\int_a^0 f(x)\,dx = -[\text{area } A - \text{area } B] = -[1.408 - 2.475] = 1.067$

27. $\int_d^b f(x)\,dx = -\int_b^d f(x)\,dx = -[\text{area } B + \text{area } C - \text{area } D]$
$$= -[-2.475 + 5.333 - 1.792] = -1.066$$

29. $\int_1^4 2x\,dx = 2\int_1^4 x\,dx = 2(7.5) = 15$

31. $\int_1^4 (5x + x^2)\,dx = 5\int_1^4 x\,dx + \int_1^4 x^2\,dx = 5(7.5) + 21 = 58.5$

33. $\int_1^4 (x^2 - 10x)\,dx = \int_1^4 x^2\,dx - 10\int_1^4 x\,dx = 21 - 10(7.5) = -54$

35. $\int_1^5 6x^2\,dx = 6\int_1^5 x^2\,dx = 6\left[\int_1^4 x^2\,dx + \int_4^5 x^2\,dx\right] = 6\left[21 + \dfrac{61}{3}\right] = 126 + 122 = 248$

37. $\int_4^4 (7x - 2)^2\,dx = 0$

39. $\int_5^4 9x^2\,dx = -\int_4^5 9x^2\,dx = -9\int_4^5 x^2\,dx = -9\left(\dfrac{61}{3}\right) = -183$

41. (A) $f(x) = x^2 - 2x$ on $[0, 2]$.
  $f'(x) = 2x - 2 = 2(x - 1)$; $f'(x) < 0$ on $[0, 1)$,
  $f'(x) > 0$ on $(1, 2]$
  False: f is not increasing on $[0, 2]$
  (B) $f(x) = x^2 - 2x$ on $[1, 3]$
  $f'(x) = 2x - 2 = 2(x - 1)$; $f'(x) > 0$ on $(1, 3]$
  True: f is increasing on $[1, 3]$

43. $h(x)$ is an increasing function; $\Delta x = 100$
  $L_{10} = h(0)100 + h(100)100 + h(200)100 + \ldots + h(900)(100)$
  $\quad = [0 + 183 + 235 + 245 + 260 + 286 + 322 + 388 + 453 + 489]100$
  $\quad = (2,861)100 = 286,100$ sq ft

  Error bound for L_{10}:

  Error $\leq |h(1,000) - h(0)|\left(\dfrac{1000 - 0}{10}\right) = 500(100) = 50,000$ sq ft

  We want to find n such that $|I - L_n| \leq 2,500$:

  $|h(1000) - h(0)|\left(\dfrac{1000 - 0}{n}\right) \leq 2,500$

  $\qquad 500\left(\dfrac{1000}{n}\right) \leq 2,500$

  $\qquad\quad 500,000 \leq 2,500n$

  $\qquad\qquad n \geq 200$

45. $f(x) = 0.25x^2 - 4$ on $[2, 5]$

$L_6 = f(2)\Delta x + f(2.5)\Delta x + f(3)\Delta x + f(3.5)\Delta x + f(4)\Delta x + f(4.5)\Delta x$

where $\Delta x = 0.5$

Thus,

$L_6 = [-3 - 2.44 - 1.75 - 0.94 + 0 + 1.06](0.5) = -3.53$

$R_6 = f(2.5)\Delta x + f(3)\Delta x + f(3.5)\Delta x + f(4)\Delta x + f(4.5)\Delta x + f(5)\Delta x$

where $\Delta x = 0.5$

Thus,

$R_6 = [-2.44 - 1.75 - 0.94 + 0 + 1.06 + 2.25](0.5) = -0.91$

Error bound for L_6 and R_6: Since f is increasing on $[2, 5]$,

$$\text{Error} \leq |f(5) - f(2)|\left(\frac{5-2}{6}\right) = |2.25 - (-3)|(0.5) = 2.63$$

Geometrically, the definite integral over the interval $[2, 5]$ is the area of the region which lies above the x-axis minus the area of the region which lies below the x-axis. From the figure, if R_1 represents the region bounded by the graph of f and the x-axis for $2 \leq x \leq 4$ and R_2 represents the region bounded by the graph of f and the x-axis for $4 \leq x \leq 5$, then

$$\int_2^5 f(x)dx = \text{area}(R_2) - \text{area}(R_1)$$

47. $f(x) = e^{-x^2}$

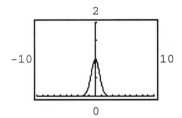

Thus, f is increasing on $(-\infty, 0]$ and decreasing on $[0, \infty)$.

49. $f(x) = x^4 - 2x^2 + 3$

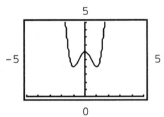

Thus, f is decreasing on $(-\infty, -1]$ and on $[0, 1]$, and increasing on $[-1, 0]$ and on $[1, \infty)$.

51. $\int_1^3 \ln x\, dx$

$|I - R_n| \leq |\ln 3 - \ln 1|\frac{3-1}{n} \approx \frac{(1.0986)2}{n} = \frac{2.1972}{n}$

Now $\frac{2.1972}{n} \leq 0.1$ implies $n \geq \frac{2.1972}{0.1} = 21.972$

so $n \geq 22$.

53. $\int_1^3 x^x dx$

$|I - L_n| \leq |3^3 - 1^1|\frac{3-1}{n} = \frac{26 \cdot 2}{n} = \frac{52}{n}$

Now $\frac{52}{n} \leq 0.5$ implies $n \geq \frac{52}{0.5} = 104$

55. From $t = 0$ to $t = 60$

$$L_3 = N(0)20 + N(20)20 + N(40)20$$
$$= (10 + 51 + 68)20 = 2580$$

$$R_3 = N(20)20 + N(40)20 + N(60)20$$
$$= (51 + 68 + 76)20 = 3900$$

Error bound for L_3 and R_3: Since $N(t)$ is increasing,

$$\text{Error} \leq |N(60) - N(0)|\left(\frac{60 - 0}{3}\right) = (76 - 10)20 = 1{,}320 \text{ units}$$

57. (A) $L_5 = A'(0)1 + A'(1)1 + A'(2)1 + A'(3)1 + A'(4)1$
$$= 0.90 + 0.81 + 0.74 + 0.67 + 0.60$$
$$= 3.72 \text{ sq cm}$$

$R_5 = A'(1)1 + A'(2)1 + A'(3)1 + A'(4)1 + A'(5)1$
$$= (0.81 + 0.74 + 0.67 + 0.60 + 0.55)$$
$$= 3.37 \text{ sq cm}$$

(B) Since $A'(t)$ is a decreasing function
$$R_5 = 3.37 \leq \int_0^5 A'(t)dt \leq 3.72 = L_5$$

59. $L_3 = N'(6)2 + N'(8)2 + N'(10)2$
$$= (21 + 19 + 17)2 = 114$$

$R_3 = N'(8)2 + N'(10)2 + N'(12)2$
$$= (19 + 17 + 15)2 = 102$$

Error bound for L_3 and R_3: Since $N'(x)$ is decreasing

$$\text{Error} \leq |N'(12) - N'(6)|\left(\frac{12 - 6}{3}\right) = |15 - 21|(2) = 12 \text{ code symbols}$$

EXERCISE 6-5

1. <u>FUNDAMENTAL THEOREM OF CALCULUS</u>

   If f is a continuous function on the closed interval $[a, b]$ and F is any antiderivative of f, then

   $$\int_a^b f(x)dx = F(x)\Big|_a^b = F(b) - F(a);$$
   $$F'(x) = f(x)$$

2. <u>AVERAGE VALUE OF A CONTINUOUS FUNCTION OVER</u> $[a, b]$

   Let f be continuous on $[a, b]$. Then the AVERAGE VALUE of f over $[a, b]$ is:

   $$\frac{1}{b - a}\int_a^b f(x)dx$$

---

1. $F(x) = 3x^2 + 160$

(A) $F(15) - F(10) = 3(15)^2 + 160 - [3(10)^2 + 160]$
$$= 675 - 300 = 375$$

(B)

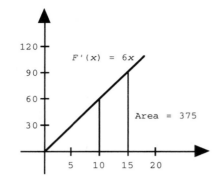

Area of trapezoid:

$$\frac{F'(15) + F'(10)}{2} \cdot 5 = \frac{90 + 60}{2} \cdot 5$$
$$= 75(5) = 375$$

(C) By the Fundamental Theorem of Calculus:
$$\int_{10}^{15} 6x \, dx = 3x^2 \Big]_{10}^{15} = 3(15)^2 - 3(10)^2 = 375$$

3. $F(x) = -x^2 + 42x + 240$

(A) $F(15) - F(10) = -(15)^2 + 42(15) + 240 - [-(10)^2 + 42(10) + 240]$
$$= -225 + 630 + 240 - (-100 + 420 + 240)$$
$$= -225 + 630 + 100 - 420 = 85$$

(B)

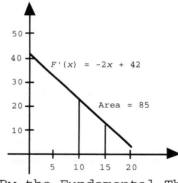

Area of trapezoid:

$$\frac{F'(15) + F'(10)}{2} \cdot 5 = \frac{(-30 + 42) + (-20 + 42)}{2} \cdot 5$$
$$= 17(5) = 85$$

(C) By the Fundamental Theorem of Calculus:
$$\int_{10}^{15} (-2x + 42) \, dx = \left[-x^2 + 42x\right]_{10}^{15} = -(15)^2 + 42(15) - [-(10)^2 + 42(10)]$$
$$= -225 + 630 + 100 - 420 = 85$$

5. $\int_{2}^{3} 2x\,dx = 2 \cdot \dfrac{x^2}{2} \Big|_{2}^{3} = 3^2 - 2^2 = 5$ **7.** $\int_{3}^{4} 5 \, dx = 5x \Big|_{3}^{4} = 5 \cdot 4 - 5 \cdot 3 = 5$

9. $\int_{1}^{3} (2x - 3)\,dx = (x^2 - 3x) \Big|_{1}^{3} = (3^2 - 3 \cdot 3) - (1^2 - 3 \cdot 1) = 2$

11. $\int_{-3}^{4} (4 - x^2)\,dx = \left(4x - \dfrac{x^3}{3}\right) \Big|_{-3}^{4} = \left(4 \cdot 4 - \dfrac{4^3}{3}\right) - \left(4(-3) - \dfrac{(-3)^3}{3}\right)$
$$= 16 - \frac{64}{3} + 3 = -\frac{7}{3}$$

13. $\int_0^1 24x^{11}dx = 24\left.\dfrac{x^{12}}{12}\right|_0^1 = 2x^{12}\Big|_0^1 = 2 \cdot 1^{12} - 2\cdot 0^{12} = 2$

15. $\int_0^1 e^{2x}dx = \left.\dfrac{1}{2}e^{2x}\right|_0^1 = \dfrac{1}{2}e^{2\cdot 1} - \dfrac{1}{2}e^{2\cdot 0} = \dfrac{1}{2}(e^2 - 1)$

17. $\int_1^{3.5} 2x^{-1}dx = 2\ln x\Big|_1^{3.5} = 2\ln 3.5 - 2\ln 1$

$\qquad\qquad\qquad\qquad\qquad = 2\ln 3.5 \quad \text{(Recall: } \ln 1 = 0\text{)}$

19. $\int_1^2 \dfrac{2}{x^3}dx = 2\int_1^2 x^{-3}dx = 2\left.\dfrac{x^{-2}}{-2}\right|_1^2 = -\dfrac{1}{x^2}\Big|_1^2$

$\qquad\qquad\qquad\qquad = -\dfrac{1}{4} - (-1) = \dfrac{3}{4}$

21. $\int_1^4 6x^{-1/2}dx = 6\int_1^4 x^{-1/2}dx = 12x^{1/2}\Big|_1^4 = 12(4)^{1/2} - 12(1)^{1/2} = 12$

23. $\int_1^2 (2x^{-2} - 3)dx = (-2x^{-1} - 3x)\Big|_1^2 = \left(-\dfrac{2}{x} - 3x\right)\Big|_1^2$

$\qquad\qquad\qquad = -\dfrac{2}{2} - 3\cdot 2 - \left(-\dfrac{2}{1} - 3\cdot 1\right) = -7 - (-5) = -2$

25. $\int_1^4 3\sqrt{x}dx = 3\int_1^4 x^{1/2}dx3 = 3\cdot\dfrac{2}{3}x^{3/2}\Big|_1^4 = 2x^{3/2}\Big|_1^4$

$\qquad\qquad\qquad = 2\cdot 4^{3/2} - 2\cdot 1^{3/2} = 16 - 2 = 14$

27. $\int_2^3 12(x^2 - 4)^5 xdx$. Consider the indefinite integral $\int 12(x^2 - 4)^5 x\,dx$.

Let $u = x^2 - 4$, then $du = 2x\,dx$.

$\int 12(x^2 - 4)^5 x\,dx = 6\int (x^2 - 4)^5 2x\,dx = 6\int u^5 du$

$\qquad\qquad = 6\dfrac{u^6}{6} + C = u^6 + C = (x^2 - 4)^6 + C$

Thus,

$\int_2^3 12(x^2 - 4)^5 xdx = (x^2 - 4)^6\Big|_2^3 = (3^2 - 4)^6 - (2^2 - 4)^6 = 5^6 = 15{,}625.$

29. $\int_3^9 \dfrac{1}{x - 1}dx$

Let $u = x - 1$. Then $du = dx$ and $u = 8$ when $x = 9$, $u = 2$ when $x = 3$.

Thus,

$\int_3^9 \dfrac{1}{x - 1}dx = \int_2^8 \dfrac{1}{u}du = \ln u\Big|_2^8 = \ln 8 - \ln 2 = \ln 4 \approx 1.386.$

31. $\displaystyle\int_{-5}^{10} e^{-0.05x}dx$

Let $u = -0.05x$. Then $du = -0.05\ dx$ and $u = -0.5$ when $x = 10$, $u = 0.25$ when $x = -5$. Thus,

$$\int_{-5}^{10} e^{-0.05x}dx = -\frac{1}{0.05}\int_{-5}^{10} e^{-0.05x}(-0.05)dx = -\frac{1}{0.05}\int_{0.25}^{-0.5} e^{u}du$$

$$= -\frac{1}{0.05}e^{u}\Big|_{0.25}^{-0.5} = -\frac{1}{0.05}\left[e^{-0.5} - e^{0.25}\right]$$

$$= 20(e^{0.25} - e^{-0.5}) \approx 13.550$$

33. $\displaystyle\int_{1}^{e}\frac{\ln t}{t}dt = \int_{0}^{1}u\,du = \frac{1}{2}u^2\Big|_{0}^{1} = \frac{1}{2}$

Let $u = \ln t$

Then $du = \frac{1}{t}dt$

$t = 1$ implies $u = \ln 1 = 0$

$t = e$ implies $u = \ln e = 1$

35. $\displaystyle\int_{0}^{2} x\sqrt{4 - x^2}\,dx$

We evaluate the indefinite integral $\displaystyle\int x\sqrt{4 - x^2}\,dx$ first.

Let $u = 4 - x^2$. Then $du = -2x\,dx$ and

$$\int x\sqrt{4 - x^2}\,dx = \int \sqrt{4 - x^2}\left(\frac{-2}{-2}\right)x\,dx = -\frac{1}{2}\int u^{1/2}du$$

$$= -\frac{1}{2}\frac{u^{3/2}}{3/2} + C$$

$$= \frac{1}{3}u^{3/2} + C$$

$$= -\frac{1}{3}(4 - x^2)^{3/2} + C$$

Now $\displaystyle\int_{0}^{2} x\sqrt{4 - x^2}\,dx = -\frac{1}{3}(4 - x^2)^{3/2}\Big|_{0}^{2} = -\frac{1}{3}(4 - 4)^{3/2} + \frac{1}{3}(4)^{3/2}$

$$= \frac{8}{3} \approx 2.667.$$

37. $\displaystyle\int_{0}^{1} xe^{-x^2}dx = \int_{0}^{1} e^{-x^2}\left(\frac{-2}{-2}\right)x\,dx$

Let $u = -x^2$

Then $du = -2x\,dx$

$x = 0$ implies $u = 0$

$x = 1$ implies $u = -1$

$$= -\frac{1}{2}\int_{0}^{-1} e^{u}du$$

$$= -\frac{1}{2}e^{u}\Big|_{0}^{-1} = -\frac{1}{2}e^{-1} + \frac{1}{2}e^{0}$$

$$= \frac{1}{2}(1 - e^{-1})$$

$$\approx 0.316$$

39. $\displaystyle\int_{-2}^{-1} \frac{x^2 + 1}{x}\,dx = \int_{-2}^{-1}\left(x + \frac{1}{x}\right)dx = \left[\frac{1}{2}\,x^2 + \ln|x|\right]_{-2}^{-1}$

$$= \left(\frac{1}{2}\,(-1)^2 + \ln 1\right) - \left(\frac{1}{2}\,(-2)^2 + \ln 2\right)$$

$$= -\frac{3}{2} - \ln 2 \approx -2.193$$

41. $f(x) = 500 - 50x$ on $[0, 10]$

    (A) Avg. $f(x) = \dfrac{1}{10 - 0}\displaystyle\int_0^{10}(500 - 50x)\,dx$ (B)

$$= \frac{1}{10}\,(500x - 25x^2)\Big|_0^{10}$$

$$= \frac{1}{10}\,[5{,}000 - 2{,}500] = 250$$

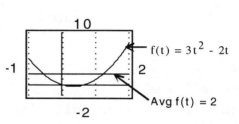

43. $f(t) = 3t^2 - 2t$ on $[-1, 2]$

    (A) Avg. $f(t) = \dfrac{1}{2 - (-1)}\displaystyle\int_{-1}^{2}(3t^2 - 2t)\,dt$ (B)

$$= \frac{1}{3}\,(t^3 - t^2)\Big|_{-1}^{2}$$

$$= \frac{1}{3}\,[4 - (-2)] = 2$$

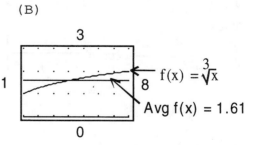

45. $f(x) = \sqrt[3]{x} = x^{1/3}$ on $[1, 8]$

    (A) Avg. $f(x) = \dfrac{1}{8 - 1}\displaystyle\int_1^{8} x^{1/3}\,dx$ (B)

$$= \frac{1}{7}\left(\frac{3}{4}\,x^{4/3}\right)\Big|_1^{8}$$

$$= \frac{3}{28}\,(16 - 1) = \frac{45}{28} \approx 1.61$$

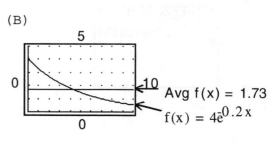

47. $f(x) = 4e^{-0.2x}$ on $[0, 10]$

    (A) Avg. $f(x) = \dfrac{1}{10 - 0}\displaystyle\int_0^{10} 4e^{-0.2x}\,dx$ (B)

$$= \frac{1}{10}\,(-20e^{-0.2x})\Big|_0^{10}$$

$$= \frac{1}{10}\,(20 - 20e^{-2}) \approx 1.73$$

49. $\displaystyle\int_2^3 x\sqrt{2x^2 - 3}\,dx = \int_2^3 x(2x^2 - 3)^{1/2}dx$

$$= \frac{1}{4}\int_2^3 (2x^2 - 3)^{1/2}4x\,dx$$

[Note: The integrand has the form $u^{1/2}du$; the antiderivative is $\dfrac{2}{3}u^{3/2} = \dfrac{2}{3}(2x^2 - 3)^{3/2}$.]

$$= \frac{1}{4}\left(\frac{2}{3}\right)(2x^2 - 3)^{3/2}\Big|_2^3$$

$$= \frac{1}{6}[2(3)^2 - 3]^{3/2} - \frac{1}{6}[2(2)^2 - 3]^{3/2}$$

$$= \frac{1}{6}(15)^{3/2} - \frac{1}{6}(5)^{3/2} = \frac{1}{6}[15^{3/2} - 5^{3/2}] \approx 7.819$$

51. $\displaystyle\int_0^1 \frac{x - 1}{x^2 - 2x + 3}\,dx$

Consider the indefinite integral and let $u = x^2 - 2x + 3$.
Then $du = (2x - 2)\,dx = 2(x - 1)\,dx$.

$$\int \frac{x - 1}{x^2 - 2x + 3}\,dx = \frac{1}{2}\int \frac{2(x - 1)}{x^2 - 2x + 3}\,dx = \frac{1}{2}\int \frac{1}{u}\,du = \frac{1}{2}\ln|u| + C$$

Thus,

$$\int_0^1 \frac{x - 1}{x^2 - 2x + 3}\,dx = \frac{1}{2}\ln|x^2 - 2x + 3|\,\Big|_0^1$$

$$= \frac{1}{2}\ln 2 - \frac{1}{2}\ln 3 = \frac{1}{2}(\ln 2 - \ln 3) \approx -0.203$$

53. $\displaystyle\int_{-1}^1 \frac{e^{-x} - e^x}{(e^{-x} + e^x)^2}\,dx$

Consider the indefinite integral and let $u = e^{-x} + e^x$.
Then $du = (-e^{-x} + e^x)\,dx = -(e^{-x} - e^x)\,dx$.

$$\int \frac{e^{-x} - e^x}{(e^{-x} + e^x)^2}\,dx = -\int \frac{-(e^{-x} - e^x)}{(e^{-x} + e^x)^2}\,dx = -\int u^{-2}\,du = \frac{-u^{-1}}{-1} + C = \frac{1}{u} + C$$

Thus,

$$\int_{-1}^1 \frac{e^{-x} - e^x}{(e^{-x} + e^x)^2}\,dx = \frac{1}{e^{-x} + e^x}\,\Big|_{-1}^1 = \frac{1}{e^{-1} + e^1} - \frac{1}{e^{-(-1)} + e^{-1}}$$

$$= \frac{1}{e^{-1} + e} - \frac{1}{e^{-1} + e} = 0$$

55. $\displaystyle\int_{1.7}^{3.5} x\ln x\,dx \approx 4.566$

```
fnInt(X*ln X,X,1
.7,3.5)
       4.566415359
■
```

57. $\displaystyle\int_{-2}^2 \frac{1}{1 + x^2}\,dx \approx 2.214$

```
fnInt(1/(1+X²),X
,-2,2)
       2.214297436
■
```

59. If $F(t)$ denotes the position of the car at time t, then the average velocity over the time interval $t = a$ to $t = b$ is given by

$$\frac{F(b) - F(a)}{b - a}.$$

$F'(t)$ gives the instantaneous velocity of the car at time t. By the Mean Value Theorem, there exists at least one time $t = c$ at which

$$\frac{F(b) - F(a)}{b - a} = F'(c).$$

Thus, if $\dfrac{F(b) - F(a)}{b - a} = 60$, then the instantaneous velocity must equal 60 at least once during the 10 minute time interval.

61. $C'(x) = 500 - \dfrac{x}{3}$ on $[300, 900]$

The increase in cost from a production level of 300 bikes per month to a production level of 900 bikes per month is given by:

$$\int_{300}^{900} \left(500 - \frac{x}{3}\right) dx = \left(500x - \frac{1}{6}x^2\right)\Big|_{300}^{900}$$
$$= 315,000 - (135,000)$$
$$= \$180,000$$

63. Total loss in value in the first 5 years:

$$V(5) - V(0) = \int_0^5 V'(t)\,dt = \int_0^5 500(t - 12)\,dt = 500\left(\frac{t^2}{2} - 12t\right)\Big|_0^5$$
$$= 500\left(\frac{25}{2} - 60\right) = -\$23,750$$

Total loss in value in the second 5 years:

$$V(10) - V(5) = \int_5^{10} V'(t)\,dt = \int_5^{10} 500(t - 12)\,dt = 500\left(\frac{t^2}{2} - 12t\right)\Big|_5^{10}$$
$$= 500\left[(50 - 120) - \left(\frac{25}{2} - 60\right)\right] = -\$11,250$$

65. (A)

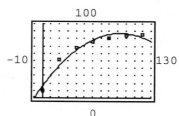

```
QuadReg
y=ax²+bx+c
a=-.0082142857
b=1.528571429
c=16
```

(B) Let $q(t)$ be the quadratic regression model found in part (A). The number of units produced by a new employee during the first 100 days is given (approximately) by

$$\int_0^{100} q(t)\,dt \approx 6505$$

```
fnInt(Y₁,X,0,100
)
        6504.761912
```

67. (A) To find the useful life, set $C'(t) = R'(t)$ and solve for t.

$$\frac{1}{11}t = 5te^{-t^2}$$

$$e^{t^2} = 55$$

$$t^2 = \ln 55$$

$$t = \sqrt{\ln 55} \approx 2 \text{ years}$$

(B) The total profit accumulated during the useful life is:

$$P(2) - P(0) = \int_0^2 [R'(t) - C'(t)]\,dt = \int_0^2 \left(5te^{-t^2} - \frac{1}{11}t\right)dt$$

$$= \int_0^2 5te^{-t^2}\,dt - \int_0^2 \frac{1}{11}t\,dt$$

$$= -\frac{5}{2}\int_0^2 e^{-t^2}(-2t)\,dt - \frac{1}{11}\int_0^2 t\,dt \qquad$$

[Note: In the first integral, the integrand has the form $e^u\,du$, where $u = -t^2$; an antiderivative is $e^u = e^{-t^2}$.]

$$= -\frac{5}{2}e^{-t^2}\Big|_0^2 - \frac{1}{22}t^2\Big|_0^2$$

$$= -\frac{5}{2}e^{-4} + \frac{5}{2} - \frac{4}{22} = \frac{51}{22} - \frac{5}{2}e^{-4} \approx 2.272$$

Thus, the total profit is approximately $2,272.

69. $C(x) = 60,000 + 300x$

(A) Average cost per unit:

$$\overline{C}(x) = \frac{C(x)}{x} = \frac{60,000}{x} + 300$$

$$\overline{C}(500) = \frac{60,000}{500} + 300 = \$420$$

(B) Avg. $C(x) = \dfrac{1}{500}\displaystyle\int_0^{500}(60,000 + 300x)\,dx$

$$= \frac{1}{500}(60,000x + 150x^2)\Big|_0^{500}$$

$$= \frac{1}{500}(30,000,000 + 37,500,000) = \$135,000$$

(C) $\overline{C}(500)$ is the average cost per unit at a production level of 500 units; Ave $C(x)$ is the average value of the total cost as production increases from 0 units to 500 units.

71. (A)

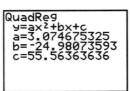
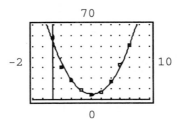

(B) Let $q(x)$ be the quadratic regression model found in part (A). The increase in cost in going from a production level of 2 thousand watches per month to 8 thousand watches per month is given (approximately) by

$$\int_2^8 q(x)\,dx \approx 100.505$$

Therefore, the increase in cost is approximately $100,505.

73. Average price:

$$\text{Avg. } S(x) = \frac{1}{30 - 20} \int_{20}^{30} 10(e^{0.02x} - 1)\,dx = \int_{20}^{30} (e^{0.02x} - 1)\,dx$$

$$= \int_{20}^{30} e^{0.02x}\,dx - \int_{20}^{30} dx$$

$$= \frac{1}{0.02} \int_{20}^{30} e^{0.02x}(0.02)\,dx - x\Big|_{20}^{30}$$

$$= 50e^{0.02x}\Big|_{20}^{30} - (30 - 20)$$

$$= 50e^{0.6} - 50e^{0.4} - 10$$

$$\approx 6.51 \text{ or } \$6.51$$

75. $g(x) = 2400x^{-1/2}$ and $L'(x) = g(x)$.
The number of labor hours to assemble the 17th through the 25th control units is:

$$L(25) - L(16) = \int_{16}^{25} g(x)\,dx = \int_{16}^{25} 2400x^{-1/2}\,dx = 2400(2)x^{1/2}\Big|_{16}^{25}$$

$$= 4800x^{1/2}\Big|_{16}^{25} = 4800[25^{1/2} - 16^{1/2}] = 4800 \text{ labor hours}$$

77. (A) The inventory function is obtained by finding the equation of the line joining (0, 600) and (3, 0).

Slope: $m = \dfrac{0 - 600}{3 - 0} = -200$, y intercept: $b = 600$

Thus, the equation of the line is: $I = -200t + 600$

(B) The average of I over [0, 3] is given by:

$$\text{Avg. } I(t) = \frac{1}{3 - 0} \int_0^3 I(t)\,dt = \frac{1}{3} \int_0^3 (-200t + 600)\,dt$$

$$= \frac{1}{3}(-100t^2 + 600t)\Big|_0^3$$

$$= \frac{1}{3}[-100(3^2) + 600(3) - 0]$$

$$= \frac{900}{3} = 300 \text{ units}$$

79. Rate of production: $R(t) = \dfrac{100}{t + 1} + 5$, $0 \le t \le 20$

Total production from year N to year M is given by:

$$P = \int_N^M R(t)\,dt = \int_N^M \left(\frac{100}{t + 1} + 5\right)dt = 100\int_N^M \frac{1}{t + 1} + 5dt$$

$$= 100\ln|t + 1|\Big|_N^M + 5t\Big|_N^M$$

$$= 100\ln(M + 1) - 100\ln(N + 1) + 5(M - N)$$

Thus, for total production during the first 10 years, let $M = 10$ and $N = 0$.

$P = 100\ln 11 - 100\ln 1 + 5(10 - 0)$
$= 100\ln 11 + 50 \approx 290$ thousand barrels

For the total production from the end of the 10th year to the end of the 20th year, let $M = 20$ and $N = 10$.

$P = 100\ln 21 - 100\ln 11 + 5(20 - 10)$
$= 100\ln 21 - 100\ln 11 + 50 \approx 115$ thousand barrels

81. $W'(t) = 0.2e^{0.1t}$

The weight increase during the first eight hours is given by:

$$W(8) - W(0) = \int_0^8 W'(t)\,dt = \int_0^8 0.2e^{0.1t}dt = 0.2\int_0^8 e^{0.1t}dt$$

$$= \frac{0.2}{0.1}\int_0^8 e^{0.1t}(0.1)\,dt \qquad \text{(Let } u = 0.1t, \text{ then } du = 0.1dt.)$$

$$= 2e^{0.1t}\Big|_0^8 = 2e^{0.8} - 2 \approx 2.45 \text{ grams}$$

The weight increase during the second eight hours, i.e., from the 8th hour through the 16th hour, is given by:

$$W(16) - W(8) = \int_8^{16} W'(t)\,dt = \int_8^{16} 0.2e^{0.1t}dt = 2e^{0.1t}\Big|_8^{16}$$

$$= 2e^{1.6} - 2e^{0.8} \approx 5.45 \text{ grams}$$

83. Average temperature over time period $[0, 2]$ is given by:

$$\frac{1}{2-0}\int_0^2 C(t)\,dt = \frac{1}{2}\int_0^2 (t^3 - 2t + 10)\,dt = \frac{1}{2}\left(\frac{t^4}{4} - \frac{2t^2}{2} + 10t\right)\Big|_0^2$$

$$= \frac{1}{2}(4 - 4 + 20) = 10°\text{ Celsius}$$

85. $P(t) = \dfrac{8.4t}{t^2 + 49} + 0.1, \quad 0 \le t \le 24$

(A) Average fraction of people during the first seven months:

$$\frac{1}{7-0}\int_0^7\left[\frac{8.4t}{t^2+49} + 0.1\right]dt = \frac{4.2}{7}\int_0^7 \frac{2t}{t^2+49}dt + \frac{1}{7}\int_0^7 0.1dt$$

$$= 0.6\ln(t^2+49)\Big|_0^7 + \frac{0.1}{7}t\Big|_0^7$$

$$= 0.6[\ln 98 - \ln 49] + 0.1$$

$$= 0.6\ln 2 + 0.1 \approx 0.516$$

(B) Average fraction of people during the first two years:

$$\frac{1}{24-0}\int_0^{24}\left[\frac{8.4t}{t^2+49} + 0.1\right]dt = \frac{4.2}{24}\int_0^{24}\frac{2t}{t^2+49}dt + \frac{1}{24}\int_0^{24}0.1dt$$

$$= 0.175\ln(t^2+49)\Big|_0^{24} + \frac{0.1}{24}t\Big|_0^{24}$$

$$= 0.175[\ln 625 - \ln 49] + 0.1 \approx 0.546$$

CHAPTER 6 REVIEW

1. $\int(6x + 3)\,dx = 6\int x\,dx + \int 3\,dx = 6\cdot\dfrac{x^2}{2} + 3x + C$

$$= 3x^2 + 3x + C \tag{6-1}$$

2. $\displaystyle\int_{10}^{20} 5dx = 5x\Big]_{10}^{20} = 5(20) - 5(10) = 50 \tag{6-5}$

3. $\displaystyle\int_0^9 (4 - t^2)dt = \int_0^9 4dt - \int_0^9 t^2 dt = 4t\Big]_0^9 - \frac{t^3}{3}\Big]_0^9$

$$= 36 - 243 = -207 \tag{6-5}$$

4. $\int (1 - t^2)^3 t\,dt = \int (1 - t^2)^3 \left(\dfrac{-2}{-2}\right) t\,dt = -\dfrac{1}{2}\int (1 - t^2)^3 (-2t)\,dt$

$$= -\dfrac{1}{2}\int u^3\,du = -\dfrac{1}{2}\cdot\dfrac{u^4}{4} + C$$

$$= -\dfrac{1}{8}(1 - t^2)^4 + C \qquad (6\text{-}2)$$

5. $\int \dfrac{1 + u^4}{u}\,du = \int \left(\dfrac{1}{u} + u^3\right)du = \int \dfrac{1}{u}\,du + \int u^3\,du$

$$= \ln|u| + \dfrac{1}{4}u^4 + C \qquad (6\text{-}1)$$

6. $\int_0^1 xe^{-2x^2}\,dx$

Let $\quad u = -2x^2 \qquad \int xe^{-2x^2}\,dx = \int e^{-2x^2}\left(\dfrac{-4}{-4}\right)x\,dx = -\dfrac{1}{4}\int e^u\,du$

Then $du = -4x\,dx$

$$= -\dfrac{1}{4}e^u + C$$

$$= -\dfrac{1}{4}e^{-2x^2} + C$$

$\int_0^1 xe^{-2x^2}\,dx = -\dfrac{1}{4}e^{-2x^2}\Big]_0^1 = -\dfrac{1}{4}e^{-2} + \dfrac{1}{4} \approx 0.216 \qquad (6\text{-}5)$

7. $\dfrac{d}{dx}\left[\int e^{-2x^2}\,dx\right] = e^{-x^2} \quad (6\text{-}1) \qquad$ **8.** $\int \dfrac{d}{dx}(\sqrt{4 + 5x})\,dx = \sqrt{4 + 5x} + C \qquad (6\text{-}1)$

9. $\dfrac{dy}{dx} = 3x^2 - 2$

$\quad y = f(x) = \int (3x^2 - 2)\,dx$

$\quad\quad f(x) = x^3 - 2x + C$
$\quad\quad f(0) = C = 4$
$\quad\quad f(x) = x^3 - 2x + 4 \qquad (6\text{-}3)$

10. (A) $\int (8x^3 - 4x - 1)\,dx = 8\int x^3\,dx - 4\int x\,dx - \int dx$

$$= 8\cdot\dfrac{1}{4}x^4 - 4\dfrac{1}{2}x^2 - x + C$$

$$= 2x^4 - 2x^2 - x + C \qquad (6\text{-}1)$$

(B) $\int (e^t - 4^{t-1})\,dt = \int e^t - 4\int \dfrac{1}{t}\,dt$

$$= e^t - 4\ln|t| + C \qquad (6\text{-}1)$$

11. $f(x) = x^2 + 1,\ a = 1,\ b = 5,\ n = 2,\ \Delta x = \dfrac{5 - 1}{2} = 2;$

$\quad R_2 = f(3)2 + f(5)2 = 10(2) + 26(2) = 72$

Error bound for R_2: f is increasing on $[1, 5]$, so

$|I - R_2| \le [f(5) - f(1)]\dfrac{5 - 1}{2} = (26 - 2)(2) = 48$

Thus, $I = 72 \pm 48$.

$\qquad (6\text{-}5)$

12. $\int_1^5 (x^2 + 1)\, dx = \frac{1}{3}x^3 + x \Big]_1^5 = \frac{125}{3} + 5 - \left(\frac{1}{3} + 1\right) = \frac{136}{3} = 45\frac{1}{3}$

$|I - R_2| = \left|45\frac{1}{3} - 72\right| = 26\frac{2}{3} \approx 26.67$

(6-5)

13. Using the values of f in the table with $a = 1$, $b = 17$, $n = 4$

$\Delta x = \dfrac{17 - 1}{4} = 4$, we have

$L_4 = f(1)4 + f(5)4 + f(9)4 + f(13)4$

$\quad = [1.2 + 3.4 + 2.6 + 0.5]4 = 30.8$

(6-5)

14. $f(x) = 6x^2 + 2x$ on $[-1, 2]$;

Ave $f(x) = \dfrac{1}{2 - (-1)} \int_{-1}^2 (6x^2 + 2x)\, dx$

$\quad = \frac{1}{3}(2x^3 + x^2)\Big|_{-1}^2 = \frac{1}{3}[20 - (-1)] = 7$

(6-5)

15. width $= 2 - (-1) = 3$, height $=$ Avg. $f(x) = 7$

(6-5)

16. $f(x) = 100 - x^2$

$\Delta x = \dfrac{11 - 3}{4} = \dfrac{8}{4} = 2$; $c_i = \dfrac{x_{i-1} + x_i}{2}$ (= midpoint of interval)

$S_4 = f(4)2 + f(6)2 + f(8)\cdot 2 + f(10)\cdot 2$

$\quad = [84 + 64 + 36 + 0]2 = (184)2 = 368$

(6-5)

17. $f(x) = 100 - x^2$

$\Delta x = \dfrac{5 - (-5)}{5} = \dfrac{10}{5} = 2$

$S_5 = f(-4)2 + f(-1)2 + f(1)2 + f(2)2 + f(5)2$

$\quad = [84 + 99 + 99 + 96 + 75]2 = (453)2 = 906$

(6-5)

18. $\int_a^b 5f(x)\, dx = 5\int_a^b f(x)\, dx = 5(-2) = -10$

(6-4, 6-5)

19. $\int_b^c \dfrac{f(x)}{5}\, dx = \frac{1}{5}\int_b^c f(x)\, dx = \frac{1}{5}(2) = \frac{2}{5} = 0.4$

(6-4, 6-5)

20. $\int_b^d f(x)\, dx = \int_b^c f(x)\, dx + \int_c^d f(x)\, dx = 2 - 0.6 = 1.4$

(6-4, 6-5)

21. $\int_a^c f(x)\, dx = \int_a^b f(x)\, dx + \int_b^c f(x)\, dx = -2 + 2 = 0$

(6-4, 6-5)

22. $\int_0^d f(x)\, dx = \int_0^a f(x)\, dx + \int_a^b f(x)\, dx + \int_b^c f(x)\, dx + \int_c^d f(x)\, dx$

$\quad = 1 - 2 + 2 - 0.6 = 0.4$

(6-4, 6-5)

23. $\int_b^a f(x)\, dx = -\int_a^b f(x)\, dx = -(-2) = 2$

(6-4, 6-5)

24. $\int_c^b f(x)\, dx = -\int_b^c f(x)\, dx = -2$

(6-4, 6-5)

25. $\int_d^0 f(x)\,dx = -\int_0^d f(x)\,dx = -0.4$ (from Problem 22) $\quad$ (6-4, 6-5)

26. (A) $\dfrac{dy}{dx} = \dfrac{2y}{x}$; $\left.\dfrac{dy}{dx}\right|_{(2,\,1)} = \dfrac{2(1)}{2} = 1$, $\left.\dfrac{dy}{dx}\right|_{(-2,\,-1)} = \dfrac{2(-1)}{-2} = 1$

(B) $\dfrac{dy}{dx} = \dfrac{2x}{y}$; $\left.\dfrac{dy}{dx}\right|_{(2,\,1)} = \dfrac{2(2)}{1} = 4$, $\left.\dfrac{dy}{dx}\right|_{(-2,\,-1)} = \dfrac{2(-2)}{-1} = 4$ $\quad$ (6-3)

27. $\dfrac{dy}{dx} = \dfrac{2y}{x}$; from the figure, the slopes at (2, 1) and (-2, -1) are approximately equal to 1 as computed in Problem 26(A), not 4 as computed in Problem 26(B). $\quad$ (6-3)

28. Let $y = Cx^2$. Then $\dfrac{dy}{dx} = 2Cx$. From the original equation, $C = \dfrac{y}{x^2}$ so

$$\dfrac{dy}{dx} = 2x\left(\dfrac{y}{x^2}\right) = \dfrac{2y}{x} \qquad (6\text{-}3)$$

29. Letting $x = 2$ and $y = 1$ in $y = Cx^2$, we get

$1 = 4C$ so $C = \dfrac{1}{4}$ and $y = \dfrac{1}{4}x^2$

Letting $x = -2$ and $y = -1$ in $y = Cx^2$, we get

$-1 = 4C$ so $C = -\dfrac{1}{4}$ and $y = -\dfrac{1}{4}x^2$ $\quad$ (6-3)

30.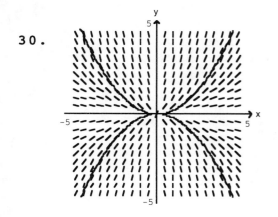

$\quad$ (6-3)

31.

$\quad$ (6-3)

32. $\int_{-1}^{1} \sqrt{1 + x}\,dx = \int_0^2 u^{1/2}\,du = \left.\dfrac{u^{3/2}}{3/2}\right|_0^2 = \dfrac{2}{3}(2)^{3/2} \approx 1.886$

Let $u = 1 + x$
$\quad du = dx$
when $x = -1$, $u = 0$,
when $x = 1$, $u = 2$ $\quad$ (6-5)

33. $\int_{-1}^{0} x^2(x^3 + 2)^{-2}dx = \int_{-1}^{0} (x^3 + 2)^{-2}\left(\frac{3}{3}\right)x^2dx = \frac{1}{3}\int_{-1}^{0} (x^3 + 2)^{-2}3x^2dx$

Let $u = x^3 + 2$
Then $du = 3x^2dx$
When $x = -1$, $u = 1$
when $x = 0$, $u = 2$

$= \frac{1}{3}\int_{1}^{2} u^{-2}du$

$= \frac{1}{3}\cdot\frac{u^{-1}}{-1}\Big]_{1}^{2} = -\frac{1}{3u}\Big]_{1}^{2}$

$= -\frac{1}{6} + \frac{1}{3} = \frac{1}{6}$

34. $\int 5e^{-t}dt = -\int 5e^{-t}(-dt) = -5\int e^{u}du = -5e^{u} + C$

Let $u = -t$
Then $du = -dt$

$= -5e^{-t} + C$

(6-2)

35. $\int_{1}^{e} \frac{1 + t^2}{t} dt = \int_{1}^{e} \left(\frac{1}{t} + t\right)dt = \int_{1}^{e} \frac{1}{t} dt + \int_{1}^{e} t\, dt$

$= \ln t \Big]_{1}^{e} + \frac{1}{2}t^2 \Big]_{1}^{e}$

$= \ln e - \ln 1 + \frac{1}{2}e^2 - \frac{1}{2}$

$= \frac{1}{2} + \frac{1}{2}e^2$

(6-5)

36. $\int xe^{3x^2}dx = \int e^{3x^2}\frac{6}{6}xdx = \frac{1}{6}\int e^{u}du = \frac{1}{6}e^{u} + C$

Let $u = 3x^2$
Then $du = 6xdx$

$= \frac{1}{6}e^{3x^2} + C$

(6-2)

37. $\int_{-3}^{1} \frac{1}{\sqrt{2 - x}} dx = -\int_{-3}^{1} \frac{1}{\sqrt{2 - x}}(-dx) = -\int_{5}^{1} u^{-1/2}du$

Let $u = 2 - x$
Then $du = -dx$
When $x = -3$, $u = 5$
when $x = 1$, $u = 1$

$= \int_{1}^{5} u^{-1/2}du$

$= 2u^{1/2}\Big]_{1}^{5}$

$= 2\sqrt{5} - 2 \approx 2.472$

(6-5)

38. Let $u = 1 + x^2$, then $du = 2x\, dx$.

$\int_{0}^{3} \frac{x}{1 + x^2}dx = \int_{0}^{3} \frac{1}{1 + x^2}\frac{2}{2}x\, dx$

$= \frac{1}{2}\int_{0}^{3} \frac{1}{1 + x^2}\frac{2}{2}2x\, dx = \frac{1}{2}\ln(1 + x^2)\Big|_{0}^{3}$

$= \frac{1}{2}\ln 10 - \frac{1}{2}\ln 1 = \frac{1}{2}\ln 10 \approx 1.151$

(6-5)

39. Let $u = 1 + x^2$, then $du = 2x\,dx$.

$$\int_0^3 \frac{x}{(1 + x^2)^2}\,dx = \int_0^3 (1 + x^2)^{-2}\frac{2}{2}x\,dx = \frac{1}{2}\int_0^3 (1 + x^2)^{-2}\,2x\,dx$$

$$= \frac{1}{2} \cdot \frac{(1 + x^2)^{-1}}{-1}\bigg|_0^3 = \frac{-1}{2(1 + x^2)}\bigg|_0^3 = -\frac{1}{20} + \frac{1}{2} = \frac{9}{20} = 0.45$$

(6-5)

40. Let $u = 2x^4 + 5$, then $du = 8x^3\,dx$.

$$\int x^3 (2x^4 + 5)^5\,dx = \int (2x^4 + 5)^5 x^3\,dx = \frac{1}{8}\int u^5\,du$$

$$= \frac{1}{8} \cdot \frac{u^6}{6} + C = \frac{(2x^4 + 5)^6}{48} + C$$

(6-2)

41. Let $u = e^{-x} + 3$, then $du = -e^{-x}\,dx$.

$$\int \frac{e^{-x}}{e^{-x} + 3}\,dx = \int \frac{1}{e^{-x} + 3} \cdot \frac{(-1)}{(-1)}e^{-x}\,dx = -\int \frac{1}{u}\,du$$

$$= -\ln|u| + C = -\ln|e^{-x} + 3| + C = -\ln(e^{-x} + 3) + C$$

[<u>Note</u>: Absolute value not needed since $e^{-x} + 3 > 0$.]

(6-2)

42. Let $u = e^x + 2$, then $du = e^x\,dx$.

$$\int \frac{e^x}{(e^x + 2)^2}\,dx = \int (e^x + 2)^{-2}e^x\,dx = \int u^{-2}\,du$$

$$= \frac{u^{-1}}{-1} + C = -(e^x + 2)^{-1} + C = \frac{-1}{(e^x + 2)} + C$$

(6-2)

43. $\dfrac{dy}{dx} = 3x^{-1} - x^{-2}$

$$y = \int (3x^{-1} - x^{-2})\,dx = 3\int \frac{1}{x}\,dx - \int x^{-2}\,dx$$

$$= 3\ln|x| - \frac{x^{-1}}{-1} + C = 3\ln|x| + x^{-1} + C$$

Given $y(1) = 5$:

$5 = 3\ln 1 + 1 + C$ and $C = 4$

Thus, $y = 3\ln|x| + x^{-1} + 4$.

(6-2, 6-3)

44. $\dfrac{dy}{dx} = 6x + 1$

$$f(x) = y = \int (6x + 1)\,dx = \frac{6x^2}{2} + x + C = 3x^2 + x + C$$

We have $y = 10$ when $x = 2$: $3(2)^2 + 2 + C = 10$

$$C = 10 - 12 - 2 = -4$$

Thus, the equation of the curve is $y = 3x^2 + x - 4$.

(6-3)

45. (A) $f(x) = 3\sqrt{x} = 3x^{1/2}$ on $[1, 9]$

Avg. $f(x) = \dfrac{1}{9-1}\displaystyle\int_1^9 3x^{1/2}dx$

$= \dfrac{3}{8}\cdot\dfrac{x^{3/2}}{3/2}\bigg|_1^9 = \dfrac{1}{4}x^{3/2}\bigg|_1^9$

$= \dfrac{27}{4} - \dfrac{1}{4} = \dfrac{26}{4} = 6.5$

(B)

(6-5)

46. Let $u = \ln x$, then $du = \dfrac{1}{x}dx$.

$\displaystyle\int\dfrac{(\ln x)^2}{x}dx = \int(\ln x)^2\dfrac{1}{x}dx = \int u^2 du = \dfrac{u^3}{3} + C = \dfrac{(\ln x)^3}{3} + C$ (6-2)

47. $\displaystyle\int x(x^3 - 1)^2 dx = \int x(x^6 - 2x^3 + 1)\, dx$ (square $x^3 - 1$)

$= \displaystyle\int(x^7 - 2x^4 + x)\, dx = \dfrac{x^8}{8} - \dfrac{2x^5}{5} + \dfrac{x^2}{2} + C$ (6-2)

48. Let $u = 6 - x$, then $x = 6 - u$ and $dx = -du$.

$\displaystyle\int\dfrac{x}{\sqrt{6-x}}dx = -\int\dfrac{(6-u)du}{u^{1/2}} = \int(u^{1/2} - 6u^{-1/2})\, du$

$= \dfrac{u^{3/2}}{3/2} - \dfrac{6u^{1/2}}{1/2} + C = \dfrac{2}{3}u^{3/2} - 12u^{1/2} + C$

$= \dfrac{2}{3}(6-x)^{3/2} - 12(6-x)^{1/2} + C$ (6-2)

49. $\displaystyle\int_0^7 x\sqrt{16-x}\,dx$. First consider the indefinite integral:

Let $u = 16 - x$, then $x = 16 - u$ and $dx = -du$.

$\displaystyle\int x\sqrt{16-x}\,dx = -\int(16-u)u^{1/2}du = \int(u^{3/2} - 16u^{1/2})\,du = \dfrac{u^{5/2}}{5/2} - \dfrac{16u^{3/2}}{3/2} + C$

$= \dfrac{2}{5}u^{5/2} - \dfrac{32}{3}u^{3/2} + C = \dfrac{2(16-x)^{5/2}}{5} - \dfrac{32(16-x)^{3/2}}{3} + C$

$\displaystyle\int_0^7 x\sqrt{16-x}\,dx = \left[\dfrac{2(16-x)^{5/2}}{5} - \dfrac{32(16-x)^{3/2}}{3}\right]\bigg|_0^7$

$= \dfrac{2\cdot 9^{5/2}}{5} - \dfrac{32\cdot 9^{3/2}}{3} - \left(\dfrac{2\cdot 16^{5/2}}{5} - \dfrac{32\cdot 16^{3/2}}{3}\right)$

$= \dfrac{2\cdot 3^5}{5} - \dfrac{32\cdot 3^3}{3} - \left(\dfrac{2\cdot 4^5}{5} - \dfrac{32\cdot 4^3}{3}\right)$

$= \dfrac{486}{5} - 288 - \left(\dfrac{2048}{5} - \dfrac{2048}{3}\right) = \dfrac{1234}{15} \approx 82.267$ (6-5)

50. Let $u = x + 1$, then $x = u - 1$, $dx = du$; and $u = 0$ when $x = -1$, $u = 2$ when $x = 1$.

$$\int_{-1}^{1} x(x + 1)^4 dx = \int_{0}^{2} (u - 1)u^4 du = \int_{0}^{2} (u^5 - u^4)du$$

$$= \left[\frac{u^6}{6} - \frac{u^5}{5}\right]\Big|_{0}^{2} = \frac{2^6}{6} - \frac{2^5}{5} = \frac{32}{3} - \frac{32}{5}$$

$$= \frac{160 - 96}{15} = \frac{64}{15} \approx 4.267 \qquad (6\text{-}5)$$

51. $\dfrac{dy}{dx} = 9x^2 e^{x^3}$, $f(0) = 2$

Let $u = x^3$, then $du = 3x^2 dx$.

$$y = \int 9x^2 e^{x^3} dx = 3\int e^{x^3} \cdot 3x^2 dx = 3\int e^u du = 3e^u + C = 3e^{x^3} + C$$

Given $f(0) = 2$:

$2 = 3e^0 + C = 3 + C$

Hence, $C = -1$ and $y = f(x) = 3e^{x^3} - 1$. $\qquad (6\text{-}3)$

52. $\dfrac{dN}{dt} = 0.06N$, $N(0) = 800$, $N > 0$

From the differential equation, $N(t) = Ce^{0.06t}$, where C is an arbitrary constant. Since $N(0) = 800$, we have

$\quad 800 = Ce^0 = C$.

Hence, $C = 800$ and $N(t) = 800e^{0.06t}$. $\qquad (6\text{-}3)$

53. $N = 50(1 - e^{-0.07t})$,
$0 \le t \le 80$, $0 \le N \le 60$

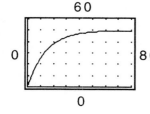

Limited growth
$(6\text{-}3)$

54. $p = 500e^{-0.03x}$,
$0 \le x \le 100$, $0 \le p \le 500$

Exponential decay
$(6\text{-}3)$

55. $A = 200e^{0.08t}$,
$0 \le t \le 20$, $0 \le A \le 1{,}000$

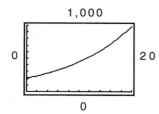

Unlimited growth
$(6\text{-}3)$

56. $N = \dfrac{100}{1 + 9e^{-0.3t}}$,
$0 \le t \le 25$, $0 \le N \le 100$

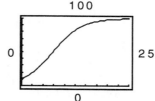

Logistic growth
$(6\text{-}3)$

57. $\int_{-0.5}^{0.6} \dfrac{1}{\sqrt{1-x^2}}\, dx \approx 1.167$

```
fnInt(Y₁,X, -0.5,
0.6)
        1.167099884
■
```

(6-5)

58. $\int_{-2}^{3} x^2 e^x dx \approx 99.074$

```
fnInt(Y₁,X, -2,3)
        99.07433178
```

(6-5)

59. $\int_{0.5}^{2.5} \dfrac{\ln x}{x^2}\, dx \approx -0.153$

```
fnInt(Y₁,X,0.5,2
.5)
        -.1528106539
■
```

(6-5)

60. $a = 200$, $b = 600$, $n = 2$, $\Delta x = \dfrac{600 - 200}{2} = 200$

$L_2 = C'(200)\Delta x + C'(400)\Delta x$

$\quad\,\, = [500 + 400]200 = \$180,000$

$R_2 = C'(400)\Delta x + C'(600)\Delta x$

$\quad\,\, = [400 + 300]200 = \$140,000$

$140,000 \le \int_{200}^{600} C'(x)dx \le 180,000$

(6-4)

61. The graph of $C'(x)$ is a straight line with y-intercept $= 600$ and

$\qquad$ slope $= \dfrac{300 - 600}{600 - 0} = -\dfrac{1}{2}$

Thus, $C'(x) = -\dfrac{1}{2}x + 600$

Increase in costs:

$\int_{200}^{600} \left(600 - \dfrac{1}{2}x\right)dx = \left(600x - \dfrac{1}{4}x^2\right)\Big|_{200}^{600}$

$\qquad\qquad\qquad\qquad = 270,000 - 110,000$

$\qquad\qquad\qquad\qquad = \$160,000$

(6-5)

62. The total change in profit for a production change from 10 units per week to 40 units per week is given by:

$\int_{10}^{40} \left(150 - \dfrac{x}{10}\right)dx = \left(150x - \dfrac{x^2}{20}\right)\Big|_{10}^{40}$

$\qquad\qquad\qquad\qquad = \left(150(40) - \dfrac{40^2}{20}\right) - \left(150(10) - \dfrac{10^2}{20}\right)$

$\qquad\qquad\qquad\qquad = 5920 - 1495 = \$4425$

(6-5)

63. $P'(x) = 100 - 0.02x$

$$P(x) = \int (100 - 0.02x)\,dx = 100x - 0.02\frac{x^2}{2} + C = 100x - 0.01x^2 + C$$

$$P(0) = 0 - 0 + C = 0$$
$$C = 0$$

Thus, $P(x) = 100x - 0.01x^2$.
The profit on 10 units of production is given by:
$$P(10) = 100(10) - 0.01(10)^2 = \$999 \tag{6-3}$$

64. The required definite integral is:

$$\int_0^{15} (60 - 4t)\,dt = (60t - 2t^2)\Big|_0^{15}$$

$$= 60(15) - 2(15)^2 = 450 \text{ or } 450,000 \text{ barrels}$$

The total production in 15 years is 450,000 barrels. $\tag{6-5}$

65. Average inventory from $t = 3$ to $t = 6$:

$$\text{Avg. } I(t) = \frac{1}{6 - 3}\int_3^6 (10 + 36t - 3t^2)\,dt$$

$$= \frac{1}{3}[10t + 18t^2 - t^3]\Big|_3^6$$

$$= \frac{1}{3}[60 + 648 - 216 - (30 + 162 - 27)]$$

$$= 109 \text{ items} \tag{6-5}$$

66. $S(x) = 8(e^{0.05x} - 1)$

Average price over the interval $[40, 50]$:

$$\text{Avg. } S(x) = \frac{1}{50 - 40}\int_{40}^{50} 8(e^{0.05x} - 1)\,dx = \frac{8}{10}\int_{40}^{50}(e^{0.05x} - 1)\,dx$$

$$= \frac{4}{5}\left[\frac{e^{0.05x}}{0.05} - x\right]\Big|_{40}^{50}$$

$$= \frac{4}{5}[20e^{2.5} - 50 - (20e^2 - 40)]$$

$$= 16e^{2.5} - 16e^2 - 8 \approx \$68.70 \tag{6-5}$$

67. To find the useful life, set $R'(t) = C'(t)$:

$$20e^{-0.1t} = 3$$

$$e^{-0.1t} = \frac{3}{20}$$

$$-0.1t = \ln\left(\frac{3}{20}\right) \approx -1.897$$

$$t = 18.97 \text{ or } 19 \text{ years}$$

$$\text{Total profit} = \int_0^{19} [R'(t) - C(t)]\,dt = \int_0^{19}(20e^{-0.1t} - 3)\,dt$$

$$= 20\int_0^{19} e^{-0.1t}(-0.1)\,dt - \int_0^{19} 3\,dt = \frac{20}{-0.1}\int_0^{19} e^{-0.1t}(-0.1)\,dt - \int_0^{19} 3\,dt$$

$$= -200e^{-0.1t}\Big|_0^{19} - 3t\Big|_0^{19}$$

$$= -200e^{-1.9} + 200 - 57 \approx 113.086 \text{ or } \$113,086 \tag{6-5}$$

68. $S'(t) = 4e^{-0.08t}$, $0 \leq t \leq 24$.   Therefore,

$$S(t) = \int 4e^{-0.08t}dt = \frac{4e^{-0.08t}}{-0.08} + C = -50e^{-0.08t} + C.$$

Now, $S(0) = 0$, so
$$0 = -50e^{-0.08(0)} + C = -50 + C.$$
Thus, $C = 50$, and $S(t) = 50(1 - e^{-0.08t})$ gives the total sales after t months.

Estimated sales after 12 months:
$$S(12) = 50(1 - e^{-0.08(12)}) = 50(1 - e^{-0.96}) \approx 31 \text{ or } \$31 \text{ million.}$$

To find the time to reach $40 million in sales, solve
$$40 = 50(1 - e^{-0.08t})$$
for t.

$$0.8 = 1 - e^{-0.08t}$$
$$e^{-0.08t} = 0.2$$
$$-0.08t = \ln(0.2)$$
$$t = \frac{\ln(0.2)}{-0.08} \approx 20 \text{ months}$$

$(6-3)$

69. $\frac{dA}{dt} = -5t^{-2}$, $1 \leq t \leq 5$

$$A = \int -5t^{-2}dt = -5\int t^{-2}dt = -5 \cdot \frac{t^{-1}}{-1} + C = \frac{5}{t} + C$$

Now $A(1) = \frac{5}{1} + C = 5$.   Therefore, $C = 0$ and

$$A(t) = \frac{5}{t}$$

$$A(5) = \frac{5}{5} = 1$$

The area of the wound after 5 days is 1 cm^2.

$(6-3)$

70. The total amount of seepage during the first four years is given by:

$$T = \int_0^4 R(t)dt = \int_0^4 \frac{1000}{1 + t^2}dt = 1000\int_0^4 (1 + t)^{-2}dt = 1000 \frac{(1 + t)^{-1}}{-1}\Big|_0^4$$

$$[\text{Let } u = 1 + t, \text{ then } du = dt.] = \frac{-1000}{1 + t}\Big|_0^4 = \frac{-1000}{5} + 1000 = 800 \text{ gallons}$$

$(6-5)$

71. (A) The exponential growth law applies and we have:
$$\frac{dP}{dt} = 0.015P, \quad P(0) = 100 \text{ (million)}$$
Thus $P(t) = 100e^{0.015t}$
and $P(25) = 100e^{0.015(25)} = 100e^{0.375} \approx 145$

Assuming that the population continues to grow at the rate 1.5% per year, the population in 2025 will be approximately 145 million.

(B) Time to double:
$$100e^{0.015t} = 200$$
$$e^{0.015t} = 2$$
$$0.015t = \ln 2$$
$$t = \frac{\ln 2}{0.015} \approx 46$$

At the current growth rate it will take approximately 46 years for the population to double. (6-3)

72. Let $Q = Q(t)$ be the amount of carbon-14 present in the bone at time t. Then,

$$\frac{dQ}{dt} = -0.0001238Q \quad \text{and} \quad Q(t) = Q_0 e^{-0.0001238t},$$

where Q_0 is the amount present originally (i.e., at the time the animal died). We want to find t such that $Q(t) = 0.04Q_0$.

$$0.04Q_0 = Q_0 e^{-0.0001238t}$$
$$e^{-0.0001238t} = 0.04$$
$$-0.0001238t = \ln 0.04$$
$$t = \frac{\ln 0.04}{-0.0001238} \approx 26{,}000 \text{ years}$$ (6-3)

73. $N'(t) = 7e^{-0.1t}$ and $N(0) = 25$.

$$N(t) = \int 7e^{-0.1t}dt = 7\int e^{-0.1t}dt = \frac{7}{-0.1}\int e^{-0.1t}(-0.1)\,dt$$

$$= -70e^{-0.1t} + C, \ 0 \le t \le 15$$

Given $N(0) = 25$: $25 = -70e^0 + C = -70 + C$

Hence, $C = 95$ and $N(t) = 95 - 70e^{-0.1t}$. The student would be expected to type $N(15) = 95 - 70e^{-0.1(15)} = 95 - 70e^{-1.5} \approx 79$ words per minute after completing the course. (6-3)

EXERCISE 7-1

Things to remember:

1. AREA BETWEEN TWO CURVES
   If f and g are continuous and $f(x) \geq g(x)$ over the interval $[a, b]$, then the area bounded by $y = f(x)$ and $y = g(x)$, for $a \leq x \leq b$, is given exactly by:

   $$A = \int_a^b [f(x) - g(x)]dx.$$

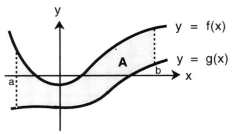

2. GINI INDEX OF INCOME CONCENTRATION
   If $y = f(x)$ is the equation of a Lorenz curve, then the
   $$\text{Gini Index} = 2\int_0^1 [x - f(x)]dx.$$

---

1. $A = \int_a^b g(x)dx$

3. $A = \int_a^b [-h(x)]dx)$

5. Since the shaded region in Figure (c) is below the x-axis, $h(x) \leq 0$. Thus, $\int_a^b h(x)dx$ represents the negative of the area of the region.

7. $A = \int_0^4 -[-2x - 1]dx$

$= \int_0^4 [2x + 1]dx = (x^2 + x)\Big|_0^4 = 20$

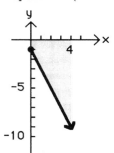

9. $A = \int_{-1}^0 (x^2 + 2)dx = \left(\dfrac{x^3}{3} + 2x\right)\Big|_{-1}^0$

$= 0 - \left(-\dfrac{1}{3} - 2\right) = \dfrac{7}{3} \approx 2.333$

$y = x^2 + 2$

11. $A = \int_0^2 [x^3 + 1]dx = \left(\dfrac{1}{4}x^4 + x\right)\Big|_0^2 = 4 + 2 = 6$

13. $A = \int_{-1}^{2} e^x dx = e^x \Big|_{-1}^{2}$

$\qquad = e^2 - e^{-1} \approx 7.021$

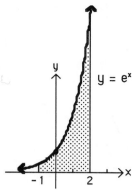

$y = e^x$

15. $A = \int_{0.5}^{1} -\left[-\dfrac{1}{t}\right] dt = \int_{0.5}^{1} \dfrac{1}{t} dt = \ln t \Big|_{0.5}^{1} = \ln 1 - \ln(0.5) \approx 0.693$

17. $A = \int_{a}^{b} [-f(x)] dx$ **19.** $a = \int_{b}^{c} f(x) dx + \int_{c}^{d} [-f(x)] dx$

21. $A = \int_{c}^{d} [f(x) - g(x)] dx$ **23.** $A = \int_{a}^{b} [f(x) - g(x)] dx + \int_{b}^{c} [g(x) - f(x)] dx$

25. Find the x-coordinates of the points of intersection of the two curves on $[a, d]$ by solving the equation $f(x) = g(x)$, $a \leq x \leq d$, to find $x = b$ and $x = c$. Then note that $f(x) \geq g(x)$ on $[a, b]$, $g(x) \geq f(x)$ on $[b, c]$ and $f(x) \geq g(x)$ on $[c, d]$.

Thus,

$$\text{Area} = \int_{a}^{b} [f(x) - g(x)] dx + \int_{b}^{c} [g(x) - f(x)] dx + \int_{c}^{d} [f(x) - g(x)] dx$$

27. $A = A_1 + A_2 = \int_{-2}^{0} -x dx + \int_{0}^{1} -(-x) dx$

$\qquad = \int_{-2}^{0} x dx + \int_{0}^{1} x dx$

$\qquad = -\dfrac{x^2}{2} \Big|_{-2}^{0} + \dfrac{x^2}{2} \Big|_{0}^{1}$

$\qquad = -\left(0 - \dfrac{(-2)^2}{2}\right) + \left(\dfrac{1^2}{2} - 0\right)$

$\qquad = 2 + \dfrac{1}{2} = \dfrac{5}{2} = 2.5$

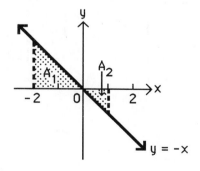

$y = -x$

29. $A = A_1 + A_2 = \int_{0}^{2} -(x^2 - 4) dx + \int_{2}^{3} (x^2 - 4) dx$

$\qquad = \int_{0}^{2} (4 - x^2) dx + \int_{2}^{3} (x^2 - 4) dx$

$\qquad = \left(4x - \dfrac{x^3}{3}\right) \Big|_{0}^{2} + \left(\dfrac{x^3}{3} - 4x\right) \Big|_{2}^{3}$

$\qquad = \left(8 - \dfrac{8}{3}\right) + \left(\dfrac{27}{3} - 12\right) - \left(\dfrac{8}{3} - 8\right)$

$\qquad = 13 - \dfrac{16}{3} = \dfrac{39}{3} - \dfrac{16}{3} = \dfrac{23}{3} \approx 7.667$

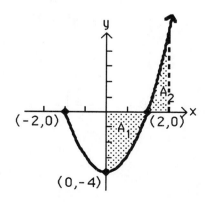

$(-2,0)$ $(0,-4)$ $(2,0)$

31. $A = A_1 + A_2 = \int_{-2}^{0} (x^2 - 3x)\, dx + \int_{0}^{2} -(x^2 - 3x)\, dx$

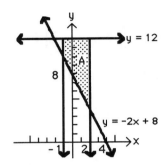

$$= \int_{-2}^{0} (x^2 - 3x)\, dx + \int_{0}^{2} (3x - x^2)\, dx$$

$$= \left(\frac{1}{3}x^3 - \frac{3}{2}x^2 \right)\Big|_{-2}^{0} + \left(\frac{3}{2}x^2 - \frac{1}{3}x^3 \right)\Big|_{0}^{2}$$

$$= 0 - \left(-\frac{8}{3} - 6 \right) + \left(6 - \frac{8}{3} \right) - 0 = 12$$

33. $A = \int_{-1}^{2} [12 - (-2x + 8)]\, dx = \int_{-1}^{2} (2x + 4)\, dx$

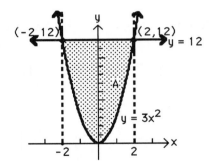

$$= \left(\frac{2x^2}{2} + 4x \right)\Big|_{-1}^{2} = (x^2 + 4x)\Big|_{-1}^{2}$$

$$= (4 + 8) - (1 - 4)$$

$$= 12 + 3 = 15$$

35. $A = \int_{-2}^{2} (12 - 3x^2)\, dx = \left(12x - \frac{3x^3}{3} \right)\Big|_{-2}^{2}$

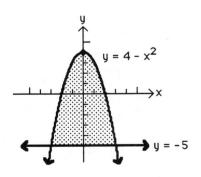

$$= (12x - x^3)\Big|_{-2}^{2}$$

$$= (12 \cdot 2 - 2^3) - [12 \cdot (-2) - (-2)^3]$$

$$= 16 - (-16) = 32$$

37. $(3, -5)$ and $(-3, -5)$ are the points of intersection.

$$A = \int_{-3}^{3} [4 - x^2 - (-5)]\, dx$$

$$= \int_{-3}^{3} (9 - x^2)\, dx = \left(9x - \frac{x^3}{3} \right)\Big|_{-3}^{3}$$

$$= \left(9 \cdot 3 - \frac{3^3}{3} \right) - \left(9(-3) - \frac{(-3)^3}{3} \right)$$

$$= 18 + 18 = 36$$

39. $A = \int_{-1}^{2} [(x^2 + 1) - (2x - 2)] \, dx$

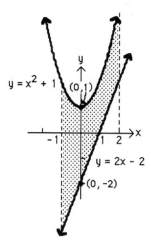

$y = x^2 + 1 \quad (0,1)$

$y = 2x - 2$

$(0, -2)$

$\quad = \int_{-1}^{2} (x^2 - 2x + 3) \, dx = \left(\dfrac{x^3}{3} - x^2 + 3x \right)\Big|_{-1}^{2}$

$\quad = \left(\dfrac{8}{3} - 4 + 6 \right) - \left(-\dfrac{1}{3} - 1 - 3 \right)$

$\quad = 3 - 4 + 6 + 1 + 3 = 9$

41. $A = \int_{1}^{2} \left[e^{0.5x} - \left(-\dfrac{1}{x} \right) \right] dx$

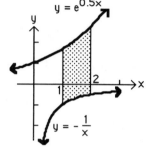

$y = e^{0.5x}$

$y = -\dfrac{1}{x}$

$\quad = \int_{1}^{2} \left(e^{0.5x} + \dfrac{1}{x} \right) dx$

$\quad = \left(\dfrac{e^{0.5x}}{0.5} + \ln|x| \right)\Big|_{1}^{2}$

$\quad = 2e + \ln 2 - 2e^{0.5}$

$\quad \approx 2.832$

43. The graphs of $y = 3 - 5x - 2x^2$ and $y = 2x^2 + 3x - 2$ are shown at the right. The x-coordinates of the points of intersection are: $x_1 = -2.5$, $x_2 = 0.5$.

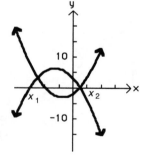

$A = \int_{-2.5}^{0.5} [(3 - 5x - 2x^2) - (2x^2 + 3x - 2)] \, dx$

$\quad = \int_{-2.5}^{0.5} (5 - 8x - 4x^2) \, dx = \left(5x - 4x^2 - \dfrac{4}{3} x^3 \right)\Big|_{-2.5}^{0.5}$

$\quad\quad\quad\quad = 1.333 + 16.667 = 18$

45. The graphs of $y = -0.5x + 2.25$ and $y = \dfrac{1}{x}$ are shown below. The x-coordinates of the points of intersection are: $x_1 = 0.5$, $x_2 = 4$.

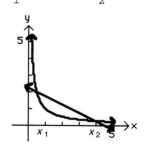

$A = \int_{0.5}^{4} \left[(-0.5x + 2.25) - \left(\dfrac{1}{x} \right) \right] dx$

$\quad = \left(-\dfrac{1}{4} x^2 + \dfrac{9}{4} x - \ln x \right)\Big|_{0.5}^{4}$

$\quad = [-4 + 9 - \ln 4] - [-0.0625 + 1.125 - \ln(0.5)]$

$\quad \approx 1.858$

47. The graphs of $y = e^x$ and $y = e^{-x}$, $0 \le x \le 4$, are shown at the right.

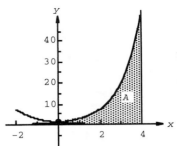

$$A = \int_0^4 (e^x - e^{-x})\, dx = (e^x + e^{-x})\Big|_0^4$$

$$= e^4 + e^{-4} - (1 + 1)$$

$$\approx 52.616$$

49. The graphs are given at the right. To find the points of intersection, solve:

$$x^3 = 4x$$
$$x^3 - 4x = 0$$
$$x(x^2 - 4) = 0$$
$$x(x + 2)(x - 2) = 0$$

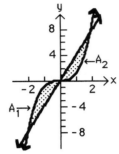

Thus, the points of intersection are $(-2, -8)$, $(0, 0)$, and $(2, 8)$.

$$A = A_1 + A_2 = \int_{-2}^0 (x^3 - 4x)\, dx + \int_0^2 (4x - x^3)\, dx$$

$$= \left(\frac{x^4}{4} - 2x^2\right)\Big|_{-2}^0 + \left(2x^2 - \frac{x^4}{4}\right)\Big|_0^2$$

$$= 0 - \left[\frac{(-2)^4}{4} - 2(-2)^2\right] + \left[2(2^2) - \frac{2^4}{4}\right] - 0$$

$$= -4 + 8 + 8 - 4 = 8$$

51. The graphs are given at the right. To find the points of intersection, solve:

$$x^3 - 3x^2 - 9x + 12 = x + 12$$
$$x^3 - 3x^2 - 10x = 0$$
$$x(x^2 - 3x - 10) = 0$$
$$x(x - 5)(x + 2) = 0$$
$$x = -2, \ x = 0, \ x = 5$$

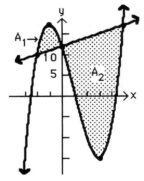

Thus, $(-2, 10)$, $(0, 12)$, and $(5, 17)$ are the points of intersection.

$$A = A_1 + A_2$$

$$= \int_{-2}^0 [x^3 - 3x^2 - 9x + 12 - (x + 12)]\, dx$$

$$\qquad\qquad + \int_0^5 [x + 12 - (x^3 - 3x^2 - 9x + 12)]\, dx$$

$$= \int_{-2}^0 (x^3 - 3x^2 - 10x)\, dx + \int_0^5 (-x^3 + 3x^2 + 10x)\, dx$$

$$= \left(\frac{x^4}{4} - x^3 - 5x^2\right)\Big|_{-2}^0 + \left(-\frac{x^4}{4} + x^3 + 5x^2\right)\Big|_0^5$$

$$= -\left[\frac{(-2)^4}{4} - (-2)^3 - 5(-2)^2\right] + \left(\frac{-5^4}{4} + 5^3 + 5 \cdot 5^2\right)$$

$$= 8 + \frac{375}{4} = \frac{407}{4} = 101.75$$

53. The graphs are given at the right. To find the points of intersection, solve:

$$x^4 - 4x^2 + 1 = x^2 - 3$$
$$x^4 - 5x^2 + 4 = 0$$
$$(x^2 - 4)(x^2 - 1) = 0$$
$$x = -2, -1, 1, 2$$

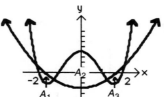

$$A = A_1 + A_2 + A_3$$

$$= \int_{-2}^{-1} [(x^2 - 3) - (x^4 - 4x^2 + 1)]\,dx + \int_{-1}^{1} [(x^4 - 4x^2 + 1) - (x^2 - 3)]\,dx$$

$$+ \int_{1}^{2} [(x^2 - 3) - (x^4 - 4x^2 + 1)]\,dx$$

$$= \int_{-2}^{-1} (-x^4 + 5x^2 - 4)\,dx + \int_{-1}^{1} (x^4 - 5x^2 + 4)\,dx + \int_{1}^{2} (-x^4 + 5x^2 - 4)\,dx$$

$$= \left(-\frac{x^5}{5} + \frac{5}{3}x^3 - 4x\right)\Big|_{-2}^{-1} + \left(\frac{x^5}{5} - \frac{5}{3}x^3 + 4x\right)\Big|_{-1}^{1} + \left(-\frac{x^5}{5} + \frac{5}{3}x^3 - 4x\right)\Big|_{1}^{2}$$

$$= \left(\frac{1}{5} - \frac{5}{3} + 4\right) - \left(\frac{32}{5} - \frac{40}{3} + 8\right) + \left(\frac{1}{5} - \frac{5}{3} + 4\right) - \left(-\frac{1}{5} + \frac{5}{3} - 4\right)$$

$$+ \left(-\frac{32}{5} + \frac{40}{3} - 8\right) - \left(-\frac{1}{5} + \frac{5}{3} - 4\right) = 8$$

55. The graphs are given below. The x-coordinates of the points of intersection are: $x_1 = -2$, $x_2 = 0.5$, $x_3 = 2$

$$A = A_1 + A_2$$

$$= \int_{-2}^{0.5} [(x^3 - x^2 + 2) - (-x^3 + 8x - 2)]\,dx$$

$$+ \int_{0.5}^{2} [(-x^3 + 8x - 2) - (x^3 - x^2 + 2)]\,dx$$

$$= \int_{-2}^{0.5} (2x^3 - x^2 - 8x + 4)\,dx + \int_{0.5}^{2} (-2x^3 + x^2 + 8x - 4)\,dx$$

$$= \left(\frac{1}{2}x^4 - \frac{1}{3}x^3 - 4x^2 + 4x\right)\Big|_{-2}^{0.5} + \left(-\frac{1}{2}x^4 + \frac{1}{3}x^3 + 4x^2 - 4x\right)\Big|_{0.5}^{2}$$

$$= \left(\frac{1}{32} - \frac{1}{24} - 1 + 2\right) - \left(8 + \frac{8}{3} - 16 - 8\right)$$

$$+ \left(-8 + \frac{8}{3} + 16 - 8\right) - \left(-\frac{1}{32} + \frac{1}{24} + 1 - 2\right)$$

$$= 18 + \frac{1}{16} - \frac{1}{12} \approx 17.979$$

57. The graphs are given at the right. The x-coordinates of the points of intersection are: $x_1 \approx -1.924$, $x_2 \approx 1.373$

$$A = \int_{-1.924}^{1.373} [(3 - 2x) - e^{-x}]\,dx$$

$$= (3x - x^2 + e^{-x}) \Big|_{-1.924}^{1.373}$$

$$\approx 2.487 - (-2.626) = 5.113$$

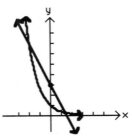

59. The graphs are given at the right. The x-coordinates of the points of intersection are: $x_1 \approx -2.247$, $x_2 \approx 0.264$, $x_3 \approx 1.439$

$$A = A_1 + A_2 = \int_{-2.247}^{0.264} [e^x - (5x - x^3)]\,dx$$

$$+ \int_{0.264}^{1.439} [5x - x^3 - e^x]\,dx$$

$$= \left(e^x - \frac{5}{2}x^2 + \frac{1}{4}x^4\right) \Big|_{-2.247}^{0.264} + \left(\frac{5}{2}x^2 - \frac{1}{4}x^4 - e^x\right) \Big|_{0.264}^{1.439}$$

$$\approx (1.129) - (-6.144) + (-0.112) - (-1.129) = 8.290$$

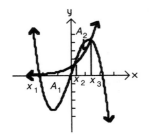

61. $y = e^{-x}$; $y = \sqrt{\ln x}$; $2 \le x \le 5$

The graphs of $y_1 = e^{-x}$ and $y_2 = \sqrt{\ln x}$ are

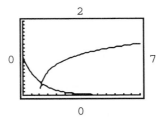

```
fnInt(Y2-Y1,X,2,
5)
          3.165511884
```

Thus, $A = \int_2^5 (\sqrt{\ln x} - e^{-x})\,dx \approx 3.166$

63. $y = e^{x^2}$; $y = x + 2$

The graphs of $y_1 = e^{x^2}$ and $y_2 = x + 2$ are

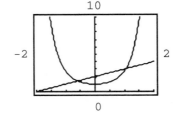

```
fnInt(Y2-Y1,X,-0
.588,1.057)
          1.385384053
```

The curves intersect at

$x \approx -0.588$ and $x \approx 1.057$

$y \approx 1.412$ and $y \approx 3.057$

$$\int_{-0.588}^{1.057} (x + 2 - e^{x^2})\,dx \approx 1.385$$

65. $\int_5^{10} R(t)\,dt = \int_5^{10}\left(\dfrac{100}{t+10}+10\right)dt = 100\int_5^{10}\dfrac{1}{t+10}\,dt + \int_5^{10} 10\,dt$

$$= 100\ \ln(t+10)\Big|_5^{10} + 10t\Big|_5^{10}$$

$$= 100\ \ln 20 - 100\ \ln 15 + 10(10-5)$$
$$= 100\ \ln 20 - 100\ \ln 15 + 50 \approx 79$$

The total production from the end of the fifth year to the end of the tenth year is approximately 79 thousand barrels.

67. To find the useful life, set $R'(t) = C'(t)$ and solve for t:

$$9e^{-0.3t} = 2$$

$$e^{-0.3t} = \dfrac{2}{9}$$

$$-0.3t = \ln\dfrac{2}{9}$$

$$-0.3t \approx -1.5$$

$$t \approx 5 \text{ years}$$

$$\int_0^5 [R'(t) - C'(t)]\,dt] = \int_0^5 [9e^{-0.3t} - 2]\,dt$$

$$= 9\int_0^5 e^{-0.3t}\,dt - \int_0^5 2\,dt = \dfrac{9}{-0.3}\ e^{-0.3t}\Big|_0^5 - 2t\Big|_0^5$$

$$= -30e^{-1.5} + 30 - 10$$
$$= 20 - 30e^{-1.5} \approx 13.306$$

The total profit over the useful life of the game is approximately $13,306.

69. For 1935: $f(x) = x^{2.4}$

Gini Index $= 2\int_0^1 [x - f(x)] = 2\int_0^1 (x - x^{2.4})\,dx$

$$= 2\left(\dfrac{x^2}{2} - \dfrac{x^{3.4}}{3.4}\right)\Big|_0^1$$

$$= 2\left(\dfrac{1}{2} - \dfrac{1}{3.4}\right) \approx 0.412$$

For 1947: $g(x) = x^{1.6}$

Gini Index $= 2\int_0^1 [x - g(x)]\,dx = 2\int_0^1 (x - x^{1.6})\,dx$

$$= 2\left(\dfrac{x^2}{2} - \dfrac{x^{2.6}}{2.6}\right)\Big|_0^1$$

$$= 2\left(\dfrac{1}{2} - \dfrac{1}{2.6}\right) \approx 0.231$$

Interpretation: Income was more equally distributed in 1947.

71. For 1963: $f(x) = x^{10}$

Gini Index $= 2\int_0^1 [x - f(x)]\,dx = 2\int_0^1 (x - x^{10})\,dx$

$$= 2\left(\frac{x^2}{2} - \frac{x^{11}}{11}\right)\Big|_0^1$$

$$= 2\left(\frac{1}{2} - \frac{1}{11}\right) \approx 0.818$$

For 1983: $g(x) = x^{12}$

Gini Index $= 2\int_0^1 [x - g(x)]\,dx = 2\int_0^1 (x - x^{12})\,dx$

$$= 2\left(\frac{x^2}{2} - \frac{x^{13}}{13}\right)\Big|_0^1$$

$$= 2\left(\frac{1}{2} - \frac{1}{13}\right) \approx 0.846$$

Interpretation: Total assets were less equally distributed in 1983.

73. (A)

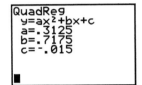

Lorenz curve:

$f(x) = 0.3125x^2 + 0.7175x - 0.015.$

(B) Gini Index:

$$2\int_0^1 [x - f(x)]\,dx \approx 0.104$$

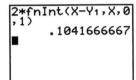

75. $W(t) = \int_0^{10} W'(t)\,dt = \int_0^{10} 0.3e^{0.1t}\,dt = 0.3\int_0^{10} e^{0.1t}\,dt$

$$= \frac{0.3}{0.1}\, e^{0.1t}\Big|_0^{10} = 3e^{0.1t}\Big|_0^{10} = 3e - 3 \approx 5.15$$

Total weight gain during the first 10 hours is approximately 5.15 grams.

77. $V = \int_2^4 \frac{15}{t}\,dt = 15\int_2^4 \frac{1}{t}\,dt = 15\ln t\Big|_2^4$

$$= 15\ln 4 - 15\ln 2 = 15\ln\left(\frac{4}{2}\right) = 15\ln 2 \approx 10$$

Average number of words learned during the second 2 hours is 10.

EXERCISE 7-2

Things to remember:

1. PROBABILITY DENSITY FUNCTION

    A function f which satisfies the following three conditions:

    a. $f(x) \geq 0$ for all real x.

    b. The area under the graph of f over the interval $(-\infty, \infty)$ is exactly 1.

<u>c</u>. If [c, d] is a subinterval of (-∞, ∞), then the probability that the outcome x of an experiment will be in the interval [c, d], denoted Probability (c ≤ x ≤ d), is given by

$$\text{Probability } (c \le x \le d) = \int_c^d f(x)\, dx$$

$$\int_c^d f(x)\, dx = \text{Probability } (c \le x \le d)$$

2. TOTAL INCOME FOR A CONTINUOUS INCOME STREAM

If $f(t)$ is the rate of flow of a continuous income stream, then the TOTAL INCOME produced during the time period from $t = a$ to $t = b$ is:

$$\text{Total income} = \int_a^b f(t)\, dt$$

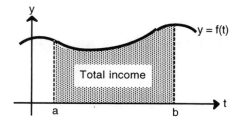

3. FUTURE VALUE OF A CONTINUOUS INCOME STREAM

If $f(t)$ is the rate of flow of a continuous income stream, $0 \le t \le T$, and if the income is continuously invested at a rate r, compounded continuously, then the FUTURE VALUE, FV, at the end of T years is given by:

$$FV = \int_0^T f(t)\, e^{r(T-t)}\, dt = e^{rT} \int_0^T f(t)\, e^{-rt} dt$$

The future value of a continuous income stream is the total value of all money produced by the continuous income stream (income and interest) at the end of T years.

4. CONSUMERS' SURPLUS

If $(\overline{x}, \overline{p})$ is a point on the graph of the price-demand equation $p = D(x)$ for a particular product, then the CONSUMERS' SURPLUS, CS, at a price level of $\overline{p}$ is

$$CS = \int_0^{\overline{x}} [D(x) - \overline{p}]\, dx$$

which is the area between $p = \overline{p}$ and $p = D(x)$ from $x = 0$ to $x = \overline{x}$.

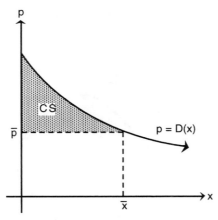

Consumers' surplus represents the total savings to consumers who are willing to pay more than $\overline{p}$ for the product but are still able to buy the product for $\overline{p}$.

5. PRODUCERS' SURPLUS

If $(\overline{x}, \overline{p})$ is a point on the graph of the price-supply equation $p = S(x)$, then the PRODUCERS' SURPLUS, PS, at a price level of $\overline{p}$ is

$$PS = \int_0^{\overline{x}} [\overline{p} - S(x)] \, dx$$

which is the area between $p = \overline{p}$ and $p = S(x)$ from $x = 0$ to $x = \overline{x}$.

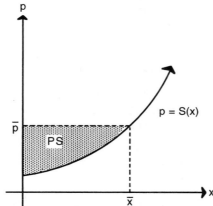

Producers' surplus represents the total gain to producers who are willing to supply units at a lower price than $\overline{p}$ but are still able to supply units at $\overline{p}$.

6. EQUILIBRIUM PRICE AND EQUILIBRIUM QUANTITY

If $p = D(x)$ and $p = S(x)$ are the price-demand and the price-supply equations, respectively, for a product and if $(\overline{x}, \overline{p})$ is the point of intersection of these equations, then $\overline{p}$ is called the EQUILIBRIUM PRICE and $\overline{x}$ is called the EQUILIBRIUM QUANTITY.

1. $\int_0^5 e^{-0.08t} dt = \dfrac{e^{-0.08t}}{-0.08}\Big|_0^5 = -12.5e^{-0.08t}\Big|_0^5$

$$= -12.5e^{-0.4} + 12.5$$
$$\approx -8.38 + 12.5 = 4.12$$

3. $\int_0^{30} e^{0.06t} \cdot e^{0.12(30-t)} dt = \int_0^{30} e^{0.06t} e^{3.6-0.12t} dt$

$$= \int_0^{30} e^{3.6-0.06t} dt = e^{3.6} \int_0^{30} e^{-0.06t} dt$$

$$= \frac{e^{3.6}}{-0.06} e^{-0.06t}\Big|_0^{30}$$

$$= -\frac{e^{3.6}}{0.06}[e^{-1.8} - 1] \approx 509.14$$

5. (A) $\int_0^8 e^{0.07(8-t)} dt = \int_0^8 e^{0.56 - 0.07t} dt = \int_0^8 e^{0.56} \cdot e^{-0.07t} dt$

$$= e^{0.56} \int_0^8 e^{-0.07t} dt = \frac{e^{0.56}}{-0.07} e^{-0.07t}\Big|_0^8$$

$$= -\frac{e^{0.56}}{0.07}[e^{-0.56} - 1] \approx 10.72$$

(B) $\int_0^8 (e^{0.56} - e^{0.07t}) dt = (e^{0.56}) t\Big|_0^8 - \dfrac{e^{0.07t}}{0.07}\Big|_0^8$

$$= 8e^{0.56} - \frac{1}{0.07}[e^{0.56} - 1] \approx 3.28$$

(C) $e^{0.56} \int_0^8 e^{-0.07t} dt \approx 10.72$ as in (A)

7. $f(x) = \begin{cases} \dfrac{2}{(x + 2)^2}, & x \geq 0 \\ 0 & x < 0 \end{cases}$

(A) Probability $(0 \leq x \leq 6) = \int_0^6 f(x)\, dx = \int_0^6 \dfrac{2}{(x + 2)^2} dx$

$$= 2\frac{(x + 2)^{-1}}{-1}\Big|_0^6 = \frac{-2}{(x + 2)}\Big|_0^6$$

$$= -\frac{1}{4} + 1 = \frac{3}{4} = 0.75$$

Thus, Probability $(0 \leq x \leq 6) = 0.75$

(B) Probability $(6 \leq x \leq 12) = \int_6^{12} f(x)\, dx = \int_6^{12} \dfrac{2}{(x + 2)^2} dx$

$$= \frac{-2}{x + 2}\Big|_6^{12} = -\frac{1}{7} + \frac{1}{4} = \frac{3}{28} \approx 0.11$$

(C)

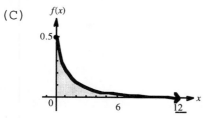

9. We want to find d such that

Probability $(0 \le x \le d) = \int_0^d f(x)\,dx = 0.8$:

$$\int_0^d f(x)\,dx = \int_0^d \frac{2}{(x+2)^2}\,dx = \left.-\frac{2}{x+2}\right|_0^d = \frac{-2}{d+2} + 1 = \frac{d}{d+2}$$

Now, $\dfrac{d}{d+2} = 0.8$

$$d = 0.8d + 1.6$$
$$0.2d = 1.6$$
$$d = 8 \text{ years}$$

11. $f(t) = \begin{cases} 0.01e^{-0.01t} & \text{if} \quad t \ge 0 \\ 0 & \text{otherwise} \end{cases}$

(A) Since t is in months, the probability of failure during the warranty period of the first year is

Probability $(0 \le t \le 12) = \int_0^{12} f(t)\,dt = \int_0^{12} 0.01e^{-0.01t}\,dt$

$$= \left.\frac{0.01}{-0.01}e^{-0.01t}\right|_0^{12} = -1(e^{-0.12} - 1) \approx 0.11$$

(B) Probability $(12 \le t \le 24 = \int_{12}^{24} 0.01e^{-0.01t}\,dt = \left.-1e^{-0.01t}\right|_{12}^{24}$

$$= -1(e^{-0.24} - e^{-0.12}) \approx 0.10$$

13. Probability $(0 \le t \le \infty) = 1 = \int_0^\infty f(t)\,dt$

But, $\int_0^\infty f(t)\,dt = \int_0^{12} f(t)\,dt + \int_{12}^\infty f(t)\,dt$

Thus, Probability $(t \ge 12) = 1 - \text{Probability } (0 \le t \le 12)$
$$\approx 1 - 0.11 = 0.89$$

15. $f(t) = 2500$

Total income $= \int_0^5 2500\,dt = \left.2500t\right|_0^5 = \$12,500$

17.

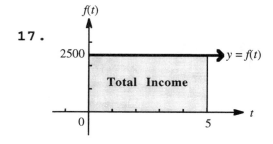

If $f(t)$ is the rate of flow of a continuous income stream, then the total income produced from 0 to 5 years is the area under the curve $y = f(t)$ from $t = 0$ to $t = 5$.

19. $f(t) = 400e^{0.05t}$

Total income $= \int_0^3 400e^{0.05t}\,dt = \dfrac{400}{0.05}e^{0.05t}\Big|_0^3 = 8000(e^{0.15} - 1) \approx \$1295$

21.

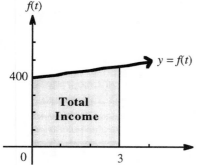

If $f(t)$ is the rate of flow of a continuous income stream, then the total income produced from 0 to 3 years is the area under the curve $y = f(t)$ from $t = 0$ to $t = 3$.

23. $f(t) = 2,000e^{0.05t}$

The amount in the account after 40 years is given by:

$$\int_0^{40} 2,000e^{0.05t}\,dt = 40,000e^{0.05t}\Big|_0^{40} = 295,562.24 - 40,000 \approx \$255,562$$

Since $\$2,000 \times 40 = \$80,000$ was deposited into the account, the interest earned is:
$$\$255,562 - \$80,000 = \$175,562$$

25. $f(t) = 1,650e^{-0.02t}$, $r = 0.0625$, $T = 4$.

$FV = e^{0.0625(4)} \int_0^4 1,650e^{-0.02t}e^{-0.0625t}\,dt$

$= 1,650e^{0.25} \int_0^4 e^{-0.0825t}\,dt$

$= 1,650e^{0.25}\dfrac{e^{-0.0825t}}{-0.0825}\Big|_0^4 = 20,000(e^{0.25} - e^{0.08}) \approx \$7,218.$

27. Total Income $= \int_0^4 1,650e^{-0.02t}\,dt = \dfrac{1650}{-0.02}e^{-0.02t}\Big|_0^4$

$= -82,500(e^{-0.08} - 1) \approx \$6,343.$

From Problem 25,
Interest earned $= \$7,218 - \$6,343 = \$875$

29. Clothing store: $f(t) = 12,000$, $r = 0.1$, $T = 5$.

$FV = e^{0.1(5)} \int_0^5 12,000e^{-0.1t}\,dt = 12,000e^{0.5} \int_0^5 e^{-0.1t}\,dt$

$= \dfrac{12,000e^{0.5}}{-0.1}e^{-0.1t}\Big|_0^5 = -120,000e^{0.5}(e^{-0.5} - 1)$

$= 120,000(e^{0.5} - 1) \approx \$77,847$

Computer store: $g(t) = 10,000e^{0.05t}$, $r = 0.1$, $T = 5$.

$$FV = e^{0.1(5)} \int_0^5 10,000e^{0.05t}e^{-0.1t}dt = 10,000e^{0.5}\int_0^5 e^{-0.05t}dt$$

$$= \frac{10,000e^{0.5}}{-0.05}e^{-0.05t}\Big|_0^5 = -200,000e^{0.5}(e^{-0.25} - 1)$$

$$= 200,000(e^{0.5} - e^{0.25}) \approx \$72,939$$

The clothing store is the better investment.

31. Bond: $P = \$10,000$, $r = 0.08$, $t = 5$.
$FV = 10,000e^{0.08(5)} = 10,000e^{0.4} \approx \$14,918$
Business: $f(t) = 2000$, $r = 0.08$, $T = 5$.
$$FV = e^{0.08(5)}\int_0^5 2000e^{-0.08t}dt = 2000e^{0.4}\int_0^5 e^{-0.08t}dt$$

$$= \frac{2000e^{0.4}}{-0.08}e^{-0.08t}\Big|_0^5 = -25,000e^{0.4}(e^{-0.4} - 1)$$

$$= 25,000(e^{0.4} - 1) \approx \$12,296$$

The bond is the better investment.

33. $f(t) = 9,000$, $r = 0.0695$, $T = 8$.
$$FV = e^{0.0695(8)}\int_0^8 9000e^{-0.0695t}dt$$

$$= 9000e^{0.556}\int_0^8 e^{-0.0695t} = \frac{9000e^{0.556}}{-0.0695}e^{-0.0695t}\Big]_0^8$$

$$\approx -225,800.78(e^{-0.556} - 1) \approx \$96,304.$$

The relationship between present value (PV) and future value (FV) at a continuously compounded interest rate r (expressed as a decimal) for t years is:

$$FV = PVe^{rt} \quad \text{or} \quad PV = FVe^{-rt}$$

Thus, we have:

$$PV = 96,304e^{-0.0695(8)} = 96,304e^{-0.556} \approx \$55,230$$

35. $f(t) = k$, rate r (expressed as a decimal), years T:
$$FV = e^{rT}\int_0^T ke^{-rt}dt = ke^{rT}\int_0^T e^{-rt}dt = \frac{ke^{rT}}{-r}e^{-rt}\Big|_0^T$$

$$= -\frac{k}{r}e^{rT}(e^{-rT} - 1) = \frac{k}{r}(e^{rT} - 1)$$

37. $D(x) = 400 - \dfrac{1}{20}x$, $\bar{p} = 150$

First, find $\bar{x}$: $150 = 400 - \dfrac{1}{20}\bar{x}$

$$\bar{x} = 5000$$

$$CS = \int_0^{5000}\left[400 - \frac{1}{20}x - 150\right]dx = \int_0^{5000}\left(250 - \frac{1}{20}x\right)dx$$

$$= \left(250x - \frac{1}{40}x^2\right)\Big|_0^{5000} = \$625,000$$

39.

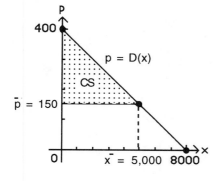

The shaded area is the consumers' surplus and represents the total savings to consumers who are willing to pay more than $150 for a product but are still able to buy the product for $150.

41. $p = S(x) = 10 + 0.1x + 0.0003x^2$, $\overline{p} = 67$.

First find $\overline{x}$: $67 = 10 + 0.1\overline{x} + 0.0003\overline{x}^2$

$$0.0003\overline{x}^2 + 0.1\overline{x} - 57 = 0$$

$$\overline{x} = \frac{-0.1 + \sqrt{0.01 + 0.0684}}{0.0006}$$

$$= \frac{-0.1 + 0.28}{0.0006} = 300$$

$$PS = \int_0^{300} [67 - (10 + 0.1x + 0.0003x^2)]\,dx$$

$$= \int_0^{300} (57 - 0.1x - 0.0003x^2)\,dx$$

$$= (57x - 0.05x^2 - 0.0001x^3)\,\Big|_0^{300} = \$9,900$$

43.

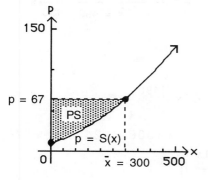

The area of the region PS is the producers' surplus and represents the total gain to producers who are willing to supply units at a lower price than $67 but are still able to supply the product at $67.

45. $p = D(x) = 50 - 0.1x$; $p = S(x) = 11 + 0.05x$

Equilibrium price: $D(x) = S(x)$

$$50 - 0.1x = 11 + 0.05x$$

$$39 = 0.15x$$

$$x = 260$$

Thus, $\overline{x} = 260$ and $\overline{p} = 50 - 0.1(260) = 24$.

$$CS = \int_0^{260} [(50 - 0.1x) - 24]\,dx = \int_0^{260} (26 - 0.1x)\,dx$$

$$= (26x - 0.05x^2)\Big|_0^{260}$$

$$= \$3,380$$

$$PS = \int_0^{260} [24 - (11 + 0.05x)]\,dx = \int_0^{260} [13 - 0.05x]\,dx$$

$$= (13x - 0.025x^2)\Big|_0^{260}$$

$$= \$1,690$$

47. $D(x) = 80e^{-0.001x}$ and $S(x) = 30e^{0.001x}$

Equilibrium price: $D(x) = S(x)$

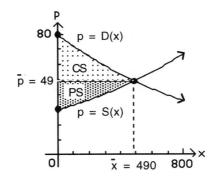

$$80e^{-0.001x} = 30e^{0.001x}$$

$$e^{0.002x} = \frac{8}{3}$$

$$0.002x = \ln\left(\frac{8}{3}\right)$$

$$\overline{x} = \frac{\ln\left(\dfrac{8}{3}\right)}{0.002} \approx 490$$

Thus, $\overline{p} = 30e^{0.001(490)} \approx 49$.

$$CS = \int_0^{490} [80e^{-0.001x} - 49]\,dx = \left(\frac{80e^{-0.001x}}{-0.001} - 49x\right)\Big|_0^{490}$$

$$= -80,000e^{-0.49} + 80,000 - 24,010 \approx \$6,980$$

$$PS = \int_0^{490} [49 - 30e^{0.001x}]\,dx = \left(49x - \frac{30e^{0.001x}}{0.001}\right)\Big|_0^{490}$$

$$= 24,010 - 30,000(e^{0.49} - 1) \approx \$5,041$$

49. $D(x) = 80 - 0.04x;\; S(x) = 30e^{0.001x}$

Equilibrium price: $D(x) = S(x)$

$$80 - 0.04x = 30e^{0.001x}$$

Using a graphing utility, we find that

$$\overline{x} \approx 614$$

Thus, $\overline{p} = 80 - (0.04)614 \approx 55$

$$CS = \int_0^{614}[80 - 0.04x - 55]\,dx = \int_0^{614}(25 - 0.04x)\,dx$$

$$= (25x - 0.02x^2)\Big|_0^{614}$$

$$\approx \$7,810$$

$$PS = \int_0^{614}[55 - (30e^{0.001x})]\,dx = \int_0^{614}(55 - 30e^{0.001x})\,dx$$

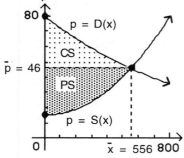

$$= (55x - 30,000e^{0.001x})\Big|_0^{614}$$

$$\approx \$8,336$$

51. $D(x) = 80e^{-0.001x}$; $S(x) = 15 + 0.0001x^2$
Equilibrium price: $D(x) = S(x)$
Using a graphing utility, we find that
$$\overline{x} \approx 556$$
Thus, $\overline{p} = 15 + 0.0001(556)^2 \approx 46$

$$CS = \int_0^{556}[80e^{-0.001x} - 46]\,dx = (-80,000e^{-0.001x} - 46x)\Big|_0^{556}$$

$$\approx \$8,544$$

$$PS = \int_0^{556}[46 - (15 + 0.0001x^2)]\,dx = \int_0^{556}(31 - 0.0001x^2)\,dx$$

$$= \left(31x - \frac{0.0001}{3}x^3\right)\Big|_0^{556}$$

$$\approx \$11,507$$

53. (A) <u>Price-Demand</u>   <u>Price-Supply</u>

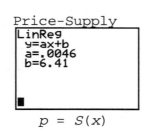

$p = D(x)$ $p = S(x)$

Graph the price-demand and price-supply models and find their point of intersection.

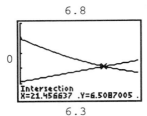

6.8

0   30

Intersection
X=21.456637 .Y=6.5087005 .

6.3

Equilibrium quantity $\overline{x}$ = 21.457
Equilibrium price $\overline{p}$ = 6.51

(B) Let $D(x)$ be the quadratic regression model in part (A).

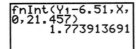

fnInt(Y₁-6.51,X,
0,21.457)
         1.773913691

Consumers' surplus:

$$CS = \int_0^{21.457} [D(x) - 6.51]\,dx \approx \$1,774.$$

Let $S(x)$ be the linear regression model in part (A).

fnInt(6.51-Y₂,X,
0,21.457)
         1.086773447

Producers' surplus

$$PS = \int_0^{21.457} [6.51 - S(x)]\,dx \approx \$1,087$$

EXERCISE 7-3

Things to remember:

1. INTEGRATION-BY-PARTS FORMULA

$$\int u\,dv = uv - \int v\,du$$

2. INTEGRATION-BY-PARTS: SELECTION OF u AND dv

   (a) The product $u\,dv$ must equal the original integrand.

   (b) It must be possible to integrate dv (preferably by using standard formulas or simple substitutions.)

   (c) The new integral, $\int v\,du$, should not be more complicated than the original integral $\int u\,dv$.

   (d) For integrals involving $x^p e^{ax}$, try
   $$u = x^p;\ dv = e^{ax}dx.$$

   (e) For integrals involving $x^p (\ln x)^q$, try
   $$u = (\ln x)^q;\ dv = x^p dx.$$

---

1. $\int xe^{3x}dx$

Let $u = x$ and $dv = e^{3x}dx$. Then $du = dx$ and $v = \dfrac{e^{3x}}{3}$.

$$\int xe^{3x}dx = \frac{xe^{3x}}{3} - \int \frac{e^{3x}}{3}\,dx = \frac{1}{3}xe^{3x} - \frac{1}{3}\int e^{3x}dx = \frac{1}{3}xe^{3x} - \frac{1}{9}e^{3x} + C$$

3. $\int x^2 \ln x \, dx$

Let $u = \ln x$ and $dv = x^2 dx$. Then $du = \dfrac{dx}{x}$ and $v = \dfrac{x^3}{3}$.

$$\int x^2 \ln x \, dx = (\ln x)\left(\frac{x^3}{3}\right) - \int \frac{x^3}{3} \cdot \frac{dx}{x} = \frac{1}{3}x^3 \ln x - \frac{1}{3}\int x^2 dx$$

$$= \frac{x^3 \ln x}{3} - \frac{1}{3} \cdot \frac{x^3}{3} + C = \frac{x^3 \ln x}{3} - \frac{x^3}{9} + C$$

5. $\int (x + 1)^5 (x + 2) \, dx$

The better choice is $u = x + 2$, $dv = (x + 1)^5 dx$
The alternative is $u = (x + 1)^5$, $dv = (x + 2)dx$, which will lead to an integral of the form
$$\int (x + 1)^4 (x + 2)^2 dx.$$

Let $u = x + 2$ and $dv = (x + 1)^5 dx$. Then $du = dx$ and $v = \dfrac{1}{6}(x + 1)^6$.

Substitute into the integration by parts formula:

$$\int (x + 1)^5 (x + 2) \, dx = \frac{1}{6}(x + 1)^6(x + 2) - \int \frac{1}{6}(x + 1)^6 dx$$

$$= \frac{1}{6}(x + 1)^6(x + 2) - \frac{1}{42}(x + 1)^7 + C$$

7. $\int xe^{-x} dx$

Let $u = x$ and $dv = e^{-x} dx$. Then $du = dx$ and $v = -e^{-x}$.
$$\int xe^{-x} dx = x(-e^{-x}) - \int (-e^{-x}) \, dx = -xe^{-x} + \int e^{-x} dx = -xe^{-x} - e^{-x} + C$$

9. $\int xe^{x^2} dx = \int e^{x^2} \dfrac{2}{2} x \, dx = \dfrac{1}{2}\int e^{x^2} 2x \, dx = \dfrac{1}{2}\int e^u du$

Let $u = x^2$,
then $du = 2x \, dx$. $\qquad = \dfrac{1}{2}e^u + C = \dfrac{1}{2}e^{x^2} + C$

11. $\int_0^1 (x - 3) e^x dx$

Let $u = (x - 3)$ and $dv = e^x dx$. Then $du = dx$ and $v = e^x$.
$$\int (x - 3) e^x dx = (x - 3) e^x - \int e^x dx = (x - 3) e^x - e^x + C$$

$$= xe^x - 4e^x + C.$$

Thus, $\displaystyle\int_0^1 (x - 3) e^x dx = (xe^x - 4e^x)\Big|_0^1 = (e - 4e) - (-4)$

$$= -3e + 4 \approx -4.1548.$$

13. $\int_1^3 \ln 2x\,dx$

Let $u = \ln 2x$ and $dv = dx$. Then $du = \dfrac{dx}{x}$ and $v = x$.

$$\int \ln 2x\,dx = (\ln 2x)(x) - \int x \cdot \frac{dx}{x} = x \ln 2x - x + C$$

Thus, $\int_1^3 \ln 2x\,dx = (x \ln 2x - x)\Big|_1^3$

$$= (3 \ln 6 - 3) - (\ln 2 - 1) \approx 2.6821.$$

15. $\int \dfrac{2x}{x^2 + 1}\,dx = \int \dfrac{1}{u}\,du = \ln|u| + C = \ln(x^2 + 1) + C$

Substitution: $u = x^2 + 1$
$du = 2x\,dx$

[<u>Note</u>: Absolute value not needed, since $x^2 + 1 \geq 0$.]

17. $\int \dfrac{\ln x}{x}\,dx = \int u\,du = \dfrac{u^2}{2} + C = \dfrac{(\ln x)^2}{2} + C$

Substitution: $u = \ln x$
$du = \dfrac{1}{x}\,dx$

19. $\int \sqrt{x}\,\ln x\,dx = \int x^{1/2}\ln x\,dx$

Let $u = \ln x$ and $dv = x^{1/2}\,dx$. Then $du = \dfrac{dx}{x}$ and $v = \dfrac{2}{3}x^{3/2}$.

$$\int x^{1/2}\ln x\,dx = \frac{2}{3}x^{3/2}\ln x - \int \frac{2}{3}x^{3/2}\frac{dx}{x} = \frac{2}{3}x^{3/2}\ln x - \frac{2}{3}\int x^{1/2}\,dx$$

$$= \frac{2}{3}x^{3/2}\ln x - \frac{4}{9}x^{3/2} + C$$

21.

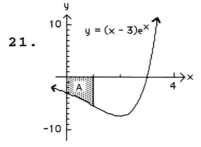

Since $f(x) = (x - 3)e^x < 0$ on $[0, 1]$, the integral represents the negative of the area between the graph of f and the x-axis from $x = 0$ to $x = 1$.

23.

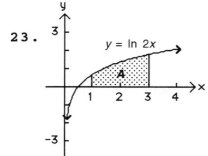

The integral represents the area between the curve $y = \ln 2x$ and the x-axis from $x = 1$ to $x = 3$.

25. $\int x^2 e^x dx$

Let $u = x^2$ and $dv = e^x dx$. Then $du = 2x\, dx$ and $v = e^x$.
$\int x^2 e^x dx = x^2 e^x - \int e^x (2x)\, dx = x^2 e^x - 2 \int x e^x dx$

$\int x e^x dx$ can be computed by using integration-by-parts again.

Let $u = x$ and $dv = e^x dx$. Then $du = dx$ and $v = e^x$.
$\int x e^x dx = x e^x - \int e^x dx = x e^x - e^x + C$
and
$\int x^2 e^x dx = x^2 e^x - 2(x e^x - e^x) + C = x^2 e^x - 2x e^x + 2 e^x + C$
$$= (x^2 - 2x + 2) e^x + C$$

27. $\int x e^{ax} dx$

Let $u = x$ and $dv = e^{ax} dx$. Then $du = dx$ and $v = \dfrac{e^{ax}}{a}$.

$\int x e^{ax} dx = x \cdot \dfrac{e^{ax}}{a} - \int \dfrac{e^{ax}}{a}\, dx = \dfrac{x e^{ax}}{a} - \dfrac{e^{ax}}{a^2} + C$

29. $\int_1^e \dfrac{\ln x}{x^2}\, dx$

Let $u = \ln x$ and $dv = \dfrac{dx}{x^2}$. Then $du = \dfrac{dx}{x}$ and $v = \dfrac{-1}{x}$.

$\int \dfrac{\ln x}{x^2}\, dx = (\ln x)\left(-\dfrac{1}{x}\right) - \int -\dfrac{1}{x} \cdot \dfrac{dx}{x} = -\dfrac{\ln x}{x} + \int \dfrac{dx}{x^2} = -\dfrac{\ln x}{x} - \dfrac{1}{x} + C$

Thus, $\int_1^e \dfrac{\ln x}{x^2}\, dx = \left(-\dfrac{\ln x}{x} - \dfrac{1}{x}\right)\Big|_1^e = -\dfrac{\ln e}{e} - \dfrac{1}{e} - \left(-\dfrac{\ln 1}{1} - \dfrac{1}{1}\right)$
$$= -\dfrac{2}{e} + 1 \approx 0.2642.$$

[<u>Note</u>: $\ln e = 1$.]

31. $\int_0^2 \ln(x + 4)\, dx$

Let $t = x + 4$. Then $dt = dx$ and
$\int \ln(x + 4)\, dx = \int \ln t\, dt$.

Now, let $u = \ln t$ and $dv = dt$. Then $du = \dfrac{dt}{t}$ and $v = t$.

$\int \ln t\, dt = t \ln t - \int t\left(\dfrac{1}{t}\right) dt = t \ln t - \int dt = t \ln t - t + C$

Thus, $\int \ln(x + 4)\, dx = (x + 4)\ \ln(x + 4) - (x + 4) + C$
and
$\int_0^2 \ln(x + 4)\, dx = [(x + 4)\ \ln(x + 4) - (x + 4)]\Big|_0^2$
$$= 6 \ln 6 - 6 - (4 \ln 4 - 4) = 6 \ln 6 - 4 \ln 4 - 2 \approx 3.205.$$

33. $\int xe^{x-2}dx$

Let $u = x$ and $dv = e^{x-2}dx$. Then $du = dx$ and $v = e^{x-2}$.
$\int xe^{x-2}dx = xe^{x-2} - \int e^{x-2}\,dx = xe^{x-2} - e^{x-2} + C$

35. $\int x\,\ln(1 + x^2)\,dx$

Let $t = 1 + x^2$. Then $dt = 2x\,dx$ and
$\int x\,\ln(1 + x^2)\,dx = \int \ln(1 + x^2)x\,dx = \int \ln t\,\dfrac{dt}{2} = \dfrac{1}{2}\int \ln t\,dt$.

Now, for $\int \ln t\,dt$, let $u = \ln t$, $dv = dt$. Then $du = \dfrac{dt}{t}$ and $v = t$.

$\dfrac{1}{2}\int \ln t\,dt = t\,\ln t - \int t\left(\dfrac{1}{t}\right)dt = t\,\ln t - \int dt = t\,\ln t - t + C$

Therefore,
$\int x\,\ln(1 + x^2)\,dx = \dfrac{1}{2}(1 + x^2)\ln(1 + x^2) - \dfrac{1}{2}(1 + x^2) + C$.

37. $\int e^x\,\ln(1 + e^x)\,dx$

Let $t = 1 + e^x$. Then $dt = e^x dx$ and
$\int e^x\,\ln(1 + e^x)\,dx = \int \ln t\,dt$.

Now, as shown in Problems 31 and 35,
$\int \ln t\,dt = t\,\ln t - t + C$.

Thus, $\int e^x\,\ln(1 + e^x)\,dx = (1 + e^x)\ln(1 + e^x) - (1 + e^x) + C$.

39. $\int (\ln x)^2 dx$

Let $u = (\ln x)^2$ and $dv = dx$. Then $du = \dfrac{2\ln x}{x}dx$ and $v = x$.

$\int (\ln x)^2 dx = x(\ln x)^2 - \int x \cdot \dfrac{2\ln x}{x}dx = x(\ln x)^2 - 2\int \ln x\,dx$

$\int \ln x\,dx$ can be computed by using integration-by-parts again.

As shown in Problems 31 and 35,
$\int \ln x\,dx = x\,\ln x - x + C$.

Thus, $\int (\ln x)^2 dx = x(\ln x)^2 - 2(x\,\ln x - x) + C$
$= x(\ln x)^2 - 2x\,\ln x + 2x + C$.

41. $\int (\ln x^3)\,dx$

Let $u = (\ln x)^3$ and $dv = dx$. Then $du = 3(\ln x)^2 \cdot \dfrac{1}{x}dx$ and $v = x$.

$\int (\ln x^3)\,dx = x(\ln x)^3 - \int x \cdot 3(\ln x)^2 \cdot \dfrac{1}{x}dx = x(\ln x)^3 - 3\int (\ln x^3)\,dx$

Now, using Problem 39,

$$\int (\ln x^2)\, dx = x(\ln x)^2 - 2x \ln x + 2x + C.$$

Therefore, $\int (\ln x^3)\, dx = x(\ln x)^3 - 3[x(\ln x)^2 - 2x \ln x + 2x] + C$

$$= x(\ln x)^3 - 3x(\ln x)^2 + 6x \ln x - 6x + C.$$

43. $y = x - 2 - \ln x,\ 1 \le x \le 4$

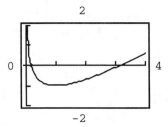

$y = 0$ at $x \approx 3.146$

$$A = \int_1^{3.146} [-(x - 2 - \ln x)]\, dx + \int_{3.146}^4 (x - 2 - \ln x)\, dx$$

$$= \int_1^{3.146} (\ln x + 2 - x)\, dx + \int_{3.146}^4 (x - 2 - \ln x)\, dx$$

Now, $\int \ln x\, dx$ is found using integration-by-parts. Let $u = \ln x$ and $dv = dx$. Then $du = \dfrac{1}{x}\, dx$ and $v = x$.

$$\int \ln x\, dx = x \ln x - \int x\left(\frac{1}{x}\right) dx = x \ln x - \int dx = x \ln x - x + C$$

Thus,

$$A = \left(x \ln x - x + 2x - \frac{1}{2} x^2\right)\Big|_1^{3.146} + \left(\frac{1}{2} x^2 - 2x - x \ln x + x\right)\Big|_{3.146}^4$$

$$= \left(x \ln x + x - \frac{1}{2} x^2\right)\Big|_1^{3.146} + \left(\frac{1}{2} x^2 - x - x \ln x\right)\Big|_{3.146}^4$$

$$\approx (1.803 - 0.5) + (-1.545 + 1.803) = 1.561$$

45. $y = 5 - xe^x,\ 0 \le x \le 3$

$y = 0$ at $x \approx 1.327$

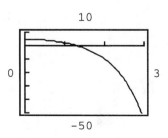

$$A = \int_0^{1.327} (5 - xe^x)\, dx + \int_{1.327}^3 [-(5 - xe^x)]\, dx$$

$$= \int_0^{1.327} (5 - xe^x)\, dx + \int_{1.327}^3 (xe^x - 5)\, dx$$

Now, $\int xe^x\, dx$ is found using integration-by-parts. Let $u = x$ and $dv = e^x\, dx$. Then, $du = dx$ and $v = e^x$.

$$\int xe^x\, dx = xe^x - \int e^x\, dx = xe^x - e^x + C$$

Thus,

$$A = (5x - [xe^x - e^x])\Big|_0^{1.327} + (xe^x - e^x - 5x)\Big|_{1.327}^3$$

$$\approx (5.402 - 1) + (25.171 - [-5.402]) \approx 34.98$$

47. Marginal profit: $P'(t) = 2t - te^{-t}$.

The total profit over the first 5 years is given by the definite integral:

$$\int_0^5 (2t - te^{-t})\,dt = \int_0^5 2t\,dt - \int_0^5 te^{-t}\,dt$$

We calculate the second integral using integration-by-parts. Let $u = t$ and $dv = e^{-t}\,dt$. Then $du = dt$ and $v = -e^{-t}$

$$\int te^{-t}\,dt = -te^{-t} - \int -e^{-t}\,dt = -te^{-t} - e^{-t} + C = -e^{-t}[t + 1] + C$$

Thus,

$$\text{Total profit} = t^2 \Big|_0^5 + (e^{-t}[t + 1])\Big|_0^5$$

$$\approx 25 + (0.040 - 1) = 24.040$$

To the nearest million, the total profit is $24 million.

49.

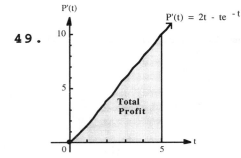

The total profit for the first five years (in millions of dollars) is the same as the area under the marginal profit function, $P'(t) = 2t - te^{-t}$, from $t = 0$ to $t = 5$.

51. From Exercise 7-2, Future Value $= e^{rT}\int_0^T f(t)e^{-rt}\,dt$. Now $r = 0.08$, $T = 5$, $f(t) = 1000 - 200t$. Thus,

$$FV = e^{(0.08)5}\int_0^5 (1000 - 200t)e^{-0.08t}\,dt$$

$$= 1000e^{0.4}\int_0^5 e^{-0.08t}\,dt - 200e^{0.4}\int_0^5 te^{-0.08t}\,dt.$$

We calculate the second integral using integration-by-parts.

Let $u = t$, $dv = e^{-0.08t}\,dt$. Then $du = dt$ and $v = \dfrac{e^{-0.08t}}{-0.08}$.

$$\int te^{-0.08t}\,dt = \frac{te^{-0.08t}}{-0.08} - \int \frac{e^{-0.08t}}{-0.08}\,dt = -12.5te^{-0.08t} - \frac{e^{-0.08t}}{0.0064} + C$$

$$= -12.5te^{-0.08t} - 156.25e^{-0.08t} + C$$

Thus, we have:

$$FV = 1000e^{0.4}\frac{e^{-0.08t}}{-0.08}\Big|_0^5 - 200e^{0.4}[-12.5te^{-0.08t} - 156.25e^{-0.08t}]\Big|_0^5$$

$$= -12{,}500 + 12{,}500e^{0.4} - 200e^{0.4}[-62.5e^{-0.4} - 156.25e^{-0.4} + 156.25]$$

$$= -12{,}500 + 12{,}500e^{0.4} + 43{,}750 - 31{,}250e^{0.4}$$

$$= 31{,}250 - 18{,}750e^{0.4} \approx 3{,}278 \text{ or } \$3{,}278$$

53. Gini Index $= 2\int_0^1 (x - xe^{x-1})\,dx$

$$= 2\int_0^1 x\,dx - 2\int_0^1 xe^{x-1}\,dx$$

We calculate the second integral using integration-by-parts.
Let $u = x$, $dv = e^{x-1}dx$. Then $du = dx$, $v = e^{x-1}$.

$$\int xe^{x-1}\,dx = xe^{x-1} - \int e^{x-1}\,dx = xe^{x-1} - e^{x-1} + C$$

Therefore, $2\int_0^1 x\,dx - 2\int_0^1 xe^{x-1}\,dx = x^2\Big|_0^1 - 2[xe^{x-1} - e^{x-1}]\Big|_0^1$

$$= 1 - 2[1 - 1 + (e^{-1})]$$
$$= 1 - 2e^{-1} \approx 0.264.$$

55.

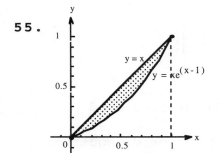

The area bounded by $y = x$ and the Lorenz curve $y = xe^{(x-1)}$ divided by the area under the curve $y = x$ from $x = 0$ to $x = 1$ is the index of income concentration, in this case 0.264. It is a measure of the concentration of income—the closer to zero, the closer to all the income being equally distributed; the closer to one, the closer to all the income being concentrated in a few hands.

57. $S'(t) = -4te^{0.1t}$, $S(0) = 2,000$

$$S(t) = \int -4te^{0.1t}\,dt = -4\int te^{0.1t}\,dt$$

Let $u = t$ and $dv = e^{0.1t}\,dt$. Then $du = dt$ and $v = \dfrac{e^{0.1t}}{0.1} = 10e^{0.1t}$

$$\int te^{0.1t}\,dt = 10te^{0.1t} - \int 10e^{0.1t}\,dt = 10te^{0.1t} - 100e^{0.1t} + C$$

Now, $S(t) = -40te^{0.1t} + 400e^{0.1t} + C$

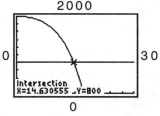

Since $S(0) = 2,000$, we have
$2,000 = 400 + C$, $C = 1,600$

Thus,
$$S(t) = 1,600 + 400e^{0.1t} - 40te^{0.1t}$$

To find how long the company will continue to manufacture this computer, solve $S(t) = 800$ for t.

The company will manufacture the computer for 15 months.

59. $p = D(x) = 9 - \ln(x + 4)$; $\overline{p} = \$2.089$. To find $\overline{x}$, solve

$$9 - \ln(\overline{x} + 4) = 2.089$$
$$\ln(\overline{x} + 4) = 6.911$$
$$\overline{x} + 4 = e^{6.911} \quad \text{(take the exponential of both sides)}$$
$$\overline{x} \approx 1,000$$

Now,

$$CS = \int_0^{1,000} (D(x) - \overline{p})\,dx = \int_0^{1,000} [9 - \ln(x + 4) - 2.089]\,dx$$

$$= \int_0^{1,000} 6.911\,dx - \int_0^{1,000} \ln(x + 4)\,dx$$

To calculate the second integral, we first let $z = x + 4$ and $dz = dx$ to get

$$\int \ln(x + 4)\,dx = \int \ln z\,dz$$

Then we use integration-by-parts. Let $u = \ln z$ and $dv = dz$.
Then $du = \dfrac{1}{z}dz$ and $v = z$.

$$\int \ln z\,dz = z \ln z - \int z \cdot \frac{1}{z}dz = z \ln z - z + C$$

Therefore,

$$\int \ln(x + 4)\,dx = (x + 4)\ln(x + 4) - (x + 4) + C$$

and

$$CS = 6.911x \Big|_0^{1,000} - [(x + 4)\ln(x + 4) - (x + 4)] \Big|_0^{1,000}$$

$$\approx 6911 - (5935.39 - 1.55) \approx \$977$$

61.

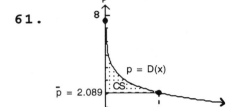

The area bounded by the price-demand equation,
$p = 9 - \ln(x + 4)$, and the price equation,
$y = \bar{p} = 2.089$, from $x = 0$ to $x = \bar{x} = 1,000$,
represents the consumers' surplus. This is the amount saved by consumer's who are willing to pay more than \$2.089.

63. Average concentration: $= \dfrac{1}{5 - 0}\displaystyle\int_0^5 \frac{20 \ln(t + 1)}{(t + 1)^2}dt = 4\displaystyle\int_0^5 \frac{\ln(t + 1)}{(t + 1)^2}$

$\displaystyle\int \frac{\ln(t + 1)}{(t + 1)^2}dt$ is found using integration-by-parts.

Let $u = \ln(t + 1)$ and $dv = (t + 1)^{-2}dt$.
Then $du = \dfrac{1}{t + 1}dt = (t + 1)^{-1}dt$ and $v = -(t + 1)^{-1}$.

$$\int \frac{\ln(t + 1)}{(t + 1)^2}dt = -\frac{\ln(t + 1)}{t + 1} - \int -(t + 1)^{-1}(t + 1)^{-1}dt$$

$$= -\frac{\ln(t + 1)}{t + 1} + \int (t + 1)^{-2}dt = -\frac{\ln(t + 1)}{t + 1} - \frac{1}{t + 1} + C$$

Therefore, the average concentration is:

$$\frac{1}{5}\int_0^5 \frac{20 \ln(t + 1)}{(t + 1)^2}dt = 4\left[-\frac{\ln(t + 1)}{t + 1} - \frac{1}{t + 1}\right]\Big|_0^5$$

$$= 4\left(-\frac{\ln 6}{6} - \frac{1}{6}\right) - 4(-\ln 1 - 1)$$

$$= 4 - \frac{2}{3}\ln 6 - \frac{2}{3} = \frac{1}{3}(10 - 2 \ln 6) \approx 2.1388 \text{ ppm}$$

65. $N'(t) = (t + 6)e^{-0.25t}$, $0 \leq t \leq 15$; $N(0) = 40$

$N(t) - N(0) = \int_0^t N'(x)\,dx$;

$N(t) = 40 + \int_0^t (x + 6)e^{-0.25x}dx = 40 + 6\int_0^t e^{-0.25x}dx + \int_0^t xe^{-0.25x}dx$

$\qquad = 40 + 6(-4e^{-0.25x})\Big|_0^t + \int_0^t xe^{-0.25x}dx$

$\qquad = 64 - 24e^{-0.25t} + \int_0^t xe^{-0.25x}dx$

Let $u = x$ and $dv = e^{-0.25x}dx$. Then $du = dx$ and $v = -4e^{-0.25x}$;

$\int xe^{-0.25x}dx = -4xe^{-0.25x} - \int -4e^{-0.25x}dx = -4xe^{-0.25x} - 16e^{-0.25x} + C$

Now, $\int_0^t xe^{-0.25x}dx = (-4xe^{-0.25x} - 16e^{-0.25x})\Big|_0^t$

$\qquad\qquad\qquad\qquad = -4te^{-0.25t} - 16e^{-0.25t} + 16$

and

$N(t) = 80 - 40e^{-0.25t} - 4te^{-0.25t}$

To find how long it will take a student to achieve the 70 words per minute level, solve $N(t) = 70$:

It will take 8 weeks.

By the end of the course, a student should be able to type $N(15) = 80 - 40e^{-0.25(15)} - 60e^{-0.25(15)} \approx 78$ words per minute.

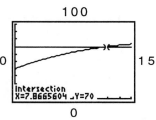

67. Average number of voters $= \dfrac{1}{5}\int_0^5 (20 + 4t - 5te^{-0.1t})\,dt$

$\qquad\qquad\qquad\qquad = \dfrac{1}{5}\int_0^5 (20 + 4t)\,dt - \int_0^5 te^{-0.1t}dt$

$\int te^{-0.1t}dt$ is found using integration-by-parts.

Let $u = t$ and $dv = e^{-0.1t}dt$. Then $du = dt$ and $v = \dfrac{e^{-0.1t}}{-0.1} = -10e^{-0.1t}$.

$\int te^{-0.1t}dt = -10te^{-0.1t} - \int -10e^{-0.1t}dt = -10te^{-0.1t} + 10\int e^{-0.1t}dt$

$\qquad\qquad = -10te^{-0.1t} + \dfrac{10e^{-0.1t}}{-0.1} + C = -10te^{-0.1t} - 100e^{-0.1t} + C$

Therefore, the average number of voters is:

$\dfrac{1}{5}\int_0^5 (20 + 4t)\,dt - \int_0^5 te^{-0.1t}dt$

$\qquad = \dfrac{1}{5}(20t + 2t^2)\Big|_0^5 - (-10te^{-0.1t} - 100e^{-0.1t})\Big|_0^5$

$\qquad = \dfrac{1}{5}(100 + 50) + (10te^{-0.1t} + 100e^{-0.1t})\Big|_0^5$

$\qquad = 30 + (50e^{-0.5} + 100e^{-0.5}) - 100$

$\qquad = 150e^{-0.5} - 70$

$\qquad \approx 20.98$ (thousands) or 20,980

1. Use Formula 9 with $a = b = 1$.

$$\int \frac{1}{x(1 + x)} dx = \frac{1}{1} \ln \left| \frac{x}{1 + x} \right| + C = \ln \left| \frac{x}{x + 1} \right| + C$$

3. Use Formula 18 with $a = 3$, $b = 1$, $c = 5$, $d = 2$:

$$\int \frac{1}{(3 + x)^2(5 + 2x)} dx = \frac{1}{3 \cdot 2 - 5 \cdot 1} \cdot \frac{1}{3 + x} + \frac{2}{(3 \cdot 2 - 5 \cdot 1)^2} \ln \left| \frac{5 + 2x}{3 + x} \right| + C$$

$$= \frac{1}{3 + x} + 2 \ln \left| \frac{5 + 2x}{3 + x} \right| + C$$

5. Use Formula 25 with $a = 16$ and $b = 1$:

$$\int \frac{x}{\sqrt{16 + x}} dx = \frac{2(x - 2 \cdot 16)}{3 \cdot 1^2} \sqrt{16 + x} + C = \frac{2(x - 32)}{3} \sqrt{16 + x} + C$$

7. Use Formula 29 with $a = 1$:

$$\int \frac{1}{x\sqrt{1 - x^2}} dx = -\frac{1}{1} \ln \left| \frac{1 + \sqrt{1 - x^2}}{x} \right| + C$$

$$= -\ln \left| \frac{1 + \sqrt{1 - x^2}}{x} \right| + C$$

9. Use Formula 37 with $a = 2$ $(a^2 = 4)$:

$$\int \frac{1}{x\sqrt{x^2 + 4}} dx = \frac{1}{2} \ln \left| \frac{x}{2 + \sqrt{x^2 + 4}} \right| + C$$

11. Use Formula 51 with $n = 2$:

$$\int x^2 \ln x \, dx = \frac{x^{2+1}}{2 + 1} \ln x - \frac{x^{2+1}}{(2 + 1)^2} + C = \frac{x^3}{3} \ln x - \frac{x^3}{9} + C$$

13. First let $u = e^x$. Then $du = e^x dx$ and $dx = \frac{1}{e^x} du = \frac{1}{u} du$.

Thus, $\int \frac{1}{1 + e^x} dx = \int \frac{1}{u(1 + u)} du$

Now use Formula 9 with $a = b = 1$:

$$\int \frac{1}{u(1 + u)} du = \frac{1}{1} \ln \left| \frac{u}{1 + u} \right| + C$$

$$= \ln \left| \frac{e^x}{1 + e^x} \right| + C$$

$$= \ln |e^x| - \ln |1 + e^x| + C$$

$$= x - \ln |1 + e^x| + C$$

15. First use Formula 5 with $a = 3$ and $b = 1$ to find the indefinite integral.

$$\int \frac{x^2}{3 + x}dx = \frac{(3 + x)^2}{2 \cdot 1^3} - \frac{2 \cdot 3(3 + x)}{1^3} + \frac{3^2}{1^3}\ln|3 + x| + C$$

$$= \frac{(3 + x)^2}{2} - 6(3 + x) + 9\ln|3 + x| + C$$

Thus, $\int_1^3 \frac{x^2}{3 + x}dx = \left[\frac{(3 + x)^2}{2} - 6(3 + x) + 9\ln|3 + x|\right]\Big|_1^3$

$$= \frac{(3 + 3)^2}{2} - 6(3 + 3) + 9\ln|3 + 3|$$

$$- \left[\frac{(3 + 1)^2}{2} - 6(3 + 1) + 9\ln|3 + 1|\right]$$

$$= 9\ln\frac{3}{2} - 2 \approx 1.6492.$$

17. First use Formula 15 with $a = 3$, $b = c = d = 1$ to find the indefinite integral.

$$\int \frac{1}{(3 + x)(1 + x)}dx = \frac{1}{3 \cdot 1 - 1 \cdot 1}\ln\left|\frac{1 + x}{3 + x}\right| + C = \frac{1}{2}\ln\left|\frac{1 + x}{3 + x}\right| + C$$

Thus, $\int_0^7 \frac{1}{(3 + x)(1 + x)}dx = \frac{1}{2}\ln\left|\frac{1 + x}{3 + x}\right|\Big|_0^7 = \frac{1}{2}\ln\left|\frac{1 + 7}{3 + 7}\right| - \frac{1}{2}\ln\left|\frac{1}{3}\right|$

$$= \frac{1}{2}\ln\left|\frac{4}{5}\right| - \frac{1}{2}\ln\left|\frac{1}{3}\right| = \frac{1}{2}\ln\frac{12}{5} \approx 0.4377.$$

19. First use Formula 36 with $a = 3$ ($a^2 = 9$) to find the indefinite integral:

$$\int \frac{1}{\sqrt{x^2 + 9}}dx = \ln\left|x + \sqrt{x^2 + 9}\right| + C$$

Thus, $\int_0^4 \frac{1}{\sqrt{x^2 + 9}}dx = \ln\left|x + \sqrt{x^2 + 9}\right|\Big|_0^4 = \ln\left|4 + \sqrt{16 + 9}\right| - \ln\left|\sqrt{9}\right|$

$$= \ln 9 - \ln 3 = \ln 3 \approx 1.0986.$$

21. Consider Formula 35. Let $u = 2x$. Then $u^2 = 4x^2$, $x = \frac{u}{2}$, and $dx = \frac{du}{2}$.

$$\int \frac{\sqrt{4x^2 + 1}}{x^2}dx = \int \frac{\sqrt{u^2 + 1}}{\frac{u^2}{4}}\frac{du}{2} = 2\int \frac{\sqrt{u^2 + 1}}{u^2}du$$

$$= 2\left[-\frac{\sqrt{u^2 + 1}}{u} + \ln\left|u + \sqrt{u^2 + 1}\right|\right] + C$$

$$= 2\left[-\frac{\sqrt{4x^2 + 1}}{2x} + \ln\left|2x + \sqrt{4x^2 + 1}\right|\right] + C$$

$$= -\frac{\sqrt{4x^2 + 1}}{x} + 2\ln\left|2x + \sqrt{4x^2 + 1}\right| + C$$

23. Let $u = x^2$. Then $du = 2x\,dx$.

$$\int \frac{x}{\sqrt{x^4 - 16}}\,dx = \frac{1}{2}\int \frac{1}{\sqrt{u^2 - 16}}\,du$$

Now use Formula 43 with $a = 4$ ($a^2 = 16$):

$$\frac{1}{2}\int \frac{1}{\sqrt{u^2 - 16}}\,du = \frac{1}{2}\ln\left|u + \sqrt{u^2 - 16}\right| + C = \frac{1}{2}\left|\ln x^2 + \sqrt{x^4 - 16}\right| + C$$

25. Let $u = x^3$. Then $du = 3x^2\,dx$.

$$\int x^2\sqrt{x^6 + 4}\,dx = \frac{1}{3}\int \sqrt{u^2 + 4}\,du$$

Now use Formula 32 with $a = 2$ ($a^2 = 4$):

$$\frac{1}{3}\int \sqrt{u^2 + 4}\,du = \frac{1}{3}\cdot\frac{1}{2}\left[u\sqrt{u^2 + 4} + 4\ln\left|u + \sqrt{u^2 + 4}\right|\right] + C$$

$$= \frac{1}{6}\left[x^3\sqrt{x^6 + 4} + 4\ln\left|x^3 + \sqrt{x^6 + 4}\right|\right] + C$$

27. $$\int \frac{1}{x^3\sqrt{4 - x^4}}\,dx = \int \frac{x}{x^4\sqrt{4 - x^4}}\,dx$$

Let $u = x^2$. Then $du = 2x\,dx$.

$$\int \frac{x}{x^4\sqrt{4 - x^4}}\,dx = \frac{1}{2}\int \frac{1}{u^2\sqrt{4 - u^2}}\,du$$

Now use Formula 30 with $a = 2$ ($a^2 = 4$):

$$\frac{1}{2}\int \frac{1}{u^2\sqrt{4 - u^2}}\,du = -\frac{1}{2}\cdot\frac{\sqrt{4 - u^2}}{4u} + C = \frac{-\sqrt{4 - x^4}}{8x^2} + C$$

29. $$\int \frac{e^x}{(2 + e^x)(3 + 4e^x)}\,dx = \int \frac{1}{(2 + u)(3 + 4u)}\,du$$

Substitution: $u = e^x$, $du = e^x\,dx$.
Now use Formula 15 with $a = 2$, $b = 1$, $c = 3$, $d = 4$:

$$\int \frac{1}{(2 + u)(3 + 4u)}\,du = \frac{1}{2\cdot 4 - 3\cdot 1}\ln\left|\frac{3 + 4u}{2 + u}\right| + C = \frac{1}{5}\ln\left|\frac{3 + 4e^x}{2 + e^x}\right| + C$$

31. $$\int \frac{\ln x}{x\sqrt{4 + \ln x}}\,dx = \int \frac{u}{\sqrt{4 + u}}\,du$$

Substitution: $u = \ln x$, $du = \dfrac{1}{x}\,dx$.

Use Formula 25 with $a = 4$, $b = 1$:

$$\int \frac{u}{\sqrt{4 + u}}\,du = \frac{2(u - 2\cdot 4)}{3\cdot 1^2}\sqrt{4 + u} + C = \frac{2(u - 8)}{3}\sqrt{4 + u} + C$$

$$= \frac{2(\ln x - 8)}{3}\sqrt{4 + \ln x} + C$$

33. Use Formula 47 with $n = 2$ and $a = 5$:

$$\int x^2 e^{5x} dx = \frac{x^2 e^{5x}}{5} - \frac{2}{5}\int x e^{5x} dx$$

To find $\int x e^{5x} dx$, use Formula 47 with $n = 1$, $a = 5$:

$$\int x e^{5x} dx = \frac{x e^{5x}}{5} - \frac{1}{5}\int e^{5x} dx = \frac{x e^{5x}}{5} - \frac{1}{5} \cdot \frac{e^{5x}}{5}$$

Thus, $\int x^2 e^{5x} dx = \frac{x^2 e^{5x}}{5} - \frac{2}{5}\left[\frac{x e^{5x}}{5} - \frac{1}{25} e^{5x}\right] + C$

$$= \frac{x^2 e^{5x}}{5} - \frac{2x e^{5x}}{25} + \frac{2 e^{5x}}{125} + C.$$

35. Use Formula 47 with $n = 3$ and $a = -1$.

$$\int x^3 e^{-x} dx = \frac{x^3 e^{-x}}{-1} - \frac{3}{-1}\int x^2 e^{-x} dx = -x^3 e^{-x} + 3\int x^2 e^{-x} dx$$

Now $\int x^2 e^{-x} dx = \frac{x^2 e^{-x}}{-1} - \frac{2}{-1}\int x e^{-x} dx = -x^2 e^{-x} + 2\int x e^{-x} dx$

and $\int x e^{-x} dx = \frac{x e^{-x}}{-1} - \frac{1}{-1}\int e^{-x} dx = -x e^{-x} - e^{-x}$, using Formula 47.

Thus, $\int x^3 e^{-x} dx = -x^3 e^{-x} + 3[-x^2 e^{-x} + 2(-x e^{-x} - e^{-x})] + C$

$$= -x^3 e^{-x} - 3x^2 e^{-x} - 6x e^{-x} - 6e^{-x} + C.$$

37. Use Formula 52 with $n = 3$:

$$\int (\ln x)^3 dx = x(\ln x)^3 - 3\int (\ln x)^2 dx$$

Now $\int (\ln x)^2 dx = x(\ln x)^2 - 2\int \ln x\, dx$ using Formula 52 again, and

$\int \ln x\, dx = x \ln x - x$ by Formula 49.

Thus, $\int (\ln x)^3 dx = x(\ln x)^3 - 3[x(\ln x)^2 - 2(x \ln x - x)] + C$

$$= x(\ln x)^3 - 3x(\ln x)^2 + 6x \ln x - 6x + C.$$

39. $\int_3^5 x\sqrt{x^2 - 9}\, dx$. First consider the indefinite integral.

Let $u = x^2 - 9$. Then $du = 2x\, dx$ or $x\, dx = \frac{1}{2} du$. Thus,

$$\int x\sqrt{x^2 - 9}\, dx = \frac{1}{2}\int u^{1/2} du = \frac{1}{2} \cdot \frac{u^{3/2}}{3/2} + C = \frac{1}{3}(x^2 - 9)^{3/2} + C.$$

Now, $\int_3^5 x\sqrt{x^2 - 9}\, dx = \frac{1}{3}(x^2 - 9)^{3/2}\Big|_3^5 = \frac{1}{3} \cdot 16^{3/2} = \frac{64}{3}.$

41. $\int_2^4 \dfrac{1}{x^2 - 1}\,dx$. Consider the indefinite integral:

$$\int \dfrac{1}{x^2 - 1}\,dx = \dfrac{1}{2 \cdot 1}\ln\left|\dfrac{x - 1}{x + 1}\right| + C,\text{ using Formula 13 with } a = 1.$$

Thus,

$$\int_2^4 \dfrac{1}{x^2 - 1}\,dx = \dfrac{1}{2}\ln\left|\dfrac{x - 1}{x + 1}\right|\Big|_2^4 = \dfrac{1}{2}\ln\left|\dfrac{3}{5}\right| - \dfrac{1}{2}\ln\left|\dfrac{1}{3}\right| = \dfrac{1}{2}\ln\dfrac{9}{5} \approx 0.2939.$$

43. $\int \dfrac{\ln x}{x^2}\,dx = \int x^{-2}\ln x\,dx$

$$= \dfrac{x^{-1}}{-1}\ln x - \dfrac{x^{-1}}{(-1)^2} + C \quad [\text{Formula 51 with } n = -2]$$

$$= -\dfrac{1}{x}\ln x - \dfrac{1}{x} + C = \dfrac{-1 - \ln x}{x} + C$$

45. $\int \dfrac{x}{\sqrt{x^2 - 1}}\,dx = \int \dfrac{1}{\sqrt{x^2 - 1}}\left(\dfrac{2}{2}\right)x\,dx = \dfrac{1}{2}\int u^{-1/2}\,du$

Let $u = x^2 - 1$ 　　　　　　　　　　　　$= u^{1/2} + C$

Then $du = 2x\,dx$ 　　　　　　　　　　$= \sqrt{x^2 - 1} + C$

47. $f(x) = \dfrac{10}{\sqrt{x^2 + 1}}$, $g(x) = x^2 + 3x$

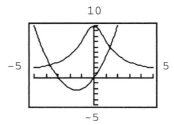

The graphs of f and g are shown at the right.
The x-coordinates of the points of intersection
are: $x_1 \approx -3.70$, $x_2 \approx 1.36$

$$A = \int_{-3.70}^{1.36}\left[\dfrac{1}{\sqrt{x^2 + 1}} - (x^2 + 3x)\right]dx$$

$$= 10\int_{-3.70}^{1.36}\dfrac{1}{\sqrt{x^2 + 1}}\,dx - \int_{-3.70}^{1.36}(x^2 + 3x)\,dx$$

For the first integral, use Formula 36 with $a = 1$:

$$A = (10\ln|x + \sqrt{x^2 + 1}|)\Big|_{-3.70}^{1.36} - \left(\dfrac{1}{3}x^3 + \dfrac{3}{2}x^2\right)\Big|_{-3.70}^{1.36}$$

$$\approx [11.15 - (-20.19)] - [3.61 - (3.65)] = 31.38$$

49. $f(x) = x\sqrt{x + 4}$, $g(x) = 1 + x$

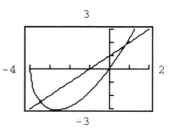

The graphs of f and g are shown at the right.
The x-coordinates of the points of intersection
are: $x_1 \approx -3.49$, $x_2 \approx 0.83$

$$A = \int_{-3.49}^{0.83}[1 + x - x\sqrt{x + 4}]\,dx = \int_{-3.49}^{0.83}(1 + x)\,dx - \int_{-3.49}^{0.83}x\sqrt{x + 4}\,dx$$

For the second integral, use Formula 22 with $a = 4$ and $b = 1$:

$$A = \left(x + \frac{1}{2}x^2\right)\Big|_{-3.49}^{0.83} - \left(\frac{2[3x - 8]}{15}\sqrt{(x + 4)^3}\right)\Big|_{-3.49}^{0.83}$$

$$\approx (1.17445 - 2.60005) - (-7.79850 + 0.89693) \approx 5.48$$

51. Find $\overline{x}$, the demand when the price $\overline{p} = 15$:

$$15 = \frac{7500 - 30\overline{x}}{300 - \overline{x}}$$

$$4500 - 15\overline{x} = 7500 - 30\overline{x}$$

$$15\overline{x} = 3000$$

$$\overline{x} = 200$$

Consumers' surplus:

$$CS = \int_0^{\overline{x}} [D(x) - \overline{p}]\,dx = \int_0^{200}\left[\frac{7500 - 30x}{300 - x} - 15\right]dx = \int_0^{200}\left[\frac{3000 - 15x}{300 - x}\right]dx$$

Use Formula 20 with $a = 3000$, $b = -15$, $c = 300$, $d = -1$:

$$CS = \left[\frac{-15x}{-1} + \frac{3000(-1) - (-15)(300)}{(-1)^2}\ln|300 - x|\right]\Big|_0^{200}$$

$$= [15x + 1500\ln|300 - x|]\Big|_0^{200}$$

$$= 3000 + 1500\ln(100) - 1500\ln(300)$$

$$= 3000 + 1500\ln\left(\frac{1}{3}\right) \approx 1352$$

Thus, the consumers' surplus is $1352.

53.

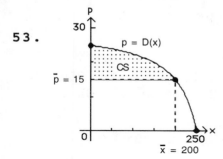

The shaded region represents the consumers' surplus.

55. $C'(x) = \dfrac{250 + 10x}{1 + 0.05x}$, $C(0) = 25,000$

$$C(x) = \int\frac{250 + 10x}{1 + 0.05x}\,dx = 250\int\frac{1}{1 + 0.05x}\,dx + 10\int\frac{x}{1 + 0.05x}\,dx$$

$$= 250\left(\frac{1}{0.05}\ln|1 + 0.05x|\right) + 10\left(\frac{x}{0.05} - \frac{1}{(0.05)^2}\ln|1 + 0.05x|\right) + K$$

(Formulas 3 and 4)

$$= 5,000\ln|1 + 0.05x| + 200x - 4,000\ln|1 + 0.05x| + K$$

$$= 1,000\ln|1 + 0.05x| + 200x + K$$

Since $C(0) = 25,000$, $K = 25,000$ and

$$C(x) = 1,000\ln(1 + 0.05x) + 200x + 25,000, \quad x \geq 0$$

To find the production level that produces a cost of \$150,000, solve $C(x) = 150,000$ for x:

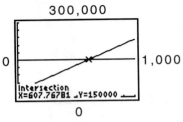

The production level is $x = 608$ pairs of skis.

At a production level of 850 pairs of skis,

$C(850) = 1,000 \ln(1 + 0.05[850]) + 200(850) + 25,000 \approx \$198,773.$

57. $FV = e^{rT} \int_0^T f(t) e^{-rt} dt$

Now, $r = 0.1$, $T = 10$, $f(t) = 50t^2$.

$FV = e^{(0.1)10} \int_0^{10} 50t^2 e^{-0.1t} dt = 50e \int_0^{10} t^2 e^{-0.1t} dt$

To evaluate the integral, use Formula 47 with $n = 2$ and $a = -0.1$:

$$\int t^2 e^{-0.1t} dt = \frac{t^2 e^{-0.1t}}{-0.1} - \frac{2}{-0.1} \int t e^{-0.1t} dt = -10t^2 e^{-0.1t} + 20 \int t e^{-0.1t} dt$$

Now, using Formula 47 again:

$$\int t e^{-0.1t} dt = \frac{t e^{-0.1t}}{-0.1} - \frac{1}{-0.1} \int e^{-0.1t} dt = -10t e^{-0.1t} + 10 \frac{e^{-0.1t}}{-0.1}$$

$$= -10t e^{-0.1t} - 100 e^{-0.1t}$$

Thus, $\int t^2 e^{-0.1t} dt = -10t^2 e^{-0.1t} - 200t e^{-0.1t} - 2000 e^{-0.1t} + C.$

$FV = 50e[-10t^2 e^{-0.1t} - 200t e^{-0.1t} - 2000 e^{-0.1t}]\Big|_0^{10}$

$= 50e[-1000 e^{-1} - 2000 e^{-1} - 2000 e^{-1} + 2000] = 100,000e - 250,000$

$\approx 21,828$ or \$21,828

59. Gini Index:

$$2\int_0^1 [x - f(x)] dx = 2\int_0^1 \left[x - \frac{1}{2} x\sqrt{1 + 3x}\right] dx = \int_0^1 [2x - x\sqrt{1 + 3x}] dx$$

$$= \int_0^1 2x\,dx - \int_0^1 x\sqrt{1 + 3x}\,dx$$

For the second integral, use Formula 22 with $a = 1$ and $b = 3$:

$$= x^2\Big|_0^1 - \frac{2(3 \cdot 3x - 2 \cdot 1)}{15(3)^2} \sqrt{(1 + 3x)^3}\,\Big|_0^1$$

$$= 1 - \frac{2(9x - 2)}{135} \sqrt{(1 + 3x)^3}\,\Big|_0^1$$

$$= 1 - \frac{14}{135} \sqrt{4^3} - \frac{4}{135} \sqrt{1^3}$$

$$= 1 - \frac{112}{135} - \frac{4}{135} = \frac{19}{135} \approx 0.1407$$

61.

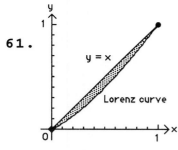

As the area bounded by the two curves gets smaller, the Lorenz curve approaches $y = x$ and the distribution of income approaches perfect equality — all individuals share equally in the income.

63. $S'(t) = \dfrac{t^2}{(1 + t)^2}$; $S(t) = \displaystyle\int \dfrac{t^2}{(1 + t)^2}\, dt$

Use Formula 7 with $a = 1$ and $b = 1$:

$$S(t) = \frac{1 + t}{1^3} - \frac{1^2}{1^3(1 + t)} - \frac{2(1)}{1^3}\ln|1 + t| + C$$

$$= 1 + t - \frac{1}{1 + t} - 2\ln|1 + t| + C$$

Since $S(0) = 0$, we have $0 = 1 - 1 - 2\ln 1 + C$ and $C = 0$. Thus,

$$S(t) = 1 + t - \frac{1}{1 + t} - 2\ln|1 + t|.$$

Now, the total sales during the first two years (= 24 months) is given by:

$$S(24) = 1 + 24 - \frac{1}{1 + 24} - 2\ln|1 + 24| = 24.96 - 2\ln 25 \approx 18.5$$

Thus, total sales during the first two years is approximately $18.5 million.

65.

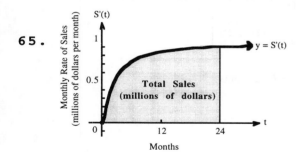

The total sales, in millions of dollars, over the first two years (24 months) is the area under the curve $y = S'(t)$ from $t = 0$ to $t = 24$.

67. $P'(x) = x\sqrt{2 + 3x}$, $P(1) = -\$2,000$

$$P(x) = \int x\sqrt{2 + 3x}\, dx = \frac{2(9x - 4)}{135}(2 + 3x)^{3/2} + C$$
(Formula 22)

$$P(1) = \frac{2(5)}{135}5^{3/2} + C = -2,000$$

$$C = -2,000 - \frac{2}{27}5^{3/2} \approx -2,000.83$$

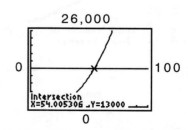

Thus, $P(x) = \dfrac{2(9x - 4)}{135}(2 + 3x)^{3/2} - 2,000.83$.

The number of cars that must be sold to have a profit of $13,000: 54

Profit if 10 cars are sold per week:

$$P(10) = \frac{2(86)}{135}(32)^{3/2} - 2,000.83 \approx -\$1,770$$

69. $\dfrac{dR}{dt} = \dfrac{100}{\sqrt{t^2 + 9}}$. Therefore,

$$R = \int \frac{100}{\sqrt{t^2 + 9}}\,dt = 100\int \frac{1}{\sqrt{t^2 + 9}}\,dt$$

Using Formula 36 with $a = 3$ ($a^2 = 9$), we have:

$R = 100\,\ln\left|t + \sqrt{t^2 + 9}\right| + C$

Now $R(0) = 0$, so $0 = 100\,\ln|3| + C$ or $C = -100\,\ln 3$. Thus,

$R(t) = 100\,\ln\left|t + \sqrt{t^2 + 9}\right| - 100\,\ln 3$

and

$$\begin{aligned}
R(4) &= 100\,\ln(4 + \sqrt{4^2 + 9}) - 100\,\ln 3 \\
&= 100\,\ln 9 - 100\,\ln 3 \\
&= 100\,\ln 3 \approx 110 \text{ feet}
\end{aligned}$$

71. $N'(t) = \dfrac{60}{\sqrt{t^2 + 25}}$

The number of items learned in the first twelve hours of study is given by:

$$\begin{aligned}
N &= \int_0^{12} \frac{60}{\sqrt{t^2 + 25}}\,dt = 60\int_0^{12} \frac{1}{\sqrt{t^2 + 25}}\,dt \\
&= 60\left(\ln\left|t + \sqrt{t^2 + 25}\right|\right)\Big|_0^{12}, \text{ using Formula 36} \\
&= 60\left[\ln\left|12 + \sqrt{12^2 + 25}\right| - \ln\sqrt{25}\right] \\
&= 60(\ln 25 - \ln 5) \\
&= 60\,\ln 5 \approx 96.57 \text{ or } 97 \text{ items}
\end{aligned}$$

73.

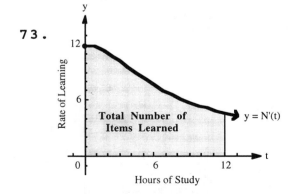

The area under the rate of learning curve, $y = N'(t)$, from $t = 0$ to $t = 12$ represents the total number of items learned in that time interval.

CHAPTER 7 REVIEW

1. $A = \displaystyle\int_a^b f(x)\,dx$ (7-1)

2. $A = \displaystyle\int_b^c [-f(x)]\,dx$ (7-1)

3. $A = \displaystyle\int_a^b f(x)\,dx + \int_b^c [-f(x)]\,dx$ (7-1)

4. $A = \int_{0.5}^{1} [-\ln x]\, dx + \int_{1}^{e} \ln x\, dx$

We evaluate the integral using integration-by-parts.
Let $u = \ln x$, $dv = dx$.

Then $du = \dfrac{1}{x}dx$, $v = x$, and $\int \ln x\, dx =$

$x \ln x - \int x\left(\dfrac{1}{x}\right)dx = x \ln x - x + C$

Thus,

$A = -\int_{0.5}^{1} \ln x\, dx + \int_{1}^{e} \ln x\, dx$

$= (-x \ln x + x)\Big|_{0.5}^{1} + (x \ln x - x)\Big|_{1}^{e}$

$\approx (1 - 0.847) + (1) = 1.153$

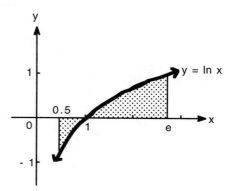

5. $\int xe^{4x}dx$. Use integration-by-parts:

Let $u = x$ and $dv = e^{4x}dx$. Then $du = dx$ and $v = \dfrac{e^{4x}}{4}$.

$\int xe^{4x}dx = \dfrac{xe^{4x}}{4} - \int \dfrac{e^{4x}}{4}dx = \dfrac{xe^{4x}}{4} - \dfrac{e^{4x}}{16} + C$ $\qquad$ (7-3, 7-4)

6. $\int x \ln x\, dx$. Use integration-by-parts:

Let $u = \ln x$ and $dv = x\, dx$. Then $du = \dfrac{1}{x}dx$ and $v = \dfrac{x^2}{2}$.

$\int x \ln x\, dx = \dfrac{x^2 \ln x}{2} - \int \dfrac{1}{x} \cdot \dfrac{x^2}{2}dx = \dfrac{x^2 \ln x}{2} - \dfrac{1}{2}\int x\, dx$

$= \dfrac{x^2 \ln x}{2} - \dfrac{x^2}{4} + C$ $\qquad$ (7-3, 7-4)

7. $\int \dfrac{\ln x}{x}dx$

Let $u = \ln x$. Then $du = \dfrac{1}{x}dx$ and

$\int \dfrac{\ln x}{x}dx = \int u\, du = \dfrac{1}{2}u^2 + C = \dfrac{1}{2}[\ln x]^2 + C$ $\qquad$ (7-2)

8. $\int \dfrac{x}{1 + x^2}dx$

Let $u = 1 + x^2$. Then $du = 2x\, dx$ and

$\int \dfrac{x}{1 + x^2}dx = \int \dfrac{1/2\, du}{u} = \dfrac{1}{2}\int \dfrac{1}{u}du = \dfrac{1}{2} \ln|u| + C = \dfrac{1}{2} \ln(1 + x^2) + C$ $\qquad$ (7-2)

9. Use Formula 11 with $a = 1$ and $b = 1$.

$\int \dfrac{1}{x(1 + x)^2}dx = \dfrac{1}{1(1 + x)} + \dfrac{1}{1^2} \ln\left|\dfrac{x}{1 + x}\right| + C = \dfrac{1}{1 + x} + \ln\left|\dfrac{x}{1 + x}\right| + C$

$\qquad$ (7-4)

10. Use Formula 28 with $a = 1$ and $b = 1$.

$$\int \frac{1}{x^2\sqrt{1+x}}\,dx = -\frac{\sqrt{1+x}}{1\cdot x} - \frac{1}{2\cdot 1\sqrt{1}}\ln\left|\frac{\sqrt{1+x}-\sqrt{1}}{\sqrt{1+x}+\sqrt{1}}\right| + C$$

$$= -\frac{\sqrt{1+x}}{x} - \frac{1}{2}\ln\left|\frac{\sqrt{1+x}-1}{\sqrt{1+x}+1}\right| + C \qquad (7\text{-}4)$$

11. $A = \int_a^b [f(x) - g(x)]\,dx$ (7-1)   **12.** $A = \int_b^c [g(x) - f(x)]\,dx$ (7-1)

13. $A = \int_b^c [g(x) - f(x)]\,dx + \int_c^d [f(x) - g(x)]\,dx$ (7-1)

14. $A = \int_a^b [f(x) - g(x)]\,dx + \int_b^c [g(x) - f(x)]\,dx + \int_c^d [f(x) - g(x)]\,dx$ (7-1)

15. $A = \int_0^5 [(9 - x) - (x^2 - 6x + 9)]\,dx$

$$= \int_0^5 (5x - x^2)\,dx$$

$$= \left(\frac{5}{2}x^2 - \frac{1}{3}x^3\right)\Big|_0^5$$

$$= \frac{125}{2} - \frac{125}{3} = \frac{125}{6} \approx 20.833$$

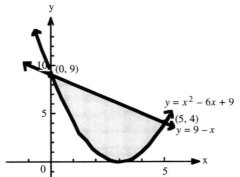

16. $\int_0^1 xe^x\,dx$.   Use integration-by-parts.

Let $u = x$ and $dv = e^x\,dx$.   Then $du = dx$ and $v = e^x$.
$$\int xe^x\,dx = xe^x - \int e^x\,dx = xe^x - e^x + C$$

Therefore, $\int_0^1 xe^x\,dx = (xe^x - e^x)\Big|_0^1 = 1\cdot e - e - (0\cdot 1 - 1)$

$$= 1 \qquad (7\text{-}3,\ 7\text{-}4)$$

17. Use Formula 38 with $a = 4$

$$\int_0^3 \frac{x^2}{\sqrt{x^2+16}}\,dx = \frac{1}{2}\left[x\sqrt{x^2+16} - 16\ln\left|x + \sqrt{x^2+16}\right|\right]\Big|_0^3$$

$$= \frac{1}{2}\left[3\sqrt{25} - 16\ln(3 + \sqrt{25})\right] - \frac{1}{2}(-16\ln\sqrt{16})$$

$$= \frac{1}{2}[15 - 16\ln 8] + 8\ln 4$$

$$= \frac{15}{2} - 8\ln 8 + 8\ln 4 \approx 1.955 \qquad (7\text{-}4)$$

18. Let $u = 3x$, then $du = 3\,dx$.   Now, use Formula 40 with $a = 7$.
$$\int \sqrt{9x^2 - 49}\,dx = \frac{1}{3}\int \sqrt{u^2 - 49}\,du$$

$$= \frac{1}{3}\cdot\frac{1}{2}\left(u\sqrt{u^2 - 49} - 49\ln\left|u + \sqrt{u^2 - 49}\right|\right) + C$$

$$= \frac{1}{6}\left(3x\sqrt{9x^2 - 49} - 49\ln\left|3x + \sqrt{9x^2 - 49}\right|\right) + C \qquad (7\text{-}4)$$

19. $\int te^{-0.5t}\,dt.$ Use integration-by-parts.

Let $u = t$ and $dv = e^{-0.5t}dt.$ Then $du = dt$ and $v = \dfrac{e^{-0.5t}}{-0.5}$.

$$\int te^{-0.5t}\,dt = \frac{-te^{-0.5t}}{0.5} + \int \frac{e^{-0.5t}}{0.5}\,dt = \frac{-te^{-0.5t}}{0.5} + \frac{e^{-0.5t}}{-0.25} + C$$

$$= -2te^{-0.5t} - 4e^{-0.5t} + C \qquad\qquad (7\text{-}3,\ 7\text{-}4)$$

20. $\int x^2 \ln x\,dx.$ Use integration-by-parts.

Let $u = \ln x$ and $dv = x^2 dx.$ Then $du = \dfrac{1}{x}\,dx$ and $v = \dfrac{x^3}{3}$.

$$\int x^2 \ln x\,dx = \frac{x^3 \ln x}{3} - \int \frac{1}{x}\cdot\frac{x^3}{3}\,dx = \frac{x^3 \ln x}{3} - \frac{1}{3}\int x^2 dx$$

$$= \frac{x^3 \ln x}{3} - \frac{x^3}{9} + C \qquad\qquad (7\text{-}3,\ 7\text{-}4)$$

21. Use Formula 48 with $a = 1,\ c = 1,$ and $d = 2.$

$$\int \frac{1}{1 + 2e^x}\,dx = \frac{x}{1} - \frac{1}{1\cdot 1}\ln|1 + 2e^x| + C = x - \ln|1 + 2e^x| + C \qquad (7\text{-}4)$$

22. (A)

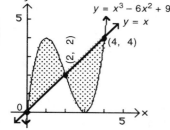

$$A = \int_0^2 [(x^3 - 6x^2 + 9x) - x]\,dx + \int_2^4 [x - (x^3 - 6x^2 + 9x)]\,dx$$

$$= \int_0^2 (x^3 - 6x^2 + 8x)\,dx + \int_2^4 (-x^3 + 6x^2 - 8x)\,dx$$

$$= \left(\frac{1}{4}x^4 - 2x^3 + 4x^2\right)\Big|_0^2 + \left(-\frac{1}{4}x^4 + 2x^3 - 4x^2\right)\Big|_2^4$$

$$= 4 + 4 = 8$$

(B)

The x-coordinates of the points of intersection are: $x_1 \approx 0.14,$ $x_2 \approx 1.75,$ $x_3 \approx 4.11.$

$$A = \int_{0.14}^{1.75} [(x^3 - 6x^2 + 9x) - (x + 1)]\,dx$$

$$+ \int_{1.75}^{4.11} [(x + 1) - (x^3 - 6x^2 + 9x)]\,dx$$

$$= \int_{0.14}^{1.75} (x^3 - 6x^2 + 8x - 1)\,dx + \int_{1.75}^{4.11} (1 - x^3 + 6x^2 - 8x)\,dx$$

$$= \left(\frac{1}{4}x^4 - 2x^3 + 4x^2 - x\right)\Big|_{0.14}^{1.75} + \left(x - \frac{1}{4}x^4 + 2x^3 - 4x^2\right)\Big|_{1.75}^{4.11}$$

$$= [2.126 - (-0.066)] + [4.059 - (-2.126)] \approx 8.38 \qquad (7\text{-}1)$$

23. $\int \dfrac{(\ln x)^2}{x}\,dx = \int u^2\,du = \dfrac{u^3}{3} + C = \dfrac{(\ln x)^3}{3} + C$ Substitution: $u = \ln x$

$$du = \frac{1}{x}\,dx \qquad (7\text{-}2)$$

24. $\int x(\ln x)^2\,dx$. Use integration-by-parts.

Let $u = (\ln x)^2$ and $dv = x\,dx$. Then $du = 2(\ln x)\dfrac{1}{x}\,dx$ and $v = \dfrac{x^2}{2}$.

$$\int x(\ln x)^2\,dx = \frac{x^2(\ln x)^2}{2} - \int 2(\ln x)\frac{1}{x}\cdot\frac{x^2}{2}\,dx = \frac{x^2(\ln x)^2}{2} - \int x\ln x\,dx$$

Let $u = \ln x$ and $dv = x\,dx$. Then $du = \dfrac{1}{x}\,dx$ and $v = \dfrac{x^2}{2}$.

$$\int x\ln x\,dx$$

Thus, $\int x(\ln x)^2\,dx = \dfrac{x^2(\ln x)^2}{2} - \left[\dfrac{x^2\ln x}{2} - \dfrac{x^2}{4}\right] + C$

$$= \frac{x^2(\ln x)^2}{2} - \frac{x^2\ln x}{2} + \frac{x^2}{4} + C. \qquad (7\text{-}3,\ 7\text{-}4)$$

25. Let $u = x^2 - 36$. Then $du = 2x\,dx$.

$$\int \frac{x}{\sqrt{x^2 - 36}}\,dx = \int \frac{x}{(x^2 - 36)^{1/2}}\,dx = \frac{1}{2}\int \frac{1}{u^{1/2}}\,du = \frac{1}{2}\int u^{-1/2}\,du$$

$$= \frac{1}{2}\cdot\frac{u^{1/2}}{1/2} + C = u^{1/2} + C = \sqrt{x^2 - 36} + C \qquad (6\text{-}2)$$

26. Let $u = x^2$, $du = 2x\,dx$.

Then use Formula 43 with $a = 6$.

$$\int \frac{x}{\sqrt{x^4 - 36}}\,dx = \frac{1}{2}\int \frac{du}{\sqrt{u^2 - 36}} = \frac{1}{2}\ln\left|u + \sqrt{u^2 - 36}\right| + C$$

$$= \frac{1}{2}\ln\left|x^2 + \sqrt{x^4 - 36}\right| + C \qquad (7\text{-}4)$$

27. $\int_0^4 x \ln(10 - x)\,dx$

Consider

Substitution: $t = 10 - x$
$dt = -dx$
$x = 10 - t$

$$\int x \ln(10 - x)\,dx = \int (10 - t) \ln t\,(-dt)$$

$$= \int t \ln t\,dt - 10\int \ln t\,dt.$$

Now use integration-by-parts on the two integrals.

Let $u = \ln t$, $dv = t\,dt$. Then $du = \dfrac{1}{t}\,dt$, $v = \dfrac{t^2}{2}$.

$$\int t \ln t\,dt = \frac{t^2}{2}\ln t - \int \frac{t^2}{2}\cdot\frac{1}{t}\,dt = \frac{t^2 \ln t}{2} - \frac{t^2}{4} + C$$

Let $u = \ln t$, $dv = dt$. Then $du = \dfrac{1}{t}\,dt$, $v = t$.

$$\int t \ln t\,dt = t \ln t - \int t\cdot\frac{1}{t}\,dt = t \ln t - t + C$$

Thus, $\displaystyle\int_0^4 x \ln(10 - x)\,dx = \left[\dfrac{(10 - x)^2 \ln(10 - x)}{2} - \dfrac{(10 - x)^2}{4}\right.$

$$\left.-10(10 - x)\ln(10 - x) + 10(10 - x)\right]\Big|_0^4$$

$$= \frac{36 \ln 6}{2} - \frac{36}{4} - 10(6)\ln 6 + 10(6)$$

$$- \left[\frac{100 \ln 10}{2} - \frac{100}{4} - 10(10)\ln 10 + 10(10)\right]$$

$$= 18 \ln 6 - 9 - 60 \ln 6 + 60 - 50 \ln 10 + 25$$
$$+ 100 \ln 10 - 100$$

$$= 50 \ln 10 - 42 \ln 6 - 24 \approx 15.875. \qquad \text{(7-3, 7-4)}$$

28. Use Formula 52 with $n = 2$.

$$\int (\ln x)^2\,dx = x(\ln x)^2 - 2\int \ln x\,dx$$

Now use integration-by-parts to calculate $\int \ln x\,dx$.

Let $u = \ln x$, $dv = dx$. Then $du = \dfrac{1}{x}\,dx$, $v = x$.

$$\int \ln x\,dx = x \ln x - \int x\cdot\frac{1}{x}\,dx = x \ln x - x + C$$

Therefore, $\displaystyle\int (\ln x)^2\,dx = x(\ln x)^2 - 2[x \ln x - x] + C$

$$= x(\ln x)^2 - 2x \ln x + 2x + C. \qquad \text{(7-3, 7-4)}$$

29. $\int xe^{-2x^2}\,dx$

Let $u = -2x^2$. Then $du = -4x\,dx$.
$$\int xe^{-2x^2}\,dx = -\frac{1}{4}\int e^u\,du = -\frac{1}{4}e^u + C$$

$$= -\frac{1}{4}e^{-2x^2} + C \qquad \text{(6-2)}$$

30. $\int x^2 e^{-2x}\, dx$. Use integration-by-parts. Let $u = x^2$ and $dv = e^{-2x}dx$.

Then $du = 2x\, dx$ and $v = -\dfrac{1}{2}e^{-2x}$.

$$\int x^2 e^{-2x}\, dx = -\frac{1}{2}x^2 e^{-2x} + \int xe^{-2x}\, dx$$

Now use integration-by-parts again. Let $u = x$ and $dv = e^{-2x}dx$.

Then $du = dx$ and $v = -\dfrac{1}{2}e^{-2x}$.

$$\int xe^{-2x}\, dx = -\frac{1}{2}xe^{-2x} + \frac{1}{2}\int e^{-2x}\, dx$$

$$= -\frac{1}{2}xe^{-2x} - \frac{1}{4}e^{-2x} + C$$

Thus,

$$\int x^2 e^{-2x}\, dx = -\frac{1}{2}x^2 e^{-2x} + \left[-\frac{1}{2}xe^{-2x} - \frac{1}{4}e^{-2x}\right] + C$$

$$= -\frac{1}{2}x^2 e^{-2x} - \frac{1}{2}xe^{-2x} - \frac{1}{4}e^{-2x} + C \qquad\qquad \text{(7-3, 7-4)}$$

31. First graph the two functions to find the points of intersection.

The curves intersect at the points where $x = 1.448$ and $x = 6.915$.

$$\text{Area } A = \int_{1.448}^{6.915}\left(\frac{6}{2 + 5e^{-x}} - [0.2x + 1.6]\right)dx$$

$$\approx 1.703$$

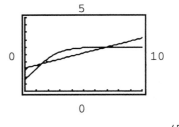

(7-1)

32. (A) Probability $(0 \le t \le 1) = \displaystyle\int_0^1 0.21e^{-0.21t}\, dt$

$$= -e^{-0.21t}\Big|_0^1$$

$$= -e^{-0.21} + 1 \approx 0.189$$

(B) Probability $(1 \le t \le 2) = \displaystyle\int_1^2 0.21e^{-0.21t}\, dt$

$$= -e^{-0.21t}\Big|_1^2$$

$$= e^{-0.21} - e^{-0.42} \approx 0.154 \qquad\qquad \text{(7-2)}$$

33.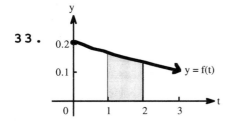

The probability that the product will fail during the second year of warranty is the area under the probability density function $y = f(t)$ from $t = 1$ to $t = 2$.

34. $R'(x) = 65 - 6\ln(x + 1)$, $R(0) = 0$

$R(x) = \int[65 - 6\ln(x + 1)]dx = 65x - 6\int\ln(x + 1)dx$

Let $z = x + 1$. Then $dz = dx$ and $\int\ln(x + 1)dx = \int\ln z\, dz$.

Now, let $u = \ln z$ and $dv = dz$. Then $du = \frac{1}{z}dz$ and $v = z$:

$$\int\ln z\, dz = z\ln z - \int z\left(\frac{1}{z}\right)dz = z\ln z - \int dz = z\ln z - z + C$$

Therefore, $\int\ln(x + 1)dx = (x + 1)\ln(x + 1) - (x + 1) + C$ and

$R(x) = 65x - 6[(x + 1)\ln(x + 1) - (x + 1)] + C$

Since $R(0) = 0$, $C = -6$. Thus,

$R(x) = 65x - 6[(x + 1)\ln(x + 1) - x]$

To find the production level for a revenue of \$20,000 per week, solve $R(x) = 20,000$ for x.

The production level should be 618 hair dryers per week.

At a production level of 1,000 hair dryers per week, revenue

$R(1,000) = 65,000 - 6[(1,001)\ln(1,001) - 1,000] \approx \$29,506$ (7-3)

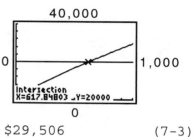

35. (A)

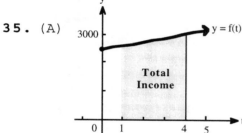

(B) Total income $= \int_1^4 2,500e^{0.05t}\, dt$

$= 50,000e^{0.05t}\Big|_1^4$

$= 50,000[e^{0.2} - e^{0.05}] \approx \$8,507$ (7-2)

36. $f(t) = 2,500e^{0.05t}$, $r = 0.15$, $T = 5$

(A) $FV = e^{(0.15)5}\int_0^5 2,500e^{0.05t}\, e^{-0.15t}\, dt = 2,500e^{0.75}\int_0^5 e^{-0.1t}\, dt$

$= -25,000e^{0.75}\, e^{-0.1t}\Big|_0^5$

$= 25,000[e^{0.75} - e^{0.25}] \approx \$20,824$

(B) Total income $= \int_0^5 2,500e^{0.05t}\, dt = 50,000e^{0.05t}\Big|_0^5$

$= 50,000[e^{0.25} - 1]$

$\approx \$14,201$

Interest $= FV -$ Total income $= \$20,824 - \$14,201 = \$6,623$ (7-2)

37. (A)

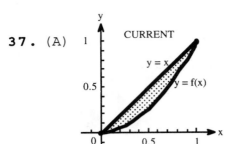

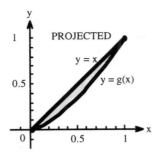

(B) The income will be more equally distributed 10 years from now since the area between $y = x$ and the projected Lorenz curve is less than the area between $y = x$ and the current Lorenz curve.

(C) Current:

$$\text{Gini Index} = 2\int_0^1 [x - (0.1x + 0.9x^2)]\,dx$$

$$= 2\int_0^1 (0.9x - 0.9x^2)\,dx = 2(0.45x^2 - 0.3x^3)\Big|_0^1 = 0.30$$

Projected:

$$\text{Gini Index} = 2\int_0^1 (x - x^{1.5})\,dx$$

$$= 2\int_0^1 (x - x^{3/2})\,dx = 2\left(\frac{1}{2}x^2 - \frac{2}{5}x^{5/2}\right)\Big|_0^1 = 2\left(\frac{1}{10}\right) = 0.2$$

Thus, income will be more equally distributed 10 years from now, as indicated in part (B). (7-1)

38. (A) $p = D(x) = 70 - 0.2x$, $p = S(x) = 13 + 0.0012x^2$

Equilibrium price: $D(x) = S(x)$

$$70 - 0.2x = 13 + 0.0012x^2$$

$$0.0012x^2 + 0.2x - 57 = 0$$

$$x = \frac{-0.2 \pm \sqrt{0.04 + 0.2736}}{0.0024} = \frac{-0.2 \pm 0.56}{0.0024}$$

Therefore, $\overline{x} = \dfrac{-0.2 + 0.56}{0.0024} = 150$, and $\overline{p} = 70 - 0.2(150) = 40$.

$$CS = \int_0^{150} (70 - 0.2x - 40)\,dx = \int_0^{150} (30 - 0.2x)\,dx$$

$$= (30x - 0.1x^2)\Big|_0^{150}$$

$$= \$2,250$$

$$PS = \int_0^{150} [40 - (13 + 0.012x^2)]\,dx = \int_0^{150} (27 - 0.012x^2)\,dx$$

$$= (27x - 0.0004x^3)\Big|_0^{150}$$

$$= \$2,700$$

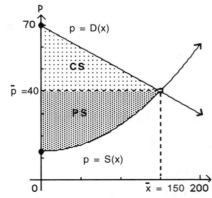

(B) $p = D(x) = 70 - 0.2x$, $p = S(x) = 13e^{0.006x}$

Equilibrium price: $D(x) = S(x)$

$$70 - 0.2x = 13e^{0.006x}$$

Using a graphing utility to solve for x, we get $\bar{x} \approx 170$
and $\bar{p} = 70 - 0.2(170) \approx 36$.

$$CS = \int_0^{170} (70 - 0.2x - 36)\,dx = \int_0^{170} (34 - 0.2x)\,dx$$

$$= (34x - 0.1x^2) \Big|_0^{170}$$

$$= \$2,890$$

$$PS = \int_0^{170} (36 - 13e^{0.006x})\,dx = (36x - 2,166.67e^{0.006x}) \Big|_0^{170}$$

$$\approx \$2,278$$

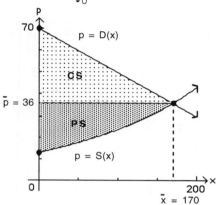

(7-2)

39. (A)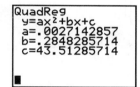

Graph the quadratic regression model and the line
$p = 52.50$ to find the point of intersection.

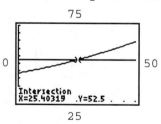

The demand at a price of 52.50 cents per pound is
25,403 lbs.

(B) Let $S(x)$ be the quadratic regression model found in part (A). Then
the producers' surplus at the price level of 52.5 cents per pound is
given by

$$PS = \int_0^{25.403} [52.5 - S(x)]\,dx \approx \$1,216$$

(7-2)

40. $R(t) = \dfrac{60t}{(t + 1)^2(t + 2)}$

The amount of the drug eliminated during the first hour is given by

$$A = \int_0^1 \frac{60t}{(t + 1)^2(t + 2)}\, dt$$

We will use the Table of Integration Formulas to calculate this integral. First, let $u = t + 2$. Then $t = u - 2$, $t + 1 = u - 1$, $du = dt$ and

$$\int \frac{60t}{(t + 1)^2(t + 2)}\, dt = 60\int \frac{u - 2}{(u - 1)^2 \cdot u}\, du$$

$$= 60\int \frac{1}{(u - 1)^2}\, du - 120\int \frac{1}{u(u - 1)^2}\, du$$

In the first integral, let $v = u - 1$, $dv = du$. Then

$$60\int \frac{1}{(u - 1)^2}\, du = 60\int v^{-2}\, dv = -60v^{-1} = \frac{-60}{u - 1}$$

For the second integral, use Formula 11 with $a = -1$, $b = 1$:

$$-120\int \frac{1}{u(u - 1)^2}\, du = -120\left[\frac{-1}{u - 1} + \ln\left|\frac{u}{u - 1}\right|\right]$$

Combining these results and replacing u by $t + 2$, we have:

$$\int \frac{60t}{(t + 1)^2(t + 2)}\, dt = \frac{-60}{t + 1} + \frac{120}{t + 1} - 120\ln\left|\frac{t + 2}{t + 1}\right| + C$$

$$= \frac{60}{t + 1} - 120\ln\left|\frac{t + 2}{t + 1}\right| + C$$

Now,

$$A = \int_0^1 \frac{60t}{(t + 1)^2(t + 2)}\, dt = \left[\frac{60}{t + 1} - 120\ln\left(\frac{t + 2}{t + 1}\right)\right]\Bigg|_0^1$$

$$= 30 - 120\ln\left(\frac{3}{2}\right) - 60 + 120\ln 2$$

$$\approx 4.522 \text{ milliliters}$$

The amount of drug eliminated during the 4th hour is given by:

$$A = \int_3^4 \frac{60t}{(t + 1)^2(t + 2)}\, dt = \left[\frac{60}{t + 1} - 120\ln\left(\frac{t + 2}{t + 1}\right)\right]\Bigg|_3^4$$

$$= 12 - 120\ln\left(\frac{6}{5}\right) - 15 + 120\ln\left(\frac{5}{4}\right)$$

$$\approx 1.899 \text{ milliliters}$$ (6-5, 7-4)

41.

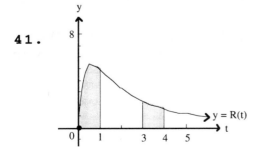

(7-2)

42. $f(t) = \begin{cases} \dfrac{4/3}{(t+1)^2} & 0 \le t \le 3 \\ 0 & \text{otherwise} \end{cases}$

(A) Probability $(0 \le t \le 1) = \displaystyle\int_0^1 \frac{4/3}{(t+1)^2}\,dt$

To calculate the integral, let $u = t + 1$, $du = dt$. Then,

$$\int \frac{4/3}{(t+1)^2}\,dt = \frac{4}{3}\int u^{-2}\,du = \frac{4}{3}\frac{u^{-1}}{-1} = -\frac{4}{3u} + C = \frac{-4}{3(t+1)} + C$$

Thus,

$$\int_0^1 \frac{4/3}{(t+1)^2}\,dt = \frac{-4}{3(t+1)}\Big|_0^1 = -\frac{2}{3} + \frac{4}{3} = \frac{2}{3} \approx 0.667$$

(B) Probability $(t \ge 1) = \displaystyle\int_1^3 \frac{4/3}{(t+1)^2}\,dt$

$$= \frac{-4}{3(t+1)}\Big|_1^3$$

$$= -\frac{1}{3} + \frac{2}{3} = \frac{1}{3} \approx 0.333 \hspace{2cm} (7\text{-}2)$$

43.

The probability that the doctor will spend more than an hour with a randomly selected patient is the area under the probability density function $y = f(t)$ from $t = 1$ to $t = 3$.

44. $N'(t) = \dfrac{100t}{(1 + t^2)^2}$. To find $N(t)$, we calculate

$$\int \frac{100t}{(1 + t^2)^2}\,dt$$

Let $u = 1 + t^2$. Then $du = 2t\,dt$, and

$$N(t) = \int \frac{100t}{(1 + t^2)^2}\,dt = 50\int \frac{1}{u^2}\,du = 50\int u^{-2}\,du$$

$$= -50\frac{1}{u} + C$$

$$= \frac{-50}{1 + t^2} + C$$

At $t = 0$, we have

$$N(0) = -50 + C$$

Therefore, $C = N(0) + 50$ and

$$N(t) = \frac{-50}{1 + t^2} + 50 + N(0)$$

Now,

$$N(3) = \frac{-5}{1 + 3^2} + 50 + N(0) = 45 + N(0)$$

Thus, the population will increase by 45 thousand during the next 3 years.

$(6\text{-}5, 7\text{-}1)$

45. We want to find Probability $(t \geq 2) = \int_2^\infty f(t)\,dt$

Since

$$\int_{-\infty}^\infty f(t)\,dt = \int_{-\infty}^2 f(t)\,dt + \int_2^\infty f(t)\,dt = 1,$$

$$\int_2^\infty f(t)\,dt = 1 - \int_{-\infty}^2 f(t)\,dt = 1 - \int_0^2 f(t)\,dt \text{ (since } f(t) = 0 \text{ for } t \leq 0)$$

$$= 1 - \text{Probability } (0 \leq t \leq 2)$$

Now, Probability $(0 \leq t \leq 2) = \int_0^2 0.5e^{-0.5t}\,dt$

$$= -e^{-0.5t}\Big|_0^2$$

$$= -e^{-1} + 1 \approx 0.632$$

Therefore, Probability $(t \geq 2) = 1 - 0.632 = 0.368$ (7-2)

8 MULTIVARIABLE CALCULUS

Things to remember:

1. An equation of the form $z = f(x, y)$ describes a FUNCTION OF TWO INDEPENDENT VARIABLES if for each permissible ordered pair (x, y) there is one and only one value of z determined by $f(x, y)$. The variables x and y are INDEPENDENT VARIABLES, and the variable z is a DEPENDENT VARIABLE. The set of all ordered pairs of permissible values of x and y is the DOMAIN of the function, and the set of all corresponding values $f(x, y)$ is the RANGE of the function.

2. CONVENTION ON DOMAINS

   Unless otherwise stated, the domain of a function specified by an equation of the form $z = f(x, y)$ is the set of all ordered pairs of real numbers (x, y) such that $f(x, y)$ is also a real number.

3. Functions of three independent variables $w = f(x, y, z)$, four independent variables $u = f(x, y, z, w)$, and so on, are defined similarly.

In Problems 1 - 9, $f(x, y) = 2x + 7y - 5$ and $g(x, y) = \dfrac{88}{x^2 + 3y}$.

1. $f(4, -1) = 2(4) + 7(-1) - 5 = -4$ **3.** $f(8, 0) = 2(8) + 7(0) - 5 = 11$

5. $g(1, 7) = \dfrac{88}{1^2 + 3(7)} = \dfrac{88}{22} = 4$ **7.** $g(3, -3)$ not defined; $3^2 + 3(-3) = 0$

9. $3f(-2, 2) + 5g(-2, 2) = 3[2(-2) + 7(2) - 5] + 5 \cdot \dfrac{88}{(-2)^2 + 3(2)}$

$$= 3(5) + 5 \cdot \dfrac{88}{10} = 59$$

In Problems 11 - 13, $f(x, y, z) = 2x - 3y^2 + 5z^3 - 1$.

11. $f(0, 0, 0) = 2(0) - 3(0) + 5(0) - 1 = -1$

13. $f(6, -5, 0) = 2(6) - 3(-5)^2 + 5(0) - 1 = 12 - 75 - 1 = -64$

15. $V(r, h) = \pi r^2 h$

$V(2, 4) = \pi \cdot 2^2 \cdot 4 = 16\pi$

($r = 2$ and $h = 4$)

17. $R(x, y) = -5x^2 + 6xy - 4y^2 + 200x + 300y$

$R(1, 2) = -5(1)^2 + 6 \cdot 1 \cdot 2 - 4 \cdot 2^2 + 200 \cdot 1 + 300 \cdot 2$

$= -5 + 12 - 16 + 200 + 600$

$= 791$

($x = 1$ and $y = 2$)

19. $R(L, r) = .002 \dfrac{L}{r^4}$

$R(6, 0.5) = 0.002 \dfrac{6}{(0.5)^4} = \dfrac{0.012}{0.0625} = 0.192$

($L = 6$ and $r = 0.5$)

21. $A(P, r, t) = P + Prt$

$A(100, 0.06, 3) = 100 + 100(0.06)3 = 118$

($P = 100$, $r = 0.06$, and $t = 3$)

23. $P(r, t) = \displaystyle\int_0^T 4000e^{-rt} dt$,

$P(0.05, 12) = \displaystyle\int_0^{12} 4000e^{-0.05t} dt = \dfrac{4000}{-0.05} e^{-0.05t} \Big|_0^{12}$

$= -80,000[e^{-0.6} - 1]$

$\approx 36,095.07$

25. $F(x, y) = x^2 + e^x y - y^2$; $F(x, 2) = x^2 + 2e^x - 4$.

We use a graphing utility to solve $F(x, 2) = 0$.
The graph of $u = F(x, 2)$ is shown at the right.

The solutions of $F(x, 2) = 0$ are: $x_1 \approx -1.926$,
$x_2 \approx 0.599$

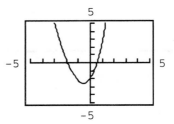

27. $f(x, y) = x^2 + 2y^2$

$\dfrac{f(x + h, y) - f(x, y)}{h} = \dfrac{(x + h)^2 + 2y^2 - (x^2 + 2y^2)}{h}$

$= \dfrac{x^2 + 2xh + h^2 + 2y^2 - x^2 - 2y^2}{h}$

$= \dfrac{2xh + h^2}{h} = \dfrac{h(2x + h)}{h} = 2x + h, \ h \neq 0$

29. $f(x, y) = 2xy^2$

$\dfrac{f(x + h, y) - f(x, y)}{h} = \dfrac{2(x + h)y^2 - 2xy^2}{h}$

$= \dfrac{2xy^2 + 2hy^2 - 2xy^2}{h} = \dfrac{2hy^2}{h} = 2y^2, \ h \neq 0$

31. Coordinates of point $E = E(0, 0, 3)$.
Coordinates of point $F = F(2, 0, 3)$.

33. $f(x, y) = x^2$

(A) In the plane $y = c$, c any constant, the graph of $z = x^2$ is a parabola.

(B) Cross-section corresponding to $x = 0$: the y-axis

Cross-section corresponding to $x = 1$: the line passing through $(1, 0, 1)$ parallel to the y-axis.

Cross-section corresponding to $x = 2$: the line passing through $(2, 0, 4)$ parallel to the y-axis.

(C) The surface $z = x^2$ is a parabolic trough lying on the y-axis.

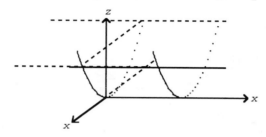

35. $f(x, y) = \sqrt{36 - x^2 - y^2}$

(A) Cross-sections corresponding to $y = 1$, $y = 2$, $y = 3$, $y = 4$, $y = 5$: Upper semicircles with centers at $(0, 1, 0)$, $(0, 2, 0)$, $(0, 3, 0)$, $(0, 4, 0)$, and $(0, 5, 0)$, respectively.

(B) Cross-sections corresponding to $x = 0$, $x = 1$, $x = 2$, $x = 3$, $x = 4$, $x = 5$: Upper semicircles with centers at $(0, 0, 0)$, $(1, 0, 0)$, $(2, 0, 0)$, $(3, 0, 0)$, $(4, 0, 0)$ and $(5, 0, 0)$, respectively.

(C) The upper hemisphere of radius 6 with center at the origin.

37. (A) If the points (a, b) and (c, d) both lie on the same circle centered at the origin, then $a^2 + b^2 = r^2 = c^2 + d^2$, where r is the radius of the circle.

(B) The cross-sections are:

(i) $x = 0$, $f(0, y) = e^{-y^2}$

(ii) $y = 0$, $f(x, 0) = e^{-x^2}$

(iii) $x = y$, $f(x, x) = e^{-2x^2}$

These are bell-shaped curves with maximum value 1 at $y = 0$ in (i) and $x = 0$ in (ii) and (iii).

(C) A "bell" with maximum value 1 at the origin, extending infinitely far in all directions, and approaching the x-y plane as x, $y \to \pm\infty$.

39. Monthly cost function $= C(x, y) = 2000 + 70x + 100y$

$$C(20, 10) = 2000 + 70 \cdot 20 + 100 \cdot 10 = \$4400$$
$$C(50, 5) = 2000 + 70 \cdot 50 + 100 \cdot 5 = \$6000$$
$$C(30, 30) = 2000 + 70 \cdot 30 + 100 \cdot 30 = \$7100$$

41. $R(p, q) = p \cdot x + q \cdot y = 200p - 5p^2 + 4pq + 300q - 4q^2 + 2pq$ or

$R(p, q) = -5p^2 + 6pq - 4q^2 + 200p + 300q$

$R(2, 3) = -5 \cdot 2^2 + 6 \cdot 2 \cdot 3 - 4 \cdot 3^2 + 200 \cdot 2 + 300 \cdot 3 = 1280$ or $\$1280$

$R(3, 2) = -5 \cdot 3^2 + 6 \cdot 3 \cdot 2 - 4 \cdot 2^2 + 200 \cdot 3 + 300 \cdot 2 = 1175$ or $\$1175$

43. $f(x, y) = 20x^{0.4}y^{0.6}$

$f(1250, 1700) = 20(1250)^{0.4}(1700)^{0.6}$
$$\approx 20(17.3286)(86.7500) \approx 30,065 \text{ units}$$

45. $F(p, i, n) = p\dfrac{(1 + i)^n - 1}{i}$

(A) $p = 2,000, \quad i = 0.09, \quad n = 30$

$F(2000, 0.09, 30) = 2000\dfrac{(1.09)^{30} - 1}{0.09} = \$272,615.08$

(B) Set $y_1 = 2000\dfrac{(1 + i)^{30} - 1}{i}, \quad y_2 = 500,000$

and find the intersection of the two curves.

Rate of interest: $i = 12.18\%$

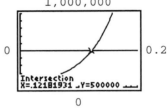

47. $T(V, x) = \dfrac{33V}{x + 33}$

$T(70, 47) = \dfrac{33 \cdot 70}{47 + 33} = \dfrac{33 \cdot 70}{80} = 28.8 \approx 29 \text{ minutes}$

$T(60, 27) = \dfrac{33 \cdot 60}{27 + 33} = 33 \text{ minutes}$

49. $C(W, L) = 100\dfrac{W}{L}$

$C(6, 8) = 100\dfrac{6}{8} = 75$

$C(8.1, 9) = 100\dfrac{8.1}{9} = 90$

51. $Q(M, C) = \dfrac{M}{C}100$

$Q(12, 10) = \dfrac{12}{10}100 = 120$

$Q(10, 12) = \dfrac{10}{12}100 = 83.33 \approx 83$

EXERCISE 8-2

Things to remember:

<u>1.</u> Let $z = f(x, y)$ be a function of two independent variables. The PARTIAL DERIVATIVE OF z WITH RESPECT TO x, denoted by $\dfrac{\partial z}{\partial x}$, f_x, or $f_x(x, y)$, is given by

$$\frac{\partial z}{\partial x} = \lim_{h \to 0} \frac{f(x + h, y) - f(x, y)}{h}$$

provided this limit exists. Similarly, the PARTIAL DERIVATIVE OF z WITH RESPECT TO y, denoted by $\frac{\partial z}{\partial y}$, $f_{y'}$ or $f_y(x, y)$, is given by

$$\frac{\partial z}{\partial y} = \lim_{k \to 0} \frac{f(x, y + k) - f(x, y)}{k}$$

provided this limit exists.

2. SECOND-ORDER PARTIAL DERIVATIVES

If $z = f(x, y)$, then:

$$\frac{\partial^2 z}{\partial x^2} = \frac{\partial \left(\frac{\partial z}{\partial x} \right)}{\partial x} = f_{xx}(x, y) = f_{xx}$$

$$\frac{\partial^2 z}{\partial x \partial y} = \frac{\partial \left(\frac{\partial z}{\partial y} \right)}{\partial x} = f_{yx}(x, y) = f_{yx}$$

$$\frac{\partial^2 z}{\partial y \partial x} = \frac{\partial \left(\frac{\partial z}{\partial x} \right)}{\partial y} = f_{xy}(x, y) = f_{xy}$$

$$\frac{\partial^2 z}{\partial y^2} = \frac{\partial \left(\frac{\partial z}{\partial y} \right)}{\partial y} = f_{yy}(x, y) = f_{yy}$$

$\Big[$ Note: For the functions being considered in this text, the mixed partial derivatives f_{xy} and f_{yx} are equal, i.e., $\dfrac{\partial^2 z}{\partial x \partial y} = \dfrac{\partial^2 z}{\partial y \partial x}$. $\Big]$

---

1. $z = 3 + 4x - 5y^2$
$\frac{\partial z}{\partial x} = 0 + 4 - 0 = 4$

3. $z = 3 + 4x - 5y^2$
$f_y = 0 + 0 - 10y;\ f_y(1, 2) = -20$

In Problems 5 - 9, $z = f(x, y) = 8x + 6y^3 - 3xy^2$.

5. $\frac{\partial z}{\partial y} = 18y^2 - 6xy$

7. From Problem 5, $\frac{\partial^2 z}{\partial y^2} = 36y - 6x$.

9. $f_x = 8 - 3y^2;\ f_x(2, 3) = 8 - 27 = -19$

In Problems 11 - 17, $C(x, y) = -7x^2 + 10xy + 4y^2 - 9x + 8y + 12$.

11. $C_x(x, y) = -14x + 10y - 9$

13. From Problem 11, $C_x(2, 2) = -28 + 20 - 9 = -17$

15. From Problem 11, $C_{xy} = 10$.

17. From Problem 11, $C_{xx} = -14$.

In Problems 19-23, $S(x, y) = 2y^3 e^x + 5x^4 \ln y$.

19. $S_x(x, y) = 2y^3 e^x + 20x^3 \ln y$

21. $S_y(x, y) = 6y^2 e^x + \dfrac{5x^4}{y}$; $S_y(2, 1) = 6e^2 + 80$

23. From Problem 19, $S_{xy}(x, y) = 6y^2 e^x + \dfrac{20x^3}{y}$.

In Problems 25 - 32, $z = f(x, y) = e^{4x^2+5y}$.

25. $\dfrac{\partial z}{\partial x} = e^{4x^2+5y} \cdot \dfrac{\partial}{\partial x}(4x^2 + 5y) = e^{4x^2+5y}(8x) = 8xe^{4x^2+5y}$

27. From Problem 25, $\dfrac{\partial z}{\partial x} = 8xe^{4x^2+5y}$. Therefore,

$$\dfrac{\partial^2 z}{\partial x \partial y} = \dfrac{\partial}{\partial y}(8xe^{4x^2+5y}) = 8xe^{4x^2+5y}\dfrac{\partial}{\partial y}(4x^2 + 5y)$$
$$= 8xe^{4x^2+5y}(5)$$
$$= 40xe^{4x^2+5y}$$

29. From Problem 27, $f_{xy} = 40xe^{4x^2+5y}$. Therefore,

$f_{xy}(1, 0) = 40e^4$

31. From Problem 25, $f_x = 8xe^{4x^2+5y}$. Therefore,

$$f_{xx} = 8xe^{4x^2+5y}\dfrac{\partial}{\partial x}(4x^2 + 5y) + e^{4x^2+5y}(8)$$
$$= 8xe^{4x^2+5y}(8x) + 8e^{4x^2+5y}$$
$$= 64x^2 e^{4x^2+5y} + 8e^{4x^2+5y}$$
$$f_{xx}(0, 1) = 8e^5$$

33. $f(x, y) = (x^2 - y^3)^3$

$f_x(x, y) = 3(x^2 - y^3)^2 \dfrac{\partial(x^2 - y^3)}{\partial x} = 3(x^2 - y^3)^2 2x = 6x(x^2 - y^3)^2$

$f_y(x, y) = 3(x^2 - y^3)^2 \dfrac{\partial(x^2 - y^3)}{\partial y} = 3(x^2 - y^3)^2(-3y^2) = -9y^2(x^2 - y^3)^2$

35. $f(x, y) = (3x^2y - 1)^4$

$f_x(x, y) = 4(3x^2y - 1)^3 \dfrac{\partial(3x^2y - 1)}{\partial x} = 4(3x^2y - 1)^3 6xy = 24xy(3x^2y - 1)^3$

$f_y(x, y) = 4(3x^2y - 1)^3 \dfrac{\partial(3x^2y - 1)}{\partial y} = 4(3x^2y - 1)^3 3x^2 = 12x^2(3x^2y - 1)^3$

37. $f(x, y) = \ln(x^2 + y^2)$

$f_x(x, y) = \dfrac{1}{x^2 + y^2} \cdot \dfrac{\partial(x^2 + y^2)}{\partial x} = \dfrac{2x}{x^2 + y^2}$

$f_y(x, y) = \dfrac{1}{x^2 + y^2} \cdot \dfrac{\partial(x^2 + y^2)}{\partial y} = \dfrac{2y}{x^2 + y^2}$

39. $f(x, y) = y^2 e^{xy^2}$

$f_x(x, y) = y^2 e^{xy^2} \dfrac{\partial(xy^2)}{\partial x} = y^2 e^{xy^2} y^2 = y^4 e^{xy^2}$

$f_y(x, y) = y^2 \dfrac{\partial(e^{xy^2})}{\partial y} + e^{xy^2} \dfrac{\partial(y^2)}{\partial y} \quad \text{(Product rule)}$

$= y^2 e^{xy^2} 2yx + y^2 e^{xy^2} 2y = 2xy^3 e^{xy^2} + 2y e^{xy^2}$

41. $f(x, y) = \dfrac{x^2 - y^2}{x^2 + y^2}$

Applying the quotient rule:

$f_x(x, y) = \dfrac{(x^2 + y^2) \dfrac{\partial(x^2 - y^2)}{\partial x} - (x^2 - y^2) \dfrac{\partial(x^2 + y^2)}{\partial x}}{(x^2 + y^2)^2}$

$= \dfrac{(x^2 + y^2)(2x) - (x^2 - y^2)(2x)}{(x^2 + y^2)^2}$

$= \dfrac{2x^3 + 2y^2x - 2x^3 + 2y^2x}{(x^2 + y^2)^2} = \dfrac{4xy^2}{(x^2 + y^2)^2}$

Again, applying the quotient rule:

$f_y(x, y) = \dfrac{(x^2 + y^2)(-2y) - (x^2 - y^2)(2y)}{(x^2 + y^2)^2} = \dfrac{-4x^2y}{(x^2 + y^2)^2}$

43. (A) $f(x, y) = y^3 + 4y^2 - 5y + 3$

Since f is independent of x, $\dfrac{\partial f}{\partial x} = 0$

(B) If $g(x, y)$ depends on y only, that is, if $g(x, y) = G(y)$ is independent of x, then
$$\dfrac{\partial g}{\partial x} = 0$$
Clearly there are an infinite number of such functions.

45. $f(x, y) = x^2 y^2 + x^3 + y$

$f_x(x, y) = 2xy^2 + 3x^2$ $\qquad\qquad$ $f_y(x, y) = 2x^2 y + 1$

$f_{xx}(x, y) = 2y^2 + 6x$ $\qquad\qquad$ $f_{yx}(x, y) = 4xy$

$f_{xy}(x, y) = 4xy$ $\qquad\qquad$ $f_{yy}(x, y) = 2x^2$

47. $f(x, y) = \dfrac{x}{y} - \dfrac{y}{x}$

$f_x(x, y) = \dfrac{1}{y} + \dfrac{y}{x^2}$ $\qquad\qquad$ $f_y(x, y) = -\dfrac{x}{y^2} - \dfrac{1}{x}$

$f_{xx}(x, y) = -\dfrac{2y}{x^3}$ $\qquad\qquad$ $f_{yx}(x, y) = -\dfrac{1}{y^2} + \dfrac{1}{x^2}$

$f_{xy}(x, y) = -\dfrac{1}{y^2} + \dfrac{1}{x^2}$ $\qquad\qquad$ $f_{yy}(x, y) = \dfrac{2x}{y^3}$

49. $f(x, y) = xe^{xy}$

$f_x(x, y) = xye^{xy} + e^{xy}$ $\qquad\qquad$ $f_y(x, y) = x^2 e^{xy}$

$f_{xx}(x, y) = xy^2 e^{xy} + 2ye^{xy}$ $\qquad\qquad$ $f_{yx}(x, y) = x^2 y e^{xy} + 2xe^{xy}$

$f_{xy}(x, y) = x^2 y e^{xy} + 2xe^{xy}$ $\qquad\qquad$ $f_{yy}(x, y) = x^3 e^{xy}$

51. $P(x, y) = -x^2 + 2xy - 2y^2 - 4x + 12y - 5$

$P_x(x, y) = -2x + 2y - 0 - 4 + 0 - 0 = -2x + 2y - 4$

$P_y(x, y) = 0 + 2x - 4y - 0 + 12 - 0 = 2x - 4y + 12$

$P_x(x, y) = 0$ and $P_y(x, y) = 0$ when

$\qquad$ $-2x + 2y - 4 = 0$ $\qquad$ (1)
$\qquad$ $2x - 4y + 12 = 0$ $\qquad$ (2)

Add equations (1) and (2): $-2y + 8 = 0$
$\qquad\qquad\qquad\qquad\qquad\qquad$ $y = 4$

Substitute $y = 4$ into (1): $-2x + 2 \cdot 4 - 4 = 0$
$\qquad\qquad\qquad\qquad\qquad\qquad$ $-2x + 4 = 0$
$\qquad\qquad\qquad\qquad\qquad\qquad\qquad$ $x = 2$

Thus, $P_x(x, y) = 0$ and $P_y(x, y) = 0$ when $x = 2$ and $y = 4$.

53. $F(x, y) = x^3 - 2x^2y^2 - 2x - 4y + 10$;

$F_x(x, y) = 3x^2 - 4xy^2 - 2$; $F_y(x, y) = -4x^2y - 4$.

Set $F_x(x, y) = 0$ and $F_y(x, y) = 0$ and solve simultaneously:

$$3x^2 - 4xy^2 - 2 = 0 \qquad (1)$$
$$-4x^2y - 4 = 0 \qquad (2)$$

From (2), $y = -\dfrac{1}{x^2}$. Substituting this into (1),

$$3x^2 - 4x\left(-\frac{1}{x^2}\right)^2 - 2 = 0$$

$$3x^2 - 4x\left(\frac{1}{x^4}\right) - 2 = 0$$

$$3x^5 - 2x^3 - 4 = 0$$

Using a graphing utility, we find that
    $x \approx 1.200$
Then, $y \approx -0.694$.

55. $f(x, y) = 3x^2 + y^2 - 4x - 6y + 2$

(A) $f(x, 1) = 3x^2 + 1 - 4x - 6 + 2$
$$= 3x^2 - 4x - 3$$

$\dfrac{d}{dx}[f(x, 1)] = 6x - 4$; critical values: $6x - 4 = 0$

$$x = \frac{2}{3}$$

$\dfrac{d^2}{dx^2}[f(x, 1)] = 6 > 0$

Therefore, $f\left(\dfrac{2}{3}, 1\right) = 3\left(\dfrac{2}{3}\right)^2 - 4\left(\dfrac{2}{3}\right) - 3 = -\dfrac{13}{3}$ is the minimum value of $f(x, 1)$.

(B) $-\dfrac{13}{3}$ is the minimum value of $f(x, y)$ on the curve $f(x, 1)$; $f(x, y)$ may have smaller values on other curves $f(x, k)$, k constant, or $f(h, y)$, h constant. For example, the minimum value of $f(x, 2) = 3x^2 - 4x - 6$ is $f\left(\dfrac{2}{3}, 2\right) = -\dfrac{22}{3}$; the minimum value of $f(0, y) = y^2 - 6y + 2$ is $f(0, 3) = -7$.

57. $f(x, y) = 4 - x^4y + 3xy^2 + y^5$

(A) Let $y = 2$ and find the maximum value of $f(x, 2) = 4 - 2x^4 + 12x + 32$ $= -2x^4 + 12x + 36$. Using a graphing utility we find that the maximum value of $f(x, 2)$ is 46.302 at $x = 1.1447152 \approx 1.145$.

(B) $f_x(x, y) = -4x^3y + 3y^2$
$f_x(1.145, 2) = -0.008989 \approx 0$

$f_y(x, y) = -x^4 + 6xy + 5y^4$
$f_y(1.145, 2) = 92.021$

59. $f(x, y) = \ln(x^2 + y^2)$ (see Problem 37)

$$f_x(x, y) = \frac{2x}{x^2 + y^2} \qquad\qquad f_y(x, y) = \frac{2y}{x^2 + y^2}$$

$$f_{xx}(x, y) = \frac{(x^2 + y^2)2 - 2x(2x)}{(x^2 + y^2)^2} \qquad f_{yy}(x, y) = \frac{(x^2 + y^2)2 - 2y(2y)}{(x^2 + y^2)^2}$$

$$= \frac{2(y^2 - x^2)}{(x^2 + y^2)^2} \qquad\qquad = \frac{2(x^2 - y^2)}{(x^2 + y^2)^2} = \frac{-2(y^2 - x^2)}{(x^2 + y^2)^2}$$

$$f_{xx}(x, y) + f_{yy}(x, y) = \frac{2(y^2 - x^2)}{(x^2 + y^2)^2} + \frac{-2(y^2 - x^2)}{(x^2 + y^2)^2} = 0$$

61. $f(x, y) = x^2 + 2y^2$

(A) $\displaystyle\lim_{h \to 0} \frac{f(x + h, y) - f(x, y)}{h} = \lim_{h \to 0} \frac{(x + h)^2 + 2y^2 - (x^2 + 2y^2)}{h}$

$$= \lim_{h \to 0} \frac{x^2 + 2xh + h^2 + 2y^2 - x^2 - 2y^2}{h}$$

$$= \lim_{h \to 0} \frac{h(2x + h)}{h} = \lim_{h \to 0} (2x + h)$$

$$= 2x$$

(B) $\displaystyle\lim_{k \to 0} \frac{f(x, y + k) - f(x, y)}{k} = \lim_{k \to 0} \frac{x^2 + 2(y + k)^2 - (x^2 + 2y^2)}{k}$

$$= \lim_{k \to 0} \frac{x^2 + 2(y^2 + 2yk + k^2) - x^2 - 2y^2}{k}$$

$$= \lim_{k \to 0} \frac{4yk + 2k^2}{k} = \lim_{k \to 0} (4y + 2k)$$

$$= 4y$$

63. $R(x, y) = 80x + 90y + 0.04xy - 0.05x^2 - 0.05y^2$
$C(x, y) = 8x + 6y + 20,000$
The profit $P(x, y)$ is given by:
$P(x, y) = R(x, y) - C(x, y)$

$$= 80x + 90y + 0.04xy - 0.05x^2 - 0.05y^2 - (8x + 6y + 20,000)$$

$$= 72x + 84y + 0.04xy - 0.05x^2 - 0.05y^2 - 20,000$$

Now
$P_x(x, y) = 72 + 0.04y - 0.1x$
and
$P_x(1200, 1800) = 72 + 0.04(1800) - 0.1(1200)$

$$= 72 + 72 - 120 = 24;$$

$P_y(x, y) = 84 + 0.04x - 0.1y$
and
$P_y(1200, 1800) = 84 + 0.04(1200) - 0.1(1800)$

$$= 84 + 48 - 180 = -48.$$

Thus, at the (1200, 1800) output level, profit will increase approximately $24 per unit increase in production of type A calculators; and profit will decrease $48 per unit increase in production of type B calculators.

65. $x = 200 - 5p + 4q$
$y = 300 - 4q + 2p$
$\dfrac{\partial x}{\partial p} = -5, \quad \dfrac{\partial y}{\partial p} = 2$

A \$1 increase in the price of brand A will decrease the demand for brand A by 5 pounds at any price level (p, q).

A \$1 increase in the price of brand A will increase the demand for brand B by 2 pounds at any price level (p, q).

67. $f(x, y) = 10x^{0.75}y^{0.25}$

(A) $f_x(x, y) = 10(0.75)x^{-0.25}y^{0.25} = 7.5x^{-0.25}y^{0.25}$

$f_y(x, y) = 10(0.25)x^{0.75}y^{-0.75} = 2.5x^{0.75}y^{-0.75}$

(B) Marginal productivity of labor $= f_x(600, 100)$
$$= 7.5(600)^{-0.25}(100)^{0.25} \approx 4.79$$

Marginal productivity of capital $= f_y(600, 100)$
$$= 2.5(600)^{0.75}(100)^{-0.75} \approx 9.58$$

(C) The government should encourage the increased use of capital.

69. $x = f(p, q) = 8000 - 0.09p^2 + 0.08q^2$ (Butter)
$y = g(p, q) = 15,000 + 0.04p^2 - 0.3q^2$ (Margarine)
$f_q(p, q) = 0.08(2)q = 0.16q > 0$
$g_p(p, q) = 0.04(2)p = 0.08p > 0$
Thus, the products are competitive.

71. $x = f(p, q) = 800 - 0.004p^2 - 0.003q^2$ (Skis)
$y = g(p, q) = 600 - 0.003p^2 - 0.002q^2$ (Ski boots)
$f_q(p, q) = -0.003(2)q = -0.006q < 0$
$g_p(p, q) = -0.003(2)p = -0.006p < 0$
Thus, the products are complementary.

73. $A = f(w, h) = 15.64w^{0.425}h^{0.725}$

(A) $f_w(w, h) = 15.64(0.425)w^{-0.575}h^{0.725} \approx 6.65w^{-0.575}h^{0.725}$

$f_h(w, h) = 15.64(0.725)w^{0.425}h^{-0.275} \approx 11.34w^{0.425}h^{-0.275}$

(B) $f_w(65, 57) = 6.65(65)^{-0.575}(57)^{0.725} \approx 11.31$

For a 65 pound child 57 inches tall, the rate of change of surface area is approximately 11.31 square inches for a one-pound gain in weight, height held fixed.

$f_h(65, 57) = 11.34(65)^{0.425}(57)^{-0.275} \approx 21.99$

For a 65 pound child 57 inches tall, the rate of change of surface area is approximately 21.99 square inches for a one-inch gain in height, weight held fixed.

75. $C(W, L) = 100\dfrac{W}{L}$

$C_W(W, L) = \dfrac{100}{L}$

$C_W(6, 8) = \dfrac{100}{8} = 12.5$

The index increases 12.5 units per 1-inch increase in the width of the head (length held fixed) when $W = 6$ and $L = 8$.

$C_L(W, L) = -\dfrac{100W}{L^2}$

$C_L(6, 8) = -\dfrac{100 \times 6}{8^2}$

$= -\dfrac{600}{64} = -9.38$

The index decreases 9.38 units per 1-inch increase in length (width held fixed) when $W = 6$ and $L = 8$.

EXERCISE 8-3

Things to remember:

<u>1</u>. $f(a, b)$ is a LOCAL MAXIMUM if there exists a circular region in the domain of $f(x, y)$ with (a, b) as the center, such that $f(a, b) \geq f(x, y)$ for all (x, y) in the region. Similarly, $f(a, b)$ is a LOCAL MINIMUM if $f(a, b) \leq f(x, y)$ for all (x, y) in the region.

<u>2</u>. LOCAL EXTREMA AND PARTIAL DERIVATIVES

Let $f(a, b)$ be a local extremum (a local maximum or a local minimum) for the function f. If both f_x and f_y exist at (a, b) then

$$f_x(a, b) = 0 \quad \text{and} \quad f_y(a, b) = 0$$

<u>3</u>. SECOND-DERIVATIVE TEST FOR LOCAL EXTREMA FOR $z = f(x, y)$
Given:

(a) $f_x(a, b) = 0$ and $f_y(a, b) = 0$ [(a, b) is a critical point].

(b) All second-order partial derivatives of f exist in some circular region containing (a, b) as center.

(c) $A = f_{xx}(a, b)$, $B = f_{xy}(a, b)$, $C = f_{yy}(a, b)$.

   Then:

   i) If $AC - B^2 > 0$ and $A < 0$, then $f(a, b)$ is a local maximum.

   ii) If $AC - B^2 > 0$ and $A > 0$, then $f(a, b)$ is a local minimum.

   iii) If $AC - B^2 < 0$, then f has a saddle point at (a, b).

   iv) If $AC - B^2 = 0$, then the test fails.

---

1. $f(x, y) = 4x + 5y - 6$
$f_x(x, y) = 4 \neq 0$; $f_y(x, y) = 5 \neq 0$; the functions $f_x(x, y)$ and $f_y(x, y)$ are nonzero for all (x, y).

3. $f(x, y) = 3.7 - 1.2x + 6.8y + 0.2y^3 + x^4$
$f_x(x, y) = -1.2 + 4x^3$; $f_y = 6.8 + 0.6y^2$; the function $f_y(x, y)$ is nonzero for all (x, y).

5. $f(x, y) = 6 - x^2 - 4x - y^2$

$f_x(x, y) = -2x - 4 = 0$

$$x = -2$$

$f_y(x, y) = -2y = 0$

$$y = 0$$

Thus, $(-2, 0)$ is a critical point.

$f_{xx} = -2$, $f_{xy} = 0$, $f_{yy} = -2$,

$f_{xx}(-2, 0) \cdot f_{yy}(-2, 0) - [f_{xy}(-2, 0)]^2 = (-2)(-2) - 0^2 = 4 > 0$

and $\qquad\qquad\qquad\qquad f_{xx}(-2, 0) = -2 < 0$.

Thus, $f(-2, 0) = 6 - (-2)^2 - 4(-2) - 0^2 = 10$ is a local maximum (using <u>3</u>).

7. $f(x, y) = x^2 + y^2 + 2x - 6y + 14$

$f_x(x, y) = 2x + 2 = 0$

$$x = -1$$

$f_y(x, y) = 2y - 6 = 0$

$$y = 3$$

Thus, $(-1, 3)$ is a critical point.

$f_{xx} = 2 \qquad\qquad\qquad f_{xy} = 0 \qquad\qquad\qquad f_{yy} = 2$

$f_{xx}(-1, 3) = 2 > 0 \qquad\quad f_{xy}(-1, 3) = 0 \qquad\quad f_{yy}(-1, 3) = 2$

$f_{xx}(-1, 3) \cdot f_{yy}(-1, 3) - [f_{xy}(-1, 3)]^2 = 2 \cdot 2 - 0^2 = 4 > 0$

Thus, using <u>3</u>, $f(-1, 3) = 4$ is a local minimum.

9. $f(x, y) = xy + 2x - 3y - 2$

$f_x = y + 2 = 0$

$$y = -2$$

$f_y = x - 3 = 0$

$$x = 3$$

Thus, $(3, -2)$ is a critical point.

$f_{xx} = 0 \qquad\qquad\qquad f_{xy} = 1 \qquad\qquad\qquad f_{yy} = 0$

$f_{xx}(3, -2) = 0 \qquad\quad f_{xy}(3, -2) = 1 \qquad\quad f_{yy}(3, -2) = 0$

$f_{xx}(3, -2) \cdot f_{yy}(3, -2) - [f_{xy}(3, -2)]^2 = 0 \cdot 0 - [1]^2 = -1 < 0$

Thus, using <u>3</u>, f has a saddle point at $(3, -2)$.

11. $f(x, y) = -3x^2 + 2xy - 2y^2 + 14x + 2y + 10$

$f_x = -6x + 2y + 14 = 0 \qquad (1)$

$f_y = 2x - 4y + 2 = 0 \qquad (2)$

Solving (1) and (2) for x and y, we obtain $x = 3$ and $y = 2$.

Thus, $(3, 2)$ is a critical point.

$f_{xx} = -6 \qquad\qquad\qquad f_{xy} = 2 \qquad\qquad\qquad f_{yy} = -4$

$f_{xx}(3, 2) = -6 < 0 \qquad\quad f_{xy}(3, 2) = 2 \qquad\quad f_{yy}(3, 2) = -4$

$f_{xx}(3, 2) \cdot f_{yy}(3, 2) - [f_{xy}(3, 2)]^2 = (-6)(-4) - 2^2 = 20 > 0$

Thus, using <u>3</u>, $f(3, 2)$ is a local maximum and

$f(3, 2) = -3 \cdot 3^2 + 2 \cdot 3 \cdot 2 - 2 \cdot 2^2 + 14 \cdot 3 + 2 \cdot 2 + 10 = 33$.

13. $f(x, y) = 2x^2 - 2xy + 3y^2 - 4x - 8y + 20$

$f_x = 4x - 2y - 4 = 0$ (1)

$f_y = -2x + 6y - 8 = 0$ (2)

Solving (1) and (2) for x and y, we obtain $x = 2$ and $y = 2$.
Thus, (2, 2) is a critical point.

$f_{xx} = 4$ $f_{xy} = -2$ $f_{yy} = 6$

$f_{xx}(2, 2) = 4 > 0$ $f_{xy}(2, 2) = -2$ $f_{yy}(2, 2) = 6$

$f_{xx}(2, 2) \cdot f_{yy}(2, 2) - [f_{xy}(2, 2)]^2 = 4 \cdot 6 - [-2]^2 = 20 > 0$

Thus, using 3, $f(2, 2)$ is a local minimum and

$f(2, 2) = 2 \cdot 2^2 - 2 \cdot 2 \cdot 2 + 3 \cdot 2^2 - 4 \cdot 2 - 8 \cdot 2 + 20 = 8.$

15. $f(x, y) = e^{xy}$

$f_x = e^{xy} \dfrac{\partial(xy)}{\partial x}$ $f_y = e^{xy} \dfrac{\partial(xy)}{\partial y}$

    $= e^{xy} y = 0$ $= e^{xy} x = 0$

       $y = 0$ $(e^{xy} \neq 0)$ $x = 0$ $(e^{xy} \neq 0)$

Thus, (0, 0) is a critical point.

$f_{xx} = ye^{xy} \dfrac{\partial(xy)}{\partial x}$ $f_{xy} = e^{xy} \cdot 1 + ye^{xy} x$ $f_{yy} = xe^{xy} \dfrac{\partial(xy)}{\partial y}$

     $= ye^{xy} y$ $= e^{xy} + xye^{xy}$ $= x^2 e^{xy}$

     $= y^2 e^{xy}$

$f_{xx}(0, 0) = 0$ $f_{xy}(0, 0) = 1 + 0 = 1$ $f_{yy}(0, 0) = 0$

$f_{xx}(0, 0) \cdot f_{yy}(0, 0) - [f_{xy}(0, 0)]^2 = 0 - [1]^2 = -1 < 0$

Thus, using 3, $f(x, y)$ has a saddle point at (0, 0).

17. $f(x, y) = x^3 + y^3 - 3xy$

$f_x = 3x^2 - 3y = 3(x^2 - y) = 0$

Thus, $y = x^2$.   (1)

$f_y = 3y^2 - 3x = 3(y^2 - x) = 0$

Thus, $y^2 = x$.   (2)

Combining (1) and (2), we obtain $x = x^4$ or $x(x^3 - 1) = 0$. Therefore, $x = 0$ or $x = 1$, and the critical points are (0, 0) and (1, 1).

$f_{xx} = 6x$ $f_{xy} = -3$ $f_{yy} = 6y$

For the critical point (0, 0):

$f_{xx}(0, 0) = 0$ $f_{xy}(0, 0) = -3$ $f_{yy}(0, 0) = 0$

$f_{xx}(0, 0) \cdot f_{yy}(0, 0) - [f_{xy}(0, 0)]^2 = 0 - (-3)^2 = -9 < 0$

Thus, using 3, $f(x, y)$ has a saddle point at (0, 0).
For the critical point (1, 1):

$f_{xx}(1, 1) = 6$ $f_{xy}(1, 1) = -3$ $f_{yy}(1, 1) = 6$

$f_{xx}(1, 1) \cdot f_{yy}(1, 1) - [f_{xy}(1, 1)]^2 = 6 \cdot 6 - (-3)^2 = 27 > 0$

$f_{xx}(1, 1) > 0$

Thus, using 3, $f(1, 1)$ is a local minimum and

$f(1, 1) = 1^3 + 1^3 - 3 \cdot 1 \cdot 1 = 2 - 3 = -1.$

19. $f(x, y) = 2x^4 + y^2 - 12xy$

$f_x = 8x^3 - 12y = 0$

Thus, $y = \dfrac{2}{3}x^3$.

$f_y = 2y - 12x = 0$

Thus, $y = 6x$

Therefore, $6x = \dfrac{2}{3}x^3$

$x^3 - 9x = 0$

$x(x^2 - 9) = 0$

$x = 0, x = 3, x = -3$

Thus, the critical points are $(0, 0)$, $(3, 18)$, $(-3, -18)$. Now,

$f_{xx} = 24x^2 \qquad\qquad f_{xy} = -12 \qquad\qquad f_{yy} = 2$

For the critical point $(0, 0)$:

$f_{xx}(0, 0) = 0 \qquad\qquad f_{xy}(0, 0) = -12 \qquad\qquad f_{yy}(0, 0) = 2$

and

$f_{xx}(0, 0) \cdot f_{yy}(0, 0) - [f_{xy}(0, 0)]^2 = 0 \cdot 2 - (-12)^2 = -144.$

Thus, $f(x, y)$ has a saddle point at $(0, 0)$.

For the critical point $(3, 18)$:

$f_{xx}(3, 18) = 24 \cdot 3^2 = 216 > 0 \qquad f_{xy}(3, 18) = -12 \qquad f_{yy}(3, 18) = 2$

and

$f_{xx}(3, 18) \cdot f_{yy}(3, 18) - [f_{xy}(3, 18)]^2 = 216 \cdot 2 - (-12)^2 = 288 > 0$

Thus, $f(3, 18) = -162$ is a local minimum.

For the critical point $(-3, -18)$:

$f_{xx}(-3, -18) = 216 > 0 \qquad f_{xy}(-3, -18) = -12 \qquad f_{yy}(-3, -18) = 2$

and

$f_{xx}(-3, -18) \cdot f_{yy}(-3, -18) - [f_{xy}(-3, -18)]^2 = 288 > 0$

Thus, $f(-3, -18) = -162$ is a local minimum.

21. $f(x, y) = x^3 - 3xy^2 + 6y^2$

$f_x = 3x^2 - 3y^2 = 0$

Thus, $y^2 = x^2$ or $y = \pm x$.

$f_y = -6xy + 12y = 0$ or $-6y(x - 2) = 0$

Thus, $y = 0$ or $x = 2$.

Therefore, the critical points are $(0, 0)$, $(2, 2)$, and $(2, -2)$.

Now,

$f_{xx} = 6x \qquad\qquad f_{xy} = -6y \qquad\qquad f_{yy} = -6x + 12$

For the critical point $(0, 0)$:

$f_{xx}(0, 0) \cdot f_{yy}(0, 0) - [f_{xy}(0, 0]^2 = 0 \cdot 12 - 0^2 = 0$

Thus, the second-derivative test fails.

For the critical point $(2, 2)$:

$f_{xx}(2, 2) \cdot f_{yy}(2, 2) - [f_{xy}(2, 2)]^2 = 12 \cdot 0 - (-12)^2 = -144 < 0$

Thus, $f(x, y)$ has a saddle point at $(2, 2)$.

For the critical point $(2, -2)$:

$f_{xx}(2, -2) \cdot f_{yy}(2, -2) - [f_{xy}(2, -2)]^2 = 12 \cdot 0 - (12)^2 = -144 < 0$

Thus, $f(x, y)$ has a saddle point at $(2, -2)$.

23. $f(x, y) = y^3 + 2x^2 y^2 - 3x - 2y + 8$;

$f_x = 4xy^2 - 3$; $f_y = 3y^2 + 4x^2 y - 2$

Set $f_x = 0$ and $f_y = 0$ to find the critical points:

$$4xy^2 - 3 = 0 \qquad (1)$$
$$3y^2 + 4x^2 y - 2 = 0 \qquad (2)$$

From (1) $x = \dfrac{3}{4y^2}$. Substituting this into (2), we have

$$3y^2 + 4\left(\frac{3}{4y^2}\right)^2 y - 2 = 0$$

$$3y^2 + 4\left(\frac{9}{16y^4}\right) y - 2 = 0$$

$$12y^5 - 8y^3 + 9 = 0$$

Using a graphing utility, we find that $y \approx -1.105$ and $x \approx 0.614$.

Now, $f_{xx} = 4y^2$ and $f_{xx}(0.614, -1.105) \approx 4.884$

$f_{xy} = 8xy$ and $f_{xy}(0.614, -1.105) \approx -5.428$

$f_{yy} = 6y + 4x^2$ and $f_{yy}(0.614, -1.105) \approx -5.122$

$f_{xx}(0.614, -1.105) \cdot f_{yy}(0.614, -1.105) - [f_{xy}(0.614, -1.105)]^2$

$\approx -54.479 < 0$

Thus, $f(x, y)$ has a saddle point at $(0.614, -1.105)$.

25. $f(x, y) = x^2 \geq 0$ for all (x, y) and $f(x, y) = 0$ when $x = 0$. Thus, f has a local minimum at each point $(0, y, 0)$ on the y-axis.

27. $f(x, y) = x^4 e^y + x^2 y^4 + 1$

(A) $f_x = 4x^3 e^y + 2xy^4 = 0$ (1)

$f_y = x^4 e^y + 4x^2 y^3 = 0$ (2)

The values $x = 0$, $y = 0$ satisfy (1) and (2) so $(0, 0)$ is a critical point.

$A = f_{xx} = 12x^2 e^y + 2y^4 = 0$ at $(0, 0)$,

$B = f_{xy} = 4x^3 e^y + 8xy^3 = 0$ at $(0, 0)$,

$C = f_{yy} = x^4 e^y + 12x^2 y^2 = 0$ at $(0, 0)$.

$AC - B^2 = 0$; the second derivative test fails.

(B) Cross-sections of f by the planes $y = 0$, $x = 0$, $y = x$ and $y = -x$ are shown at the right.

The cross-sections indicate that f has a local minimum at $(0, 0)$.

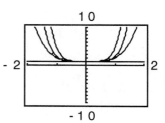

29. $P(x, y) = R(x, y) - C(x, y)$
$= 2x + 3y - (x^2 - 2xy + 2y^2 + 6x - 9y + 5)$
$= -x^2 + 2xy - 2y^2 - 4x + 12y - 5$
$P_x = -2x + 2y - 4 = 0$ (1)
$P_y = 2x - 4y + 12 = 0$ (2)
Solving (1) and (2) for x and y, we obtain $x = 2$ and $y = 4$. Thus, $(2, 4)$ is a critical point.

$P_{xx} = -2$ and $P_{xx}(2, 4) = -2 < 0$
$P_{xy} = 2$ and $P_{xy}(2, 4) = 2$
$P_{yy} = -4$ and $P_{yy}(2, 4) = -4$

$P_{xx}(2, 4) \cdot P_{yy}(2, 4) - [P_{xy}(2, 4)]^2 = (-2)(-4) - [2]^2 = 4 > 0$
The maximum occurs when 2000 type A and 4000 type B calculators are produced. The maximum profit is given by $P(2, 4)$. Hence,
$\max P = P(2, 4) = -(2)^2 + 2 \cdot 2 \cdot 4 - 2 \cdot 4^2 - 4 \cdot 2 + 12 \cdot 4 - 5$
$= -4 + 16 - 32 - 8 + 48 - 5 = \$15$ million.

31. $x = 116 - 30p + 20q$ (Brand A)
$y = 144 + 16p - 24q$ (Brand B)

(A)

p	q	x	y
10	12	56	16
11	11	6	56

(B) In terms of p and q, the cost function C is given by:
$C = 6x + 8y = 6(116 - 30p + 20q) + 8(144 + 16p - 24q)$
$= 1848 - 52p - 72q$
The revenue function R is given by:
$R = px + qy = p(116 - 30p + 20q) + q(144 + 16p - 24q)$
$= 116p - 30p^2 + 20pq + 144q + 16pq - 24q^2$
$= -30p^2 + 36pq - 24q^2 + 116p + 144q$

Thus, the profit $P = R - C$ is given by:
$P = -30p^2 + 36pq - 24q^2 + 116p + 144q - (1848 - 52p - 72q)$
$= -30p^2 + 36pq - 24q^2 + 168p + 216q - 1848$

Now, calculating P_p and P_q and setting these equal to 0, we have:
$P_p = -60p + 36q + 168 = 0$ (1)
$P_q = 36p - 48q + 216 = 0$ (2)
Solving (1) and (2) for p and q, we get $p = 10$ and $q = 12$. Thus, $(10, 12)$ is a critical point of the profit function P.

$$P_{pp} = -60 \quad \text{and} \quad P_{pp}(10, 12) = -60$$
$$P_{pq} = 36 \quad \text{and} \quad P_{pq}(10, 12) = 36$$
$$P_{qq} = -48 \quad \text{and} \quad P_{qq}(10, 12) = -48$$
$$P_{pp} \cdot P_{qq} - [P_{pq}]^2 = (-60)(-48) - (36)^2 = 1584 > 0$$

Since $P_{pp}(10, 12) = -60 < 0$, we conclude that the maximum profit occurs when $p = \$10$ and $q = \$12$. The maximum profit is:

$$P(10, 12) = -30(10)^2 + 36(10)(12) - 24(12)^2 + 168(10) + 216(12) - 1848$$
$$= \$288$$

33. The square of the distance from P to A is: $x^2 + y^2$
The square of the distance from P to B is:
$(x - 2)^2 + (y - 6)^2 = x^2 - 4x + y^2 - 12y + 40$
The square of the distance from P to C is:
$(x - 10)^2 + y^2 = x^2 - 20x + y^2 + 100$
Thus, we have:
$$P(x, y) = 3x^2 - 24x + 3y^2 - 12y + 140$$

$$P_x = 6x - 24 = 0 \qquad\qquad P_y = 6y - 12 = 0$$
$$x = 4 \qquad\qquad\qquad\qquad y = 2$$
Therefore, $(4, 2)$ is a critical point.

$$P_{xx} = 6 \quad \text{and} \quad P_{xx}(4, 2) = 6 > 0$$
$$P_{xy} = 0 \quad \text{and} \quad P_{xy}(4, 2) = 0$$
$$P_{yy} = 6 \quad \text{and} \quad P_{yy}(4, 2) = 6$$
$$P_{xx} \cdot P_{yy} - [P_{xy}]^2 = 6 \cdot 6 - 0 = 36 > 0$$
Therefore, P has a minimum at the point $(4, 2)$.

35. Let $x =$ length, $y =$ width, and $z =$ height. Then $V = xyz = 64$ or $z = \dfrac{64}{xy}$. The surface area of the box is:

$$S = xy + 2xz + 4yz \quad \text{or} \quad S(x, y) = xy + \frac{128}{y} + \frac{256}{x}, \quad x > 0, \ y > 0$$

$$S_x = y - \frac{256}{x^2} = 0 \qquad \text{or} \quad y = \frac{256}{x^2} \qquad (1)$$

$$S_y = x - \frac{128}{y^2} = 0 \qquad \text{or} \quad x = \frac{128}{y^2}$$

Thus, $y = \dfrac{256}{\dfrac{(128)^2}{y^4}}$ or $y^4 - 64y = 0$

$y(y^3 - 64) = 0$ (Since $y > 0$, $y = 0$ does not
and $y = 4$ yield a critical point.)

Setting $y = 4$ in (1), we find $x = 8$. Therefore, the critical point is $(8, 4)$.

Now we have:

$$S_{xx} = \frac{512}{x^3} \quad \text{and} \quad S_{xx}(8, 4) = 1 > 0$$

$$S_{xy} = 1$$

$$S_{yy} = \frac{256}{y^3} \quad \text{and} \quad S_{yy}(8, 4) = 4$$

$$S_{xx}(8, 4) \cdot S_{yy}(8, 4) - [S_{xy}(8, 4)]^2 = 1 \cdot 4 - 1^2 = 3 > 0$$

Thus, the dimensions that will require the least amount of material are:

Length $x = 8$ inches; Width $y = 4$ inches; Height $z = \dfrac{64}{8(4)} = 2$ inches.

37. Let x = length of the package, y = width, and z = height. Then

$$x + 2y + 2z = 120 \qquad (1)$$

Volume = $V = xyz$.

From (1), $z = \dfrac{120 - x - 2y}{2}$. Thus, we have:

$$V(x, y) = xy\left(\frac{120 - x - 2y}{2}\right) = 60xy - \frac{x^2 y}{2} - xy^2, \quad x > 0, \; y > 0$$

$$V_x = 60y - xy - y^2 = 0$$

$$y(60 - x - y) = 0$$

$$60 - x - y = 0 \qquad (2) \qquad \text{(Since } y > 0, \; y = 0 \text{ does not yield}$$
$$\text{a critical point.)}$$

$$V_y = 60x - \frac{x^2}{2} - 2xy = 0$$

$$x\left(60 - \frac{x}{2} - 2y\right) = 0$$

$$120 - x - 4y = 0 \qquad (3) \qquad \text{(Since } x > 0, \; x = 0 \text{ does not yield}$$
$$\text{a critical point.)}$$

Solving (2) and (3) for x and y, we obtain $x = 40$ and $y = 20$. Thus, (40, 20) is the critical point.

$$V_{xx} = -y \qquad \text{and} \quad V_{xx}(40, 20) = -20 < 0$$

$$V_{xy} = 60 - x - 2y \quad \text{and} \quad V_{xy}(40, 20) = 60 - 40 - 40 = -20$$

$$V_{yy} = -2x \qquad \text{and} \quad V_{yy}(40, 20) = -80$$

$$V_{xx}(40, 20) \cdot V_{yy}(40, 20) - [V_{xy}(40, 20)]^2 = (-20)(-80) - [-20]^2$$
$$= 1600 - 400$$
$$= 1200 > 0$$

Thus, the maximum volume of the package is obtained when $x = 40$, $y = 20$, and $z = \dfrac{120 - 40 - 2 \cdot 20}{2} = 20$ inches. The package has dimensions:

Length $x = 40$ inches; Width $y = 20$ inches; Height $z = 20$ inches.

Things to remember:

1. Any local maxima or minima of the function $z = f(x, y)$ subject to the constraint $g(x, y) = 0$ will be among those points (x_0, y_0) for which (x_0, y_0, λ_0) is a solution to the system:

$$F_x(x, y, \lambda) = 0$$
$$F_y(x, y, \lambda) = 0$$
$$F_\lambda(x, y, \lambda) = 0$$

where $F(x, y, \lambda) = f(x, y) + \lambda g(x, y)$, provided all the partial derivatives exist.

2. METHOD OF LAGRANGE MULTIPLIERS FOR FUNCTIONS OF TWO INDEPENDENT VARIABLES
   (a) Formulate the problem in the form:
       Maximize (or Minimize) $z = f(x, y)$
       Subject to: $g(x, y) = 0$
   (b) Form the function F:
       $$F(x, y, \lambda) = f(x, y) + \lambda g(x, y)$$
   (c) Find the critical points (x_0, y_0, λ_0) for F, that is, solve the system:

   $$F_x(x, y, \lambda) = 0$$
   $$F_y(x, y, \lambda) = 0$$
   $$F_\lambda(x, y, \lambda) = 0$$

   (d) If (x_0, y_0, λ_0) is the only critical point of F, then assume that (x_0, y_0) is the solution to the problem. If F has more than one critical point, then evaluate $z = f(x, y)$ at (x_0, y_0) for each critical point (x_0, y_0, λ_0) of F.
       Assume that the largest of these values is the maximum value of $f(x, y)$ subject to the constraint $g(x, y) = 0$, and the smallest is the minimum value of $f(x, y)$ subject to the constraint $g(x, y) = 0$.

3. METHOD OF LAGRANGE MULTIPLIERS FOR FUNCTIONS OF THREE VARIABLES
   Any local maxima or minima of the function $w = f(x, y, z)$ subject to the constraint $g(x, y, z) = 0$ will be among the set of points (x_0, y_0, z_0) for which $(x_0, y_0, z_0, \lambda_0)$ is a solution to the system

   $$F_x(x, y, z, \lambda) = 0$$
   $$F_y(x, y, z, \lambda) = 0$$
   $$F_z(x, y, z, \lambda) = 0$$
   $$F_\lambda(x, y, z, \lambda) = 0$$

   where $F(x, y, z, \lambda) = f(x, y, z) + \lambda g(x, y, z)$, provided that all the partial derivatives exist.

1. Step 1. Maximize $f(x, y) = 2xy$
Subject to: $g(x, y) = x + y - 6 = 0$

Step 2. $F(x, y, \lambda) = f(x, y) + \lambda g(x, y)$
$$= 2xy + \lambda(x + y - 6)$$

Step 3. $F_x = 2y + \lambda = 0$ (1)

$F_y = 2x + \lambda = 0$ (2)

$F_\lambda = x + y - 6 = 0$ (3)

From (1) and (2), we obtain:

$x = -\dfrac{\lambda}{2}, \ y = -\dfrac{\lambda}{2}$

Substituting these into (3), we have:

$-\dfrac{\lambda}{2} - \dfrac{\lambda}{2} - 6 = 0$

$\lambda = -6.$

Thus, the critical point is $(3, 3, -6)$.

Step 4. Since $(3, 3, -6)$ is the only critical point for F, we conclude that max $f(x, y) = f(3, 3) = 2 \cdot 3 \cdot 3 = 18$.

3. Step 1. Minimize $f(x, y) = x^2 + y^2$
Subject to: $g(x, y) = 3x + 4y - 25 = 0$

Step 2. $F(x, y, \lambda) = f(x, y) + \lambda g(x, y)$
$$= x^2 + y^2 + \lambda(3x + 4y - 25)$$

Step 3. $F_x = 2x + 3\lambda = 0$ (1)

$F_y = 2y + 4\lambda = 0$ (2)

$F_\lambda = 3x + 4y - 25 = 0$ (3)

From (1) and (2), we obtain:

$x = -\dfrac{3\lambda}{2}, \ y = -2\lambda$

Substituting these into (3), we have:

$3\left(-\dfrac{3\lambda}{2}\right) + 4(-2\lambda) - 25 = 0$

$\dfrac{25}{2}\lambda = -25$

$\lambda = -2$

The critical point is $(3, 4, -2)$.

Step 4. Since $(3, 4, -2)$ is the only critical point for F, we conclude that min $f(x, y) = f(3, 4) = 3^2 + 4^2 = 25$.

5. Step 1. Maximize $f(x, y) = 4y - 3x$ subject to $2x + 5y - 3 = 0$

Step 2. $F(x, y, \lambda) = f(x, y) + \lambda g(x, y) = 4y - 3x + \lambda(2x + 5y - 3)$

Step 3. $F_x = -3 + 2\lambda = 0 \qquad (1)$

$F_y = 4 + 5\lambda = 0 \qquad (2)$

$F_\lambda = 2x + 5y - 3 = 0 \qquad (3)$

From (1), $\lambda = \dfrac{3}{2}$, from (2), $\lambda = -\dfrac{4}{5}$. Thus, the system (1),

(2), (3) does not have a solution.

7. Step 1. Maximize and minimize $f(x, y) = 2xy$

Subject to: $g(x, y) = x^2 + y^2 - 18 = 0$

Step 2. $F(x, y, \lambda) = f(x, y) + \lambda g(x, y)$

$= 2xy + \lambda(x^2 + y^2 - 18)$

Step 3. $F_x = 2y + 2\lambda x = 0 \qquad (1)$

$F_y = 2x + 2\lambda y = 0 \qquad (2)$

$F_\lambda = x^2 + y^2 - 18 = 0 \qquad (3)$

From (1), (2), and (3), we obtain the critical points
(3, 3, -1), (3, -3, 1), (-3, 3, 1) and (-3, -3, -1).

Step 4. $f(3, 3) = 2 \cdot 3 \cdot 3 = 18$

$f(3, -3) = 2 \cdot 3(-3) = -18$

$f(-3, 3) = 2(-3) \cdot 3 = -18$

$f(-3, -3) = 2(-3)(-3) = 18$

Thus, max $f(x, y) = f(3, 3) = f(-3, -3) = 18$;

min $f(x, y) = f(3, -3) = f(-3, 3) = -18$.

9. Let x and y be the required numbers.

Step 1. Maximize $f(x, y) = xy$

Subject to: $x + y = 10$ or $g(x, y) = x + y - 10 = 0$

Step 2. $F(x, y, \lambda) = xy + \lambda(x + y - 10)$

Step 3. $F_x = y + \lambda = 0 \qquad (1)$

$F_y = x + \lambda = 0 \qquad (2)$

$F_\lambda = x + y - 10 = 0 \qquad (3)$

From (1) and (2), we obtain:

$x = -\lambda, \ y = -\lambda$

Substituting these into (3), we have:

$\lambda = -5$

The critical point is (5, 5, -5).

Step 4. Since (5, 5, -5) is the only critical point for F, we conclude
that max $f(x, y) = f(5, 5) = 5 \cdot 5 = 25$. Thus, the maximum
product is 25 when $x = 5$ and $y = 5$.

11. Step 1. Minimize $f(x, y, z) = x^2 + y^2 + z^2$
Subject to: $g(x, y) = 2x - y + 3z + 28 = 0$

Step 2. $F(x, y, z, \lambda) = x^2 + y^2 + z^2 + \lambda(2x - y + 3z + 28)$

Step 3. $F_x = 2x + 2\lambda = 0$ (1)

$F_y = 2y - \lambda = 0$ (2)

$F_z = 2z + 3\lambda = 0$ (3)

$F_\lambda = 2x - y + 3z + 28 = 0$ (4)

From (1), (2), and (3), we obtain:

$x = -\lambda, \; y = \dfrac{\lambda}{2}, \; z = -\dfrac{3}{2}\lambda$

Substituting these into (4), we have:

$2(-\lambda) - \dfrac{\lambda}{2} + 3\left(-\dfrac{3}{2}\lambda\right) + 28 = 0$

$-\dfrac{14}{2}\lambda + 28 = 0$

$\lambda = 4$

The critical point is $(-4, 2, -6, 4)$.

Step 4. Since $(-4, 2, -6, 4)$ is the only critical point for F, we conclude that min $f(x, y, z) = f(-4, 2, -6) = 56$.

13. Step 1. Maximize and minimize $f(x, y, z) = x + y + z$
Subject to: $g(x, y, z) = x^2 + y^2 + z^2 - 12 = 0$

Step 2. $F(x, y, z, \lambda) = f(x, y, z) + \lambda g(x, y, z)$
$= x + y + z + \lambda(x^2 + y^2 + z^2 - 12)$

Step 3. $F_x = 1 + 2x\lambda = 0$ (1)

$F_y = 1 + 2y\lambda = 0$ (2)

$F_z = 1 + 2z\lambda = 0$ (3)

$F_\lambda = x^2 + y^2 + z^2 - 12 = 0$ (4)

From (1), (2), and (3), we obtain:

$x = -\dfrac{1}{2\lambda}, \; y = -\dfrac{1}{2\lambda}, \; z = -\dfrac{1}{2\lambda}$

Substituting these into (4), we have:

$\left(-\dfrac{1}{2\lambda}\right)^2 + \left(-\dfrac{1}{2\lambda}\right)^2 + \left(-\dfrac{1}{2\lambda}\right)^2 - 12 = 0$

$\dfrac{3}{4\lambda^2} - 12 = 0$

$1 - 16\lambda^2 = 0$

$\lambda = \pm\dfrac{1}{4}$

Thus, the critical points are $\left(2, 2, 2, -\dfrac{1}{4}\right)$ and $\left(-2, -2, -2, \dfrac{1}{4}\right)$.

Step 4. $f(2, 2, 2) = 2 + 2 + 2 = 6$
$f(-2, -2, -2) = -2 - 2 - 2 = -6$
Thus, max $f(x, y, z) = f(2, 2, 2) = 6$;
min $f(x, y, z) = f(-2, -2, -2) = -6$.

15. **Step 1.** Maximize $f(x, y) = y + xy^2$
Subject to: $x + y^2 = 1$ or $g(x, y) = x + y^2 - 1 = 0$

Step 2. $F(x, y, \lambda) = y + xy^2 + \lambda(x + y^2 - 1)$

Step 3. $F_x = y^2 + \lambda = 0$ (1)
$F_y = 1 + 2xy + 2y\lambda = 0$ (2)
$F_\lambda = x + y^2 - 1 = 0$ (3)

From (1), $\lambda = -y^2$ and from (3), $x = 1 - y^2$. Substituting these values into (2), we have

$$1 + 2(1 - y^2)y - 2y^3 = 0$$
$$\text{or} \qquad 4y^3 - 2y - 1 = 0$$

Using a graphing utility to solve this equation, we get $y \approx 0.885$. Then $x \approx 0.217$ and max $f(x, y) = f(0.217, 0.885) \approx 1.055$.

17. **Step 1.** Maximize $f(x, y) = e^x + 3e^y$ subject to $g(x, y) = x - 2y - 6 = 0$

Step 2. $F(x, y, \lambda) = f(x, y) + \lambda g(x, y) = e^x + 3e^y + \lambda(x - 2y - 6)$

Step 3. $F_x = e^x + \lambda = 0$ (1)
$F_y = 3e^y - 2\lambda = 0$ (2)
$F_\lambda = x - 2y - 6 = 0$ (3)

From (1), $\lambda = -e^x$, which implies λ is negative.
From (2), $\lambda = \dfrac{3}{2}e^y$ which implies λ is positive.
Thus, (1) and (2) have no simultaneous solution.

19. The constraint $g(x, y) = y - 5 = 0$ implies $y = 5$. Replacing y by 5 in the function f, the problem reduces to maximizing the function $h(x) = f(x, 5)$, a function of one independent variable.

21. Maximize $f(x, y) = e^{-(x^2 + y^2)}$

Subject to: $g(x, y) = x^2 + y - 1 = 0$

(A) $x^2 + y - 1 = 0$; $y = 1 - x^2$

Substituting $y = 1 - x^2$ into $f(x, y)$, we get
$$h(x) = f(x, 1 - x^2) = e^{-(x^2 + [1 - x^2]^2)}$$
$$= e^{-(x^4 - x^2 + 1)}$$

Now, $h'(x) = e^{-(x^4 - x^2 + 1)}(-4x^3 + 2x)$.

Critical numbers: $(2x - 4x^3)e^{-(x^4 - x^2 + 1)} = 0$
$$2x(1 - 2x^2) = 0$$
$$x = 0, \quad \frac{\sqrt{2}}{2}, \quad -\frac{\sqrt{2}}{2}$$

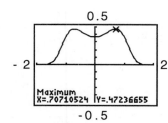

0.5

-2   2

Maximum
X=.70710524   Y=.47236655

-0.5

From the constraint equation, $y = \frac{1}{2}$ when $x = \pm\frac{\sqrt{2}}{2}$.

Max $f(x, y) = f\left(-\frac{\sqrt{2}}{2}, \frac{1}{2}\right) = f\left(\frac{\sqrt{2}}{2}, \frac{1}{2}\right) \approx 0.47$.

(B) $F(x, y, \lambda) = e^{-(x^2 + y^2)} + \lambda(x^2 + y - 1)$

$F_x = -2xe^{-(x^2 + y^2)} + 2x\lambda = 0$ (1)

$F_y = -2ye^{-(x^2 + y^2)} + \lambda = 0$ (2)

$F_\lambda = x^2 + y - 1 = 0$ (3)

From (3), $y = 1 - x^2$ and from (2)
$$\lambda = 2ye^{-(x^2 + y^2)} = 2(1 - x^2)e^{-(x^4 - x^2 + 1)}$$

Substituting these values into (1), we have
$$-2xe^{-(x^4 - x^2 + 1)} + 2x[2(1 - x^2)e^{-(x^4 - x^2 + 1)}] = 0$$
$$2x[2 - 2x^2 - 1] = 0$$
$$2x(1 - 2x^2) = 0$$
$$x = 0, \quad \frac{\sqrt{2}}{2}, \quad -\frac{\sqrt{2}}{2}$$

Now, $y = 1$ when $x = 0$, and $y = \frac{1}{2}$ when $x = \pm\frac{\sqrt{2}}{2}$.

$f(0, 1) = e^{-1} \approx 0.37$

$f\left(\frac{\sqrt{2}}{2}, \frac{1}{2}\right) = f\left(-\frac{\sqrt{2}}{2}, \frac{1}{2}\right) \approx 0.47$

Thus, Max $f(x, y) \approx 0.47$.

23. <u>Step 1</u>. Minimize cost function $C(x, y) = 6x^2 + 12y^2$

Subject to: $x + y = 90$ or $g(x, y) = x + y - 90 = 0$

<u>Step 2</u>. $F(x, y, \lambda) = 6x^2 + 12y^2 + \lambda(x + y - 90)$

Step 3.　$F_x = 12x + \lambda = 0$　　　　(1)

$F_y = 24y + \lambda = 0$　　　　(2)

$F_\lambda = x + y - 90 = 0$　　　(3)

From (1) and (2), we obtain

$$x = -\frac{\lambda}{12}, \quad y = -\frac{\lambda}{24}$$

Substituting these into (3), we have:

$$-\frac{\lambda}{12} - \frac{\lambda}{24} - 90 = 0$$

$$\frac{3\lambda}{24} = -90$$

$$\lambda = -720$$

The critical point is (60, 30, -720).

Step 4.　Since (60, 30, -720) is the only critical point for F, we conclude that:

$$\min C(x, y) = C(60, 30) = 6 \cdot 60^2 + 12 \cdot 30^2$$
$$= 21,600 + 10,800$$
$$= \$32,400$$

Thus, 60 of model A and 30 of model B will yield a minimum cost of \$32,400 per week.

25. (A) Step 1.　Maximize the production function $N(x, y) = 50x^{0.8}y^{0.2}$

Subject to the constraint: $C(x, y) = 40x + 80y = 400,000$

i.e., $g(x, y) = 40x + 80y - 400,000 = 0$

Step 2.　$F(x, y, \lambda) = 50x^{0.8}y^{0.2} + \lambda(40x + 80y - 400,000)$

Step 3.　$F_x = 40x^{-0.2}y^{0.2} + 40\lambda = 0$　　(1)

$F_y = 10x^{0.8}y^{-0.8} + 80\lambda = 0$　　(2)

$F_\lambda = 40x + 80y - 400,000 = 0$ (3)

From (1), $\lambda = -\dfrac{y^{0.2}}{x^{0.2}}$.　From (2), $\lambda = -\dfrac{x^{0.8}}{8y^{0.8}}$.

Thus, we obtain

$$-\frac{y^{0.2}}{x^{0.2}} = -\frac{x^{0.8}}{8y^{0.8}} \quad \text{or} \quad x = 8y$$

Substituting into (3), we have:

$320y + 80y - 400,000 = 0$

$$y = 1000$$

Therefore, $x = 8000$, $\lambda \approx -0.6598$, and the critical point is (8000, 1000, -0.6598). Thus, we conclude that:

$$\max N(x, y) = N(8000, 1000) = 50(8000)^{0.8}(1000)^{0.2}$$
$$\approx 263,902 \text{ units}$$

and production is maximized when 8000 labor units and 1000 capital units are used.

(B) The marginal productivity of money is $-\lambda \approx 0.6598$. The increase in production if an additional \$50,000 is budgeted for production is: $0.6598(50,000) = 32,990$ units

27. Let x = length, y = width, and z = height.

   Step 1. Maximize volume $V = xyz$
   Subject to: $S(x, y, z) = xy + 3xz + 3yz - 192 = 0$

   Step 2. $F(x, y, z, \lambda) = xyz + \lambda(xy + 3xz + 3yz - 192)$

   Step 3. $F_x = yz + \lambda(y + 3z) = 0$ (1)
   $F_y = xz + \lambda(x + 3z) = 0$ (2)
   $F_z = xy + \lambda(3x + 3y) = 0$ (3)
   $F_\lambda = xy + 3xz + 3yz - 192 = 0$ (4)

   Solving this system of equations, (1)-(4), simultaneously, yields:
   $x = 8, \ y = 8, \ z = \dfrac{8}{3}, \ \lambda = -\dfrac{4}{3}$

   Thus, the critical point is $\left(8, 8, \dfrac{8}{3}, -\dfrac{4}{3}\right)$.

   Step 4. Since $\left(8, 8, \dfrac{8}{3}, -\dfrac{4}{3}\right)$ is the only critical point for F:

   $\max V(x, y, z) = V\left(8, 8, \dfrac{8}{3}\right) = \dfrac{512}{3} \approx 170.67$

   Thus, the dimensions that will maximize the volume of the box are: Length $x = 8$ inches; Width $y = 8$ inches; Height $z = \dfrac{8}{3}$ inches.

29. Step 1. Maximize $A = xy$
   Subject to: $P(x, y) = y + 4x - 400 = 0$

   Step 2. $F(x, y, \lambda) = xy + \lambda(y + 4x - 400)$

   Step 3. $F_x = y + 4\lambda = 0$ (1)
   $F_y = x + \lambda = 0$ (2)
   $F_\lambda = y + 4x - 400 = 0$ (3)

   From (1) and (2), we have:
   $y = -4\lambda$ and $x = -\lambda$
   Substituting these into (3), we obtain:
   $-4\lambda - 4\lambda - 400 = 0$
   Thus, $\lambda = -50$ and the critical point is $(50, 200, -50)$.

   Step 4. Since $(50, 200, -50)$ is the only critical point for F,
   $\max A(x, y) = A(50, 200) = 10,000$.
   Therefore, $x = 50$ feet, $y = 200$ feet will produce the maximum area $A(50, 200) = 10,000$ square feet.

Things to remember:

1. LEAST SQUARES APPROXIMATION FORMULAS

   For a set of n points (x_1, y_1), (x_2, y_2), ... , (x_n, y_n), the coefficients of the least squares line $y = ax + b$ are the solutions of the system of the NORMAL EQUATIONS

   $$\left(\sum_{k=1}^{n} x_k^2\right) a + \left(\sum_{k=1}^{n} x_k\right) b = \sum_{k=1}^{n} x_k y_k \tag{1}$$

   $$\left(\sum_{k=1}^{n} x_k\right) a + nb = \sum_{k=1}^{n} y_k$$

   and are given by the formulas

   $$a = \frac{n\left(\sum_{k=1}^{n} x_k y_k\right) - \left(\sum_{k=1}^{n} x_k\right)\left(\sum_{k=1}^{n} y_k\right)}{n\left(\sum_{k=1}^{n} x_k^2\right) - \left(\sum_{k=1}^{n} x_k\right)^2} \tag{2}$$

   $$b = \frac{\sum_{k=1}^{n} y_k - a\left(\sum_{k=1}^{n} x_k\right)}{n} \tag{3}$$

   [Note: To find a and b, either solve system (1) directly, or use formulas (2) and (3). If the formulas are used, the value of a must be calculated first since it is used in the formula for b.

1.

	x_k	y_k	$x_k y_k$	x_k^2
	1	1	1	1
	2	3	6	4
	3	4	12	9
	4	3	12	16
Totals	10	11	31	30

Thus, $\sum_{k=1}^{4} x_k = 10$, $\sum_{k=1}^{4} y_k = 11$, $\sum_{k=1}^{4} x_k y_k = 31$, $\sum_{k=1}^{4} x_k^2 = 30$.

Substituting these values into formulas (2) and (3) for m and d, respectively, we have:

$$m = \frac{n\left(\sum_{k=1}^{n} x_k y_k\right) - \left(\sum_{k=1}^{n} x_k\right)\left(\sum_{k=1}^{n} y_k\right)}{n\left(\sum_{k=1}^{n} x_k^2\right) - \left(\sum_{k=1}^{n} x_k\right)^2} = \frac{4(31) - (10)(11)}{4(30) - (10)^2} = \frac{14}{20} = 0.7$$

$$d = \frac{\sum\limits_{k=1}^{n} y_k - m\left(\sum\limits_{k=1}^{n} x_k\right)}{n} = \frac{11 - 0.7(10)}{4} = 1$$

Thus, the least squares line is $y = mx + d = 0.7x + 1$. Refer to the graph at the right.

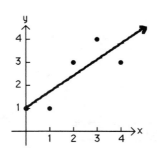

3.

x_k	y_k	$x_k y_k$	x_k^2
1	8	8	1
2	5	10	4
3	4	12	9
4	0	0	16
Totals 10	17	30	30

Thus, $\sum\limits_{k=1}^{4} x_k = 10$, $\sum\limits_{k=1}^{4} y_k = 17$, $\sum\limits_{k=1}^{4} x_k y_k = 30$, $\sum\limits_{k=1}^{4} x_k^2 = 30$.

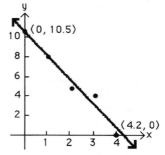

Substituting these values into system (1), we have:

$$10m + 4d = 17$$
$$30m + 10d = 30$$

The solution of this system is $m = -2.5$, $d = 10.5$. Thus, the least squares line is $y = mx + d = -2.5x + 10.5$. Refer to the graph above.

5.

x_k	y_k	$x_k y_k$	x_k^2
1	3	3	1
2	4	8	4
3	5	15	9
4	6	24	16
Totals 10	18	50	30

Thus, $\sum\limits_{k=1}^{4} x_k = 10$, $\sum\limits_{k=1}^{4} y_k = 18$, $\sum\limits_{k=1}^{4} x_k y_k = 50$, $\sum\limits_{k=1}^{4} x_k^2 = 30$.

Substituting these values into the formulas for m and d [formulas (2) and (3)], we have:

$$m = \frac{4(50) - (10)(18)}{4(30) - (10)^2} = \frac{20}{20} = 1$$

$$d = \frac{18 - 1(10)}{4} = \frac{8}{4} = 2$$

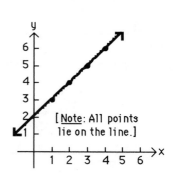

[Note: All points lie on the line.]

Thus, the least squares line is $y = mx + d = x + 2$. Refer to the graph at the right.

7.

x_k	y_k	$x_k y_k$	x_k^2
1	3	3	1
2	1	2	4
2	2	4	4
3	0	0	9
Totals 8	6	9	18

Thus, $\sum\limits_{k=1}^{4} x_k = 8$, $\sum\limits_{k=1}^{4} y_k = 6$, $\sum\limits_{k=1}^{4} x_k y_k = 9$, $\sum\limits_{k=1}^{4} x_k^2 = 18$.

Substituting these values into formulas (2) and (3) for m and d, respectively, we have:

$$m = \frac{4(9) - 8(6)}{4(18) - 8^2} = \frac{36 - 48}{72 - 64} = \frac{-12}{8} = -\frac{3}{2} = -1.5$$

$$d = \frac{6 - (-3/2)(8)}{4} = \frac{6 + 12}{4} = \frac{9}{2} = 4.5$$

Thus, the least squares line is $y = -1.5x + 4.5$.
When $x = 2.5$, $y = -1.5(2.5) + 4.5 = 0.75$.

9.

x_k	y_k	$x_k y_k$	x_k^2
0	10	0	0
5	22	110	25
10	31	310	100
15	46	690	225
20	51	1020	400
Totals 50	160	2130	750

Thus, $\sum\limits_{k=1}^{5} x_k = 50$, $\sum\limits_{k=1}^{5} y_k = 160$, $\sum\limits_{k=1}^{5} x_k y_k = 2130$, $\sum\limits_{k=1}^{5} x_k^2 = 750$.

Substituting these values into formulas (2) and (3) for m and d, respectively, we have:

$$m = \frac{5(2130) - (50)(160)}{5(750) - (50)^2} = \frac{2650}{1250} = 2.12$$

$$d = \frac{160 - 2.12(50)}{5} = \frac{54}{5} = 10.8$$

Thus, the least squares line is $y = 2.12x + 10.8$.
When $x = 25$, $y = 2.12(25) + 10.8 = 63.8$.

11.

x_k	y_k	$x_k y_k$	x_k^2
-1	14	-14	1
1	12	12	1
3	8	24	9
5	6	30	25
7	5	35	49
Totals 15	45	87	85

Thus, $\displaystyle\sum_{k=1}^{5} x_k = 15$, $\displaystyle\sum_{k=1}^{5} y_k = 45$, $\displaystyle\sum_{k=1}^{5} x_k y_k = 87$, $\displaystyle\sum_{k=1}^{5} x_k^2 = 85$.

Substituting these values into formulas (2) and (3) for m and d, respectively, we have:

$$m = \frac{5(87) - (15)(45)}{5(85) - (15)^2} = \frac{-240}{200} = -1.2$$

$$d = \frac{45 - (-1.2)(15)}{5} = 12.6$$

Thus, the least squares line is
$y = -1.2x + 12.6$.
When $x = 2$, $y = -1.2(2) + 12.6 = 10.2$.

13.

x_k	y_k	$x_k y_k$	x_k^2
0.5	25	12.5	0.25
2.0	22	44.0	4.00
3.5	21	73.5	12.25
5.0	21	105.0	25.00
6.5	18	117.0	42.25
9.5	12	114.0	90.25
11.0	11	121.0	121.00
12.5	8	100.0	156.25
14.0	5	70.0	196.00
15.5	1	15.5	240.25
Totals 80.0	144	772.5	887.50

Thus, $\displaystyle\sum_{k=1}^{10} x_k = 80$, $\displaystyle\sum_{k=1}^{10} y_k = 144$, $\displaystyle\sum_{k=1}^{10} x_k y_k = 772.5$, $\displaystyle\sum_{k=1}^{10} x_k^2 = 887.5$.

Substituting these values into formulas (2) and (3) for m and d, respectively, we have:

$$m = \frac{10(772.5) - (80)(144)}{10(887.5) - (80)^2} = \frac{-3795}{2475} \approx -1.53$$

$$d = \frac{144 - (-1.53)(80)}{10} = \frac{266.4}{10} = 26.64$$

Thus, the least squares line is
$y = -1.53x + 26.64$.
When $x = 8$, $y = -1.53(8) + 26.64 = 14.4$.

15. Minimize

$$F(a, b, c) = (a + b + c - 2)^2 + (4a + 2b + c - 1)^2$$
$$+ (9a + 3b + c - 1)^2 + (16a + 4b + c - 3)^2$$

$$F_a(a, b, c) = 2(a + b + c - 2) + 8(4a + 2b + c - 1)$$
$$+ 18(9a + 3b + c - 1) + 32(16a + 4b + c - 3)$$
$$= 708a + 200b + 60c - 126$$

$$F_b(a,\ b,\ c)\ =\ 2(a\ +\ b\ +\ c\ -\ 2)\ +\ 4(4a\ +\ 2b\ +\ c\ -\ 1)$$
$$+\ 6(9a\ +\ 3b\ +\ c\ -\ 1)\ +\ 8(16a\ +\ 4b\ +\ c\ -\ 3)$$
$$=\ 200a\ +\ 60b\ +\ 20c\ -\ 38$$

$$F_c(a,\ b,\ c)\ =\ 2(a\ +\ b\ +\ c\ -\ 2)\ +\ 2(4a\ +\ 2b\ +\ c\ -\ 1)$$
$$+\ 2(9a\ +\ 3b\ +\ c\ -\ 1)\ +\ 2(16a\ +\ 4b\ +\ c\ -\ 3)$$
$$=\ 60a\ +\ 20b\ +\ 8c\ -\ 14$$

The system is: $F_a(a,\ b,\ c)\ =\ 0$

$\qquad\qquad\qquad\ F_b(a,\ b,\ c)\ =\ 0$

$\qquad\qquad\qquad\ F_c(a,\ b,\ c)\ =\ 0$

or:

$\qquad\qquad\ 708a\ +\ 200b\ +\ 60c\ =\ 126$

$\qquad\qquad\ 200a\ +\ \ 60b\ +\ 20c\ =\ \ 38$

$\qquad\qquad\ \ 60a\ +\ \ 20b\ +\ \ 8c\ =\ \ 14$

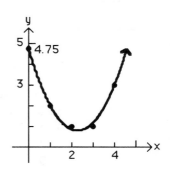

The solution is $(a,\ b,\ c)\ =\ (0.75,\ -3.45,\ 4.75)$, which gives us the equation for the parabola shown at the right:

$$y\ =\ ax^2\ +\ bx\ +\ c$$

or

$$y\ =\ 0.75x^2\ -\ 3.45x\ +\ 4.75$$

The given points: $(1,\ 2),\ (2,\ 1),\ (3,\ 1),\ (4,\ 3)$ also appear on the graph.

17. System (1) is:

$$\left(\sum_{k=1}^{n} x_k\right)m\ +\ nd\ =\ \sum_{k=1}^{n} y_k \qquad\qquad \text{(a)}$$

$$\left(\sum_{k=1}^{n} x_k^2\right)m\ +\ \left(\sum_{k=1}^{n} x_k\right)d\ =\ \sum_{k=1}^{n} x_k y_k \quad \text{(b)}$$

Multiply equation (a) by $-\left(\displaystyle\sum_{k=1}^{n} x_k\right)$, equation (b) by n, and add the resulting equations. This will eliminate d from the system.

$$\left[-\left(\sum_{k=1}^{n} x_k\right)^2\ +\ n\sum_{k=1}^{n} x_k^2\right]m\ =\ -\left(\sum_{k=1}^{n} x_k\right)\left(\sum_{k=1}^{n} y_k\right)\ +\ n\sum_{k=1}^{n} x_k y_k$$

Thus,

$$m\ =\ \frac{n\left(\displaystyle\sum_{k=1}^{n} x_k y_k\right)\ -\ \left(\displaystyle\sum_{k=1}^{n} x_k\right)\left(\displaystyle\sum_{k=1}^{n} y_k\right)}{n\left(\displaystyle\sum_{k=1}^{n} x_k^2\right)\ -\ \left(\displaystyle\sum_{k=1}^{n} x_k\right)^2}$$

which is equation (2). Solving equation (a) for d, we have

$$d\ =\ \frac{\displaystyle\sum_{k=1}^{n} y_k\ -\ m\left(\displaystyle\sum_{k=1}^{n} x_k\right)}{n}$$

which is equation (3).

19. (A) Suppose that $n = 5$ and $x_1 = -2$, $x_2 = -1$, $x_3 = 0$, $x_4 = 1$, $x_5 = 2$.

Then $\sum\limits_{k=1}^{5} x_k = -2 - 1 + 0 + 1 + 2 = 0$. Therefore, from formula (2),

$$m = \frac{5\sum\limits_{k=1}^{5} x_k y_k}{5\sum\limits_{k=1}^{5} x_k^2} = \frac{\sum x_k y_k}{\sum x_k^2} \qquad \text{From formula (3),} \quad d = \frac{\sum\limits_{k=1}^{5} y_k}{5},$$

which is the average of y_1, y_2, y_3, y_4, and y_5.

(B) If the average of the x-coordinates is 0, then

$$\frac{\sum\limits_{k=1}^{n} x_k}{n} = 0$$

Then all calculations will be the same as in part (A) with "n" instead of 5.

21. (A)

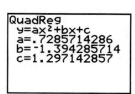
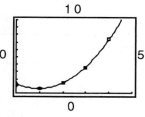

```
LinReg
 y=ax+b
 a=1.52
 b=-.16
 r=.8696654103
```

```
QuadReg
 y=ax²+bx+c
 a=.7285714286
 b=-1.394285714
 c=1.297142857
```

(B) The quadratic regression function best fits the data.

23. The cubic regression function has the form $y = ax^3 + bx^2 + cx + d$. The normal equations form a system of 4 linear equations in the 4 variables a, b, c and d. The system can be solved using Gauss-Jordan elimination.

25. (A) We use the linear regression feature on a graphing utility with 1990 as $x = 0$, 1991 as $x = 1$, etc.

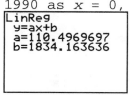

```
LinReg
 y=ax+b
 a=110.4969697
 b=1834.163636
```

Thus, the least squares line is: $y = 110.5x + 1834$.

(B) The year 2010 corresponds to $x = 20$;
$y(20) \approx 4{,}044$ thousand or $4{,}044{,}000$

27. (A)

x_k	y_k	$x_k y_k$	x_k^2
5.0	2.0	10.0	25.00
5.5	1.8	9.9	30.25
6.0	1.4	8.4	36.00
6.5	1.2	7.8	42.25
7.0	1.1	7.7	49.00
Totals 30.0	7.5	43.8	182.50

Thus, $\sum\limits_{k=1}^{5} x_k = 30$, $\sum\limits_{k=1}^{5} y_k = 7.5$, $\sum\limits_{k=1}^{5} x_k y_k = 43.8$, $\sum\limits_{k=1}^{5} x_k^2 = 182.5$.

Substituting these values into the formulas for m and d, we have:

$$m = \frac{5(43.8) - (30)(7.5)}{5(182.5) - (30)^2} = \frac{-6}{12.5} = -0.48$$

$$d = \frac{7.5 - (-0.48)(30)}{5} = 4.38$$

Thus, a demand equation is $y = -0.48x + 4.38$.

(B) Cost: $C = 4y$

Revenue: $R = xy = -0.48x^2 + 4.38x$

Profit: $P = R - C = -0.48x^2 + 4.38x - 4(-0.48x + 4.38)$

$\quad\quad$ or $P(x) = -0.48x^2 + 6.3x - 17.52$

Now, $P'(x) = -0.96x + 6.3$.

Critical value: $P'(x) = -0.96x + 6.3 = 0$

$$x = \frac{6.3}{0.96} \approx 6.56$$

$P''(x) = -0.96$ and $P''(6.56) = -0.96 < 0$

Thus, $P(x)$ has a maximum at $x = 6.56$; the price per bottle should be $6.56 to maximize the monthly profit.

29.

x_k	y_k	$x_k y_k$	x_k^2
50	15	750	2500
55	13	715	3025
60	10	600	3600
65	6	390	4225
70	2	140	4900
Totals 300	46	2595	18,250

Thus, $\displaystyle\sum_{k=1}^{5} x_k = 300$, $\displaystyle\sum_{k=1}^{5} y_k = 46$, $\displaystyle\sum_{k=1}^{5} x_k y_k = 2595$, $\displaystyle\sum_{k=1}^{5} x_k^2 = 18,250$.

Substituting these values into the formulas for m and d, we have:

$$m = \frac{5(2595) - (300)(46)}{5(18,250) - (300)^2} = \frac{-825}{1250} = -0.66$$

$$d = \frac{46 - (-0.66)300}{5} = 48.8$$

(A) The least squares line for the data is $P = -0.66T + 48.8$.

(B) $P(57) = -0.66(57) + 48.8 = 11.18$ beats per minute.

31. (A) We use the linear regression feature on a graphing utility with 1885 as $x = 0$, 1895 as $x = 10$, ..., 1995 as $x = 110$.

```
LinReg
 y=ax+b
 a=.0085664336
 b=56.47884615
```

Thus, the least squares line is:
$\quad y = 0.0086x + 56.48$

(B) The year 2085 corresponds to $x = 200$; $y(200) \approx 58.19°F$.

33. (A) Enter the data in a calculator or computer. (We used a TI-85.)
The totals are:
$\quad n = 23$, $\quad \sum x = 1098$, $\quad \sum y = 343.61$,
$\quad \sum x^2 = 73,860$, $\quad \sum xy = 18,259.08$

Now, the least squares line can be calculated either by using formulas (2) and (3), or by using the linear regression feature. We used the latter to get

$$m = 0.08653 \quad \text{and} \quad b = 10.81$$

Therefore, the least squares line is:

$$y = 0.08653x + 10.81$$

(B) Using the result in (A), an estimate for the winning height in the pole vault in the Olympic games of 2008 is:

$$y = 0.08653(112) + 10.81 \approx 20.50 \text{ feet}$$

35. (A) We use the linear regression feature on a graphing utility with 1896 as $x = 0$, 1900 as $x = 4$, ..., 2000 as $x = 104$.

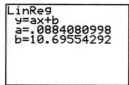

```
LinReg
 y=ax+b
 a=.0884080998
 b=10.69554292
```

Thus, the least squares line is: $y = 0.0884x + 10.70$.

(B) The year 2016 corresponds to $x = 120$; $y(120) \approx 21.30$ ft.

EXERCISE 8-6

Things to remember:

GIVEN A FUNCTION $z = f(x, y)$:

<u>1.</u> $\int f(x, y)\,dx$ means antidifferentiate $f(x, y)$ with respect to x, holding y fixed.

$\int f(x, y)\,dy$ means antidifferentiate $f(x, y)$ with respect to y, holding x fixed.

<u>2.</u> The DOUBLE INTEGRAL of $f(x, y)$ over the rectangle $R = \{(x, y) \mid a \le x \le b,\ c \le y \le d\}$ is:

$$\iint\limits_{R} f(x, y)\,dA = \int_a^b \left[\int_c^d f(x, y)\,dy \right] dx$$

$$= \int_c^d \left[\int_a^b f(x, y)\,dx \right] dy$$

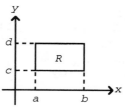

<u>3.</u> The AVERAGE VALUE of $f(x, y)$ over the rectangle $R = \{(x, y) \mid a \le x \le b,\ c \le y \le d\}$ is:

$$\frac{1}{(b - a)(d - c)} \iint\limits_{R} f(x, y)\,dA$$

VOLUME UNDER A SURFACE

If $f(x, y) \geq 0$ over a rectangle $R = \{(x, y) \mid a \leq x \leq b, \; c \leq y \leq d\}$, then the volume of the solid formed by graphing f over the rectangle R is given by:

$$V = \iint\limits_{R} f(x, y)\, dA$$

---

1. (A) $\displaystyle\int 12x^2 y^3\, dy = 12x^2 \int y^3\, dy$ (x is treated as a constant.)

$$= 12x^2 \frac{y^4}{4} + C(x)$$ (The "constant" of integration is a function of x.)

$$= 3x^2 y^4 + C(x)$$

(B) $\displaystyle\int_0^1 12x^2 y^3\, dy = 3x^2 y^4 \Big|_0^1 = 3x^2$

3. (A) $\displaystyle\int (4x + 6y + 5)\, dx$

$$= \int 4x\, dx + \int (6y + 5)\, dx$$ (y is treated as a constant.)

$$= 2x^2 + (6y + 5)x + E(y)$$ (The "constant" of integration is a function of y.)

$$= 2x^2 + 6xy + 5x + E(y)$$

(B) $\displaystyle\int_{-2}^{3} (4x + 6y + 5)\, dx = (2x^2 + 6xy + 5x)\Big|_{-2}^{3}$

$$= 2 \cdot 3^2 + 6 \cdot 3y + 5 \cdot 3 - [2(-2)^2 + 6(-2)y + 5(-2)]$$
$$= 30y + 35$$

5. (A) $\displaystyle\int \frac{x}{\sqrt{y + x^2}}\, dx = \int (y + x^2)^{-1/2} x\, dx = \frac{1}{2}\int (y + x^2)^{-1/2} 2x\, dx$

Let $u = y + x^2$, $= \dfrac{1}{2}\displaystyle\int u^{-1/2}\, du$
then $du = 2x\, dx$.

$$= u^{1/2} + E(y) = \sqrt{y + x^2} + E(y)$$

(B) $\displaystyle\int_0^2 \frac{x}{\sqrt{y + x^2}}\, dx = \sqrt{y + x^2}\Big|_0^2 = \sqrt{y + 4} - \sqrt{y}$

7. (A) $\displaystyle\int \frac{\ln x}{xy}\, dy = \frac{\ln x}{x}\int \frac{1}{y}\, dy = \frac{\ln x}{x} \cdot \ln y + C(x)$

(B) $\displaystyle\int_1^{e^2} \frac{\ln x}{xy}\, dy = \frac{\ln x \ln y}{x}\Big|_1^{e^2} = \frac{\ln x \ln e^2}{x} - \frac{\ln x \ln 1}{x} = \frac{2 \ln x}{x}$

9. $\displaystyle\int_{-1}^{2} \int_0^1 12x^2 y^3\, dy\; dx = \int_{-1}^{2} \left[\int_0^1 12x^2 y^3\, dy\right] dx = \int_{-1}^{2} 3x^2\, dx$ (see Problem 1)

$$= x^3 \Big|_{-1}^{2} = 8 + 1 = 9$$

11. $\displaystyle\int_1^4 \int_{-2}^3 (4x + 6y + 5)\, dx\, dy = \int_1^4 \left[\int_{-2}^3 (4x + 6y + 5)dx \right] dy$

$$= \int_1^4 (30y + 35)\, dy \quad \text{(see Problem 3)}$$

$$= (15y^2 + 35y)\Big|_1^4$$

$$= 15\cdot 4^2 + 35\cdot 4 - (15 + 35) = 330$$

13. $\displaystyle\int_1^5 \int_0^2 \frac{x}{\sqrt{y + x^2}}\, dx\, dy = \int_1^5 \left[\int_0^2 \frac{x}{\sqrt{y + x^2}}\, dx \right] dy$

$$= \int_1^5 (\sqrt{4 + y} - \sqrt{y})\, dy \quad \text{(see Problem 5)}$$

$$= \left[\frac{2}{3}(4 + y)^{3/2} - \frac{2}{3} y^{3/2} \right]\Big|_1^5$$

$$= \frac{2}{3}(9)^{3/2} - \frac{2}{3}(5)^{3/2} - \left(\frac{2}{3}\cdot 5^{3/2} - \frac{2}{3}\cdot 1^{3/2} \right)$$

$$= 18 - \frac{4}{3}(5)^{3/2} + \frac{2}{3} = \frac{56 - 20\sqrt{5}}{3}$$

15. $\displaystyle\int_1^e \int_1^{e^2} \frac{\ln x}{xy}\, dy\, dx = \int_1^e \left[\int_1^{e^2} \frac{\ln x}{xy}\, dy \right] dx$

$$= \int_1^e \frac{2 \ln x}{x}\, dx \quad \text{(see Problem 7)}$$

$$= 2 \int_1^e \frac{\ln x}{x}\, dx$$

$$= [\ln x]^2 \Big|_1^e \qquad\qquad \text{Substitution: } u = \ln x$$

$$= 1 \qquad\qquad\qquad\qquad\qquad du = \frac{1}{x}\, dx$$

17. $\displaystyle\iint_R xy\, dA = \int_0^2 \int_0^4 xy\, dy\, dx = \int_0^2 \left[\int_0^4 xy\, dy \right] dx = \int_0^2 \left[\frac{xy^2}{2}\Big|_0^4 \right] dx$

$$= \int_0^2 8x\, dx = 4x^2 \Big|_0^2 = 16$$

$$\iint_R xy\, dA = \int_0^4 \int_0^2 xy\, dy\, dx = \int_0^4 \left[\int_0^2 xy\, dx \right] dy = \int_0^4 \left[\frac{x^2 y}{2}\Big|_0^2 \right] dy$$

$$= \int_0^4 2y\, dy = y^2 \Big|_0^4 = 16$$

19. $\displaystyle\iint_R (x + y)^5 dA = \int_{-1}^1 \int_1^2 (x + y)^5 dy\, dx = \int_{-1}^1 \left[\int_1^2 (x + y)^5 dy \right] dx$

$$= \int_{-1}^1 \left[\frac{(x + y)^6}{6}\Big|_1^2 \right] dx = \int_{-1}^1 \left[\frac{(x + 2)^6}{6} - \frac{(x + 1)^6}{6} \right] dx$$

$$= \left[\frac{(x + 2)^7}{42} - \frac{(x + 1)^7}{42} \right]\Big|_{-1}^1 = \frac{3^7}{42} - \frac{2^7}{42} - \frac{1}{42} = 49$$

$$\iint\limits_{R} (x + y)^5 dA = \int_1^2 \int_{-1}^1 (x + y)^5 dx\, dy = \int_1^2 \left[\int_{-1}^1 (x + y)^5 dx \right] dy$$

$$= \int_1^2 \left[\frac{(x + y)^6}{6} \Big|_{-1}^1 \right] dy = \int_1^2 \left[\frac{(y + 1)^6}{6} - \frac{(y - 1)^6}{6} \right] dy$$

$$= \left[\frac{(y + 1)^7}{42} - \frac{(y - 1)^7}{42} \right]\Big|_1^2 = \frac{3^7}{42} - \frac{1}{42} - \frac{2^7}{42} = 49$$

21. Average value $= \dfrac{1}{(5 - 1)[1 - (-1)]} \iint\limits_{R} (x + y)^2 dA$

$$= \frac{1}{8} \int_{-1}^1 \int_1^5 (x + y)^2 dx\, dy = \frac{1}{8} \int_{-1}^1 \left[\frac{(x + y)^3}{3} \Big|_1^5 \right] dy$$

$$= \frac{1}{8} \int_{-1}^1 \left[\frac{(5 + y)^3}{3} - \frac{(1 + y)^3}{3} \right] dy = \frac{1}{8} \left[\frac{(5 + y)^4}{12} - \frac{(1 + y)^4}{12} \right]\Big|_{-1}^1$$

$$= \frac{1}{96} [6^4 - 2^4 - 4^4] = \frac{32}{3}$$

23. Average value $= \dfrac{1}{(4 - 1)(7 - 2)} \iint\limits_{R} \frac{x}{y} dA = \frac{1}{15} \int_1^4 \int_2^7 \frac{x}{y} dy\, dx$

$$= \frac{1}{15} \int_1^4 \left[x \ln y \right]_2^7 dx = \frac{1}{15} \int_1^4 [x \ln 7 - x \ln 2]\, dx$$

$$= \frac{\ln 7 - \ln 2}{15} \int_1^4 x\, dx = \frac{\ln 7 - \ln 2}{15} \cdot \frac{x^2}{2} \Big|_1^4$$

$$= \frac{\ln 7 - \ln 2}{15} \left(\frac{4^2}{2} - \frac{1^2}{2} \right) = \frac{1}{2} (\ln 7 - \ln 2)$$

$$= \frac{1}{2} \ln\left(\frac{7}{2} \right) \approx 0.626$$

25. $V = \iint\limits_{R} (2 - x^2 - y^2)\, dA = \int_0^1 \int_0^1 \iint\limits_{R} (2 - x^2 - y^2)\, dy\, dx$

$$= \int_0^1 \left[\int_0^1 (2 - x^2 - y^2)\, dy \right] dx = \int_0^1 \left[\left(2y - x^2 y - \frac{y^3}{3} \right) \Big|_0^1 \right] dx$$

$$= \int_0^1 \left(2 - x^2 - \frac{1}{3} \right) dx = \int_0^1 \left(\frac{5}{3} - x^2 \right) dx = \left(\frac{5}{3} x - \frac{x^3}{3} \right) \Big|_0^1 = \frac{5}{3} - \frac{1}{3} = \frac{4}{3}$$

27. $V = \iint\limits_{R} (4 - y^2)\, dA = \int_0^2 \int_0^2 (4 - y^2)\, dx\, dy = \int_0^2 \left[\int_0^2 (4 - y^2) dx \right] dy$

$$= \int_0^2 \left[(4x - xy^2) \Big|_0^2 \right] dy = \int_0^2 (8 - 2y^2)\, dy = \left(8y - \frac{2}{3} y^3 \right) \Big|_0^2$$

$$= 16 - \frac{16}{3} = \frac{32}{3}$$

29. $\displaystyle\iint\limits_R xe^{xy}\,dA = \int_0^1\int_1^2 xe^{xy}\,dy\,dx = \int_0^1\left[\int_1^2 xe^{xy}\,dy\right]dx$

$\displaystyle\qquad = \int_0^1\left[x\int_1^2 e^{xy}\,dy\right]dx = \int_0^1\left[x\cdot\frac{e^{xy}}{x}\Big|_1^2\right]dx = \int_0^1\left[\frac{e^{xy}}{x}\Big|_1^2\right]dx$

$\displaystyle\qquad = \int_0^1 (e^{2x} - e^x)\,dx = \left(\frac{e^{2x}}{2} - e^x\right)\Big|_0^1 = \frac{e^2}{2} - e - \left(\frac{1}{2} - 1\right)$

$\displaystyle\qquad = \frac{e^2}{2} - e + \frac{1}{2}$

31. $\displaystyle\iint\limits_R \frac{2y + 3xy^2}{1 + x^2}\,dA = \int_0^1\int_{-1}^1 \frac{2y + 3xy^2}{1 + x^2}\,dy\,dx = \int_0^1\left[\int_{-1}^1 \frac{2y + 3xy^2}{1 + x^2}\,dy\right]dx$

$\displaystyle\qquad = \int_0^1\left[\frac{1}{1 + x^2}(y^2 + xy^3)\Big|_{-1}^1\right]dx$

$\displaystyle\qquad = \int_0^1\left[\frac{1}{1 + x^2}(1 + x - [1 - x])\right]dx$

$\displaystyle\qquad = \int_0^1 \frac{2x}{1 + x^2}\,dx = \ln(1 + x^2)\Big|_0^1 \qquad \text{Substitution: } u = 1 + x^2$
$\displaystyle\qquad\qquad\qquad\qquad\qquad\qquad\qquad\qquad\qquad\qquad\qquad du = 2x\,dx$

$\displaystyle\qquad = \ln 2$

33. $\displaystyle\int_0^2\int_0^2 (1 - y)\,dx\,dy = \int_0^2\left[\int_0^2 (1 - y)\,dx\right]dy$

$\displaystyle\qquad = \int_0^2\left[(x - xy)\Big|_0^2\right]dy$

$\displaystyle\qquad = \int_0^2 (2 - 2y)\,dy$

$\displaystyle\qquad = (2y - y^2)\Big|_0^2 = 0$

Since $f(x, y) = 1 - y$ is NOT nonnegative over the rectangle $R = \{(x, y) \mid 0 \le x \le 2,\ 0 \le y \le 2\}$ the double integral does not represent the volume of solid.

35. $f(x, y) = x^3 + y^2 - e^{-x} - 1$ on $R = \{(x, y) \mid -2 \le x \le 2,\ -2 \le y \le 2\}$.
(A) Average value of f:

$\displaystyle\quad\frac{1}{b - a}\cdot\frac{1}{d - c}\iint\limits_R f(x, y)\,dA$

$\displaystyle\qquad = \frac{1}{2 - (-2)}\cdot\frac{1}{2 - (-2)}\int_{-2}^2\int_{-2}^2 (x^3 + y^2 - e^{-x} - 1)\,dx\,dy$

$\displaystyle\qquad = \frac{1}{16}\int_{-2}^2\left[\left(\frac{1}{4}x^4 + xy^2 + e^{-x} - x\right)\Big|_{-2}^2\right]dy$

$\displaystyle\qquad = \frac{1}{16}\int_{-2}^2 [4y^2 + e^{-2} - e^2 - 4]\,dy$

$\displaystyle\qquad = \frac{1}{16}\left[\frac{4}{3}y^3 + e^{-2}y - e^2y - 4y\right]\Big|_{-2}^2$

$\displaystyle\qquad = \frac{1}{16}\left[\frac{64}{3} + 4e^{-2} - 4e^2 - 16\right] = \frac{1}{3} + \frac{1}{4}e^{-2} - \frac{1}{4}e^2$

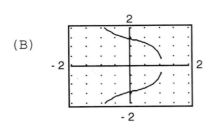

(B)

(C) $f(x, y) > 0$ at the points which lie to the right of the curve in part (B); $f(x, y) < 0$ at the points which lie to the left of the curve in part (B).

37. $S(x, y) = \dfrac{y}{1 - x}$, $0.6 \leq x \leq 0.8$, $5 \leq y \leq 7$.

The *average* total amount of spending is given by:

$$T = \frac{1}{(0.8 - 0.6)(7 - 5)} \iint\limits_{R} \frac{y}{1 - x} dA = \frac{1}{0.4} \int_{0.6}^{0.8} \int_{5}^{7} \frac{y}{1 - x} dy\, dx$$

$$= \frac{1}{0.4} \int_{0.6}^{0.8} \left[\frac{1}{1 - x} \cdot \frac{y^2}{2} \Big|_5^7 \right] dx = \frac{1}{0.4} \int_{0.6}^{0.8} \frac{1}{1 - x} \left(\frac{49}{2} - \frac{25}{2} \right) dx$$

$$= \frac{12}{0.4} \int_{0.6}^{0.8} \frac{1}{1 - x} dx = 30 [-\ln(1 - x)] \Big|_{0.6}^{0.8}$$

$$= 30 [-\ln(0.2) + \ln(0.4)] = 30 \ln 2 \approx \$20.8 \text{ billion}$$

39. $N(x, y) = x^{0.75} y^{0.25}$, $10 \leq x \leq 20$, $1 \leq y \leq 2$

Average value $= \dfrac{1}{(20 - 10)(2 - 1)} \displaystyle\int_{10}^{20} \int_{1}^{2} x^{0.75} y^{0.25} dy\, dx$

$$= \frac{1}{10} \int_{10}^{20} \left[x^{0.75} \frac{y^{1.25}}{1.25} \Big|_1^2 \right] dx = \frac{1}{10} \int_{10}^{20} \left[x^{0.75} \frac{2^{1.25} - 1}{1.25} \right] dx$$

$$= \frac{1}{12.5} (2^{1.25} - 1) \int_{10}^{20} x^{0.75} dx = \frac{1}{12.5} (2^{1.25} - 1) \frac{x^{1.75}}{1.75} \Big|_{10}^{20}$$

$$= \frac{1}{21.875} (2^{1.25} - 1)(20^{1.75} - 10^{1.75}) \approx 8.375 \text{ or } 8375 \text{ items}$$

41. $C = 10 - \dfrac{1}{10} d^2 = 10 - \dfrac{1}{10} (x^2 + y^2) = C(x, y)$, $-8 \leq x \leq 8$, $-6 \leq y \leq 6$

Average concentration

$$= \frac{1}{16(12)} \int_{-8}^{8} \int_{-6}^{6} \left[10 - \frac{1}{10} (x^2 + y^2) \right] dy\, dx$$

$$= \frac{1}{192} \int_{-8}^{8} \left[10y - \frac{1}{10} \left(x^2 y + \frac{y^3}{3} \right) \right] \Big|_{-6}^{6} dx$$

$$= \frac{1}{192} \int_{-8}^{8} \left\{ 60 - \frac{1}{10} \left(6x^2 + \frac{216}{3} \right) - \left[-60 - \frac{1}{10} \left(-6x^2 - \frac{216}{3} \right) \right] \right\} dx$$

$$= \frac{1}{192} \int_{-8}^{8} \left[120 - \frac{1}{10} (12x^2 + 144) \right] dx$$

$$= \frac{1}{192} \left[120x - \frac{1}{10} (4x^3 + 144x) \right] \Big|_{-8}^{8}$$

$$= \frac{1}{192} (1280) = \frac{20}{3} \approx 6.67 \text{ insects per square foot}$$

43. $C = 100 - 15d^2 = 100 - 15(x^2 + y^2) = C(x, y)$, $-2 \le x \le 2$, $-1 \le y \le 1$

Average concentration $= \dfrac{1}{4(2)} \displaystyle\int_{-2}^{2} \int_{-1}^{1} [100 - 15(x^2 + y^2)]\, dy\, dx$

$$= \dfrac{1}{8} \int_{-2}^{2} (100y - 15x^2 y - 5y^3)\Big|_{-1}^{1} dx$$

$$= \dfrac{1}{8} \int_{-2}^{2} (190 - 30x^2)\, dx = \dfrac{1}{8}(190x - 10x^3)\Big|_{-2}^{2}$$

$$= \dfrac{1}{8}(600) = 75 \text{ parts per million}$$

45. $L = 0.0000133xy^2$, $2000 \le x \le 3000$, $50 \le y \le 60$

Average length $= \dfrac{1}{10,000} \displaystyle\int_{2000}^{3000} \int_{50}^{60} 0.0000133xy^2\, dy\, dx$

$$= \dfrac{0.0000133}{10,000} \int_{2000}^{3000} \left[\dfrac{xy^3}{3}\Big|_{50}^{60}\right] dx$$

$$= \dfrac{0.0000133}{10,000} \int_{2000}^{3000} \dfrac{91,000}{3}x\, dx = \dfrac{1.2103}{30,000} \cdot \dfrac{x^2}{2}\Big|_{2000}^{3000}$$

$$= \dfrac{1.2103}{30,000}(5,000,000) \approx 100.86 \text{ feet}$$

47. $Q(x, y) = 100\left(\dfrac{x}{y}\right)$, $8 \le x \le 16$, $10 \le y \le 12$

Average intelligence $= \dfrac{1}{16} \displaystyle\int_{8}^{16} \int_{10}^{12} 100\left(\dfrac{x}{y}\right) dy\, dx = \dfrac{100}{16} \int_{8}^{16} \left[x \ln y \Big|_{10}^{12}\right] dx$

$$= \dfrac{100}{16} \int_{8}^{16} x(\ln 12 - \ln 10)\, dx$$

$$= \dfrac{100(\ln 12 - \ln 10)}{16} \cdot \dfrac{x^2}{2}\Big|_{8}^{16}$$

$$= \dfrac{100(\ln 12 - \ln 10)}{32}(192)$$

$$= 600 \ln(1.2) \approx 109.4$$

CHAPTER 8 REVIEW

1. $f(x, y) = 2000 + 40x + 70y$

$f(5, 10) = 2000 + 40 \cdot 5 + 70 \cdot 10 = 2900$

$f_x(x, y) = 40$

$f_y(x, y) = 70$

(8-1, 8-2)

2. $z = x^3 y^2$

$$\frac{\partial z}{\partial x} = 3x^2 y^2$$

$$\frac{\partial^2 z}{\partial x^2} = \frac{\partial\left(\frac{\partial z}{\partial x}\right)}{\partial x} = \frac{\partial(3x^2 y^2)}{\partial x} = 6xy^2$$

$$\frac{\partial z}{\partial y} = 2x^3 y$$

$$\frac{\partial^2 z}{\partial x \partial y} = \frac{\partial\left(\frac{\partial z}{\partial y}\right)}{\partial x} = \frac{\partial(2x^3 y)}{\partial x} = 6x^2 y \qquad (8\text{-}2)$$

3. $\int(6xy^2 + 4y)\,dy = 6x\int y^2\,dy + 4\int y\,dy = 6x \cdot \frac{y^3}{3} + 4 \cdot \frac{y^2}{2} + C(x)$

$$= 2xy^3 + 2y^2 + C(x) \qquad (8\text{-}6)$$

4. $\int(6xy^2 + 4y)\,dx = 6y^2\int x\,dx + 4y\int dx = 6y^2 \cdot \frac{x^2}{2} + 4yx + E(y)$

$$= 3x^2 y^2 + 4xy + E(y) \qquad (8\text{-}6)$$

5. $\int_0^1 \int_0^1 4xy\,dy\,dx = \int_0^1 \left[\int_0^1 4xy\,dy\right]dx = \int_0^1 \left[2xy^2\,\Big|_0^1\right]dx$

$$= \int_0^1 2x\,dx = x^2\,\Big|_0^1 = 1 \qquad (8\text{-}6)$$

6. $f(x, y) = 6 + 5x - 2y + 3x^2 + x^3$

$f_x(x, y) = 5 + 6x + 3x^2$

$f_y(x, y) = -2 \neq 0$

The function $f_y(x, y)$ is nonzero for all (x, y). $\qquad (8\text{-}3)$

7. $f(x, y) = 3x^2 - 2xy + y^2 - 2x + 3y - 7$

$f(2, 3) = 3 \cdot 2^2 - 2 \cdot 2 \cdot 3 + 3^2 - 2 \cdot 2 + 3 \cdot 3 - 7 = 7$

$f_y(x, y) = -2x + 2y + 3$

$f_y(2, 3) = -2 \cdot 2 + 2 \cdot 3 + 3 = 5 \qquad (8\text{-}1,\ 8\text{-}2)$

8. $f(x, y) = -4x^2 + 4xy - 3y^2 + 4x + 10y + 81$

$f_x(x, y) = -8x + 4y + 4 \qquad\qquad f_y(x, y) = 4x - 6y + 10$

$f_{xx}(x, y) = -8 \qquad\qquad\qquad\qquad f_{yy}(x, y) = -6$

$f_{xy}(x, y) = 4$

Now, $f_{xx}(2, 3) \cdot f_{yy}(2, 3) - [f_{xy}(2, 3)]^2 = (-8)(-6) - 4^2 = 32.$ $\qquad (8\text{-}2)$

9. $f(x, y) = x + 3y$ and $g(x, y) = x^2 + y^2 - 10$.

Let $F(x, y, \lambda) = f(x, y) + \lambda g(x, y) = x + 3y + \lambda(x^2 + y^2 - 10)$.

Then, we have:

$F_x = 1 + 2x\lambda$

$F_y = 3 + 2y\lambda$

$F_\lambda = x^2 + y^2 - 10$

Setting $F_x = F_y = F_\lambda = 0$, we obtain:

$1 + 2x\lambda = 0 \qquad (1)$

$3 + 2y\lambda = 0 \qquad (2)$

$x^2 + y^2 - 10 = 0 \qquad (3)$

From the first equation, $x = -\dfrac{1}{2\lambda}$; from the second equation, $y = -\dfrac{3}{2\lambda}$.

Substituting these into the third equation gives:

$\dfrac{1}{4\lambda^2} + \dfrac{9}{4\lambda^2} - 10 = 0$

$$40\lambda^2 = 10$$

$$\lambda^2 = \frac{1}{4}$$

$$\lambda = \pm\frac{1}{2}$$

Thus, the critical points are $\left(-1, -3, \dfrac{1}{2}\right)$ and $\left(1, 3, -\dfrac{1}{2}\right)$. $\qquad\qquad$ (8-4)

10.

x_k	y_k	$x_k y_k$	x_k^2
2	12	24	4
4	10	40	16
6	7	42	36
8	3	24	64
Totals 20	32	130	120

Thus, $\displaystyle\sum_{k=1}^{4} x_k = 20$, $\displaystyle\sum_{k=1}^{4} y_k = 32$, $\displaystyle\sum_{k=1}^{4} x_k y_k = 130$, $\displaystyle\sum_{k=1}^{4} x_k^2 = 120$.

Substituting these values into the formulas for m and d, we have:

$$m = \frac{4\left(\displaystyle\sum_{k=1}^{4} x_k y_k\right) - \left(\displaystyle\sum_{k=1}^{4} x_k\right)\left(\displaystyle\sum_{k=1}^{4} y_k\right)}{4\left(\displaystyle\sum_{k=1}^{4} x_k^2\right) - \left(\displaystyle\sum_{k=1}^{4} x_k\right)^2} = \frac{4(130) - (20)(32)}{4(120) - (20)^2} = \frac{-120}{80} = -1.5$$

$$d = \frac{\displaystyle\sum_{k=1}^{4} y_k - (-1.5)\sum_{k=1}^{4} x_k}{4} = \frac{32 + (1.5)(20)}{4} = \frac{62}{4} = 15.5$$

Thus, the least squares line is:

$y = mx + d = -1.5x + 15.5$

When $x = 10$, $y = -1.5(10) + 15.5 = 0.5$. $\qquad\qquad$ (8-5)

11. $\displaystyle\iint\limits_R (4x + 6y)\,dA = \int_{-1}^{1}\int_{1}^{2}(4x+6y)\,dy\,dx = \int_{-1}^{1}\left[\int_{1}^{2}(4x+6y)dy\right]dx$

$$= \int_{-1}^{1}\left[(4xy + 3y^2)\Big|_1^2\right]dx = \int_{-1}^{1}(8x + 12 - 4x - 3)\,dx$$

$$= \int_{-1}^{1}(4x + 9)\,dx = (2x^2 + 9x)\Big|_{-1}^{1} = 2 + 9 - (2 - 9) = 18$$

$\displaystyle\iint\limits_R (4x + 6y)\,dA = \int_{1}^{2}\int_{-1}^{1}(4x+6y)\,dx\,dy = \int_{1}^{2}\left[\int_{-1}^{1}(4x+6y)dx\right]dy$

$$= \int_{1}^{2}\left[(2x^2 + 6xy)\Big|_{-1}^{1}\right]dy = \int_{1}^{2}[2 + 6y - (2 - 6y)]\,dy$$

$$= \int_{1}^{2} 12y\,dy = 6y^2\Big|_1^2 = 24 - 6 = 18 \tag{8-6}$$

12. $f(x, y) = e^{x^2+2y}$

$f_x(x, y) = e^{x^2+2y}\cdot 2x = 2xe^{x^2+2y}$

$f_y(x, y) = e^{x^2+2y}\cdot 2 = 2e^{x^2+2y}$

$f_{xy}(x, y) = 2xe^{x^2+2y}\cdot 2 = 4xe^{x^2+2y}$ $\tag{8-2}$

13. $f(x, y) = (x^2 + y^2)^5$

$f_x(x, y) = 5(x^2 + y^2)^4\cdot 2x = 10x(x^2 + y^2)^4$

$f_{xy}(x, y) = 10x(4)(x^2 + y^2)^3\cdot 2y = 80xy(x^2 + y^2)^3$ $\tag{8-2}$

14. $f(x, y) = x^3 - 12x + y^2 - 6y$

$f_x(x, y) = 3x^2 - 12$ $\qquad\qquad$ $f_y(x, y) = 2y - 6$

$3x^2 - 12 = 0$ $\qquad\qquad\qquad$ $2y - 6 = 0$

$\qquad x^2 = 4$ $\qquad\qquad\qquad\qquad$ $y = 3$

$\qquad\quad x = \pm 2$

Thus, the critical points are (2, 3) an (-2, 3).

$f_{xx}(x, y) = 6x$ $\qquad$ $f_{xy}(x, y) = 0$ $\qquad$ $f_{yy}(x, y) = 2$

For the critical point (2, 3):

$f_{xx}(2, 3) = 12 > 0$

$f_{xy}(2, 3) = 0$

$f_{yy}(2, 3) = 2$

$f_{xx}(2, 3)\cdot f_{yy}(2, 3) - [f_{xy}(2, 3)]^2 = 12\cdot 2 = 24 > 0$

Therefore, $f(2, 3) = 2^3 - 12\cdot 2 + 3^2 - 6\cdot 3 = -25$ is a local minimum.

For the critical point (-2, 3):

$f_{xx}(-2, 3) = -12 < 0$

$f_{xy}(-2, 3) = 0$

$f_{yy}(-2, 3) = 2$

$f_{xx}(-2, 3)\cdot f_{yy}(-2, 3) - [f_{xy}(-2, 3)]^2 = -12\cdot 2 - 0 = -24 < 0$

Thus, f has a saddle point at (-2, 3). $\tag{8-3}$

15. <u>Step 1</u>. Maximize $f(x, y) = xy$

Subject to: $g(x, y) = 2x + 3y - 24 = 0$

<u>Step 2</u>. $F(x, y, \lambda) = f(x, y) + \lambda g(x, y) = xy + \lambda(2x + 3y - 24)$

<u>Step 3</u>. $F_x = y + 2\lambda = 0$ (1)

$F_y = x + 3\lambda = 0$ (2)

$F_\lambda = 2x + 3y - 24 = 0$ (3)

From (1) and (2), we obtain:

$y = -2\lambda$ and $x = -3\lambda$

Substituting these into (3), we have:

$-6\lambda - 6\lambda - 24 = 0$

$\lambda = -2$

Thus, the critical point is $(6, 4, -2)$.

<u>Step 4</u>. Since $(6, 4, -2)$ is the only critical point for F, we conclude that max $f(x, y) = f(6, 4) = 6 \cdot 4 = 24$.   (8-4)

16. <u>Step 1</u>. Minimize $f(x, y, z) = x^2 + y^2 + z^2$

Subject to: $2x + y + 2z = 9$ or $g(x, y, z) = 2x + y + 2z - 9 = 0$

<u>Step 2</u>. $F(x, y, z, \lambda) = x^2 + y^2 + z^2 + \lambda(2x + y + 2z - 9)$

<u>Step 3</u>. $F_x = 2x + 2\lambda = 0$ (1)

$F_y = 2y + \lambda = 0$ (2)

$F_z = 2z + 2\lambda = 0$ (3)

$F_\lambda = 2x + y + 2z - 9 = 0$ (4)

From equations (1), (2), and (3), we have:

$x = -\lambda, \ y = -\dfrac{\lambda}{2}, \ $ and $z = -\lambda$

Substituting these into (4), we obtain:

$-2\lambda - \dfrac{\lambda}{2} - 2\lambda - 9 = 0$

$\dfrac{9}{2}\lambda = -9$

$\lambda = -2$

The critical point is: $(2, 1, 2, -2)$

<u>Step 4</u>. Since $(2, 1, 2, -2)$ is the only critical point for F, we conclude that min $f(x, y, z) = f(2, 1, 2) = 2^2 + 1^2 + 2^2 = 9$.   (8-4)

17.

x_k	y_k	$x_k y_k$	x_k^2
10	50	500	100
20	45	900	400
30	50	1,500	900
40	55	2,200	1,600
50	65	3,250	2,500
60	80	4,800	3,600
70	85	5,950	4,900
80	90	7,200	6,400
90	90	8,100	8,100
100	110	11,000	10,000
Totals 550	720	45,400	38,500

Thus, $\displaystyle\sum_{k=1}^{10} x_k = 550$, $\displaystyle\sum_{k=1}^{10} y_k = 720$, $\displaystyle\sum_{k=1}^{10} x_k y_k = 45,400$, $\displaystyle\sum_{k=1}^{10} x_k^2 = 38,500$.

Substituting these values into the formulas for m and d, we have:

$$m = \frac{10(45,400) - (550)(720)}{10(38,500) - (550)^2} = \frac{58,000}{82,500} = \frac{116}{165}$$

$$d = \frac{720 - \left(\frac{116}{165}\right)550}{10} = \frac{100}{3}$$

Therefore, the least squares line is:

$$y = \frac{116}{165}x + \frac{100}{3} \approx 0.703x + 33.33 \tag{8-5}$$

18.
$$\frac{1}{(b-a)(d-c)} \iint_R f(x, y)\, dA = \frac{1}{[8-(-8)](27-0)} \int_{-8}^{8} \int_{0}^{27} x^{2/3} y^{1/3}\, dy\, dx$$

$$= \frac{1}{16 \cdot 27} \int_{-8}^{8} \left(\frac{3}{4} x^{2/3} y^{4/3} \Big|_{y=0}^{y=27} \right) dx$$

$$= \frac{1}{16 \cdot 27} \int_{-8}^{8} \frac{3^5}{4} x^{2/3}\, dx = \frac{9}{64} \int_{-8}^{8} x^{2/3}\, dx$$

$$= \frac{9}{64} \cdot \frac{3}{5} x^{5/3} \Big|_{-8}^{8} = \frac{9}{64} \cdot \frac{3}{5} [2^5 - (-2)^5]$$

$$= \frac{9}{64} \cdot \frac{3}{5} \cdot 2^6 = \frac{27}{5} \tag{8-6}$$

19.
$$V = \iint_R (3x^2 + 3y^2)\, dA = \int_0^1 \int_{-1}^1 (3x^2 + 3y^2)\, dy\, dx = \int_0^1 \left[\int_{-1}^1 (3x^2 + 3y^2)\, dy \right] dx$$

$$= \int_0^1 \left[(3x^2 y + y^3) \Big|_{-1}^1 \right] dx = \int_0^1 [3x^2 + 1 - (-3x^2 - 1)]\, dx$$

$$= \int_0^1 (6x^2 + 2)\, dx = (2x^3 + 2x) \Big|_0^1 = 4 \text{ cubic units} \tag{8-6}$$

20. $f(x, y) = x + y;$ $-10 \le x \le 10,$ $-10 \le y \le 10$

Prediction: average value $= f(0, 0) = 0.$

Verification:

$$\text{average value} = \frac{1}{[10 - (-10)][10 - (-10)]} \int_{-10}^{10} \int_{-10}^{10} (x + y)\,dy\,dx$$

$$= \frac{1}{400} \int_{-10}^{10} \left[\left(xy + \frac{1}{2}y^2 \right) \Big|_{-10}^{10} \right] dy$$

$$= \frac{1}{400} \int_{-10}^{10} 20x\,dx$$

$$= \frac{1}{400} (10x^2) \Big|_{-10}^{10} = 0 \tag{8-6}$$

21. $f(x, y) = \dfrac{e^x}{y + 10}$

(A) $S = \{x, y) \mid -a \le x \le a,\ -a \le y \le a\}$

The average value of f over S is given by:

$$\frac{1}{[a - (-a)][a - (-a)]} \int_{-a}^{a} \int_{-a}^{a} \frac{e^x}{y + 10}\,dx\,dy$$

$$= \frac{1}{4a^2} \int_{-a}^{a} \left[\frac{e^x}{y + 10} \Big|_{-a}^{a} \right] dy$$

$$= \frac{1}{4a^2} \int_{-a}^{a} \left(\frac{e^a}{y + 10} - \frac{e^{-a}}{y + 10} \right) dy$$

$$= \frac{e^a - e^{-a}}{4a^2} \int_{-a}^{a} \frac{1}{y + 10}\,dy$$

$$= \frac{e^a - e^{-a}}{4a^2} (\ln|y + 10|) \Big|_{-a}^{a}$$

$$= \frac{e^a - e^{-a}}{4a^2} [\ln(10 + a) - \ln(10 - a)]$$

$$= \frac{e^a - e^{-a}}{4a^2} \ln\left(\frac{10 + a}{10 - a} \right)$$

Now, $\dfrac{e^a - e^{-a}}{4a^2} \ln\left(\dfrac{10 + a}{10 - a} \right) = 5$ is equivalent to

$(e^a - e^{-a}) \ln\left(\dfrac{10 + a}{10 - a} \right) - 20a^2 = 0.$

Using a graphing utility, the graph of

$$f(x) = (e^x - e^{-x}) \ln\left(\frac{10 + x}{10 - x} \right) - 20x^2$$

is shown at the right and $f(x) = 0$ at $x \approx \pm 6.28.$

The dimensions of the square are: $12.56 \times 12.56.$

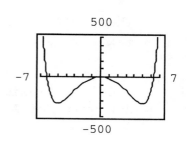

(B) To determine whether there is a square centered at (0, 0) such that

$$\frac{e^a - e^{-a}}{4a^2}\ln\!\left(\frac{10 + a}{10 - a}\right) = 0.05,$$

graph,

$$f(x) = (e^x - e^{-x})\ln\!\left(\frac{10 + x}{10 - x}\right) - 0.20x^2$$

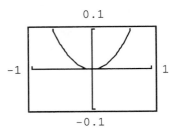

The result is shown at the right
and $f(x) = 0$ only at $x = 0$.
Thus, there does not exist a square
centered at (0, 0) such that the average
value of $f = 0.05$.

(8-6)

22. Step 1. Extremize $f(x, y) = 4x^3 - 5y^3$
   subject to $g(x, y) = 3x + 2y - 7 = 0$.

   Step 2. $F(x, y, \lambda) = 4x^3 - 5y^3 + \lambda(3x + 2y - 7)$

   Step 3. $F_x = 12x^2 + 3\lambda = 0$ (1)

   $\ F_y = -15y^2 + 2\lambda = 0 \qquad (2)$

   $\ F_\lambda = 3x + 2y - 7 = 0 \qquad (3)$

   From (1), $\lambda = -4x^2 \le 0$; from (2), $\lambda = \dfrac{15}{2}y^2 \ge 0$. This implies

   $x = y = \lambda = 0$ and $x = y = 0$ does not satisfy (3). The system
   (1), (2), (3) does not have a simultaneous solution. (8-4)

23. $P(x, y) = -4x^2 + 4xy - 3y^2 + 4x + 10y + 81$

   (A) $P_x(x, y) = -8x + 4y + 4$
   $\ P_x(1, 3) = -8\cdot1 + 4\cdot3 + 4 = 8$

   At the output level (1, 3), profit will increase by \$8000 for 100
   units increase in product A if the production of product B is held
   fixed.

   (B) $P_x = -8x + 4y + 4 = 0 \qquad (1)$
   $\ P_y = 4x - 6y + 10 = 0 \qquad (2)$

   Solving (1) and (2) for x and y, we obtain $x = 2$, $y = 3$.
   Thus, (2, 3) is a critical point.

$P_{xx} = -8$	$P_{yy} = -6$	$P_{xy} = 4$
$P_{xx}(2, 3) = -8 < 0$	$P_{yy}(2, 3) = -6$	$P_{xy}(2, 3) = 4$

   $P_{xx}(2, 3)\cdot P_{yy}(2, 3) - [P_{xy}(2, 3)]^2 = (-8)(-6) - 4^2 = 32 > 0$

   Thus, $P(2, 3)$ is a maximum and
   $\max P(x, y) = P(2, 3) = -4\cdot2^2 + 4\cdot2\cdot3 - 3\cdot3^2 + 4\cdot2 + 10\cdot3 + 81$
   $ = -16 + 24 - 27 + 8 + 30 + 81$
   $ = 100.$

   Thus, the maximum profit is \$100,000. This is obtained when
   200 units of A and 300 units of B are produced per month.

   (8-2, 8-3)

24. Minimize $S(x, y, z) = xy + 4yz + 3xz$

Subject to: $V(x, y, z) = xyz - 96 = 0$

Put $F(x, y, z, \lambda) = S(x, y, z) + \lambda V(x, y, z) = xy + 4yz + 3xz + \lambda(xyz - 96)$. Then, we have:

$$F_x = y + 3z + \lambda yz = 0 \qquad (1)$$

$$F_y = x + 4z + \lambda xz = 0 \qquad (2)$$

$$F_z = 4y + 3x + \lambda xy = 0 \qquad (3)$$

$$F_\lambda = xyz - 96 = 0 \qquad (4)$$

Solving the system of equations, (1)–(4), simultaneously, yields $x = 8$, $y = 6$, $z = 2$, and $\lambda = -1$. Thus, the critical point is $(8, 6, 2, -1)$ and $S(8, 6, 2) = 8 \cdot 6 + 4 \cdot 6 \cdot 2 + 3 \cdot 8 \cdot 2 = 144$ is the minimum value of S subject to the constraint $V = xyz - 96 = 0$.

The dimensions of the box that will require the minimum amount of material are:

Length $x = 8$ inches; Width $y = 6$ inches; Height $z = 2$ inches $\hspace{2em}$ (8-3)

25.

x_k	y_k	$x_k y_k$	x_k^2
1	2.0	2.0	1
2	2.5	5.0	4
3	3.1	9.3	9
4	4.2	16.8	16
5	4.3	21.5	25
Totals 15	16.1	54.6	55

Thus, $\sum\limits_{k=1}^{5} x_k = 15$, $\sum\limits_{k=1}^{5} y_k = 16.1$, $\sum\limits_{k=1}^{5} x_k y_k = 54.6$, $\sum\limits_{k=1}^{5} x_k^2 = 55$.

Substituting these values into the formulas for m and d, we have:

$$m = \frac{5(54.6) - (15)(16.1)}{5(55) - (15)^2} = \frac{31.5}{50} \approx 0.63$$

$$d = \frac{16.1 - (0.63)(15)}{5} = 1.33$$

Therefore, the least squares line is:

$y = 0.63x + 1.33$

When $x = 6$, $y = 0.63(6) + 1.33 = 5.11$, and the profit for the sixth year is estimated to be \$5.11 million. $\hspace{2em}$ (8-4)

26. $N(x, y) = 10x^{0.8}y^{0.2}$

(A) $N_x(x, y) = 8x^{-0.2}y^{0.2}$

$N_x(40, 50) = 8(40)^{-0.2}(50)^{0.2} \approx 8.36$

$N_y(x, y) = 2x^{0.8}y^{-0.8}$

$N_y(40, 50) = 2(40)^{0.8}(50)^{-0.8} \approx 1.67$

Thus, at the level of 40 units of labor and 50 units of capital, the marginal productivity of labor is approximately 8.36 and the marginal productivity of capital is approximately 1.67. Management should encourage increased use of labor.

(B) <u>Step 1</u>. Maximize the production function $N(x, y) = 10x^{0.8}y^{0.2}$
Subject to the constraint: $C(x, y) = 100x + 50y = 10,000$
i.e., $g(x, y) = 100x + 50y - 10,000 = 0$

<u>Step 2</u>. $F(x, y, \lambda) = 10x^{0.8}y^{0.2} + \lambda(100x + 50y - 10,000)$

<u>Step 3</u>. $F_x = 8x^{-0.2}y^{0.2} + 100\lambda = 0$ (1)

$F_y = 2x^{0.8}y^{-0.8} + 50\lambda = 0$ (2)

$F_\lambda = 100x + 50y - 10,000 = 0$ (3)

From equation (1), $\lambda = \dfrac{-0.08y^{0.2}}{x^{0.2}}$, and from (2),

$\lambda = \dfrac{-0.04x^{0.8}}{y^{0.8}}$.   Thus, $\dfrac{0.08y^{0.2}}{x^{0.2}} = \dfrac{0.04x^{0.8}}{y^{0.8}}$ and $x = 2y$.

Substituting into (3) yields:
$200y + 50y = 10,000$
$250y = 10,000$
$y = 40$

Therefore, $x = 80$ and $\lambda \approx -0.0696$. The critical point is
$(80, 40, -0.0696)$. Thus, we conclude that max $N(x, y) = N(80, 40) = 10(80)^{0.8}(40)^{0.2} \approx 696$ units.

Production is maximized when 80 units of labor and 40 units of capital are used.

The marginal productivity of money is $-\lambda \approx 0.0696$. The increase in production resulting from an increase of \$2000 in the budget is: $0.0696(2000) \approx 139$ units

(C) Average number of units
$= \dfrac{1}{(100 - 50)(40 - 20)} \displaystyle\int_{50}^{100} \int_{20}^{40} 10x^{0.8}y^{0.2}\, dy\, dx$

$= \dfrac{1}{(50)(20)} \displaystyle\int_{50}^{100} \left[\dfrac{10x^{0.8}y^{1.2}}{1.2} \Big|_{20}^{40} \right] dx = \dfrac{1}{1000} \int_{50}^{100} \dfrac{10}{1.2}x^{0.8}(40^{1.2} - 20^{1.2})\, dx$

$= \dfrac{40^{1.2} - 20^{1.2}}{120} \displaystyle\int_{50}^{100} x^{0.8}\, dx = \dfrac{40^{1.2} - 20^{1.2}}{120} \cdot \dfrac{x^{1.8}}{1.8} \Big|_{50}^{100}$

$= \dfrac{(40^{1.2} - 20^{1.2})(100^{1.8} - 50^{1.8})}{216} \approx \dfrac{(47.24)(2837.81)}{216} \approx 621$

Thus, the average number of units produced is approximately 621.

                                                           (8-4)

27. $T(V, x) = \dfrac{33V}{x + 33} = 33V(x + 33)^{-1}$

$T_x(V, x) = -33V(x + 33)^{-2} = \dfrac{-33V}{(x + 33)^2}$

$T_x(70, 17) = \dfrac{-33(70)}{(17 + 33)^2} = \dfrac{-33(70)}{2500}$

                 $= -0.924$ minutes per unit increase in depth when
$V = 70$ cubic feet and $x = 17$ ft.   (8-2)

28. $C = 100 - 24d^2 = 100 - 24(x^2 + y^2)$

$C(x, y) = 100 - 24(x^2 + y^2)$, $-2 \le x \le 2$, $-2 \le y \le 2$

Average concentration

$$= \frac{1}{4(4)} \int_{-2}^{2} \int_{-2}^{2} [100 - 24(x^2 + y^2)]\, dy\, dx$$

$$= \frac{1}{16} \int_{-2}^{2} [100y - 24x^2 y - 8y^3]\Big|_{-2}^{2}\, dx$$

$$= \frac{1}{16} \int_{-2}^{2} [400 - 96x^2 - 128]\, dx = \frac{1}{16} \int_{-2}^{2} (272 - 96x^2)\, dx$$

$$= \frac{1}{16} [272x - 32x^3]\Big|_{-2}^{2} = \frac{1}{16}(544 - 256) - \frac{1}{16}(-544 + 256)$$

$$= 18 + 18 = 36 \text{ parts per million}$$

(8-6)

29. $n(P_1, P_2, d) = 0.001\dfrac{P_1 P_2}{d}$

$$n(100{,}000,\ 50{,}000,\ 100) = 0.001\frac{100{,}000 \times 50{,}000}{100} = 50{,}000$$

(8-1)

30.

x_k	y_k	$x_k y_k$	x_k^2
30	60	1,800	900
50	75	3,750	2,500
60	80	4,800	3,600
70	85	5,950	4,900
90	90	8,100	8,100
Totals 300	390	24,400	20,000

Thus, $\displaystyle\sum_{k=1}^{5} x_k = 300$, $\displaystyle\sum_{k=1}^{5} y_k = 390$, $\displaystyle\sum_{k=1}^{5} x_k y_k = 24{,}400$, $\displaystyle\sum_{k=1}^{5} x_k^2 = 20{,}000$.

Substituting these values into the formulas for m and d, we have:

$$m = \frac{5(24{,}400) - (300)(390)}{5(20{,}000) - (300)^2} = \frac{5000}{10{,}000} = 0.5$$

$$d = \frac{390 - 0.5(300)}{5} = \frac{240}{5} = 48$$

Therefore, the least squares line is:

$y = 0.5x + 48$

When $x = 40$, $y = 0.5(40) + 48 = 68$.

(8-5)

31. (A) We use the linear regression feature on a graphing utility with 1900 as $x = 0$, 1910 as $x = 10$, ..., 2000 as $x = 100$.

```
LinReg
y=ax+b
a=.4932727273
b=25.2
```

Thus, the least squares line is:
  $y = 0.4933x + 25.20$.

(B) The year 2020 corresponds to $x = 120$; $y(120) \approx 84.40$ people/sq. mi.

(C)

```
QuadReg
 y=ax²+bx+c
 a=.0012587413
 b=.3673986014
 c=27.08811189
```

```
ExpReg
 y=a*b^x
 a=28.18046065
 b=1.010414421
```

Quadratic regression: Exponential regression:
$y(120) \approx 89.30$ people/sq. mi. $y(120) \approx 97.70$ people/sq. mi.   (8-5)

32.
```
LinReg
 y=ax+b
 a=1.069267604
 b=.5223226384
 r=.9793163189
```

(A) The least squares line is $y \approx 1.069x + 0.522$.

(B) Evaluate the result in (A) at $x = 60$: $y \approx 64.68$ yr

(C)

```
QuadReg
 y=ax²+bx+c
 a=-.0083659329
 b=2.13769365
 c=-33.36800618
```

```
LnReg
 y=a+blnx
 a=-213.2879278
 b=67.91982728
 r=.9800944981
```

Evaluate at $x = 60$: $y \approx 64.78$ yr   Evaluate at $x = 60$: $y \approx 64.80$ yr   (8-5)

33. (A) A scatter plot of the data points is shown at the right.

   A continuous curve that passes through these points would intersect certain horizontal lines in three places. Thus we would expect cubic regression to give a better fit than either linear or quadratic regression.

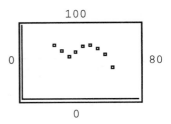

(B) The cubic regression curve clearly gives the best fit.

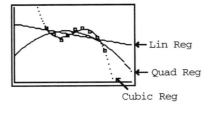

←— Lin Reg

←— Quad Reg

Cubic Reg

```
LinReg
 y=ax+b
 a=-.3633333333
 b=78.48222222
```

```
QuadReg
 y=ax²+bx+c
 a=-.0267965368
 b=1.887575758
 c=35.67922078
```

```
CubicReg
 y=ax³+bx²+cx+d
 a=-.0042356902
 b=.5069004329
 c=-19.27816835
 d=297.0128369
```

(8-5)

EXERCISE 9-1

Things to remember:

1. θ_{rad} = radian measure of θ

    $= \dfrac{\text{Arc length}}{\text{Radius}}$

    $= \dfrac{s}{R}$ [<u>Note</u>: If $R = 1$, then $\theta_{rad} = s$.]

2. DEGREE-RADIAN CONVERSION FORMULA

    $$\dfrac{\theta_{deg}}{180°} = \dfrac{\theta_{rad}}{\pi_{rad}}$$

3. On a unit circle, where the origin is at the center, cos θ and sin θ are measured by the abscissa and ordinate of point P, respectively, as shown in the figure.

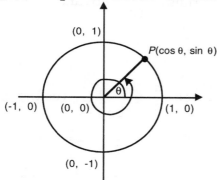

    For any real number x, sin x = sin(x radians), cos x = cos(x radians).

4. $\tan x = \dfrac{\sin x}{\cos x}$, $\cos x \neq 0$

5. $\cot x = \dfrac{\cos x}{\sin x}$, $\sin x \neq 0$

6. $\sec x = \dfrac{1}{\cos x}$, $\cos x \neq 0$

7. $\csc x = \dfrac{1}{\sin x}$, $\sin x \neq 0$

In Problems 1 - 5, use $\theta_{rad} = \dfrac{\pi}{180}\theta_{deg}$.

1. $\theta_{rad} = \dfrac{\pi}{180} \cdot 18$
$= \dfrac{\pi}{10} \text{rad}$

3. $\theta_{rad} = \dfrac{\pi}{180} \cdot 90$
$= \dfrac{\pi}{2} \text{rad}$

5. $\theta_{rad} = \dfrac{\pi}{180} \cdot 540$
$= 3\pi \text{ rad}$

7. I   **9.** II   **11.** III   **13.** -1   **15.** 0   **17.** 0

In Problems 19 - 23, use $\theta_{deg} = \dfrac{180}{\pi}\theta_{rad}$.

19. $\theta_{deg} = \dfrac{180}{\pi} \cdot \dfrac{2\pi}{3}$
$= 120°$

21. $\theta_{deg} = \dfrac{180}{\pi} \cdot 2\pi$
$= 360°$

23. $\theta_{deg} = \dfrac{180}{\pi} \cdot \dfrac{3\pi}{4}$
$= 135°$

25. $\cos 60° = \dfrac{1}{2}$

27. $\sin(-30°) = -\dfrac{1}{2}$

29. $\cos\left(\dfrac{3\pi}{4}\right) = \dfrac{-\sqrt{2}}{2}$

31. $\sin 3 = 0.1411$

33. $\cos 33.74 = -0.6840$

35. $\sin(-43.06) = 0.7970$

37. $\theta° = 27°$
Using 2, $\dfrac{27°}{180°} = \dfrac{\theta}{\pi \text{ radians}}$
$\theta = \dfrac{27\pi}{180} \text{radians}$
$= \dfrac{3\pi}{20} \text{radians}$

39. Using 2, $\dfrac{\theta°}{180°} = \dfrac{\dfrac{\pi}{12}}{\pi}$
Thus, $\dfrac{\pi}{12}$ radians $= \dfrac{180°}{12} = 15°$

41. From Figure 6 and using 4,
$\tan 45° = \dfrac{\sin 45°}{\cos 45°}$
$= \dfrac{\dfrac{1}{\sqrt{2}}}{\dfrac{1}{\sqrt{2}}} = 1$

43. $\sec\dfrac{\pi}{3} = \dfrac{1}{\cos\dfrac{\pi}{3}}$ (using 6)
$= \dfrac{1}{\dfrac{1}{2}} = 2$

45. $\cot\dfrac{\pi}{3} = \dfrac{\cos\dfrac{\pi}{3}}{\sin\dfrac{\pi}{3}} = \dfrac{\dfrac{1}{2}}{\dfrac{\sqrt{3}}{2}} = \dfrac{1}{\sqrt{3}} = \dfrac{1}{\sqrt{3}} \cdot \dfrac{\sqrt{3}}{\sqrt{3}} = \dfrac{\sqrt{3}}{3}$

47. Applying the Pythagorean Theorem to the triangle *OPQ*, we obtain:
$(\sin x)^2 + (\cos x)^2 = 1$

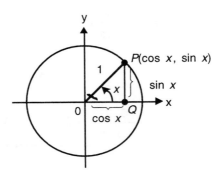

49. $y = 2 \sin \pi x$;
$0 \le x \le 2$, $-2 \le y \le 2$

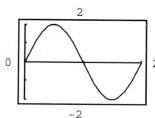

51. $y = 4 - 4 \cos \dfrac{\pi x}{2}$;
$0 \le x \le 8$, $0 \le y \le 8$

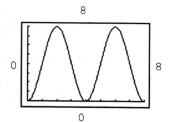

53. (A) $P(t) = 5 - 5 \cos\left(\dfrac{\pi}{26}\right)t$

$P(13) = 5 - 5 \cos\left(\dfrac{\pi}{26}\right)13 = 5 - 5 \cos\left(\dfrac{\pi}{2}\right) = 5 - 5(0) = 5$

$P(26) = 5 - 5 \cos\left(\dfrac{\pi}{26}\right)26 = 5 - 5 \cos(\pi) = 5 - 5(-1) = 10$

$P(39) = 5 - 5 \cos\left(\dfrac{\pi}{26}\right)39 = 5 - 5 \cos\left(\dfrac{3\pi}{2}\right) = 5 - 5(0) = 5$

$P(52) = 5 - 5 \cos\left(\dfrac{\pi}{26}\right)52 = 5 - 5 \cos(2\pi) = 5 - 5(1) = 0$

(B) $P(30) = 5 - 5 \cos\left(\dfrac{\pi}{26}\right)30 \approx 5 - 5(0.886) \approx 5 + 4.43 \approx 9.43$

$P(100) = 5 - 5 \cos\left(\dfrac{\pi}{26}\right)100 \approx 5 - 5(-0.886) \approx 5 - 4.43 \approx 0.57$

Interpretation: 30 weeks after January 1, the profit on a week's sales of bathing suits is $943; 100 weeks after January 1, the profit on a week's sales of bathing suits is $57.

(C)

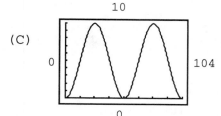

55. $V(t) = 0.45 - 0.35 \cos \dfrac{\pi t}{2}$, $0 \le t \le 8$

(A) $V(0) = 0.45 - 0.35 \cos(0) = 0.45 - 0.35 = 0.10$

$V(1) = 0.45 - 0.35 \cos\left(\dfrac{\pi}{2}\right) = 0.45 - 0 = 0.45$

$V(2) = 0.45 - 0.35 \cos(\pi) = 0.45 + 0.35 = 0.80$

$V(3) = 0.45 - 0.35 \cos\left(\dfrac{3\pi}{2}\right) = 0.45 - 0 = 0.45$

$V(7) = 0.45 - 0.35 \cos\left(\dfrac{7\pi}{2}\right) = 0.45 - 0 = 0.45$

(B) $V(3.5) = 0.45 - 0.35 \cos\left(\dfrac{3.5\pi}{2}\right) \approx 0.45 - 0.2475 \approx 0.20$

$V(5.7) = 0.45 - 0.35 \cos\left(\dfrac{5.7\pi}{2}\right) \approx 0.45 + 0.3119 \approx 0.76$

Interpretation: The volume of air in the lungs of a normal seated adult 3.5 seconds after exhaling is approximately 0.20 liters; the volume of air is approximately 0.76 liters 5.7 seconds after exhaling.

(C)

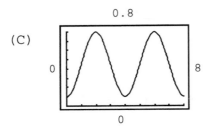

57. $d = -2.1 - 4 \sin 4\theta$

(A) $\theta = 30°$
$d = -2.1 - 4 \sin 4(30°)$
$= -2.1 - 4 \sin 120°$
$= -2.1 - 4 \cdot \dfrac{\sqrt{3}}{2} \approx -5.6°$

(B) $\theta = 10°$
$d = -2.1 - 4 \sin 4(10°)$
$= -2.1 - 4 \sin 40°$
$-2.1 - 4(0.6428) \approx -4.7°$

EXERCISE 9-2

Things to remember:

DERIVATIVE FORMULAS FOR SINE AND COSINE

1. Basic Form

$$\dfrac{d}{dx} \sin x = \cos x \qquad \dfrac{d}{dx} \cos x = -\sin x$$

2. Generalized Form
For $u = u(x)$:

$$\dfrac{d}{dx} \sin u = \cos u \dfrac{du}{dx} \qquad \dfrac{d}{dx} \cos u = -\sin u \dfrac{du}{dx}$$

1. $\dfrac{d}{dt} \cos t = -\sin t$ (using 2)

3. $\dfrac{d}{dx} \sin x^3 = \cos x^3 \dfrac{d}{dx} x^3$ (using 3)
$= \cos x^3 (3x^2)$
$= 3x^2 \cos x^3$

5. $\dfrac{d}{dt} t \sin t = t \dfrac{d}{dt} \sin t + \sin t \dfrac{d}{dt} t$
$= t \cos t + (\sin t)1$
$= t \cos t + \sin t$

7. $\dfrac{d}{dx} \sin x \cos x = \sin x \dfrac{d}{dx} \cos x + \cos x \dfrac{d}{dx} \sin x$

$$= -\sin x \sin x + \cos x \cos x$$

$$= (\cos x)^2 - (\sin x)^2$$

9. $\dfrac{d}{dx} (\sin x)^5 = 5(\sin x)^4 \dfrac{d}{dx} \sin x = 5(\sin x)^4 \cos x$

11. $\dfrac{d}{dx} \sqrt{\sin x} = \dfrac{d}{dx} (\sin x)^{1/2} = \dfrac{1}{2}(\sin x)^{-1/2}\dfrac{d}{dx}\sin x$

$$= \dfrac{1}{2}(\sin x)^{-1/2}\cos x = \dfrac{\cos x}{2\sqrt{\sin x}}$$

13. $\dfrac{d}{dx} \cos \sqrt{x} = -\sin\sqrt{x}\,\dfrac{d}{dx}\sqrt{x}$ (using $\underline{4}$)

$$= -\dfrac{1}{2}x^{-1/2}\sin\sqrt{x} = -\dfrac{\sin\sqrt{x}}{2\sqrt{x}}$$

15. $f(x) = \sin x$
$f'(x) = \cos x$

The slope of the graph of f at $x = \dfrac{\pi}{6}$ is: $f'\left(\dfrac{\pi}{6}\right) = \cos\dfrac{\pi}{6} = \dfrac{\sqrt{3}}{2} \approx 0.866$

17. f is increasing on $[-\pi, 0]$ ($f'(x) > 0$); f is decreasing on $[0, \pi]$
($f'(x) < 0$); f has a local maximum at $x = 0$;

the graph of f is concave upward on $\left(-\pi, -\dfrac{\pi}{2}\right)$ and

on $\left(\dfrac{\pi}{2}, \pi\right)$ (f' is increasing on these intervals);

the graph of f is concave downward on $\left(-\dfrac{\pi}{2}, \dfrac{\pi}{2}\right)$

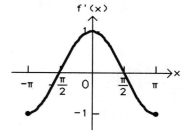

(f' is decreasing on this interval); $f(x) = \cos x$,
$f'(x) = -\sin x$.

19. $\dfrac{d}{dx}\tan x = \dfrac{d}{dx}\dfrac{\sin x}{\cos x} = \dfrac{\cos x \dfrac{d}{dx}\sin x - \sin x \dfrac{d}{dx}\cos x}{(\cos x)^2}$

$$= \dfrac{\cos x(\cos x) - \sin x(-\sin x)}{(\cos x)^2} = \dfrac{\cos x \cos x + \sin x \sin x}{(\cos x)^2}$$

$$= \dfrac{(\cos x)^2 + (\sin x)^2}{(\cos x)^2} = \dfrac{1}{(\cos x)^2} = (\sec x)^2$$

21. $\dfrac{d}{dx}\sin\sqrt{x^2 - 1} = \cos\sqrt{x^2 - 1}\,\dfrac{d}{dx}\sqrt{x^2 - 1}$

$$= \cos\sqrt{x^2 - 1}\,\dfrac{1}{2}(x^2 - 1)^{-1/2}\dfrac{d}{dx}(x^2 - 1)$$

$$= \dfrac{2x\cos\sqrt{x^2 - 1}}{2\sqrt{x^2 - 1}} = \dfrac{x\cos\sqrt{x^2 - 1}}{\sqrt{x^2 - 1}}$$

23. $f(x) = e^x \sin x$

$f'(x) = e^x(\cos x) + (\sin x)e^x = e^x(\sin x + \cos x)$

$f''(x) = e^x(\cos x - \sin x) + (\sin x + \cos x)e^x = 2e^x \cos x$

25. $y = x \sin \pi x;$

$0 \le x \le 9, \ -9 \le y \le 9$

27. $y = \dfrac{\cos \pi x}{x};$

$0 \le x \le 8, \ -2 \le y \le 3$

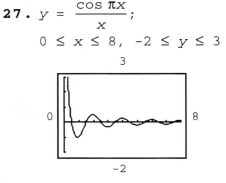

29. $y = e^{-0.3x} \sin \pi x,$
$0 \le x \le 10, \ -1 \le y \le 1$

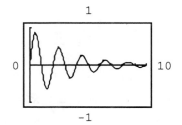

31. $P(t) = 5 - 5\cos\left(\dfrac{\pi t}{26}\right), \ 0 \le t \le 104$

(A) $P'(t) = -5\left[-\sin\left(\dfrac{\pi t}{26}\right)\left(\dfrac{\pi}{26}\right)\right] = \dfrac{5\pi}{26}\sin\left(\dfrac{\pi t}{26}\right), \ 0 \le t \le 104$

(B) $P'(8) = \dfrac{5\pi}{26}\sin\left(\dfrac{8\pi}{26}\right) \approx 0.50$ (hundred) or \$50 per week

$P'(26) = \dfrac{5\pi}{26}\sin\left(\dfrac{26\pi}{26}\right) = 0$ or \$0 per week

$P'(50) = \dfrac{5\pi}{26}\sin\left(\dfrac{50\pi}{26}\right) \approx -0.14$ (hundred) or -\$14 per week

(C) $P'(t) = \dfrac{5\pi}{26}\sin\left(\dfrac{\pi t}{26}\right) = 0, \ 0 < t < 104$

$\sin\left(\dfrac{\pi t}{26}\right) = 0$

Therefore, the critical values are:

$\dfrac{\pi t}{26} = \pi$, or $t = 26$; $\qquad \dfrac{\pi t}{26} = 2\pi$ or $t = 52$; $\qquad \dfrac{\pi t}{26} = 3\pi$ or $t = 78$.

Now,

$$P''(t) = \frac{5\pi^2}{676}\cos\left(\frac{\pi t}{26}\right)$$

$$P''(26) = \frac{5\pi^2}{676}\cos(\pi) = -\frac{5\pi^2}{676} < 0$$

$$P''(52) = \frac{5\pi^2}{676}\cos(2\pi) = \frac{5\pi^2}{676} > 0$$

$$P''(78) = \frac{5\pi^2}{676}\cos(3\pi) = -\frac{5\pi^2}{676} < 0$$

Thus,

t	$P(t)$	
26	\$1000	local maximum
52	\$0	local minimum
78	\$1000	local maximum

(D)

t	$P(t)$	
0	\$0	absolute minimum
26	\$1000	absolute maximum
52	\$0	absolute minimum
78	\$1000	absolute maximum
104	\$0	absolute minimum

(E) The results in part (C) are illustrated by the graph of f shown at the right.

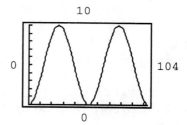

33. $V(t) = 0.45 - 0.35\cos\left(\dfrac{\pi t}{2}\right)$, $0 \le t \le 8$

(A) $V'(t) = -0.35\left[-\sin\left(\dfrac{\pi t}{2}\right)\right]\left(\dfrac{\pi}{2}\right) = \dfrac{0.35\pi}{2}\sin\left(\dfrac{\pi t}{2}\right)$, $0 \le t \le 8$

(B) $V'(3) = \dfrac{0.35\pi}{2}\sin\left(\dfrac{3\pi}{2}\right) = -\dfrac{0.35\pi}{2} \approx -0.55$ liters per second

$V'(4) = \dfrac{0.35\pi}{2}\sin\left(\dfrac{4\pi}{2}\right) = 0.00$ liters per second

$V'(5) = \dfrac{0.35\pi}{2}\sin\left(\dfrac{5\pi}{2}\right) = \dfrac{0.35\pi}{2} \approx 0.55$ liters per second

(C) $V'(t) = \dfrac{0.35\pi}{2}\sin\left(\dfrac{\pi t}{2}\right) = 0$, $0 < t < 8$

$$\sin\left(\dfrac{\pi t}{2}\right) = 0$$

Therefore, the critical values are:

$$\frac{\pi t}{2} = \pi \text{ or } t = 2; \quad \frac{\pi t}{2} = 2\pi \text{ or } t = 4; \quad \frac{\pi t}{2} = 3\pi \text{ or } t = 6.$$

Now,

$$V''(t) = \frac{0.35\pi}{2}\cos\left(\frac{\pi t}{2}\right)\left(\frac{\pi}{2}\right) = \frac{0.35\pi^2}{4}\cos\left(\frac{\pi t}{2}\right)$$

$$V''(2) = \frac{0.35\pi^2}{4}\cos(\pi) = -\frac{0.35\pi^2}{4} < 0$$

$$V''(4) = \frac{0.35\pi^2}{4}\cos(2\pi) = \frac{0.35\pi^2}{4} > 0$$

$$V''(6) = \frac{0.35\pi^2}{4}\cos(3\pi) = -\frac{0.35\pi^2}{4} < 0$$

Thus,

t	$V(t)$	
2	0.80	local maximum
4	0.10	local minimum
6	0.80	local maximum

(D)

t	$V(t)$	
0	0.10	absolute minimum
2	0.80	absolute maximum
4	0.10	absolute minimum
6	0.80	absolute maximum
8	0.10	absolute minimum

Thus, 0.10 liters is the absolute minimum and 0.80 liters is the absolute maximum of V for $0 \le t \le 8$.

(E) The results in part (C) are illustrated by the graph of f shown at the right.

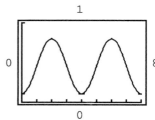

EXERCISE 9-3

Things to remember:

INDEFINITE INTEGRAL FORMULAS FOR SINE AND COSINE

<u>1</u>. Basic Formulas

$$\int \sin x \, dx = -\cos x + C \quad \text{and} \quad \int \cos x \, dx = \sin x + C$$

<u>2</u>. Generalized Formulas

For $u = u(x)$

$$\int \sin u \, du = -\cos u + C \quad \text{and} \quad \int \cos u \, du = \sin u + C$$

1. $\int \sin t \, dt = -\cos t + C$ (using $\underline{2}$)

3. $\int \cos 3x \, dx = \dfrac{1}{3}\int \cos 3x (3 \, dx)$ [Let $u = 3x$, then $du = 3 \, dx$.]

$\qquad\qquad = \dfrac{1}{3}\sin 3x + C$ (using $\underline{4}$)

5. $\int (\sin x)^{12}\cos x \, dx = \int u^{12} du$ [Let $u = \sin x$, then $du = \cos x \, dx$.]

$\qquad\qquad\qquad = \dfrac{u^{13}}{13} + C = \dfrac{(\sin x)^{13}}{13} + C$

7. $\int \sqrt[3]{\cos x}\,\sin x \, dx = -\int \sqrt[3]{\cos x}(-\sin x)dx$ [Let $u = \cos x$, then $du = -\sin x \, dx$.]

$\qquad\qquad = -\int u^{1/3} du = -\dfrac{u^{4/3}}{\frac{4}{3}} + C = -\dfrac{3}{4}(\cos x)^{4/3} + C$

9. $\int x^2 \cos x^3 \, dx = \dfrac{1}{3}\int \cos x^3 (3x^2) \, dx$ [Let $u = x^3$, then $du = 3x^2 \, dx$.]

$\qquad\qquad = \dfrac{1}{3}\sin x^3 + C$

11. $\int_0^{\pi/2} \cos x \, dx = \sin x \Big|_0^{\pi/2} = \sin \dfrac{\pi}{2} - \sin 0 = 1 - 0 = 1$

13. $\int_{\pi/2}^{\pi} \sin x \, dx = -\cos x \Big|_{\pi/2}^{\pi} = \left(\cos \pi - \cos \dfrac{\pi}{2}\right) = -(-1 - 0) = 1$

15. The shaded area $= \int_{\pi/6}^{\pi/3} \cos x \, dx = \sin x \Big|_{\pi/6}^{\pi/3} = \sin \dfrac{\pi}{3} - \sin \dfrac{\pi}{6}$

$\qquad\qquad = \dfrac{\sqrt{3}}{2} - \dfrac{1}{2} \approx 0.866 - 0.5 \approx 0.366$

17. $\int_0^2 \sin x \, dx = -\cos x \Big|_0^2 = -(\cos 2 - \cos 0) \approx -(-0.4161 - 1) \approx 1.4161$

19. $\int_1^2 \cos x \, dx = \sin x \Big|_1^2 = \sin 2 - \sin 1 \approx 0.9093 - 0.8415 \approx 0.0678$

21. $\int e^{\sin x} \cos x \, dx$ [Let $u = \sin x$, then $du = \cos x \, dx$.]

$\qquad = \int e^u \, du = e^u + C = e^{\sin x} + C$

23. $\int \dfrac{\cos x}{\sin x} dx = \int \dfrac{du}{u}$ [Let $u = \sin x$, then $du = \cos x \, dx$.]

$\qquad\qquad = \ln|u| + C = \ln|\sin x| + C$

25. $\int \tan x \, dx = \int \dfrac{\sin x}{\cos x} dx$ [Let $u = \cos x$, then $du = -\sin x \, dx$.]

$$= -\int \dfrac{du}{u} = -\ln|u| + C = -\ln|\cos x| + C$$

27. (A)

(B) $\Delta x = \dfrac{3 - 0}{6} = \dfrac{1}{2}$

$L_6 = f(0)\dfrac{1}{2} + f\left(\dfrac{1}{2}\right)\dfrac{1}{2} + f(1)\dfrac{1}{2} + f\left(\dfrac{3}{2}\right)\dfrac{1}{2} + f(2)\dfrac{1}{2} + f\left(\dfrac{5}{2}\right)\dfrac{1}{2}$

$\approx [0 + 0.291 + 0.310 + 0.223 + 0.123 + 0.049]\dfrac{1}{2}$

$= 0.498$

29. $P(t) = 5 - 5\cos\left(\dfrac{\pi t}{26}\right), \quad 0 \leq t \leq 104$

(A) Total profit during the two-year period:

$$T = \int_0^{104}\left[5 - 5\cos\left(\dfrac{\pi t}{26}\right)\right]dt = \int_0^{104} 5 \, dt - 5\int_0^{104}\cos\left(\dfrac{\pi t}{26}\right)dt$$

$$= 5t \Big|_0^{104} - 5\left(\dfrac{26}{\pi}\right)\int_0^{104}\cos\left(\dfrac{\pi t}{26}\right)\left(\dfrac{\pi}{26}\right)dt = 520 - \dfrac{130}{\pi}\sin\left(\dfrac{\pi t}{26}\right)\Big|_0^{104} = 520$$

Thus, $T = \$520$ hundred or $\$52,000$.

(B) Total profit earned from $t = 13$ to $t = 26$:

$$T = \int_{13}^{26}\left[5 - 5\cos\left(\dfrac{\pi t}{26}\right)\right]dt = \int_{13}^{26} 5 \, dt - 5\int_{13}^{26}\cos\left(\dfrac{\pi t}{26}\right)dt$$

$$= 5t \Big|_{13}^{26} - \dfrac{5(26)}{\pi}\int_{13}^{26}\cos\left(\dfrac{\pi t}{26}\right)\left(\dfrac{\pi}{26}\right)dt$$

$$= 65 - \dfrac{130}{\pi}\sin\left(\dfrac{\pi t}{26}\right)\Big|_{13}^{26} = 65 + \dfrac{130}{\pi} \approx 106.38$$

Thus, $T = \$106.38$ hundred or $\$10,638$.

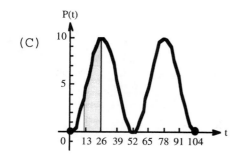

(C)

31. $P(n) = 1 + \cos\left(\dfrac{\pi n}{26}\right)$, $0 \le n \le 104$

(A) Total amount of pollutants during the two-year period:

$$T = \int_0^{104}\left[1 + \cos\left(\frac{\pi n}{26}\right)\right]dn = \int_0^{104} dn + \int_0^{104}\cos\left(\frac{\pi n}{26}\right)dn$$

$$= n\Big|_0^{104} + \frac{26}{\pi}\int_0^{104}\cos\left(\frac{\pi n}{26}\right)\left(\frac{\pi}{26}\right)dn = 104 + \frac{26}{\pi}\sin\left(\frac{\pi n}{26}\right)\Big|_0^{104} = 104 \text{ tons}$$

(B) Total amount of pollutants from the 13th week to the 52nd week:

$$T = \int_{13}^{52}\left[1 + \cos\left(\frac{\pi n}{26}\right)\right]dn = \int_{13}^{52} dn + \int_{13}^{52}\cos\left(\frac{\pi n}{26}\right)dn$$

$$= n\Big|_{13}^{52} + \frac{26}{\pi}\int_{13}^{52}\cos\left(\frac{\pi n}{26}\right)\left(\frac{\pi}{26}\right)dn = 39 + \frac{26}{\pi}\sin\left(\frac{\pi n}{26}\right)\Big|_{13}^{52}$$

$$= 39 - \frac{26}{\pi} \approx 31 \text{ tons}$$

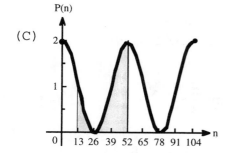

(C)

CHAPTER 9 REVIEW

1. (A) $\dfrac{\theta°}{180°} = \dfrac{\theta_{rad}}{\pi}$

$\theta_{rad} = \dfrac{\theta°\pi}{180°}$ [<u>Note</u>: θ_{rad} = radian measure of θ.]

$\theta° = 30°$

$\theta_{rad} = \dfrac{30°\pi}{180°} = \dfrac{\pi}{6}$

(B) $\theta° = 45°$

$\theta_{rad} = \dfrac{45°\pi}{180°} = \dfrac{\pi}{4}$

(C) $\theta° = 60°$

$\theta_{rad} = \dfrac{60°\pi}{180°} = \dfrac{\pi}{3}$

(D) $\theta° = 90°$

$\theta_{rad} = \dfrac{90°\pi}{180°} = \dfrac{\pi}{2}$

(9-1)

2. (A) $\cos \pi = -1$ (B) $\sin 0 = 0$ (C) $\sin \dfrac{\pi}{2} = 1$ (9-1)

3. $\dfrac{d}{dm} \cos m = -\sin m$ (9-2)   **4.** $\dfrac{d}{du} \sin u = \cos u$ (9-2)

5. $\dfrac{d}{dx} \sin(x^2 - 2x + 1) = \cos(x^2 - 2x + 1) \dfrac{d}{dx}(x^2 - 2x + 1)$

$$= (2x - 2)\cos(x^2 - 2x + 1) \qquad\qquad (9\text{-}2)$$

6. $\displaystyle\int \sin 3t\, dt = \dfrac{1}{3}\int \sin(3t)3\, dt = \dfrac{1}{3}\int \sin u\, du$ [Let $u = 3t$, then $du = 3\ dt$.]

$$= -\dfrac{1}{3}\cos u + C = -\dfrac{1}{3}\cos 3t + C \qquad\qquad (9\text{-}3)$$

7. (A) $\ \theta° = \dfrac{180°\theta_{\text{rad}}}{\pi}$ (B) $\theta_{\text{rad}} = \dfrac{\pi}{4}$

$\qquad\quad \theta_{\text{rad}} = \dfrac{\pi}{6}$

$\qquad\qquad\qquad\qquad\qquad\qquad\qquad \theta° = \dfrac{180°\left(\dfrac{\pi}{4}\right)}{\pi} = 45°$

$\qquad\quad \theta° = \dfrac{180°\left(\dfrac{\pi}{6}\right)}{\pi} = 30°$

(C) $\theta_{\text{rad}} = \dfrac{\pi}{3}$ (D) $\theta_{\text{rad}} = \dfrac{\pi}{2}$

$\qquad\quad \theta° = \dfrac{180°\left(\dfrac{\pi}{3}\right)}{\pi} = 60°$ $\qquad\qquad \theta° = \dfrac{180°\left(\dfrac{\pi}{2}\right)}{\pi} = 90°$ (9-1)

8. (A) $\sin \dfrac{\pi}{6} = \dfrac{1}{2}$ (B) $\cos \dfrac{\pi}{4} = \dfrac{\sqrt{2}}{2}$ (C) $\sin \dfrac{\pi}{3} = \dfrac{\sqrt{3}}{2}$ (9-1)

9. (A) $\cos 33.7 \approx -0.6543$ (B) $\sin(-118.4) \approx 0.8308$ (9-1)

10. $\dfrac{d}{dx}(x^2 - 1)\sin x = (x^2 - 1)\dfrac{d}{dx}\sin x + \sin x \dfrac{d}{dx}(x^2 - 1)$

$$= (x^2 - 1)\cos x + 2x \sin x \qquad\qquad (9\text{-}2)$$

11. $\dfrac{d}{dx}(\sin x)^6 = 6(\sin x)^5 \dfrac{d}{dx}\sin x = 6(\sin x)^5 \cos x$ (9-2)

12. $\dfrac{d}{dx}\sqrt[3]{\sin x} = \dfrac{d}{dx}(\sin x)^{1/3} = \dfrac{1}{3}(\sin x)^{-2/3}\dfrac{d}{dx}\sin x = \dfrac{1}{3}(\sin x)^{-2/3}\cos x$

$$(9\text{-}2)$$

13. $\int t \cos(t^2 - 1)\,dt = \dfrac{1}{2}\int \cos(t^2 - 1)\,2t\,dt$ [Let $u = (t^2 - 1)$,

then $du = 2t\,dt$.]

$= \dfrac{1}{2}\int \cos u\,du = \dfrac{1}{2}\sin u + C = \dfrac{1}{2}\sin(t^2 - 1) + C$ (9-3)

14. $\int_0^\pi \sin u\,du = -\cos u\,\Big|_0^\pi = -[\cos \pi - \cos 0] = 2$ (9-3)

15. $\int_0^{\pi/3} \cos x\,dx = \sin x\,\Big|_0^{\pi/3} = \sin \dfrac{\pi}{3} - \sin 0 = \dfrac{\sqrt{3}}{2}$ (9-3)

16. $\int_1^{2.5} \cos x\,dx = \sin x\,\Big|_1^{2.5} = \sin(2.5) - \sin(1) \approx 0.5985 - 0.8415 = -0.2430$

(9-3)

17. $y = \cos x,\ y' = -\sin x$

$y'\,\Big|_{x=\pi/4} = -\sin\left(\dfrac{\pi}{4}\right) = -\dfrac{\sqrt{2}}{2}$ (9-2)

18. $A = \int_{\pi/4}^{3\pi/4} \sin x\,dx = -\cos x\,\Big|_{\pi/4}^{3\pi/4} = \left(-\cos \dfrac{3\pi}{4}\right) - \left(-\cos \dfrac{\pi}{4}\right) = \sqrt{2}$ (9-3)

19. (A)

(B) $\Delta x = \dfrac{5 - 1}{4} = 1$

$R_4 = f(2)1 + f(3)1 + f(4)1 + f(5)1$

$\approx 0.455 + 0.047 + (-0.189) + (-0.192)$

$= 0.121$ (9-3)

20. $\theta_{rad} = \dfrac{\theta° \pi}{180°}$

Set $\theta° = 15°$. Then $\theta_{rad} = \dfrac{15° \pi}{180°} = \dfrac{\pi}{12}$. (9-1)

21. (A) $\sin\left(\dfrac{3\pi}{2}\right) = -1$ (B) $\cos\left(\dfrac{5\pi}{6}\right) = -\dfrac{\sqrt{3}}{2}$ (C) $\sin\left(-\dfrac{\pi}{6}\right) = -\dfrac{1}{2}$ (9-1)

22. $\dfrac{d}{du}\tan u = \dfrac{d}{du}\dfrac{\sin u}{\cos u} = \dfrac{\cos u \dfrac{d}{du}\sin u - \sin u \dfrac{d}{du}\cos u}{[\cos u]^2}$

$$= \dfrac{\cos u(\cos u) - \sin u(-\sin u)}{\cos^2 u}$$

$$= \dfrac{[\cos u]^2 + [\sin u]^2}{[\cos u]^2} = \dfrac{1}{[\cos u]^2} = [\sec u]^2 \qquad (9\text{-}2)$$

23. $\dfrac{d}{dx}e^{\cos x^2} = e^{\cos x^2}\dfrac{d}{dx}\cos x^2 = e^{\cos x^2}(-\sin x^2)\dfrac{d}{dx}x^2$

$$= e^{\cos x^2}(-\sin x^2)2x = -2x \sin x^2 e^{\cos x^2} \qquad (9\text{-}2)$$

24. $\displaystyle\int e^{\sin x}\cos x\, dx = \int e^u\, du \qquad$ [Let $u = \sin x$, then $du = \cos x\, dx$.]

$$= e^u + C = e^{\sin x} + C \qquad (9\text{-}3)$$

25. $\displaystyle\int \tan x\, dx = \int \dfrac{\sin x}{\cos x}dx = -\int \dfrac{1}{\cos x}(-\sin x)\,dx = -\int \dfrac{1}{u}du$

[Let $u = \cos x$, $\qquad\qquad\qquad\qquad\qquad\qquad = -\ln|u| + C$
then $du = -\sin x\, dx$.] $\qquad\qquad\qquad\qquad = -\ln|\cos x| + C \qquad (9\text{-}3)$

26. $\displaystyle\int_2^5 (5 + 2\cos 2x)\,dx = \int_2^5 5\, dx + \int_2^5 \cos(2x)2\, dx = 5x\Big|_2^5 + \sin 2x\Big|_2^5$

[Note: In the second integral, we let $u = 2x$ and $du = 2\, dx$.]

$$= 25 - 10 + \sin 10 - \sin 4$$
$$= 15 - 0.5440 + 0.7568$$
$$= 15.2128 \qquad (9\text{-}3)$$

27. $y = \dfrac{\sin \pi x}{0.2x}$;

$1 \le x \le 8,\ -4 \le y \le 4$

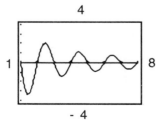

$(9\text{-}2,\ 9\text{-}3)$

28. $y = 0.5x \cos \pi x$;

$0 \le x \le 8,\ -5 \le y \le 5$

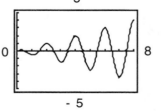

$(9\text{-}2,\ 9\text{-}3)$

29. $y = 3 - 2 \cos \pi x;$
$0 \le x \le 6, \ 0 \le y \le 5$

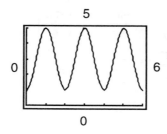

(9-2, 9-3)

30. $R(t) = 3 + 2 \cos\left(\dfrac{\pi t}{6}\right), \ 0 \le t \le 24$

(A) $R(0) = 3 + 2 \cos(0) = 3 + 2(1) = 5$

$R(2) = 3 + 2 \cos\left(\dfrac{2\pi}{6}\right) = 3 + 2\left(\dfrac{1}{2}\right) = 4$

$R(3) = 3 + 2 \cos\left(\dfrac{3\pi}{6}\right) = 3 + 2(0) = 3$

$R(6) = 3 + 2 \cos\left(\dfrac{6\pi}{6}\right) = 3 + 2(-1) = 1$

(B) $R(1) = 3 + 2 \cos\left(\dfrac{\pi}{6}\right) = 3 + 2\left(\dfrac{\sqrt{3}}{2}\right) \approx 4.732$

$R(22) = 3 + 2 \cos\left(\dfrac{22\pi}{6}\right) = 3 + 2\left(\dfrac{1}{2}\right) = 4$

Interpretation: The revenue is $4,732 for a month of sweater sales 1 month after January 1; the revenue is $4,000 for a month of sweater sales 22 months after January 1.

(9-1)

31. (A) $R'(t) = 2\left[-\sin\left(\dfrac{\pi t}{6}\right)\left(\dfrac{\pi}{6}\right)\right] = -\dfrac{\pi}{3}\sin\left(\dfrac{\pi t}{6}\right), \ 0 \le t \le 24$

(B) $R'(3) = -\dfrac{\pi}{3}\sin\left(\dfrac{3\pi}{6}\right) = -\dfrac{\pi}{3} \approx -\$1.047$ thousand or $-\$1047$ per month

$R'(10) = -\dfrac{\pi}{3}\sin\left(\dfrac{10\pi}{6}\right) = -\dfrac{\pi}{3}\left(-\dfrac{\sqrt{3}}{2}\right) \approx \$0.907$ thousand or $\$907$ per month

$R'(18) = -\dfrac{\pi}{3}\sin\left(\dfrac{18\pi}{6}\right) = -\dfrac{\pi}{3}(0) = \$0.00$

(C) Critical values: $R'(t) = -\dfrac{\pi}{3}\sin\left(\dfrac{\pi t}{6}\right) = 0$

$\sin\left(\dfrac{\pi t}{6}\right) = 0, \ 0 < t < 24$

$\dfrac{\pi t}{6} = \pi$ or $t = 6$

$\dfrac{\pi t}{6} = 2\pi$ or $t = 12$

$\dfrac{\pi t}{6} = 3\pi$ or $t = 18$

$$R''(t) = -\frac{\pi}{3} \cos\left(\frac{\pi t}{6}\right)\left(\frac{\pi}{6}\right) = \frac{-\pi^2}{18} \cos\left(\frac{\pi t}{6}\right)$$

$$R''(6) = \frac{-\pi^2}{18} \cos \pi = \frac{\pi^2}{18} > 0$$

$$R''(12) = \frac{-\pi^2}{18} \cos(2\pi) = \frac{-\pi^2}{18} < 0$$

$$R''(18) = \frac{-\pi^2}{18} \cos(3\pi) = \frac{\pi^2}{18} > 0$$

Thus,

t	$R(t)$	
6	\$1000	local minimum
12	\$5000	local maximum
18	\$1000	local minimum

(D)

t	$R(t)$	
0	\$5000	absolute maximum
6	\$1000	absolute minimum
12	\$5000	absolute maximum
18	\$1000	absolute minimum
24	\$5000	absolute maximum

(E) The results in part (C) are illustrated by the graph of R shown at the right.

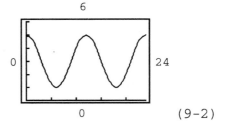

(9-2)

32. (A) Total revenue: $T = \displaystyle\int_0^{24} \left[3 + 2\cos\left(\frac{\pi t}{6}\right)\right] dt = \int_0^{24} 3\ dt + 2\int_0^{24} \cos\left(\frac{\pi t}{6}\right) dt$

$$= 3t\,\Big|_0^{24} + \frac{12}{\pi} \int_0^{24} \cos\left(\frac{\pi t}{6}\right)\left(\frac{\pi}{6}\right) dt = 72 + \frac{12}{\pi} \sin\left(\frac{\pi t}{6}\right)\Big|_0^{24}$$

$$= 72 + \frac{12}{\pi}[\sin 4\pi - \sin 0] = \$72 \text{ thousand or } \$72{,}000$$

(B) Total revenue: $T = \displaystyle\int_5^9 \left[3 + 2\cos\left(\frac{\pi t}{6}\right)\right] dt = \int_5^9 3\ dt + \frac{12}{\pi} \int_5^9 \cos\left(\frac{\pi t}{6}\right)\left(\frac{\pi}{6}\right) dt$

$$= 3t\,\Big|_5^9 + \frac{12}{\pi} \sin\left(\frac{\pi t}{6}\right)\Big|_5^9$$

$$= 3(9 - 5) + \frac{12}{\pi}\left[\sin\left(\frac{9\pi}{6}\right) - \sin\left(\frac{5\pi}{6}\right)\right]$$

$$= 12 + \frac{12}{\pi}\left(-1 - \frac{1}{2}\right) = 12 - \frac{18}{\pi}$$

$$= \$6.270 \text{ thousand or } \$6270$$

(C)

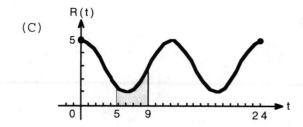

(9-2)

APPENDIX A BASIC ALGEBRA REVIEW

1. (A) Commutative $(\cdot)$: $x(y + z) = (y + z)x$
(B) Associative $(+)$: $2 + (x + y) = (2 + x) + y$
(C) Distributive: $(2 + 3)x = 2x + 3x$ $\hspace{2cm}$ (A-1)

2. $(3x - 4) + (x + 2) + (2 - 3x^2) + (x^3 + 8)$ $\cdot$
$= 3x - 4 + x + 2 + 2 - 3x^2 + x^3 + 8 = x^3 - 3x^2 + 4x + 8$ $\hspace{1cm}$ (A-2)

3. $[(x + 2) + (x^3 + 8)] - [(3x - 4) + (2 - 3x^2)]$
$= x^3 + x + 10 - [-3x^2 + 3x - 2] = x^3 + 3x^2 - 2x + 12$ $\hspace{1cm}$ (A-2)

4. $(2 - 3x^2)(x^3 + 8) = 2x^3 - 3x^5 + 16 - 24x^2 = -3x^5 + 2x^3 - 24x^2 + 16$ $\hspace{0.3cm}$ (A-2)

5. (A) 1 $\hspace{0.5cm}$ (B) 1 $\hspace{0.5cm}$ (C) 2 $\hspace{0.5cm}$ (D) 3 $\hspace{0.5cm}$ (A-2)

6. (A) 3 $\hspace{0.5cm}$ (B) 1 $\hspace{0.5cm}$ (C) -3 $\hspace{0.5cm}$ (D) 1 $\hspace{0.5cm}$ (A-2)

7. $5x^2 - 3x[4 - 3(x - 2)] = 5x^2 - 3x[4 - 3x + 6]$
$\hspace{3.3cm} = 5x^2 - 3x(-3x + 10)$
$\hspace{3.3cm} = 5x^2 + 9x^2 - 30x$
$\hspace{3.3cm} = 14x^2 - 30x$ $\hspace{2cm}$ (A-2)

8. $(2x + y)(3x - 4y) = 6x^2 - 8xy + 3xy - 4y^2$
$\hspace{3.1cm} = 6x^2 - 5xy - 4y^2$ $\hspace{1.5cm}$ (A-2)

9. $(2a - 3b)^2 = (2a)^2 - 2(2a)(3b) + (3b)^2$
$\hspace{2.3cm} = 4a^2 - 12ab + 9b^2$ $\hspace{2cm}$ (A-2)

10. $(2x - y)(2x + y) - (2x - y)^2 = (2x)^2 - y^2 - (4x^2 - 4xy + y^2)$
$\hspace{5.3cm} = 4x^2 - y^2 - 4x^2 + 4xy - y^2$
$\hspace{5.3cm} = 4xy - 2y^2$ $\hspace{1.5cm}$ (A-2)

11. $(3x^3 - 2y)^2 = (3x^3)^2 - 2(3x^3)(2y) + (2y)^2 = 9x^6 - 12x^3y + 4y^2$ $\hspace{0.5cm}$ (A-2)

12. $(x - 2y)^3 = (x - 2y)(x - 2y)^2$
$\hspace{2.1cm} = (x - 2y)(x^2 - 4xy + 4y^2)$
$\hspace{2.1cm} = x(x^2 - 4xy + 4y^2) - 2y(x^2 - 4xy + 4y^2)$
$\hspace{2.1cm} = x^3 - 4x^2y + 4xy^2 - 2x^2y + 8xy^2 - 8y^3$
$\hspace{2.1cm} = x^3 - 6x^2y + 12xy^2 - 8y^3$ $\hspace{2cm}$ (A-2)

13. (A) $4{,}065{,}000{,}000{,}000 = 4.065 \times 10^{12}$
(B) $0.0073 = 7.3 \times 10^{-3}$ $\hspace{4cm}$ (A-5)

14. (A) $2.55 \times 10^8 = 255{,}000{,}000$ $\hspace{1cm}$ (B) $4.06 \times 10^{-4} = 0.000\ 406$ $\hspace{0.5cm}$ (A-5)

15. (A) True; if n is a natural number, then $n = \dfrac{n}{1}$

(B) False; a number with a repeating decimal expansion is a rational number. $\hspace{1cm}$ (A-1)

16. Integers that are not natural numbers: 0, -1, -2, ... (A-1)

17. $6(xy^3)^5 = 6x^5y^{15}$ (A-5)   **18.** $\dfrac{9u^8v^6}{3u^4v^8} = \dfrac{3^2u^8v^6}{3u^4v^8} = \dfrac{3^{2-1}u^{8-4}}{v^{8-6}} = \dfrac{3u^4}{v^2}$ (A-5)

19. $(2 \times 10^5)(3 \times 10^{-3}) = 6 \times 10^{5-3} = 6 \times 10^2 = 600$ (A-5)

20. $(x^{-3}y^2)^{-2} = x^6y^{-4} = \dfrac{x^6}{y^4}$ (A-5)   **21.** $u^{5/3}u^{2/3} = u^{5/3 + 2/3} = u^{7/3}$ (A-6)

22. $(9a^4b^{-2})^{1/2} = (3^2a^4b^{-2})^{1/2} = (3^2)^{1/2}(a^4)^{1/2}(b^{-2})^{1/2} = 3a^2b^{-1} = \dfrac{3a^2}{b}$ (A-6)

23. $\dfrac{5^0}{3^2} + \dfrac{3^{-2}}{2^{-2}} = \dfrac{1}{3^2} + \dfrac{\frac{1}{3^2}}{\frac{1}{2^2}} = \dfrac{1}{9} + \dfrac{1}{9} \cdot \dfrac{4}{1} = \dfrac{5}{9}$ (A-5)

24. $(x^{1/2} + y^{1/2})^2 = (x^{1/2})^2 + 2x^{1/2}y^{1/2} + (y^{1/2})^2 = x + 2x^{1/2}y^{1/2} + y$ (A-6)

25. $(3x^{1/2} - y^{1/2})(2x^{1/2} + 3y^{1/2}) = 6x + 9x^{1/2}y^{1/2} - 2x^{1/2}y^{1/2} - 3y$
$$= 6x + 7x^{1/2}y^{1/2} - 3y$$ (A-6)

26. $12x^2 + 5x - 3$
$a = 12,\ b = 5,\ c = -3$
<u>Step 1</u>. Use the ac-test
$$ac = 12(-3) = -36$$

$$\underline{pq}$$
$$(1)(-36)$$
$$(-1)(36)$$
$$(2)(-18)$$
$$(-2)(18)$$
$$(3)(-12)$$
$$(-3)(12)$$
$$(4)(-9)$$
$$\boxed{(-4)(9)}$$
$$\vdots$$

$$-4 + 9 = 5 = b$$
$$12x^2 + 5x - 3 = 12x^2 - 4x + 9x - 3$$
$$= (12x^2 - 4x) + (9x - 3)$$
$$= 4x(3x - 1) + 3(3x - 1)$$
$$= (3x - 1)(4x + 3)$$ (A-8)

27. $8x^2 - 18xy + 9y^2$
$a = 8,\ b = -18,\ c = 9$
$ac = (8)(9) = 72$
Note that $(-6)(-12) = 72$ and $-12 - 6 = -18$. Thus
$$8x^2 - 18xy + 9y^2 = 8x^2 - 12xy - 6xy + 9y^2$$
$$= (8x^2 - 12xy) - (6xy - 9y^2)$$
$$= 4x(2x - 3y) - 3y(2x - 3y)$$
$$= (2x - 3y)(4x - 3y)$$ (A-8)

28. $t^2 - 4t - 6$ This polynomial cannot be factored further. (A-8)

29. $6n^3 - 9n^2 - 15n = 3n(2n^2 - 3n - 5) = 3n(2n - 5)(n + 1)$ (A-8)

30. $(4x - y)^2 - 9x^2 = (4x - y - 3x)(4x - y + 3x) = (x - y)(7x - y)$ (A-3)

31. $6x(2x + 1)^2 - 15x^2(2x + 1) = 3x(2x + 1)[2(2x + 1) - 5x]$
$$= 3x(2x + 1)(2 - x)$$ (A-3)

32. $\dfrac{2}{5b} - \dfrac{4}{3a^3} - \dfrac{1}{6a^2b^2}$ LCD $= 30a^3b^2$

$$= \frac{6a^3b}{6a^3b} \cdot \frac{2}{5b} - \frac{10b^2}{10b^2} \cdot \frac{4}{3a^3} - \frac{5a}{5a} \cdot \frac{1}{6a^2b^2}$$

$$= \frac{12a^3b}{30a^3b^2} - \frac{40b^2}{30a^3b^2} - \frac{5a}{30a^3b^2} = \frac{12a^3b - 40b^2 - 5a}{30a^3b^2}$$ (A-4)

33. $\dfrac{3x}{3x^2 - 12x} + \dfrac{1}{6x} = \dfrac{\cancel{3x}}{\cancel{3x}(x - 4)} + \dfrac{1}{6x} = \dfrac{1}{x - 4} + \dfrac{1}{6x}$

$$= \frac{6x}{6x(x - 4)} + \frac{x - 4}{6x(x - 4)} = \frac{6x + x - 4}{6x(x - 4)} = \frac{7x - 4}{6x(x - 4)}$$ (A-4)

34. $\dfrac{x}{x^2 - 16} - \dfrac{x + 4}{x^2 - 4x} = \dfrac{x}{(x - 4)(x + 4)} - \dfrac{x + 4}{x(x - 4)}$
$$[\text{LCD} = x(x - 4)(x + 4)]$$

$$= \frac{x^2}{x(x - 4)(x + 4)} - \frac{(x + 4)^2}{x(x - 4)(x + 4)}$$

$$= \frac{x^2 - (x + 4)^2}{x(x - 4)(x + 4)}$$

$$= \frac{x^2 - x^2 - 8x - 16}{x(x - 4)(x + 4)} = \frac{-8(x + 2)}{x(x - 4)(x + 4)}$$ (A-4)

35. $\dfrac{(x + y)^2 - x^2}{y} = \dfrac{x^2 + 2xy + y^2 - x^2}{y} = \dfrac{2xy + y^2}{y} = 2x + y$ (A-4)

36. $\dfrac{\dfrac{1}{7 + h} - \dfrac{1}{7}}{h} = \dfrac{\dfrac{7 - (7 + h)}{7(7 + h)}}{h} = \dfrac{\dfrac{-h}{7(7 + h)}}{\dfrac{h}{1}} = \dfrac{-h}{7(7 + h)} \cdot \dfrac{1}{h} = \dfrac{-1}{7(7 + h)}$ (A-4)

37. $\dfrac{x^{-1} + y^{-1}}{x^{-2} - y^{-2}} = \dfrac{\dfrac{1}{x} + \dfrac{1}{y}}{\dfrac{1}{x^2} - \dfrac{1}{y^2}} = \dfrac{\dfrac{x + y}{xy}}{\dfrac{y^2 - x^2}{x^2y^2}} = \dfrac{\cancel{x + y}}{\cancel{xy}} \cdot \dfrac{\cancel{xy}}{x^2y^2}}{(y - x)\cancel{(y + x)}} = \dfrac{xy}{y - x}$ (A-4)

38. (A) $(-7) - (-5) = -7 + [-(-5)]$ Subtraction

(B) $5u + (3v + 2) = (3v + 2) + 5u$ Commutative (+)

(C) $(5m - 2)(2m + 3) = (5m - 2)2m + (5m - 2)3$ Distributive

(D) $9 \cdot (49) = (9 \cdot 4)y$ Associative ($\cdot$)

(E) $\dfrac{u}{-(v - w)} = -\dfrac{u}{v - w}$ Negatives

(F) $(x - y) + 0 = (x - y)$ Identity (+) (A-1)

39. $6\sqrt[5]{x^2} - 7\sqrt[4]{(x-1)^3} = 6x^{2/5} - 7(x-1)^{3/4}$ (A-6)

40. $2x^{1/2} - 3x^{2/3} = 2\sqrt{x} - 3\sqrt[3]{x^2}$ (A-6)

41. $\dfrac{4\sqrt{x}-3}{2\sqrt{x}} = \dfrac{4x^{1/2}}{2x^{1/2}} - \dfrac{3}{2x^{1/2}} = 2 - \dfrac{3}{2}x^{-1/2}$ (A-6)

42. $\dfrac{3x}{\sqrt{3x}} = \dfrac{3x}{\sqrt{3x}} \cdot \dfrac{\sqrt{3x}}{\sqrt{3x}} = \dfrac{\cancel{3x}\sqrt{3x}}{\cancel{3x}} = \sqrt{3x}$ (A-6)

43. $\dfrac{x-5}{\sqrt{x}-\sqrt{5}} = \dfrac{x-5}{\sqrt{x}-\sqrt{5}} \cdot \dfrac{\sqrt{x}+\sqrt{5}}{\sqrt{x}+\sqrt{5}} = \dfrac{\cancel{(x-5)}(\sqrt{x}+\sqrt{5})}{\cancel{x-5}} = \sqrt{x} + \sqrt{5}$ (A-6)

44. $\dfrac{\sqrt{x-5}}{x-5} = \dfrac{\sqrt{x-5}}{x-5} \cdot \dfrac{\sqrt{x-5}}{\sqrt{x-5}} = \dfrac{\cancel{x-5}}{\cancel{(x-5)}\sqrt{x-5}} = \dfrac{1}{\sqrt{x-5}}$ (A-6)

45. $\dfrac{\sqrt{u+h}-\sqrt{u}}{h} = \dfrac{\sqrt{u+h}-\sqrt{u}}{h} \cdot \dfrac{\sqrt{u+h}+\sqrt{u}}{\sqrt{u+h}+\sqrt{u}}$

$$= \dfrac{u+h-u}{h(\sqrt{u+h}+\sqrt{u})}$$

$$= \dfrac{\cancel{h}}{\cancel{h}(\sqrt{u+h}+\sqrt{u})} = \dfrac{1}{\sqrt{u+h}+\sqrt{u}} \quad \text{(A-6)}$$

46. $\dfrac{x}{12} - \dfrac{x-3}{3} = \dfrac{1}{2}$

Multiply each term by 12: $x - 4(x-3) = 6$

$$x - 4x + 12 = 6$$
$$-3x = 6 - 12$$
$$-3x = -6$$
$$x = 2 \quad \text{(A-7)}$$

47. $x^2 = 5x$

$x^2 - 5x = 0$ (solve by factoring)

$x(x-5) = 0$

$x = 0$ or $x - 5 = 0$

        $x = 5$ (A-8)

48. $3x^2 - 21 = 0$

$x^2 - 7 = 0$ (solve by the square root method)

    $x^2 = 7$

    $x = \pm\sqrt{7}$ (A-8)

49. $x^2 - x - 20 = 0$ (solve by factoring)

$(x-5)(x+4) = 0$

$x - 5 = 0$ or $x + 4 = 0$

  $x = 5$ $x = -4$ (A-8)

50. $-6x^2 + 7x - 1$

$= (-6x + 1)(x - 1) = 0;$

$x = \dfrac{1}{6}, 1$ (A-8)

51. $2(x+4) > 5x - 4$

    $2x + 8 > 5x - 4$

    $2x - 5x > -4 - 8$

        $-3x > -12$ (Divide both sides by -3 and reverse the inequality)

          $x < 4$ or $(-\infty, 4)$

                                 (A-7)

52. $1 - \dfrac{x-3}{3} \leq \dfrac{1}{2}$

Multiply both sides of the inequality by 6. We do not reverse the direction of the inequality, since 6 > 0.

$$6 - 2(x - 3) \leq 3$$
$$6 - 2x + 6 \leq 3$$
$$-2x \leq 3 - 12$$
$$-2x \leq -9$$

Divide both sides by -2 and reverse the direction of the inequality, since -2 < 0.

$x \geq \dfrac{9}{2}$ or $\left[\dfrac{9}{2}, \infty\right)$

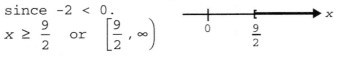

(A-7)

53. $-1 < -2x + 5 \leq 3$ (Divide the inequalities by -2 and reverse the direction.)
$-6 < -2x \leq -2$
$3 > x \geq 1$
or [1, 3]

(A-7)

54. $2x - 3y = 6$
$-3y = -2x + 6$
$y = \dfrac{2}{3}x - 2$ (A-7)

55. $3xy - 2x = y$
$3xy - y = 2x$
$y(3x - 1) = 2x$
$y = \dfrac{2x}{3x - 1}$ (A-7)

56. The GDP per person is given by:
$$\dfrac{8,511,000,000,000}{270,300,000} = \dfrac{8.511 \times 10^{12}}{2.703 \times 10^{8}} \approx 3.1487 \times 10^{4} = \$31,487/\text{person}$$ (A-5)

57. Let x = the amount invested at 8%. Then 60,000 - x = amount invested at 14%. The interest on \$60,000 at 12% for one year is:
$$0.12(60,000) = 7200$$
Thus, we want:
$$0.08x + 0.14(60,000 - x) = 7200$$
$$0.08x + 8400 - 0.14x = 7200$$
$$-0.06x = -1200$$
$$x = 20,000$$
Therefore, \$20,000 should be invested at 8% and \$40,000 should be invested at 14%.

(A-7)

58. Let x = number of tapes produced
Cost: $C = 12x + 72,000$
Revenue: $R = 30x$

To find the break-even point, set $R = C$.
$$30x = 12x + 72,000$$
$$18x = 72,000$$
$$x = 4000$$

Thus, 4000 tapes must be sold for the producer to break even.

(A-7)

Things to remember:

<u>1</u>. THE SET OF REAL NUMBERS

SYMBOL	NAME	DESCRIPTION	EXAMPLES
N	Natural numbers	Counting numbers (also called positive integers)	1, 2, 3, ...
Z	Integers	Natural numbers, their negatives, and 0	... -2, -1, 0, 1, 2, ...
Q	Rational numbers	Any number that can be represented as $\frac{a}{b}$, where a and b are integers and $b \neq 0$. Decimal representations are repeating or terminating.	-4; 0; 1; 25; $\frac{-3}{5}$; $\frac{2}{3}$; 3.67; $-0.333\overline{3}$; $5.2727\overline{27}$
I	Irrational numbers	Any number with a decimal representation that is nonrepeating and non-terminating.	$\sqrt{2}$; π; $\sqrt[3]{7}$; 1.414213...; 2.718281828...
R	Real numbers	Rationals and irrationals	

<u>2</u>. BASIC PROPERTIES OF THE SET OF REAL NUMBERS

Let a, b, and c be arbitrary elements in the set of real numbers R.

ADDITION PROPERTIES

ASSOCIATIVE: $(a + b) + c = a + (b + c)$

COMMUTATIVE: $a + b = b + a$

IDENTITY: 0 is the additive identity; that is, $0 + a = a + 0$ for all a in R, and 0 is the only element in R with this property.

INVERSE: For each a in R, $-a$ is its unique additive inverse; that is, $a + (-a) = (-a) + a = 0$, and $-a$ is the only element in R relative to a with this property.

MULTIPLICATION PROPERTIES

ASSOCIATIVE: $(ab)c = a(bc)$

COMMUTATIVE: $ab = ba$

IDENTITY: 1 is the multiplicative identity; that is, $1a = a1 = a$ for all a in R, and 1 is the only element in R with this property.

INVERSE: For each a in R, $a \neq 0$, $\dfrac{1}{a}$ is its unique multiplicative inverse; that is, $a\left(\dfrac{1}{a}\right) = \left(\dfrac{1}{a}\right)a = 1$, and $\dfrac{1}{a}$ is the only element in R relative to a with this property.

DISTRIBUTIVE PROPERTIES

$$a(b + c) = ab + ac$$

$$(a + b)c = ac + bc$$

3. SUBTRACTION AND DIVISION

For all real numbers a and b.

SUBTRACTION: $a - b = a + (-b)$
$7 - (-5) = 7 + [-(-5)] = 7 + 5 = 12$

DIVISION: $a \div b = a\left(\dfrac{1}{b}\right)$, $b \neq 0$

$9 \div 4 = 9\left(\dfrac{1}{4}\right) = \dfrac{9}{4}$

NOTE: 0 can never be used as a divisor!

4. PROPERTIES OF NEGATIVES

For all real numbers a and b.

a. $-(-a) = a$

b. $(-a)b = -(ab) = a(-b) = -ab$

c. $(-a)(-b) = ab$

d. $(-1)a = -a$

e. $\dfrac{-a}{b} = -\dfrac{a}{b} = \dfrac{a}{-b}$, $b \neq 0$

f. $\dfrac{-a}{-b} = -\dfrac{-a}{b} = -\dfrac{a}{-b} = \dfrac{a}{b}$, $b \neq 0$

ZERO PROPERTIES

For all real numbers a and b.

a. $a \cdot 0 = 0$

b. $ab = 0$ if and only if $a = 0$ or $b = 0$ (or both)

6. FRACTION PROPERTIES

For all real numbers a, b, c, d, and k (division by 0 excluded).

a. $\dfrac{a}{b} = \dfrac{c}{d}$ if and only if $ad = bc$

b. $\dfrac{ka}{kb} = \dfrac{a}{b}$

c. $\dfrac{a}{b} \cdot \dfrac{c}{d} = \dfrac{ac}{bd}$

d. $\dfrac{a}{b} \div \dfrac{c}{d} = \dfrac{a}{b} \cdot \dfrac{d}{c}$

e. $\dfrac{a}{b} + \dfrac{c}{b} = \dfrac{a + c}{b}$

f. $\dfrac{a}{b} - \dfrac{c}{b} = \dfrac{a - c}{b}$

g. $\dfrac{a}{b} + \dfrac{c}{d} = \dfrac{ad + bc}{bd}$

---

1. $uv = vu$ **3.** $3 + (7 + y) = (3 + 7) + y$ **5.** $1(u + v) = u + v$

7. T; Associative property of multiplication

9. T; Distributive property **11.** F; $-2(-a)(2x - y) = 2a(2x - y)$

13. T; Commutative property of addition **15.** T; Property of negatives

17. T; Multiplicative inverse property **19.** T; Property of negatives

21. F; $\dfrac{a}{b} + \dfrac{c}{d} = \dfrac{ad + bc}{bd}$ **23.** T; Distributive property

25. T; Zero property

27. No. For example: $2\left(\dfrac{1}{2}\right) = 1$. In general $a\left(\dfrac{1}{a}\right) = 1$ whenever $a \neq 0$.

29. (A) False. For example, -3 is an integer but not a natural number.

(B) True

(C) True. For example, for any natural number n, $n = \dfrac{n}{1}$.

31. $\sqrt{2}$, $\sqrt{3}$, ... ; in general, the square root of any rational number that is not a perfect square; π, e.

33. (A) $8 \in N, \ Z, \ Q, \ R$ (B) $\sqrt{2} \in R$

      (C) $-1.414 = -\dfrac{1414}{1000} \in Q, \ R$ (D) $\dfrac{-5}{2} \in Q, \ R$

35. (A) F; $a(b - c) = ab - ac$;

        for example $2(3 - 1) = 2 \cdot 2 = 4 \neq 2 \cdot 3 - 1 = 5$

      (B) F; For example, $(3 - 7) - 4 = -4 - 4 = -8$

                             $\neq 3 - (7 - 4) = 3 - 3 = 0.$

      (C) T; This is the associative property of multiplication.

      (D) F; For example, $(12 \div 4) \div 2 = 3 \div 2 = \dfrac{3}{2}$

                             $\neq 12 \div (4 \div 2) = 12 \div 2 = 6.$

37.
$$
\begin{aligned}
C &= 0.090909\ldots \\
100C &= 9.090909\ldots \\
100C - C &= (9.090909\ldots) - (0.090909\ldots) \\
99C &= 9 \\
C &= \frac{9}{99} = \frac{1}{11}
\end{aligned}
$$

39. (A) $\dfrac{13}{6} \approx 2.166\ 666\ 667$ (B) $\sqrt{21} \approx 4.582\ 575\ 695$

      (C) $\dfrac{7}{16} = 0.4375$ (D) $\dfrac{29}{111} \approx 0.261\ 261\ 261$

EXERCISE A-2

Things to remember:

  <u>1</u>. NATURAL NUMBER EXPONENT

     For n a natural number and b any real number,

       $b^n = b \cdot b \cdot \ldots \cdot b$, n factors of b.

     For example, $2^3 = 2 \cdot 2 \cdot 2 \ (= 8)$,

                      $3^5 = 3 \cdot 3 \cdot 3 \cdot 3 \cdot 3 \ (= 243)$.

     In the expression b^n, n is called the EXPONENT, and b is called the BASE.

  <u>2</u>. FIRST PROPERTY OF EXPONENTS

     For any natural numbers m and n, and any real number b,

       $b^m \cdot b^n = b^{m+n}$.

     For example, $3^3 \cdot 3^4 = 3^{3+4} = 3^7$.

3. POLYNOMIALS

   a. A POLYNOMIAL IN ONE VARIABLE x is constructed by adding or subtracting constants and terms of the form ax^n, where a is a real number and n is a natural number.

   b. A POLYNOMIAL IN TWO VARIABLES x AND y is constructed by adding or subtracting constants and terms of the form ax^my^n, where a is a real number and m and n are natural numbers.

   c. Polynomials in more than two variables are defined similarly.

   d. A polynomial with only one term is called a MONOMIAL.
      A polynomial with two terms is called a BINOMIAL.
      A polynomial with three terms is called a TRINOMIAL.

4. DEGREE OF A POLYNOMIAL

   a. A term of the form ax^n, $a \neq 0$, has degree n. A term of the form ax^my^n, $a \neq 0$, has degree $m + n$. A nonzero constant has degree 0.

   b. The DEGREE OF A POLYNOMIAL is the degree of the nonzero term with the highest degree. For example, $3x^4 + \sqrt{2}x^3 - 2x + 7$ has degree 4; $2x^3y^2 - 3x^2y + 7x^4 - 5y^3 + 6$ has degree 5; the polynomial 4 has degree 0.

   c. The constant 0 is a polynomial but it is not assigned a degree.

5. Two terms in a polynomial are called LIKE TERMS if they have exactly the same variable factors raised to the same powers. For example, in

   $$7x^5y^2 - 3x^3y + 2x + 4x^3y - 1,$$

   $-3x^3y$ and $4x^3y$ are like terms.

6. To multiply two polynomials, multiply each term of one by each term of the other, and then combine like terms.

7. SPECIAL PRODUCTS

   a. $(a - b)(a + b) = a^2 - b^2$

   b. $(a + b)^2 = a^2 + 2ab + b^2$

   c. $(a - b)^2 = a^2 - 2ab + b^2$

8. ORDER OF OPERATIONS

   Multiplication and division precede addition and subtraction, and taking powers precedes multiplication and division.

1. The term of highest degree in $x^3 + 2x^2 - x + 3$ is x^3 and the degree of this term is 3.

3. $(2x^2 - x + 2) + (x^3 + 2x^2 - x + 3) = x^3 + 2x^2 + 2x^2 - x - x + 2 + 3$
$$= x^3 + 4x^2 - 2x + 5$$

5. $(x^3 + 2x^2 - x + 3) - (2x^2 - x + 2) = x^3 + 2x^2 - x + 3 - 2x^2 + x - 2$
$$= x^3 + 1$$

7. Using a vertical arrangement:
$$\begin{array}{r}
x^3 + 2x^2 - x + 3 \\
\underline{2x^2 - x + 2} \\
2x^5 + 4x^4 - 2x^3 + 6x^2 \\
- x^4 - 2x^3 + x^2 - 3x \\
\underline{2x^3 + 4x^2 - 2x + 6} \\
2x^5 + 3x^4 - 2x^3 + 11x^2 - 5x + 6
\end{array}$$

9. $2(u - 1) - (3u + 2) - 2(2u - 3) = 2u - 2 - 3u - 2 - 4u + 6$
$$= -5u + 2$$

11. $4a - 2a[5 - 3(a + 2)] = 4a - 2a[5 - 3a - 6]$
$$= 4a - 2a[-3a - 1]$$
$$= 4a + 6a^2 + 2a$$
$$= 6a^2 + 6a$$

13. $(a + b)(a - b) = a^2 - b^2$ (Special product 7a)

15. $(3x - 5)(2x + 1) = 6x^2 + 3x - 10x - 5$
$$= 6x^2 - 7x - 5$$

17. $(2x - 3y)(x + 2y) = 2x^2 + 4xy - 3xy - 6y^2$
$$= 2x^2 + xy - 6y^2$$

19. $(3y + 2)(3y - 2) = (3y)^2 - 2^2 = 9y^2 - 4$ (Special product 7a)

21. $-(2x - 3)^2 = -[(2x)^2 - 2(2x)(3) + 3^2] = -[4x^2 - 12x + 9]$
$$= -4x^2 + 12x - 9$$

23. $(4m + 3n)(4m - 3n) = 16m^2 - 9n^2$

25. $(3u + 4v)^2 = 9u^2 + 24uv + 16v^2$ (Special product 7b)

27. $(a - b)(a^2 + ab + b^2) = a(a^2 + ab + b^2) - b(a^2 + ab + b^2)$
$$= a^3 + a^2b + ab^2 - a^2b - ab^2 - b^3$$
$$= a^3 - b^3$$

29. $[(x - y) + 3z][(x - y) - 3z)] = (x - y)^2 - 9z^2$
$$= x^2 - 2xy + y^2 - 9z^2$$

31. $m - \{m - [m - (m - 1)]\} = m - \{m - [m - m + 1]\}$
$$= m - \{m - 1\}$$
$$= m - m + 1$$
$$= 1$$

33. $(x^2 - 2xy + y^2)(x^2 + 2xy + y^2) = (x - y)^2(x + y)^2$

$$= [(x - y)(x + y)]^2$$
$$= [x^2 - y^2]^2$$
$$= x^4 - 2x^2y^2 + y^4$$

35. $(5a - 2b)^2 - (2b + 5a)^2 = 25a^2 - 20ab + 4b^2 - [4b^2 + 20ab + 25a^2]$

$$= -40ab$$

37. $(m - 2)^2 - (m - 2)(m + 2) = m^2 - 4m + 4 - [m^2 - 4]$

$$= m^2 - 4m + 4 - m^2 + 4$$
$$= -4m + 8$$

39. $(x - 2y)(2x + y) - (x + 2y)(2x - y)$

$$= 2x^2 - 4xy + xy - 2y^2 - [2x^2 + 4xy - xy - 2y^2]$$
$$= 2x^2 - 3xy - 2y^2 - 2x^2 - 3xy + 2y^2$$
$$= -6xy$$

41. $(u + v)^3 = (u + v)(u + v)^2 = (u + v)(u^2 + 2uv + v^2)$

$$= u^3 + 3u^2v + 3uv^2 + v^3$$

43. $(x - 2y)^3 = (x - 2y)(x - 2y)^2 = (x - 2y)(x^2 - 4xy + 4y^2)$

$$= x(x^2 - 4xy + 4y^2) - 2y(x^2 - 4xy + 4y^2)$$
$$= x^3 - 4x^2y + 4xy^2 - 2x^2y + 8xy^2 - 8y^3$$
$$= x^3 - 6x^2y + 12xy^2 - 8y^3$$

45. $[(2x^2 - 4xy + y^2) + (3xy - y^2)] - [(x^2 - 2xy - y^2) + (-x^2 + 3xy - 2y^2)]$

$$= [2x^2 - xy] - [xy - 3y^2] = 2x^2 - 2xy + 3y^2$$

47. $[(2x - 1)^2 - x(3x + 1)]^2 = [4x^2 - 4x + 1 - 3x^2 - x]^2$

$$= [x^2 - 5x + 1]^2 = (x^2 - 5x + 1)(x^2 - 5x + 1)$$
$$= x^4 - 10x^3 + 27x^2 - 10x + 1$$

49. $2\{(x - 3)(x^2 - 2x + 1) - x[3 - x(x - 2)]\}$

$$= 2\{x^3 - 5x^2 + 7x - 3 - x[3 - x^2 + 2x]\}$$
$$= 2\{x^3 - 5x^2 + 7x - 3 + x^3 - 2x^2 - 3x\}$$
$$= 2\{2x^3 - 7x^2 + 4x - 3\}$$
$$= 4x^3 - 14x^2 + 8x - 6$$

51. $m + n$

53. Given two polynomials, one with degree m and the other of degree n, their product will have degree $m + n$ regardless of the relationship between m and n.

55. Since $(a + b)^2 = a^2 + 2ab + b^2$, $(a + b)^2 = a^2 + b^2$ only when $2ab = 0$; that is, only when $a = 0$ or $b = 0$.

57. Let x = amount invested at 9%.
Then $10,000 - x$ = amount invested at 12%.
The total annual income I is:

$$I = 0.09x + 0.12(10,000 - x)$$
$$= 1,200 - 0.03x$$

59. Let x = number of tickets at \$10.
Then $3x$ = number of tickets at \$30 and $4,000 - x - 3x = 4,000 - 4x$ = number of tickets at \$50.
The total receipts R are:
$$R = 10x + 30(3x) + 50(4,000 - 4x)$$
$$= 10x + 90x + 200,000 - 200x = 200,000 - 100x$$

61. Let x = number of kilograms of food A.
Then $10 - x$ = number of kilograms of food B.
The total number of kilograms F of fat in the final food mix is:
$$F = 0.02x + 0.06(10 - x)$$
$$= 0.6 - 0.04x$$

EXERCISE A-3

Things to remember:

<u>1</u>. The discussion is limited to polynomials with integer coefficients.

<u>2</u>. FACTORED FORMS

A polynomial is in FACTORED FORM if it is written as the product of two or more polynomials. A polynomial with integer coefficients is FACTORED COMPLETELY if each factor cannot be expressed as the product of two or more polynomials with integer coefficients, other than itself and 1.

<u>3</u>. METHODS
   a. Factor out all factors common to all terms, if they are present.
   b. Try grouping terms.
   c. *ac*-Test for polynomials of the form
$$ax^2 + bx + c \quad \text{or} \quad ax^2 + bxy + cy^2$$
   If the product ac has two integer factors p and q whose sum is the coefficient b of the middle term, i.e., if integers p and q exist so that
$$pq = ac \quad \text{and} \quad p + q = b$$
   then the polynomials have first-degree factors with integer coefficients. If no such integers exist then the polynomials will not have first-degree factors with integer coefficients; the polynomials are *not factorable*.

<u>4</u>. SPECIAL FACTORING FORMULAS
   a. $u^2 + 2uv + v^2 = (u + v)^2$ Perfect square
   b. $u^2 - 2uv + v^2 = (u - v)^2$ Perfect square
   c. $u^2 - v^2 = (u - v)(u + v)$ Difference of squares
   d. $u^3 - v^3 = (u - v)(u^2 + uv + v^2)$ Difference of cubes
   e. $u^3 + v^3 = (u + v)(u^2 - uv + v^2)$ Sum of cubes

1. $3m^2$ is a common factor: $6m^4 - 9m^3 - 3m^2 = 3m^2(2m^2 - 3m - 1)$

3. $2uv$ is a common factor: $8u^3v - 6u^2v^2 + 4uv^3 = 2uv(4u^2 - 3uv + 2v^2)$

5. $(2m - 3)$ is a common factor: $7m(2m - 3) + 5(2m - 3) = (7m + 5)(2m - 3)$

7. $4ab(2c + d) - (2c + d) = (4ab - 1)(2c + d)$

9. $2x^2 - x + 4x - 2 = (2x^2 - x) + (4x - 2)$
$$= x(2x - 1) + 2(2x - 1)$$
$$= (2x - 1)(x + 2)$$

11. $3y^2 - 3y + 2y - 2 = (3y^2 - 3y) + (2y - 2)$
$$= 3y(y - 1) + 2(y - 1)$$
$$= (y - 1)(3y + 2)$$

13. $2x^2 + 8x - x - 4 = (2x^2 + 8x) - (x + 4)$
$$= 2x(x + 4) - (x + 4)$$
$$= (x + 4)(2x - 1)$$

15. $wy - wz + xy - xz = (wy - wz) + (xy - xz)$
$$= w(y - z) + x(y - z)$$
$$= (y - z)(w + x)$$
or $wy - wz + xy - xz = (wy + xy) - (wz + xz)$
$$= y(w + x) - z(w + x)$$
$$= (w + x)(y - z)$$

17. $am - 3bm + 2na - 6bn = m(a - 3b) + 2n(a - 3b)$
$$= (a - 3b)(m + 2n)$$

19. $3y^2 - y - 2$
$a = 3$, $b = -1$, $c = -2$
Step 1. Use the ac-test to test for factorability
$ac = (3)(-2) = -6$

$\underline{pq}$
$(1)(-6)$
$(-1)(6)$
$\boxed{(2)(-3)}$
$(-2)(3)$

Note that $2 + (-3) = -1 = b$. Thus, $3y^2 - y - 2$ has first-degree factors with integer coefficients.

Step 2. Split the middle term using $b = p + q$ and factor by grouping.
$-1 = -3 + 2$
$3y^2 - y - 2 = 3y^2 - 3y + 2y - 2 = (3y^2 - 3y) + (2y - 2)$
$$= 3y(y - 1) + 2(y - 1)$$
$$= (y - 1)(3y + 2)$$

21. $u^2 - 2uv - 15v^2$

$a = 1, \ b = -2, \ c = -15$

Step 1. Use the ac-test

$\qquad ac = 1(-15) = -15$

$\qquad\qquad\qquad\qquad\qquad\qquad\qquad\qquad \underline{pq}$

$\qquad\qquad\qquad\qquad\qquad\qquad\qquad\qquad (1)(-15)$

$\qquad\qquad\qquad\qquad\qquad\qquad\qquad\qquad (-1)(15)$

$\qquad\qquad\qquad\qquad\qquad\qquad\qquad\qquad \boxed{(3)(-5)}$

$\qquad\qquad\qquad\qquad\qquad\qquad\qquad\qquad (-3)(5)$

Note that $3 + (-5) = -2 = b$. Thus $u^2 - 2uv - 15v^2$ has first-degree factors with integer coefficients.

Step 2. Factor by grouping

$\qquad -2 = 3 + (-5)$

$\qquad u^2 + 3uv - 5uv - 15v^2 = (u^2 + 3uv) - (5uv + 15v^2)$

$\qquad\qquad\qquad\qquad\qquad\qquad\quad = u(u + 3v) - 5v(u + 3v)$

$\qquad\qquad\qquad\qquad\qquad\qquad\quad = (u + 3v)(u - 5v)$

23. $m^2 - 6m - 3$

$a = 1, \ b = -6, \ c = -3$

Step 1. Use the ac-test

$\qquad ac = (1)(-3) = -3$

$\qquad\qquad\qquad\qquad\qquad\qquad\qquad\qquad \underline{pq}$

$\qquad\qquad\qquad\qquad\qquad\qquad\qquad\qquad (1)(-3)$

$\qquad\qquad\qquad\qquad\qquad\qquad\qquad\qquad (-1)(3)$

None of the factors add up to $-6 = b$. Thus, this polynomial is *not factorable*.

25. $w^2x^2 - y^2 = (wx - y)(wx + y)$ (difference of squares)

27. $9m^2 - 6mn + n^2 = (3m - n)^2$ (perfect square)

29. $y^2 + 16$

$a = 1, \ b = 0, \ c = 16$

Step 1. Use the ac-test

$\qquad ac = (1)(16)$

$\qquad\qquad\qquad\qquad\qquad\qquad\qquad\qquad \underline{pq}$

$\qquad\qquad\qquad\qquad\qquad\qquad\qquad\qquad (1)(16)$

$\qquad\qquad\qquad\qquad\qquad\qquad\qquad\qquad (-1)(-16)$

$\qquad\qquad\qquad\qquad\qquad\qquad\qquad\qquad (2)(8)$

$\qquad\qquad\qquad\qquad\qquad\qquad\qquad\qquad (-2)(-8)$

$\qquad\qquad\qquad\qquad\qquad\qquad\qquad\qquad (4)(4)$

$\qquad\qquad\qquad\qquad\qquad\qquad\qquad\qquad (-4)(-4)$

None of the factors add up to $0 = b$. Thus this polynomial is *not factorable*.

31. $4z^2 - 28z + 48 = 4(z^2 - 7z + 12) = 4(z - 3)(z - 4)$

33. $2x^4 - 24x^3 + 40x^2 = 2x^2(x^2 - 12x + 20) = 2x^2(x - 2)(x - 10)$

35. $4xy^2 - 12xy + 9x = x(4y^2 - 12y + 9) = x(2y - 3)^2$

37. $6m^2 - mn - 12n^2 = (2m - 3n)(3m + 4n)$

39. $4u^3v - uv^3 = uv(4u^2 - v^2) = uv[(2u)^2 - v^2] = uv(2u - v)(2u + v)$

41. $2x^3 - 2x^2 + 8x = 2x(x^2 - x + 4)$ [Note: $x^2 - x + 4$ is *not factorable*.]

43. $8x^3 - 27y^3 = (2x)^3 - (3y)^3 = (2x - 3y)[(2x)^2 + (2x)(3y) + (3y)^2]$
$$= (2x - 3y)[4x^2 + 6xy + 9y^2]$$
$$\text{(difference of cubes)}$$

45. $x^4y + 8xy = xy[x^3 + 8] = xy(x + 2)(x^2 - 2x + 4)$

47. $(x + 2)^2 - 9y^2 = [(x + 2) - 3y][(x + 2) + 3y]$
$$= (x + 2 - 3y)(x + 2 + 3y)$$

49. $5u^2 + 4uv - 2v^2$ is *not factorable*.

51. $6(x - y)^2 + 23(x - y) - 4 = [6(x - y) - 1][(x - y) + 4]$
$$= (6x - 6y - 1)(x - y + 4)$$

53. $y^4 - 3y^2 - 4 = (y^2)^2 - 3y^2 - 4 = (y^2 - 4)(y^2 + 1)$
$$= (y - 2)(y + 2)(y^2 + 1)$$

55. $15y(x - y)^3 + 12x(x - y)^2 = 3(x - y)^2[5y(x - y) + 4x]$
$$= 3(x - y)^2[5xy - 5y^2 + 4x]$$

57. True: $u^n - v^n = (u - v)(u^{n-1} + u^{n-2}v + \dots + uv^{n-2} + v^{n-1})$

59. False; For example, $u^2 + v^2$ cannot be factored.

EXERCISE A-4
_____

Things to remember:

<u>1</u>.   FUNDAMENTAL PROPERTY OF FRACTIONS

    If a, b, and k are real numbers with b, $k \neq 0$, then
$$\frac{ka}{kb} = \frac{a}{b}.$$
    A fraction is in LOWEST TERMS if the numerator and denominator
have no common factors other than 1 or -1.

<u>2</u>.   MULTIPLICATION AND DIVISION

    For a, b, c, and d real numbers:

    a. $\dfrac{a}{b} \cdot \dfrac{c}{d} = \dfrac{ac}{bd}$, b, $d \neq 0$

    b. $\dfrac{a}{b} \div \dfrac{c}{d} = \dfrac{\frac{a}{b}}{\frac{c}{d}} = \dfrac{a}{b} \cdot \dfrac{d}{c}$, b, c, $d \neq 0$

    The same procedures are used to multiply or divide two rational
expressions.

3. ADDITION AND SUBTRACTION

For a, b, and c real numbers:

a. $\dfrac{a}{b} + \dfrac{c}{b} = \dfrac{a + c}{b}$, $b \neq 0$

b. $\dfrac{a}{b} - \dfrac{c}{b} = \dfrac{a - c}{b}$, $b \neq 0$

The same procedures are used to add or subtract two rational expressions (with the same denominator).

4. THE LEAST COMMON DENOMINATOR (LCD)

The LCD of two or more rational expressions is found as follows:

a. Factor each denominator completely, including integer factors.

b. Identify each different factor from all the denominators.

c. Form a product using each different factor to the highest power that occurs in any one denominator. This product is the LCD.

The least common denominator is used to add or subtract rational expressions having different denominators.

---

1. $\dfrac{d^5}{3a} \div \left(\dfrac{d^2}{6a^2} \cdot \dfrac{a}{4d^3} \right) = \dfrac{d^5}{3a} \div \left(\dfrac{\cancel{a}d^2}{24\underset{a}{\cancel{a^2}}\underset{d}{\cancel{d^3}}} \right) = \dfrac{d^5}{3a} \div \dfrac{1}{24ad} = \dfrac{d^5}{3\cancel{a}} \cdot \dfrac{\overset{8}{\cancel{24}}\cancel{a}d}{1} = 8d^6$

3. $\dfrac{x^2}{12} + \dfrac{x}{18} - \dfrac{1}{30} = \dfrac{15x^2}{180} + \dfrac{10x}{180} - \dfrac{6}{180}$ We find the LCD of 12, 18, 30:
$12 = 2^2 \cdot 3$, $18 = 2 \cdot 3^2$, $30 = 2 \cdot 3 \cdot 5$

$\qquad\qquad = \dfrac{15x^2 + 10x - 6}{180}$ Thus, LCD $= 2^2 \cdot 3^2 \cdot 5 = 180$.

5. $\dfrac{4m - 3}{18m^3} + \dfrac{3}{4m} - \dfrac{2m - 1}{6m^2}$ Find the LCD of $18m^3$, $4m$, $6m^2$:
$18m^3 = 2 \cdot 3^2 m^3$, $4m = 2^2 m$,

$= \dfrac{2(4m - 3)}{36m^3} + \dfrac{3(9m^2)}{36m^3} - \dfrac{6m(2m - 1)}{36m^3}$ $6m^2 = 2 \cdot 3m^2$

$\qquad\qquad\qquad\qquad\qquad\qquad$ Thus, LCD $= 36m^3$.

$= \dfrac{8m - 6 + 27m^2 - 6m(2m - 1)}{36m^3}$

$= \dfrac{8m - 6 + 27m^2 - 12m^2 + 6m}{36m^3} = \dfrac{15m^2 + 14m - 6}{36m^3}$

7. $\dfrac{x^2 - 9}{x^2 - 3x} \div (x^2 - x - 12) = \dfrac{\cancel{(x - 3)}(x + 3)}{x\cancel{(x - 3)}} \cdot \dfrac{1}{(x - 4)\cancel{(x + 3)}} = \dfrac{1}{x(x - 4)}$

9. $\dfrac{2}{x} - \dfrac{1}{x-3} = \dfrac{2(x-3)}{x(x-3)} - \dfrac{x}{x(x-3)}$ LCD $= x(x-3)$

$\qquad = \dfrac{2x-6-x}{x(x-3)} = \dfrac{x-6}{x(x-3)}$

11. $\dfrac{2}{(x+1)^2} - \dfrac{5}{x^2-x-2} = \dfrac{2}{(x+1)^2} - \dfrac{5}{(x+1)(x-2)}$ LCD $= (x+1)^2(x-2)$

$\qquad = \dfrac{2(x-2)}{(x+1)^2(x-2)} - \dfrac{5(x+1)}{(x+1)^2(x-2)}$

$\qquad = \dfrac{2x-4-5x-5}{(x+1)^2(x-2)} = \dfrac{-3x-9}{(x+1)^2(x-2)}$

13. $\dfrac{x+1}{x-1} - 1 = \dfrac{x+1}{x-1} - \dfrac{x-1}{x-1} = \dfrac{x+1-(x-1)}{x-1} = \dfrac{2}{x-1}$

15. $\dfrac{3}{a-1} - \dfrac{2}{1-a} = \dfrac{3}{a-1} - \dfrac{-2}{-(1-a)} = \dfrac{3}{a-1} + \dfrac{2}{a-1} = \dfrac{5}{a-1}$

17. $\dfrac{2x}{x^2-16} - \dfrac{x-4}{x^2+4x} = \dfrac{2x}{(x-4)(x+4)} - \dfrac{x-4}{x(x+4)}$ LCD $= x(x-4)(x+4)$

$\qquad = \dfrac{2x(x) - (x-4)(x-4)}{x(x-4)(x+4)}$

$\qquad = \dfrac{2x^2 - (x^2-8x+16)}{x(x-4)(x+4)}$

$\qquad = \dfrac{x^2+8x-16}{x(x-4)(x+4)}$

19. $\dfrac{x^2}{x^2+2x+1} + \dfrac{x-1}{3x+3} - \dfrac{1}{6} = \dfrac{x^2}{(x+1)^2} + \dfrac{x-1}{3(x+1)} - \dfrac{1}{6}$

$\quad$ LCD $= 6(x+1)^2$ $\qquad = \dfrac{6x^2}{6(x+1)^2} + \dfrac{2(x+1)(x-1)}{6(x+1)^2} - \dfrac{(x+1)^2}{6(x+1)^2}$

$\qquad = \dfrac{6x^2 + 2(x^2-1) - (x^2+2x+1)}{6(x+1)^2}$

$\qquad = \dfrac{7x^2-2x-3}{6(x+1)^2}$

21. $\dfrac{1-\dfrac{x}{y}}{2-\dfrac{y}{x}} = \dfrac{\dfrac{y-x}{y}}{\dfrac{2x-y}{x}} = \dfrac{y-x}{y} \cdot \dfrac{x}{2x-y} = \dfrac{x(y-x)}{y(2x-y)}$

23. $\dfrac{c+2}{5c-5} - \dfrac{c-2}{3c-3} + \dfrac{c}{1-c} = \dfrac{c+2}{5(c-1)} - \dfrac{c-2}{3(c-1)} - \dfrac{c}{c-1}$

$\quad$ LCD $= 15(c-1)$ $\qquad = \dfrac{3(c+2)}{15(c-1)} - \dfrac{5(c-2)}{15(c-1)} - \dfrac{15c}{15(c-1)}$

$\qquad = \dfrac{3c+6-5c+10-15c}{15(c-1)} = \dfrac{-17c+16}{15(c-1)}$

25. $\dfrac{1 + \dfrac{3}{x}}{x - \dfrac{9}{x}} = \dfrac{\dfrac{x+3}{x}}{\dfrac{x^2-9}{x}} = \dfrac{x+3}{x} \cdot \dfrac{x}{x^2-9} = \dfrac{\cancel{x+3}}{\cancel{x}} \cdot \dfrac{\cancel{x}}{\cancel{(x+3)}(x-3)} = \dfrac{1}{x-3}$

27. $\dfrac{\dfrac{1}{2(x+h)} - \dfrac{1}{2x}}{h} = \left(\dfrac{1}{2(x+h)} - \dfrac{1}{2x}\right) \div \dfrac{h}{1}$

$$= \dfrac{x - x - h}{2x(x+h)} \cdot \dfrac{1}{h}$$

$$= \dfrac{-h}{2x(x+h)h} = \dfrac{-1}{2x(x+h)}$$

29. $\dfrac{\dfrac{x}{y} - 2 + \dfrac{y}{x}}{\dfrac{x}{y} - \dfrac{y}{x}} = \dfrac{\dfrac{x^2 - 2xy + y^2}{xy}}{\dfrac{x^2 - y^2}{xy}} = \dfrac{\cancel{(x-y)}^2}{\cancel{xy}} \cdot \dfrac{\cancel{xy}}{\cancel{(x-y)}(x+y)} = \dfrac{x-y}{x+y}$

31. (A) $\dfrac{x^2 + 4x + 3}{x + 3} = x + 4$: Incorrect

(B) $\dfrac{x^2 + 4x + 3}{x + 3} = \dfrac{(x+3)(x+1)}{\cancel{x+3}} = x + 1 \quad (x \neq -3)$

33. (A) $\dfrac{(x+h)^2 - x^2}{h} = 2x + 1$: Incorrect

(B) $\dfrac{(x+h)^2 - x^2}{h} = \dfrac{x^2 + 2xh + h^2 - x^2}{h} = \dfrac{2xh + h^2}{h} = \dfrac{\cancel{h}(2x+h)}{\cancel{h}} = 2x + h$

$$(h \neq 0)$$

35. (A) $\dfrac{x^2 - 3x}{x^2 - 2x - 3} + x - 3 = 1$: Incorrect

(B) $\dfrac{x^2 - 3x}{x^2 - 2x - 3} + x - 3 = \dfrac{x\cancel{(x-3)}}{\cancel{(x-3)}(x+1)} + x - 3$

$$= \dfrac{x}{x+1} + x - 3$$

$$= \dfrac{x + (x-3)(x+1)}{x+1} = \dfrac{x^2 - x - 3}{x+1}$$

37. (A) $\dfrac{2x^2}{x^2 - 4} - \dfrac{x}{x - 2} = \dfrac{x}{x + 2}$: Correct

$$\dfrac{2x^2}{x^2 - 4} - \dfrac{x}{x - 2} = \dfrac{2x^2}{(x-2)(x+2)} - \dfrac{x}{x-2}$$

$$= \dfrac{2x^2 - x(x+2)}{(x-2)(x+2)}$$

$$= \dfrac{x^2 - 2x}{(x-2)(x+2)} = \dfrac{x\cancel{(x-2)}}{\cancel{(x-2)}(x+2)} = \dfrac{x}{x+2}$$

39. $\dfrac{\dfrac{1}{3(x+h)^2} - \dfrac{1}{3x^2}}{h} = \left[\dfrac{1}{3(x+h)^2} - \dfrac{1}{3x^2}\right] \div \dfrac{h}{1}$

$$= \dfrac{x^2 - (x+h)^2}{3x^2(x+h)^2} \cdot \dfrac{1}{h}$$

$$= \dfrac{x^2 - (x^2 + 2xh + h^2)}{3x^2(x+h)^2 h}$$

$$= \dfrac{-2xh - h^2}{3x^2(x+h)^2 h}$$

$$= \dfrac{-\not{h}(2x+h)}{3x^2(x+h)^2 \not{h}}$$

$$= -\dfrac{(2x+h)}{3x^2(x+h)^2} = \dfrac{-2x-h}{3x^2(x+h)^2}$$

41. $x - \dfrac{2}{1 - \dfrac{1}{x}} = x - \dfrac{2}{\dfrac{x-1}{x}} = x - \dfrac{2x}{x-1}$ (LCD $= x - 1$)

$$= \dfrac{x(x-1)}{x-1} - \dfrac{2x}{x-1}$$

$$= \dfrac{x^2 - x - 2x}{x-1} = \dfrac{x(x-3)}{x-1}$$

EXERCISE A-5

Things to remember:

<u>1</u>. DEFINITION OF a^n, where n is an integer and a is a real number:

  a. For n a positive integer,
    $a^n = a \cdot a \cdot \cdots \cdot a$, n factors of a.

  b. For $n = 0$,
    $a^0 = 1$, $a \neq 0$, 0^0 is not defined.

  c. For n a negative integer,
    $a^n = \dfrac{1}{a^{-n}}$, $a \neq 0$.

  [<u>Note</u>: If n is negative, then $-n$ is positive.]

2. PROPERTIES OF EXPONENTS
   GIVEN: n and m are integers and a and b are real numbers.

   a. $a^m a^n = a^{m+n}$ $\qquad$ $a^8 a^{-3} = a^{8+(-3)} = a^5$

   b. $(a^n)^m = a^{mn}$ $\qquad$ $(a^{-2})^3 = a^{3(-2)} = a^{-6}$

   c. $(ab)^m = a^m b^m$ $\qquad$ $(ab)^{-2} = a^{-2} b^{-2}$

   d. $\left(\dfrac{a}{b}\right)^m = \dfrac{a^m}{b^m}$, $b \neq 0$ $\qquad$ $\left(\dfrac{a}{b}\right)^5 = \dfrac{a^5}{b^5}$

   e. $\dfrac{a^m}{a^n} = a^{m-n} = \dfrac{1}{a^{n-m}}$, $a \neq 0$ $\qquad$ $\dfrac{a^{-3}}{a^7} = \dfrac{1}{a^{7-(-3)}} = \dfrac{1}{a^{10}}$

3. SCIENTIFIC NOTATION
   Let r be any finite decimal. Then r can be expressed as the product of a number between 1 and 10 and an integer power of 10; that is, r can be written

   $r = a \times 10^n$, $1 \leq a < 10$, a in decimal form, n an integer

   A number expressed in this form is said to be in SCIENTIFIC NOTATION.

   Examples:

   $$7 = 7 \times 10^0 \qquad\qquad 0.5 = 5 \times 10^{-1}$$
   $$67 = 6.7 \times 10 \qquad\qquad 0.45 = 4.5 \times 10^{-1}$$
   $$580 = 5.8 \times 10^2 \qquad\qquad 0.0032 = 3.2 \times 10^{-3}$$
   $$43{,}000 = 4.3 \times 10^4 \qquad\qquad 0.000\ 045 = 4.5 \times 10^{-5}$$

---

1. $2x^{-9} = \dfrac{2}{x^9}$

3. $\dfrac{3}{2w^{-7}} = \dfrac{3w^7}{2}$

5. $2x^{-8} x^5 = 2x^{-8+5} = 2x^{-3} = \dfrac{2}{x^3}$

7. $\dfrac{w^{-8}}{w^{-3}} = \dfrac{1}{w^{-3+8}} = \dfrac{1}{w^5}$

9. $(2a^{-3})^2 = 2^2(a^{-3})^2 = 4a^{-6} = \dfrac{4}{a^6}$

11. $(a^{-3})^2 = a^{-6} = \dfrac{1}{a^6}$

13. $(2x^4)^{-3} = 2^{-3}(x^4)^{-3} = \dfrac{1}{8} \cdot x^{-12} = \dfrac{1}{8x^{12}}$

15. $82{,}300{,}000{,}000 = 8.23 \times 10^{10}$

17. $0.783 = 7.83 \times 10^{-1}$

19. $0.000\ 034 = 3.4 \times 10^{-5}$

21. $4 \times 10^4 = 40{,}000$

23. $7 \times 10^{-3} = 0.007$

25. $6.171 \times 10^7 = 61{,}710{,}000$

27. $8.08 \times 10^{-4} = 0.000\ 808$

29. $(22 + 31)^0 = (53)^0 = 1$

31. $\dfrac{10^{-3} \times 10^4}{10^{-11} \times 10^{-2}} = \dfrac{10^{-3+4}}{10^{-11-2}} = \dfrac{10^1}{10^{-13}} = 10^{1+13} = 10^{14}$

33. $(5x^2y^{-3})^{-2} = 5^{-2}x^{-4}y^6 = \dfrac{y^6}{5^2x^4} = \dfrac{y^6}{25x^4}$

35. $\left(\dfrac{-5}{2x^3}\right)^{-2} = \dfrac{(-5)^{-2}}{(2x^3)^{-2}} = \dfrac{\dfrac{1}{(-5)^2}}{\dfrac{1}{(2x^3)^2}} = \dfrac{\dfrac{1}{25}}{\dfrac{1}{4x^6}} = \dfrac{4x^6}{25}$

37. $\dfrac{8x^{-3}y^{-1}}{6x^2y^{-4}} = \dfrac{4y^{-1+4}}{3x^{2+3}} = \dfrac{4y^3}{3x^5}$

39. $\dfrac{7x^5 - x^2}{4x^5} = \dfrac{7x^5}{4x^5} - \dfrac{x^2}{4x^5} = \dfrac{7}{4} - \dfrac{1}{4x^3} = \dfrac{7}{4} - \dfrac{1}{4}x^{-3}$

41. $\dfrac{5x^4 - 3x^2 + 8}{2x^2} = \dfrac{5x^4}{2x^2} - \dfrac{3x^2}{2x^2} + \dfrac{8}{2x^2}$

$\qquad = \dfrac{5}{2}x^2 - \dfrac{3}{2} + 4x^{-2}$

43. $\dfrac{3x^2(x-1)^2 - 2x^3(x-1)}{(x-1)^4} = \dfrac{x^2(x-1)[3(x-1) - 2x]}{(x-1)^4} = \dfrac{x^2(x-3)}{(x-1)^3}$

45. $2x^{-2}(x-1) - 2x^{-3}(x-1)^2 = \dfrac{2(x-1)}{x^2} - \dfrac{2(x-1)^2}{x^3}$

$\qquad = \dfrac{2x(x-1) - 2(x-1)^2}{x^3}$

$\qquad = \dfrac{2(x-1)[x - (x-1)]}{x^3}$

$\qquad = \dfrac{2(x-1)}{x^3}$

47. $\dfrac{9,600,000,000}{(1,600,000)(0.000\ 000\ 25)} = \dfrac{9.6 \times 10^9}{(1.6 \times 10^6)(2.5 \times 10^{-7})} = \dfrac{9.6 \times 10^9}{1.6(2.5) \times 10^{6-7}}$

$\qquad = \dfrac{9.6 \times 10^9}{4.0 \times 10^{-1}} = 2.4 \times 10^{9+1} = 2.4 \times 10^{10}$

$\qquad = 24,000,000,000$

49. $\dfrac{(1,250,000)(0.000\ 38)}{0.0152} = \dfrac{(1.25 \times 10^6)(3.8 \times 10^{-4})}{1.52 \times 10^{-2}} = \dfrac{1.25(3.8) \times 10^{6-4}}{1.52 \times 10^{-2}}$

$\qquad = 3.125 \times 10^4 = 31,250$

51. 2^{3^2}; 64

$\quad$ *But,* $2^{3^2} = 2^9 = 512$

53. $a^m a^0 = a^{m+0} = a^m$

Therefore, $a^m a^0 = a^m$ which implies $a^0 = 1$.

55. $\dfrac{u + v}{u^{-1} + v^{-1}} = \dfrac{u + v}{\dfrac{1}{u} + \dfrac{1}{v}} = \dfrac{u + v}{\dfrac{v + u}{uv}} = (u + v) \cdot \dfrac{uv}{v + u} = uv$

57. $\dfrac{b^{-2} - c^{-2}}{b^{-3} - c^{-3}} = \dfrac{\dfrac{1}{b^2} - \dfrac{1}{c^2}}{\dfrac{1}{b^3} - \dfrac{1}{c^3}} = \dfrac{\dfrac{c^2 - b^2}{b^2 c^2}}{\dfrac{c^3 - b^3}{b^3 c^3}} = \dfrac{\cancel{(c - b)}(c + b)}{\cancel{b^2 c^2}} \cdot \dfrac{b^{\cancel{3}} c^{\cancel{3}} \cdot bc}{\cancel{(c - b)}(c^2 + cb + b^2)}$

$\qquad = \dfrac{bc(c + b)}{c^2 + cb + b^2}$

59. (A) Citigroup's assets: 6.674×10^{11}

(B) Chase Manhattan's assets: 3.65875×10^{11}

Ratio: $\dfrac{6.674 \times 10^{11}}{3.65875 \times 10^{11}} = \dfrac{6.67400}{3.65875} \approx 1.8241$

(C) $\dfrac{3.65875 \times 10^{11}}{6.67400 \times 10^{11}} \approx 0.5482$

61. (A) Per capita debt: $\dfrac{5.5262 \times 10^{12}}{2.70299 \times 10^8} \approx 2.0445 \times 10^4 = \$20,445$

(B) Per capita interest: $\dfrac{3.63800 \times 10^{11}}{2.70299 \times 10^8} \approx 1.346 \times 10^3 = \$1,346$

(C) Percentage interest paid on debt:

$\dfrac{3.6380 \times 10^{11}}{5.5262 \times 10^{12}} = 0.658 \times 10^{-1} = 0.0658$ or 6.58%

63. (A) 9 ppm $= \dfrac{9}{1,000,000} = \dfrac{9}{10^6} = 9 \times 10^{-6}$ (B) $0.000\ 009$ (C) 0.0009%

65. $\dfrac{566.4}{100,000} \times 270,300,000 = \dfrac{5.664 \times 10^2}{10^5} \times 2.703 \times 10^8$

$\qquad \approx 15.309 \times 10^5$

To the nearest thousand, there were $1,531,000$ violent crimes committed in 1998.

Things to remember:

1. **nth ROOT**

   Let b be a real number. For any natural number n,

   $\qquad r$ is an nth ROOT of b if $r^n = b$

   If n is odd, then b has exactly one real nth root.
   If n is even, and $b < 0$, then b has NO real nth roots.
   If n is even, and $b > 0$, then b has two real nth roots;
   $\qquad$ if r is an nth root, then $-r$ is also an nth root.
   0 is an nth root of 0 for all n

2. **NOTATION**

   Let b be a real number and let $n > 1$ be a natural number. If n is odd, then the nth root of b is denoted
   $\qquad b^{1/n} \quad$ or $\quad \sqrt[n]{b}$

   If n is even and $b > 0$, then the PRINCIPAL nth ROOT OF b is the positive nth root; the principal nth root is denoted
   $\qquad b^{1/n} \quad$ or $\quad \sqrt[n]{b}$

   In the $\sqrt[n]{b}$ notation, the symbol $\sqrt{}$ is called a RADICAL, n is the INDEX of the radical and b is called the RADICAND.

3. **RATIONAL EXPONENTS**

   If m and n are natural numbers without common prime factors, b is a real number, and b is nonnegative when b is even, then

   $$b^{m/n} = \begin{cases} \left(b^{1/n}\right)^m = \left(\sqrt[n]{b}\right)^m \\ \left(b^m\right)^{1/n} = \sqrt[n]{b^m} \end{cases}$$

   and $\qquad b^{-m/n} = \dfrac{1}{b^{m/n}}, \quad b \neq 0$

   The two definitions of $b^{m/n}$ are equivalent under the indicated restrictions on m, n, and b.

4. **PROPERTIES OF RADICALS**

   If m and n are natural numbers greater than 1 and x and y are positive real numbers, then

   a. $\sqrt[n]{x^n} = x \qquad\qquad\qquad \sqrt[3]{x^3} = x$

   b. $\sqrt[n]{xy} = \sqrt[n]{x}\,\sqrt[n]{y} \qquad\quad \sqrt[5]{xy} = \sqrt[5]{x}\,\sqrt[5]{y}$

   c. $\sqrt[n]{\dfrac{x}{y}} = \dfrac{\sqrt[n]{x}}{\sqrt[n]{y}} \qquad\qquad \sqrt[4]{\dfrac{x}{y}} = \dfrac{\sqrt[4]{x}}{\sqrt[4]{y}}$

1. $6x^{3/5} = 6\sqrt[5]{x^3}$

3. $(32x^2y^3)^{3/5} = 32^{3/5}(x^2y^3)^{3/5} = (\sqrt[5]{32})^3 \sqrt[5]{(x^2y^3)^3}$
$$= 8\sqrt[5]{x^6y^9} = 8xy\sqrt[5]{xy^4}$$

5. $(x^2 + y^2)^{1/2} = \sqrt{x^2 + y^2}$ **7.** $5\sqrt[4]{x^3} = 5x^{3/4}$
[Note: $\sqrt{x^2 + y^2} \neq x + y$.]

9. $\sqrt[5]{(2x^2y)^3} = (2x^2y)^{3/5}$ **11.** $\sqrt[3]{x} + \sqrt[3]{y} = x^{1/3} + y^{1/3}$

13. $25^{1/2} = (5^2)^{1/2} = 5$ **15.** $16^{3/2} = (4^2)^{3/2} = 4^3 = 64$

17. $-49^{1/2} = -\sqrt{49} = -7$ **19.** $-64^{2/3} = -(\sqrt[3]{64})^2 = -16$

21. $\left(\dfrac{4}{25}\right)^{3/2} = \left(\left(\dfrac{2}{5}\right)^2\right)^{3/2} \left(\dfrac{2}{5}\right)^3 = \dfrac{2^3}{5^3} = \dfrac{8}{125}$ **23.** $9^{-3/2} = (3^2)^{-3/2} = 3^{-3} = \dfrac{1}{3^3} = \dfrac{1}{27}$

25. $x^{4/5}x^{-2/5} = x^{4/5-2/5} = x^{2/5}$ **27.** $\dfrac{m^{2/3}}{m^{-1/3}} = m^{2/3-(-1/3)} = m^1 = m$

29. $(8x^3y^{-6})^{1/3} = (2^3x^3y^{-6})^{1/3} = 2^{3/3}x^{3/3}y^{-6/3} = 2xy^{-2} = \dfrac{2x}{y^2}$

31. $\left(\dfrac{4x^{-2}}{y^4}\right)^{-1/2} = \left(\dfrac{2^2x^{-2}}{y^4}\right)^{-1/2} = \dfrac{2^{2(-1/2)}x^{-2(-1/2)}}{y^{4(-1/2)}} = \dfrac{2^{-1}x^1}{y^{-2}} = \dfrac{xy^2}{2}$

33. $\dfrac{(8x)^{-1/3}}{12x^{1/4}} = \dfrac{\frac{1}{(8x)^{1/3}}}{12x^{1/4}} = \dfrac{\frac{1}{2x^{1/3}}}{12x^{1/4}} = \dfrac{1}{24x^{1/4+1/3}} = \dfrac{1}{24x^{7/12}}$

35. $\sqrt[5]{(2x + 3)^5} = [(2x + 3)^5]^{1/5} = 2x + 3$

37. $\sqrt{6x}\sqrt{15x^3}\sqrt{30x^7} = \sqrt{6(15)(30)x^{11}} = \sqrt{3(30)^2x^{11}} = 30x^5\sqrt{3x}$

39. $\dfrac{\sqrt{6x}\sqrt{10}}{\sqrt{15x}} = \sqrt{\dfrac{60x}{15x}} = \sqrt{4} = 2$

41. $3x^{3/4}(4x^{1/4} - 2x^8) = 12x^{3/4+1/4} - 6x^{3/4+8}$
$$= 12x - 6x^{3/4+32/4} = 12x - 6x^{35/4}$$

43. $(3u^{1/2} - v^{1/2})(u^{1/2} - 4v^{1/2}) = 3u - 12u^{1/2}v^{1/2} - u^{1/2}v^{1/2} + 4v$
$$= 3u - 13u^{1/2}v^{1/2} + 4v$$

45. $(6m^{1/2} + n^{-1/2})(6m - n^{-1/2}) = 36m^{3/2} + 6mn^{-1/2} - 6m^{1/2}n^{-1/2} - n^{-1}$
$$= 36m^{3/2} + \dfrac{6m}{n^{1/2}} - \dfrac{6m^{1/2}}{n^{1/2}} - \dfrac{1}{n}$$

47. $(3x^{1/2} - y^{1/2})^2 = (3x^{1/2})^2 - 6x^{1/2}y^{1/2} + (y^{1/2})^2 = 9x - 6x^{1/2}y^{1/2} + y$

49. $\dfrac{\sqrt[3]{x^2} + 2}{2\sqrt[3]{x}} = \dfrac{x^{2/3} + 2}{2x^{1/3}} = \dfrac{x^{2/3}}{2x^{1/3}} + \dfrac{2}{2x^{1/3}} = \dfrac{1}{2}x^{1/3} + \dfrac{1}{x^{1/3}} = \dfrac{1}{2}x^{1/3} + x^{-1/3}$

51. $\dfrac{2\sqrt[4]{x^3} + 3\sqrt[3]{x}}{3x} = \dfrac{2x^{3/4} + 3x^{1/3}}{3x} = \dfrac{2x^{3/4}}{3x} + \dfrac{3x^{1/3}}{3x}$

$\qquad\qquad = \dfrac{2}{3}x^{3/4-1} + x^{1/3-1} = \dfrac{2}{3}x^{-1/4} + x^{-2/3}$

53. $\dfrac{2\sqrt[3]{x} - \sqrt{x}}{4\sqrt{x}} = \dfrac{2x^{1/3} - x^{1/2}}{4x^{1/2}} = \dfrac{2x^{1/3}}{4x^{1/2}} - \dfrac{x^{1/2}}{4x^{1/2}} = \dfrac{1}{2}x^{1/3-1/2} - \dfrac{1}{4} = \dfrac{1}{2}x^{-1/6} - \dfrac{1}{4}$

55. $\dfrac{12mn^2}{\sqrt{3mn}} = \dfrac{12mn^2}{\sqrt{3mn}} \cdot \dfrac{\sqrt{3mn}}{\sqrt{3mn}} = \dfrac{12mn^2\sqrt{3mn}}{3mn} = 4n\sqrt{3mn}$

57. $\dfrac{2(x+3)}{\sqrt{x-2}} = \dfrac{2(x+3)}{\sqrt{x-2}} \cdot \dfrac{\sqrt{x-2}}{\sqrt{x-2}} = \dfrac{2(x+3)\sqrt{x-2}}{x-2}$

59. $\dfrac{7(x-y)^2}{\sqrt{x}-\sqrt{y}} = \dfrac{7(x-y)^2}{\sqrt{x}-\sqrt{y}} \cdot \dfrac{\sqrt{x}+\sqrt{y}}{\sqrt{x}+\sqrt{y}} = \dfrac{7(x-y)^2\,(\sqrt{x}+\sqrt{y})}{x-y}$

$\qquad\qquad\qquad\qquad = 7(x-y)(\sqrt{x}+\sqrt{y})$

61. $\dfrac{\sqrt{5xy}}{5x^2y^2} = \dfrac{\sqrt{5xy}}{5x^2y^2} \cdot \dfrac{\sqrt{5xy}}{\sqrt{5xy}} = \dfrac{5xy}{5x^2y^2\sqrt{5xy}} = \dfrac{1}{xy\sqrt{5xy}}$

63. $\dfrac{\sqrt{x+h} - \sqrt{x}}{h} = \dfrac{\sqrt{x+h} - \sqrt{x}}{h} \cdot \dfrac{\sqrt{x+h} + \sqrt{x}}{\sqrt{x+h} + \sqrt{x}}$

$\qquad\qquad = \dfrac{x+h-x}{h(\sqrt{x+h} + \sqrt{x})} = \dfrac{h}{h(\sqrt{x+h} + \sqrt{x})}$

$\qquad\qquad = \dfrac{1}{\sqrt{x+h} + \sqrt{x}}$

65. $\dfrac{\sqrt{t} - \sqrt{x}}{t^2 - x^2} = \dfrac{\sqrt{t} - \sqrt{x}}{(t-x)(t+x)} \cdot \dfrac{\sqrt{t} + \sqrt{x}}{\sqrt{t} + \sqrt{x}} = \dfrac{t-x}{(t-x)(t+x)(\sqrt{t}+\sqrt{x})}$

$\qquad\qquad\qquad = \dfrac{1}{(t+x)(\sqrt{t}+\sqrt{x})}$

67. $(x+y)^{1/2} \overset{?}{=} x^{1/2} + y^{1/2}$

Let $x = y = 1$. Then

$(1+1)^{1/2} = 2^{1/2} = \sqrt{2} \approx 1.414$

$1^{1/2} + 1^{1/2} = \sqrt{1} + \sqrt{1} = 1 + 1 = 2; \quad \sqrt{2} \neq 2$

69. $(x+y)^{1/3} \overset{?}{=} \dfrac{1}{(x+y)^3}$

Let $x = y = 4$. Then

$(4+4)^{1/3} = 8^{1/3} = \sqrt[3]{8} = 2$

$\dfrac{1}{(4+4)^3} = \dfrac{1}{8^3} = \dfrac{1}{512}$

71. $\sqrt{x^2} = x$ for all real numbers x: False

$\sqrt{(-2)^2} = \sqrt{4} = 2 \neq -2$

73. $\sqrt[3]{x^3} = |x|$ for all real numbers x: False

$\sqrt[3]{(-1)^3} = \sqrt[3]{-1} = -1 \neq |-1| = 1$

75. False: $(-8)^{1/3} = -2$ since $(-2)^3 = -8$

77. True: $r^{1/2} = \sqrt{r}$ and $-r^{1/2} = -\sqrt{r}$ are each square roots of r.

79. True: $(\sqrt{10})^4 = (10^{1/2})^4 = 10^2 = 100$

$(-\sqrt{10})^4 = (-1)^4(\sqrt{10})^4 = (1)(100) = 100$

81. False: $5\sqrt{7} - 6\sqrt{5} \approx -0.1877$; $\sqrt{a}$ is never negative.

83. $-\dfrac{1}{2}(x - 2)(x + 3)^{-3/2} + (x + 3)^{-1/2} = \dfrac{-(x - 2)}{2(x + 3)^{3/2}} + \dfrac{1}{(x + 3)^{1/2}}$

$$= \dfrac{-x + 2 + 2(x + 3)}{2(x + 3)^{3/2}}$$

$$= \dfrac{x + 8}{2(x + 3)^{3/2}}$$

85. $\dfrac{(x - 1)^{1/2} - x\left(\dfrac{1}{2}\right)(x - 1)^{-1/2}}{x - 1} = \dfrac{(x - 1)^{1/2} - \dfrac{x}{2(x - 1)^{1/2}}}{x - 1}$

$$= \dfrac{\dfrac{2(x - 1)^{1/2}(x - 1)^{1/2}}{2(x - 1)^{1/2}} - \dfrac{x}{2(x - 1)^{1/2}}}{x - 1}$$

$$= \dfrac{\dfrac{2(x - 1) - x}{2(x - 1)^{1/2}}}{x - 1} = \dfrac{x - 2}{2(x - 1)^{3/2}}$$

87. $\dfrac{(x + 2)^{2/3} - x\left(\dfrac{2}{3}\right)(x + 2)^{-1/3}}{(x + 2)^{4/3}} = \dfrac{(x + 2)^{2/3} - \dfrac{2x}{3(x + 2)^{1/3}}}{(x + 2)^{4/3}}$

$$= \dfrac{\dfrac{3(x + 2)^{1/3}(x + 2)^{2/3}}{3(x + 2)^{1/3}} - \dfrac{2x}{3(x + 2)^{1/3}}}{(x + 2)^{4/3}}$$

$$= \dfrac{\dfrac{3(x + 2) - 2x}{3(x + 2)^{1/3}}}{(x + 2)^{4/3}} = \dfrac{x + 6}{3(x + 2)^{5/3}}$$

89. $22^{3/2} = 22^{1.5} \approx 103.2$ or $22^{3/2} = \sqrt{(22)^3} = \sqrt{10,648} \approx 103.2$

91. $827^{-3/8} = \dfrac{1}{827^{3/8}} = \dfrac{1}{827^{0.375}} \approx \dfrac{1}{12.42} \approx 0.0805$

93. $37.09^{7/3} \approx 37.09^{2.3333} \approx 4,588$

95. (A) $\sqrt{3} + \sqrt{5} \approx 1.732 + 2.236 = 3.968$

   (B) $\sqrt{2 + \sqrt{3}} + \sqrt{2 - \sqrt{3}} \approx 2.449$

   (C) $1 + \sqrt{3} \approx 2.732$

   (D) $\sqrt[3]{10 + 6\sqrt{3}} \approx 2.732$

   (E) $\sqrt{8 + \sqrt{60}} \approx 3.968$

   (F) $\sqrt{6} \approx 2.449$

   (A) and (E) have the same value:
$$\left(\sqrt{3} + \sqrt{5}\right)^2 = 3 + 2\sqrt{3}\sqrt{5} + 5 = 8 + 2\sqrt{15}$$
$$\left[\sqrt{8 + \sqrt{60}}\right]^2 = 8 + \sqrt{4 \cdot 15} = 8 + 2\sqrt{15}$$

   (B) and (F) have the same value.
$$\left(\sqrt{2 + \sqrt{3}} + \sqrt{2 - \sqrt{3}}\right)^2 = 2 + \sqrt{3} + 2\sqrt{2 + \sqrt{3}}\sqrt{2 - \sqrt{3}} + 2 - \sqrt{3}$$
$$= 4 + 2\sqrt{4 - 3} = 4 + 2 = 6$$
$$\left(\sqrt{6}\right)^2 = 6.$$

   (C) and (D) have the same value.
$$\left(1 + \sqrt{3}\right)^3 = \left(1 + \sqrt{3}\right)^2\left(1 + \sqrt{3}\right)$$
$$= (1 + 2\sqrt{3} + 3)(1 + \sqrt{3})$$
$$= (4 + 2\sqrt{3})(1 + \sqrt{3})$$
$$= 4 + 6\sqrt{3} + 6 = 10 + 6\sqrt{3}$$
$$\left(\sqrt[3]{10 + 6\sqrt{3}}\right)^3 = 10 + 6\sqrt{3}$$

EXERCISE A-7

Things to remember:

<u>1</u>.   FIRST DEGREE, OR LINEAR, EQUATIONS AND INEQUALITIES

   A FIRST DEGREE, or LINEAR, EQUATION in one variable x is an equation that can be written in the form

   STANDARD FORM: $ax + b = 0, \ a \neq 0$

   If the equality symbol = is replaced by <, > , ≤, or ≥, then the resulting expression is called a FIRST DEGREE, or LINEAR, INEQUALITY.

<u>2</u>.   SOLUTIONS

   A SOLUTION OF AN EQUATION (or inequality) involving a single variable is a number that when substituted for the variable makes the equation (or inequality) true. The set of all solutions is called the SOLUTION SET. To SOLVE AN EQUATION (or inequality) we mean that we find the solution set. Two equations (or inequalities) are EQUIVALENT if they have the same solution set.

3. EQUALITY PROPERTIES
   An equivalent equation will result if:
   a) The same quantity is added to or subtracted from each side of a given equation.
   b) Each side of a given equation is multiplied by or divided by the same nonzero quantity.

4. INEQUALITY PROPERTIES
   An equivalent inequality will result and the SENSE OR DIRECTION WILL REMAIN THE SAME if each side of the original inequality:
   a) Has the same real number added to or subtracted from it.
   b) Is multiplied or divided by the same positive number.
   An equivalent inequality will result and the SENSE OR DIRECTION WILL REVERSE if each side of the original inequality:
   c) Is multiplied or divided by the same negative number.
   NOTE: Multiplication and division by 0 is not permitted.

5. The double inequality $a \leq x \leq b$ means that $a \leq x$ and $x \leq b$. Other variations, as well as a useful interval notation, are indicated in the following table.

Interval Notation	Inequality Notation	Line Graph
$[a, b]$	$a \leq x \leq b$	
$[a, b)$	$a \leq x < b$	
$(a, b]$	$a < x \leq b$	
(a, b)	$a < x < b$	
$(-\infty, a]$	$x \leq a$	
$(-\infty, a)$	$x < a$	
$[b, \infty)$	$x \geq b$	
(b, ∞)	$x > b$	

[Note: An endpoint on a line graph has a square bracket through it if it is included in the inequality and a parenthesis through it if it is not. An interval of the form $[a, b]$ is a CLOSED INTERVAL, an interval of the form (a, b) is an OPEN INTERVAL. Intervals of the form $(a, b]$ and $[a, b)$ are HALF-OPEN and HALF-CLOSED.]

1.
$$2m + 9 = 5m - 6$$
$$2m + 9 - 9 = 5m - 6 - 9 \qquad \text{[using } \underline{3}\text{(a)]}$$
$$2m = 5m - 15$$
$$2m - 5m = 5m - 15 - 5m \qquad \text{[using } \underline{3}\text{(a)]}$$
$$-3m = -15$$
$$\frac{-3m}{-3} = \frac{-15}{-3} \qquad \text{[using } \underline{3}\text{(b)]}$$
$$m = 5$$

3.
$$2x + 3 < -4$$
$$2x + 3 - 3 < -4 - 3 \qquad \text{[using } \underline{4}\text{(a)]}$$
$$2x < -7$$
$$x < -\frac{7}{2} \qquad \text{[using } \underline{4}\text{(b)]}$$

5.
$$-3x \geq -12$$
$$\frac{-3x}{-3} \leq \frac{-12}{-3} \qquad \text{[using } \underline{4}\text{(c)]}$$
$$x \leq 4$$

7. $-4x - 7 > 5$
$$-4x > 5 + 7$$
$$-4x > 12$$
$$x < -3$$
Graph of $x < -3$ is:

9. $2 \leq x + 3 \leq 5$
$$2 - 3 \leq x \leq 5 - 3$$
$$-1 \leq x \leq 2$$
Graph of $-1 \leq x \leq 2$ is:

11. $\dfrac{x}{3} - \dfrac{1}{2} = \dfrac{1}{3}$

Multiply both sides of the equation by 6. We obtain:

$$2x - 3 = 2 \qquad \text{[using } \underline{3}\text{(b)]}$$
$$2x = 5$$
$$x = \frac{5}{2}$$

13. $\dfrac{x}{3} > -\dfrac{5}{4}$

Multiply both sides of the inequality by 12. We obtain:

$$4x > -15 \quad \text{[using } \underline{4}\text{(b)]}$$
$$x > -\frac{15}{4}$$

15. $\dfrac{y}{3} = 4 - \dfrac{y}{6}$

Multiply both sides of the equation by 6. We obtain:

$$2y = 24 - y$$
$$3y = 24$$
$$y = 8$$

17. $10x + 25(x - 3) = 275$
$$10x + 25x - 75 = 275$$
$$35x = 275 + 75$$
$$35x = 350$$
$$x = \frac{350}{35}$$
$$x = 10$$

19. $3 - y \leq 4(y - 3)$
$$3 - y \leq 4y - 12$$
$$-5y \leq -15$$
$$y \geq 3$$

[<u>Note</u>: Division by a negative number, -3.]

21. $\dfrac{x}{5} - \dfrac{x}{6} = \dfrac{6}{5}$

Multiply both sides of the equation by 30. We obtain:

$$6x - 5x = 36$$
$$x = 36$$

23. $\dfrac{m}{5} - 3 < \dfrac{3}{5} - \dfrac{m}{2}$

Multiply both sides of the inequality by 10. We obtain:

$2m - 30 < 6 - 5m$ [using $\underline{4}$(b)]

$7m < 36$

$m < \dfrac{36}{7}$

25. $0.1(x - 7) + 0.05x = 0.8$

$0.1x - 0.7 + 0.05x = 0.8$

$0.15x = 1.5$

$x = \dfrac{1.5}{0.15}$

$x = 10$

27. $2 \le 3x - 7 < 14$

$7 + 2 \le 3x < 14 + 7$

$9 \le 3x < 21$

$3 \le x < 7$

Graph of $3 \le x < 7$ is:

29. $-4 \le \dfrac{9}{5}C + 32 \le 68$

$-36 \le \dfrac{9}{5}C \le 36$

$-36\left(\dfrac{5}{9}\right) \le C \le 36\left(\dfrac{5}{9}\right)$

$-20 \le C \le 20$

Graph of $-20 \le C \le 20$ is:

31. $3x - 4y = 12$

$3x = 12 + 4y$

$3x - 12 = 4y$

$y = \dfrac{1}{4}(3x - 12)$

$y = \dfrac{3}{4}x - 3$

33. $Ax + By = C$

$By = C - Ax$

$y = \dfrac{C}{B} - \dfrac{Ax}{B}, \quad B \ne 0$

or $\quad y = -\left(\dfrac{A}{B}\right)x + \dfrac{C}{B}$

35. $F = \dfrac{9}{5}C + 32$

$\dfrac{9}{5}C + 32 = F$

$\dfrac{9}{5}C = F - 32$

$C = \dfrac{5}{9}(F - 32)$

37. $A = \dfrac{2}{3}(Bm - Bn)$

$3A = 2B(m - n)$

$B = \dfrac{3A}{2(m - n)}$

39. $-3 \le 4 - 7x < 18$

$-3 - 4 \le -7x < 18 - 4$

$-7 \le -7x < 14.$

Dividing by -7, and recalling $\underline{4}$(c), we have

$1 \ge x > -2$ or $-2 < x \le 1$

The graph is:

41. (A) $ab > 0$; $a > 0$ <u>and</u> $b > 0$, or $a < 0$ <u>and</u> $b < 0$

(B) $ab < 0$; $a > 0$ <u>and</u> $b < 0$, or $a < 0$ <u>and</u> $b > 0$

(C) $\dfrac{a}{b} > 0$; $a > 0$ <u>and</u> $b > 0$, or $a < 0$ <u>and</u> $b < 0$

(D) $\dfrac{a}{b} < 0$; $a > 0$ <u>and</u> $b < 0$, or $a < 0$ <u>and</u> $b > 0$

43. (A) If $a - b = 2$, then $a > b$.
   (B) If $c - d = -1$, then $c < d$ $(d - c = 1$ so $d > c)$.

45. Let $a, b > 0$. If $\dfrac{b}{a} > 1$, then $b > a$ so $a - b < 0$; $a - b$ is negative.

47. True: Let (a, b) and (c, d) be open intervals such that $(a, b) \cap (c, d) \neq \varnothing$. If $(a, b) \subset (c, d)$, then $(a, b) \cap (c, d) = (a, b)$ an open interval. Similarly, if $(c, d) \subset (a, b)$. If neither interval is contained in the other, then we can assume that $a < c < b < d$, and $(a, b) \cap (c, d) = (c, b)$, an open interval.

49. False: $(0, 1) \cup (2, 3)$ is **not** an open interval.

51. True: Assume $(a, b) \cap (c, d) \neq \varnothing$. Using the reasoning in Problem 47,
$(a, b) \cup (c, d) = (a, b)$ if $(c, d) \subset (a, b)$
$(a, b) \cup (c, d) = (c, d)$ if $(a, b) \subset (c, d)$
$(a, b) \cup (c, d) = (a, d)$ if $a < c < b < d$

53. Let x = number of \$15 tickets.
Then the number of \$25 tickets = $8000 - x$.
Now,

$$15x + 25(8000 - x) = 165,000$$
$$15x + 200,000 - 25x = 165,000$$
$$-10x = -35,000$$
$$x = 3,500$$

Thus, 3,500 \$15 tickets and $8,000 - 3,500 = 4,500$ \$25 tickets were sold.

55. Let x = the amount invested at 10%. Then $12,000 - x$ is the amount invested at 15%.

Required total yield = 12% of \$12,000 = $0.12 \cdot 12,000 = \$1,440$. Thus,
$$0.10x + 0.15(12,000 - x) = 0.12 \cdot 12,000$$
$$10x + 15(12,000 - x) = 12 \cdot 12,000 \quad \text{(multiply both sides by 100)}$$
$$10x + 180,000 - 15x = 144,000$$
$$-5x = -36,000$$
$$x = \$7,200$$
Thus, we get \$7,200 invested at 10% and $12,000 - 7,200 = \$4,800$ invested at 15%.

57. Let x be the price of the car in 2000. Then

$$\frac{x}{5000} = \frac{172.2}{38.8} \quad \text{(refer to Table 2, Example 9)}$$
$$x = 5,000 \cdot \frac{172.2}{38.8} \approx \$22,191$$

59. Let x = number of books produced. Then

Costs: $C = 1.60x + 55,000$

Revenue: $R = 11x$

To find the break-even point, set $R = C$:

$$11x = 1.60x + 55,000$$
$$9.40x = 55,000$$
$$x = 5851.06383$$

Thus, 5851 books will have to be sold for the publisher to break even.

61. Let x = number of books produced.

Costs: $C(x) = 55,000 + 2.10x$

Revenue: $R(x) = 11x$

(A) The obvious strategy is to raise the sales price of the book.

(B) To find the break-even point, set $R(x) = C(x)$:

$$11x = 55,000 + 2.10x$$
$$8.90x = 55,000$$
$$x = 6179.78$$

The company must sell more than 6180 books.

(C) From Problem 59, the production level at the break-even point is: 5,851 books. At this production level, the costs are

$$C(5,851) = 55,000 + 2.10(5,851) = \$67,287.10$$

If p is the new price of the book, then we need

$$5851p = 67,287.10$$

and $\quad p \approx 11.50$

The company should increase the price at least $0.50 (50 cents).

63. Let x = the number of rainbow trout in the lake. Then,

$\dfrac{x}{200} = \dfrac{200}{8}$ (since proportions are the same)

$$x = \frac{200}{8}(200)$$
$$x = 5,000$$

65. $IQ = \dfrac{\text{Mental age}}{\text{Chronological age}}(100)$

$$\frac{\text{Mental age}}{9}(100) = 140$$

$$\text{Mental age} = \frac{140}{100}(9)$$
$$= 12.6 \text{ years}$$

EXERCISE A-8

Things to remember:

<u>1</u>. A QUADRATIC EQUATION in one variable is any equation that can be written in the form

$$ax^2 + bx + c = 0, \ a \neq 0 \qquad \text{STANDARD FORM}$$

where x is a variable and a, b, and c are constants.

<u>2</u>. Quadratic equations of the form $ax^2 + c = 0$ can be solved by the SQUARE ROOT METHOD. The solutions are:

$$x = \pm\sqrt{\frac{-c}{a}} \quad \text{provided} \quad \frac{-c}{a} \geq 0;$$

otherwise, the equation has no real solutions.

3. If the left side of the quadratic equation when written in standard form can be FACTORED,

$$ax^2 + bx + c = (px + q)(rx + s),$$

then the solutions are

$$x = \frac{-q}{p} \quad \text{or} \quad x = \frac{-s}{r}.$$

4. The solutions of the quadratic equation written in standard form are given by the QUADRATIC FORMULA:

$$x = \frac{-b \pm \sqrt{b^2 - 4ac}}{2a}$$

The quantity $b^2 - 4ac$ under the radical is called the DISCRIMINANT and the equation:

(i)   Has two real solutions if $b^2 - 4ac > 0$.

(ii)   Has one real solution if $b^2 - 4ac = 0$.

(iii)   Has no real solution if $b^2 - 4ac < 0$.

5. FACTORABILITY THEOREM

The second-degree polynomial, $ax^2 + bx + c$, with integer coefficients, can be expressed as the product of two first-degree polynomials with integer coefficients if and only if $\sqrt{b^2 - 4ac}$ is an integer.

6. FACTOR THEOREM

If r_1 and r_2 are solutions of $ax^2 + bx + c = 0$, then

$$ax^2 + bx + c = a(x - r_1)(x - r_2).$$

---

1. $2x^2 - 22 = 0$
   $x^2 - 11 = 0$
   $x^2 = 11$
   $x = \pm\sqrt{11}$

3. $(3x - 1)^2 = 25$
   $3x - 1 = \pm\sqrt{25} = \pm 5$
   $3x = 1 \pm 5 = -4 \text{ or } 6$
   $x = -\dfrac{4}{3} \text{ or } 2$

5. $2u^2 - 8u - 24 = 0$
   $u^2 - 4u - 12 = 0$
   $(u - 6)(u + 2) = 0$
   $u - 6 = 0 \text{ or } u + 2 = 0$
   $u = 6 \text{ or } \quad u = -2$

7. $\quad x^2 = 2x$
   $x^2 - 2x = 0$
   $x(x - 2) = 0$
   $x = 0 \text{ or } x - 2 = 0$
   $\quad x = 2$

9. $x^2 - 6x - 3 = 0$

$$x = \frac{-b \pm \sqrt{b^2 - 4ac}}{2a}, \quad a = 1, \ b = -6, \ c = -3$$

$$= \frac{-(-6) \pm \sqrt{(-6)^2 - 4(1)(-3)}}{2(1)}$$

$$= \frac{6 \pm \sqrt{48}}{2} = \frac{6 \pm 4\sqrt{3}}{2} = 3 \pm 2\sqrt{3}$$

11. $3u^2 + 12u + 6 = 0$

Since 3 is a factor of each coefficient, divide both sides by 3.

$u^2 + 4u + 2 = 0$

$$u = \frac{-b \pm \sqrt{b^2 - 4ac}}{2a}, \quad a = 1, \ b = 4, \ c = 2$$

$$= \frac{-4 \pm \sqrt{4^2 - 4(1)(2)}}{2(1)} = \frac{-4 \pm \sqrt{8}}{2} = \frac{-4 \pm 2\sqrt{2}}{2} = -2 \pm \sqrt{2}$$

13.

$$\frac{2x^2}{3} = 5x$$

$$2x^2 = 15x$$

$2x^2 - 15x = 0$

$x(2x - 15) = 0$

$x = 0$ or $2x - 15 = 0$

$$x = \frac{15}{2}$$

15. $4u^2 - 9 = 0$

$4u^2 = 9$ (solve by square root method)

$$u^2 = \frac{9}{4}$$

$$u = \pm\sqrt{\frac{9}{4}} = \pm\frac{3}{2}$$

17.

$$8x^2 + 20x = 12$$

$8x^2 + 20x - 12 = 0$

$2x^2 + 5x - 3 = 0$

$(x + 3)(2x - 1) = 0$

$x + 3 = 0$ or $2x - 1 = 0$

$x = -3$ or $2x = 1$

$$x = \frac{1}{2}$$

19. $x^2 = 1 - x$

$x^2 + x - 1 = 0$

$$x = \frac{-b \pm \sqrt{b^2 - 4ac}}{2a}, \quad a = 1, \ b = 1, \ c = -1$$

$$= \frac{-1 \pm \sqrt{(1)^2 - 4(1)(-1)}}{2(1)} = \frac{-1 \pm \sqrt{5}}{2}$$

21. $2x^2 = 6x - 3$

$2x^2 - 6x + 3 = 0$

$$x = \frac{-b \pm \sqrt{b^2 - 4ac}}{2a}, \quad a = 2, \ b = -6, \ c = 3$$

$$= \frac{-(-6) \pm \sqrt{(-6)^2 - 4(2)(3)}}{2(2)} = \frac{6 \pm \sqrt{12}}{4} = \frac{6 \pm 2\sqrt{3}}{4} = \frac{3 \pm \sqrt{3}}{2}$$

23. $y^2 - 4y = -8$

$y^2 - 4y + 8 = 0$

$$y = \frac{-b \pm \sqrt{b^2 - 4ac}}{2a}, \quad a, = 1, \ b = -4, \ c = 8$$

$$= \frac{-(-4) \pm \sqrt{(-4)^2 - 4(1)(8)}}{2(1)} = \frac{4 \pm \sqrt{-16}}{2}$$

Since $\sqrt{-16}$ is not a real number, there are no real solutions.

25. $(2x + 3)^2 = 11$

$2x + 3 = \pm\sqrt{11}$

$2x = -3 \pm \sqrt{11}$

$x = -\dfrac{3}{2} \pm \dfrac{1}{2}\sqrt{11}$

27. $\dfrac{3}{p} = p$

$p^2 = 3$

$p = \pm\sqrt{3}$

29. $2 - \dfrac{2}{m^2} = \dfrac{3}{m}$

$2m^2 - 2 = 3m$

$2m^2 - 3m - 2 = 0$

$(2m + 1)(m - 2) = 0$

$m = -\dfrac{1}{2},\ 2$

31. $x^2 + 40x - 84$

<u>Step 1</u>. Test for factorability

$\sqrt{b^2 - 4ac} = \sqrt{(40)^2 - 4(1)(-84)} = \sqrt{1936} = 44$

Since the result is an integer, the polynomial has first-degree factors with integer coefficients.

<u>Step 2</u>. Use the factor theorem

$x^2 + 40x - 84 = 0$

$x = \dfrac{-40 \pm 44}{2} = 2,\ -42$ (by the quadratic formula)

Thus, $x^2 + 40x - 84 = (x - 2)(x - [-42]) = (x - 2)(x + 42)$

33. $x^2 - 32x + 144$

<u>Step 1</u>. Test for factorability

$\sqrt{b^2 - 4ac} = \sqrt{(-32)^2 - 4(1)(144)} = \sqrt{448} \approx 21.166$

Since this is not an integer, the polynomial is not factorable.

35. $2x^2 + 15x - 108$

<u>Step 1</u>. Test for factorability

$\sqrt{b^2 - 4ac} = \sqrt{(15)^2 - 4(2)(-108)} = \sqrt{1089} = 33$

Thus, the polynomial has first-degree factors with integer coefficients.

<u>Step 2</u>. Use the factor theorem

$2x^2 + 15x - 108$

$x = \dfrac{-15 \pm 33}{4} = \dfrac{9}{2},\ -12$

Thus, $2x^2 + 15x - 108 = 2\left(x - \dfrac{9}{2}\right)(x - [-12]) = (2x - 9)(x + 12)$

37. $4x^2 + 241x - 434$

<u>Step 1</u>. Test for factorability

$\sqrt{b^2 - 4ac} = \sqrt{(241)^2 - 4(4)(-434)} = \sqrt{65025} = 255$

Thus, the polynomial has first-degree factors with integer coefficients.

<u>Step 2</u>. Use the factor theorem

$4x^2 + 241x - 434$

$x = \dfrac{-241 \pm 255}{8} = \dfrac{14}{8},\ -\dfrac{496}{8}$ or $\dfrac{7}{4},\ -62$

Thus, $4x^2 + 241x - 434 = 4\left(x - \dfrac{7}{4}\right)(x + 62) = (4x - 7)(x + 62)$

39.
$$A = P(1 + r)^2$$
$$(1 + r)^2 = \frac{A}{P}$$
$$1 + r = \sqrt{\frac{A}{P}}$$
$$r = \sqrt{\frac{A}{P}} - 1$$

41. $x^2 + 4x + C = 0$
The discriminant is: $16 - 4c$

(A) If $16 - 4c > 0$, i.e., if $c < 4$, then the equation has two distinct real roots.

(B) If $16 - 4c = 0$, i.e., if $c = 4$, then the equation has one real double root.

(C) If $16 - 4c < 0$, i.e., if $c > 4$, then there are no real roots.

43. Setting the supply equation equal to the demand equation, we have

$$\frac{x}{450} + \frac{1}{2} = \frac{6,300}{x}$$
$$\frac{1}{450}x^2 + \frac{1}{2}x = 6,300$$
$$x^2 + 225x - 2,835,000 = 0$$
$$x = \frac{-225 \pm \sqrt{(225)^2 - 4(1)(-2,835,000)}}{2} \quad \text{(quadratic formula)}$$
$$= \frac{-225 \pm \sqrt{11,390,625}}{2}$$
$$= \frac{-225 \pm 3375}{2}$$
$$= 1,575 \text{ units}$$

Note, we discard the negative root since a negative number of units cannot be produced or sold. Substituting $x = 1,575$ into either equation (we use the demand equation), we get

$$p = \frac{6,300}{1,575} = 4$$

Supply equals demand at $4 per unit.

45. $A = P(1 + r)^2 = P(1 + 2r + r^2) = Pr^2 + 2Pr + P$

Let $A = 625$ and $P = 484$. Then,

$484r^2 + 968r + 484 = 625$

$484r^2 + 968r - 141 = 0$

Using the quadratic formula,

$$r = \frac{-968 \pm \sqrt{(968)^2 - 4(484)(-141)}}{968} = \frac{-968 \pm \sqrt{1,210,000}}{968}$$

$$= \frac{-968 \pm 1100}{968} \approx 0.1364 \text{ or } -2.136$$

Since $r > 0$, we have $r = 0.1364$ or 13.64%.

47. $v^2 = 64h$

For $h = 1$, $v^2 = 64(1) = 64$. Therefore, $v = 8$ ft/sec.

For $h = 0.5$, $v^2 = 64(0.5) = 32$.

Therefore, $v = \sqrt{32} = 4\sqrt{2} \approx 5.66$ ft/sec.

APPENDIX B   SPECIAL TOPICS

EXERCISE B-1

Things to remember:

1. **SEQUENCES**

   A SEQUENCE is a function whose domain is a set of successive integers. If the domain of a given sequence is a finite set, then the sequence is called a FINITE SEQUENCE; otherwise, the sequence is an INFINITE SEQUENCE. In general, unless stated to the contrary or the context specifies otherwise, the domain of a sequence will be understood to be the set N of natural numbers.

2. **NOTATION FOR SEQUENCES**

   Rather than function notation $f(n)$, n in the domain of a given sequence f, subscript notation a_n is normally used to denote the value in the range corresponding to n, and the sequence itself is denoted $\{a_n\}$ rather than f or $f(n)$. The elements in the range, a_n, are called the TERMS of the sequence; a_1 is the first term, a_2 is the second term, and a_n is the nth term or general term.

3. **SERIES**

   Given a sequence $\{a_n\}$. The sum of the terms of the sequence, $a_1 + a_2 + a_3 + \cdots$ is called a SERIES. If the sequence is finite, the corresponding series is a FINITE SERIES; if the sequence is infinite, then the corresponding series is an INFINITE SERIES. Only finite series are considered in this section.

4. **NOTATION FOR SERIES**

   Series are represented using SUMMATION NOTATION.
   If $\{a_k\}$, $k = 1, 2, \ldots, n$ is a finite sequence, then the series
   $$a_1 + a_2 + a_3 + \cdots + a_n$$
   is denoted
   $$\sum_{k=1}^{n} a_k.$$

   The symbol $\sum$ is called the SUMMATION SIGN and k is called the SUMMING INDEX.

5. **ARITHMETIC MEAN**

   If $\{a_k\}$, $k = 1, 2, \ldots, n$, is a finite sequence, then the ARITHMETIC MEAN $\overline{a}$ of the sequence is defined as
   $$\overline{a} = \frac{1}{n} \sum_{k=1}^{n} x_k.$$

---

1. $a_n = 2n + 3$; $a_1 = 2\cdot 1 + 3 = 5$

$\qquad\qquad\qquad a_2 = 2\cdot 2 + 3 = 7$

$\qquad\qquad\qquad a_3 = 2\cdot 3 + 3 = 9$

$\qquad\qquad\qquad a_4 = 2\cdot 4 + 3 = 11$

3. $a_n = \dfrac{n + 2}{n + 1}$; $a_1 = \dfrac{1 + 2}{1 + 1} = \dfrac{3}{2}$

$\qquad\qquad\qquad a_2 = \dfrac{2 + 2}{2 + 1} = \dfrac{4}{3}$

$\qquad\qquad\qquad a_3 = \dfrac{3 + 2}{3 + 1} = \dfrac{5}{4}$

$\qquad\qquad\qquad a_4 = \dfrac{4 + 2}{4 + 1} = \dfrac{6}{5}$

5. $a_n = (-3)^{n+1}$; $a_1 = (-3)^{1+1} = (-3)^2 = 9$

$\qquad\qquad\qquad a_2 = (-3)^{2+1} = (-3)^3 = -27$

$\qquad\qquad\qquad a_3 = (-3)^{3+1} = (-3)^4 = 81$

$\qquad\qquad\qquad a_4 = (-3)^{4+1} = (-3)^5 = -243$

7. $a_n = 2n + 3$; $a_{10} = 2\cdot 10 + 3 = 23$

9. $a_n = \dfrac{n + 2}{n + 1}$; $a_{99} = \dfrac{99 + 2}{99 + 1} = \dfrac{101}{100}$

11. $\displaystyle\sum_{k=1}^{6} k = 1 + 2 + 3 + 4 + 5 + 6 = 21$

13. $\displaystyle\sum_{k=4}^{7} (2k - 3) = (2\cdot 4 - 3) + (2\cdot 5 - 3) + (2\cdot 6 - 3) + (2\cdot 7 - 3)$

$\qquad\qquad\qquad = 5 + 7 + 9 + 11 = 32$

15. $\displaystyle\sum_{k=0}^{3} \dfrac{1}{10^k} = \dfrac{1}{10^0} + \dfrac{1}{10^1} + \dfrac{1}{10^2} + \dfrac{1}{10^3} = 1 + \dfrac{1}{10} + \dfrac{1}{100} + \dfrac{1}{1000} = \dfrac{1111}{1000} = 1.111$

17. $a_1 = 5$, $a_2 = 4$, $a_3 = 2$, $a_4 = 1$, $a_5 = 6$.   Here $n = 5$ and the arithmetic mean is given by:

$\bar{a} = \dfrac{1}{5}\displaystyle\sum_{k=1}^{5} a_k = \dfrac{1}{5}(5 + 4 + 2 + 1 + 6) = \dfrac{18}{5} = 3.6$

19. $a_1 = 96$, $a_2 = 65$, $a_3 = 82$, $a_4 = 74$, $a_5 = 91$, $a_6 = 88$, $a_7 = 87$, $a_8 = 91$, $a_9 = 77$, and $a_{10} = 74$.   Here $n = 10$ and the arithmetic mean is given by:

$\bar{a} = \dfrac{1}{10}\displaystyle\sum_{k=1}^{10} a_k = \dfrac{1}{10}(96 + 65 + 82 + 74 + 91 + 88 + 87 + 91 + 77 + 74)$

$\qquad = \dfrac{825}{10} = 82.5$

21. $a_n = \dfrac{(-1)^{n+1}}{2^n}$; $a_1 = \dfrac{(-1)^2}{2^1} = \dfrac{1}{2}$

$\qquad\qquad\qquad a_2 = \dfrac{(-1)^3}{2^2} = -\dfrac{1}{4}$

$\qquad\qquad\qquad a_3 = \dfrac{(-1)^4}{2^3} = \dfrac{1}{8}$

$\qquad\qquad\qquad a_4 = \dfrac{(-1)^5}{2^4} = -\dfrac{1}{16}$

$\qquad\qquad\qquad a_5 = \dfrac{(-1)^6}{2^5} = \dfrac{1}{32}$

23. $a_n = n[1 + (-1)^n]$; $a_1 = 1[1 + (-1)^1] = 0$

$$a_2 = 2[1 + (-1)^2] = 4$$
$$a_3 = 3[1 + (-1)^3] = 0$$
$$a_4 = 4[1 + (-1)^4] = 8$$
$$a_5 = 5[1 + (-1)^5] = 0$$

25. $a_n = \left(-\dfrac{3}{2}\right)^{n-1}$; $a_1 = \left(-\dfrac{3}{2}\right)^0 = 1$

$$a_2 = \left(-\frac{3}{2}\right)^1 = -\frac{3}{2}$$
$$a_3 = \left(-\frac{3}{2}\right)^2 = \frac{9}{4}$$
$$a_4 = \left(-\frac{3}{2}\right)^3 = -\frac{27}{8}$$
$$a_5 = \left(-\frac{3}{2}\right)^4 = \frac{81}{16}$$

27. Given -2, -1, 0, 1, … The sequence is the set of successive integers beginning with -2. Thus, $a_n = n - 3$, $n = 1, 2, 3, …$.

29. Given 4, 8, 12, 16, … The sequence is the set of positive integer multiples of 4. Thus, $a_n = 4n$, $n = 1, 2, 3, …$.

31. Given $\dfrac{1}{2}$, $\dfrac{3}{4}$, $\dfrac{5}{6}$, $\dfrac{7}{8}$, … The sequence is the set of fractions whose numerators are the odd positive integers and whose denominators are the even positive integers. Thus,

$$a_n = \frac{2n - 1}{2n}, \quad n = 1, 2, 3, … .$$

33. Given 1, -2, 3, -4, … The sequence consists of the positive integers with alternating signs. Thus,

$$a_n = (-1)^{n+1}n, \quad n = 1, 2, 3, … .$$

35. Given 1, -3, 5, -7, … The sequence consists of the odd positive integers with alternating signs. Thus,

$$a_n = (-1)^{n+1}(2n - 1), \quad n = 1, 2, 3, … .$$

37. Given 1, $\dfrac{2}{5}$, $\dfrac{4}{25}$, $\dfrac{8}{125}$, … The sequence consists of the nonnegative integral powers of $\dfrac{2}{5}$. Thus,

$$a_n = \left(\frac{2}{5}\right)^{n-1}, \quad n = 1, 2, 3, … .$$

39. Given x, x^2, x^3, x^4, … The sequence is the set of positive integral powers of x. Thus, $a_n = x^n$, $n = 1, 2, 3, …$.

41. Given x, $-x^3$, x^5, $-x^7$, ... The sequence is the set of positive odd integral powers of x with alternating signs. Thus,

$$a_n = (-1)^{n+1} x^{2n-1}, \quad n = 1, 2, 3, \ldots .$$

43. $\displaystyle\sum_{k=1}^{5} (-1)^{k+1}(2k-1)^2 = (-1)^2(2 \cdot 1 - 1)^2 + (-1)^3(2 \cdot 2 - 1)^2$

$$+ (-1)^4(2 \cdot 3 - 1)^2 + (-1)^5(2 \cdot 4 - 1)^2$$
$$+ (-1)^6(2 \cdot 5 - 1)^2$$
$$= 1 - 9 + 25 - 49 + 81$$

45. $\displaystyle\sum_{k=2}^{5} \frac{2^k}{2k+3} = \frac{2^2}{2 \cdot 2 + 3} + \frac{2^3}{2 \cdot 3 + 3} + \frac{2^4 \cdot}{2 \cdot 4 + 3} + \frac{2^5}{2 \cdot 5 + 3}$

$$= \frac{4}{7} + \frac{8}{9} + \frac{16}{11} + \frac{32}{13}$$

47. $\displaystyle\sum_{k=1}^{5} x^{k-1} = x^0 + x^1 + x^2 + x^3 + x^4 = 1 + x + x^2 + x^3 + x^4$

49. $\displaystyle\sum_{k=0}^{4} \frac{(-1)^k x^{2k+1}}{2k+1} = \frac{(-1)^0 x}{2 \cdot 0 + 1} + \frac{(-1)^2 x^5}{2 \cdot 2 + 1} + \frac{(-1)^3 x^7}{2 \cdot 3 + 1} + \frac{(-1)^4 x^9}{2 \cdot 4 + 1}$

$$= x - \frac{x^3}{3} + \frac{x^5}{5} - \frac{x^7}{7} + \frac{x^9}{9}$$

51. (A) $2 + 3 + 4 + 5 + 6 = \displaystyle\sum_{k=1}^{5} (k+1)$ (B) $2 + 3 + 4 + 5 + 6 = \displaystyle\sum_{j=0}^{4} (j+2)$

53. (A) $1 - \dfrac{1}{2} + \dfrac{1}{3} - \dfrac{1}{4} = \displaystyle\sum_{k=1}^{4} \frac{(-1)^{k+1}}{k}$ (B) $1 - \dfrac{1}{2} + \dfrac{1}{3} - \dfrac{1}{4} = \displaystyle\sum_{j=0}^{3} \frac{(-1)^j}{j+1}$

55. $2 + \dfrac{3}{2} + \dfrac{4}{3} + \ldots + \dfrac{n+1}{n} = \displaystyle\sum_{k=1}^{n} \frac{k+1}{k}$

57. $\dfrac{1}{2} - \dfrac{1}{4} + \dfrac{1}{8} - \ldots + \dfrac{(-1)^{n+1}}{2^n} = \displaystyle\sum_{k=1}^{n} \frac{(-1)^{k+1}}{2^k}$

59. False: $1 + \dfrac{1}{2} + \dfrac{1}{3} + \dfrac{1}{4} + \dfrac{1}{5} + \dfrac{1}{6} + \ldots + \dfrac{1}{64}$

$$= 1 + \frac{1}{2} + \left(\frac{1}{3} + \frac{1}{4} \right) + \left(\frac{1}{5} + \frac{1}{6} + \frac{1}{7} + \frac{1}{8} \right) + \left(\frac{1}{9} + \cdots + \frac{1}{16} \right)$$
$$+ \left(\frac{1}{7} + \cdots + \frac{1}{32} \right) + \left(\frac{1}{33} + \cdots + \frac{1}{64} \right)$$
$$> 1 + \frac{1}{2} + \frac{1}{2} + \frac{1}{2} + \frac{1}{2} + \frac{1}{2} + \frac{1}{2} = 4$$

61. True: $\dfrac{1}{2} - \dfrac{1}{4} + \dfrac{1}{8} - \dfrac{1}{16} + \dfrac{1}{32} - \ldots$

$$= \left(\dfrac{1}{2} - \dfrac{1}{4}\right) + \left(\dfrac{1}{8} - \dfrac{1}{16}\right) + \left(\dfrac{1}{32} - \dfrac{1}{64}\right) + \text{(positive terms)}$$

$$= \dfrac{1}{4} + \dfrac{1}{16} + \dfrac{1}{64} + \ldots > \dfrac{1}{4}$$

63. $a_1 = 2$ and $a_n = 3a_{n-1} + 2$
for $n \geq 2$.
$a_1 = 2$
$a_2 = 3 \cdot a_1 + 2 = 3 \cdot 2 + 2 = 8$
$a_3 = 3 \cdot a_2 + 2 = 3 \cdot 8 + 2 = 26$
$a_4 = 3 \cdot a_3 + 2 = 3 \cdot 26 + 2 = 80$
$a_5 = 3 \cdot a_4 + 2 = 3 \cdot 80 + 2 = 242$

65. $a_1 = 1$ and $a_n = 2a_{n-1}$
for $n \geq 2$.
$a_1 = 1$
$a_2 = 2 \cdot a_1 = 2 \cdot 1 = 2$
$a_3 = 2 \cdot a_2 = 2 \cdot 2 = 4$
$a_4 = 2 \cdot a_3 = 2 \cdot 4 = 8$
$a_5 = 2 \cdot a_4 = 2 \cdot 8 = 16$

67. In $a_1 = \dfrac{A}{2}$, $a_n = \dfrac{1}{2}\left(a_{n-1} + \dfrac{A}{a_{n-1}}\right)$, $n \geq 2$, let $A = 2$. Then:

$$a_1 = \dfrac{2}{2} = 1$$

$$a_2 = \dfrac{1}{2}\left(a_1 + \dfrac{A}{a_1}\right) = \dfrac{1}{2}(1 + 2) = \dfrac{3}{2}$$

$$a_3 = \dfrac{1}{2}\left(a_2 + \dfrac{A}{a_2}\right) = \dfrac{1}{2}\left(\dfrac{3}{2} + \dfrac{2}{3/2}\right) = \dfrac{1}{2}\left(\dfrac{3}{2} + \dfrac{4}{3}\right) = \dfrac{17}{12}$$

$$a_4 = \dfrac{1}{2}\left(a_3 + \dfrac{A}{a_3}\right) = \dfrac{1}{2}\left(\dfrac{17}{12} + \dfrac{2}{17/12}\right) = \dfrac{1}{2}\left(\dfrac{17}{12} + \dfrac{24}{17}\right) = \dfrac{577}{408} \approx 1.414216$$

$$\text{and } \sqrt{2} \approx 1.414214$$

69. $a_1 = 1$, $a_2 = 1$, $a_n = a_{n-1} + a_{n-2}$, $n \geq 3$
$a_3 = a_2 + a_1 = 2$, $a_4 = a_3 + a_2 = 3$, $a_5 = a_4 + a_3 = 5$,
$a_6 = a_5 + a_4 = 8$, $a_7 = a_6 + a_5 = 13$, $a_8 = a_7 + a_6 = 21$
$a_9 = a_8 + a_7 = 34$, $a_{10} = a_9 + a_8 = 55$

EXERCISE B-2

Things to remember:

<u>1</u>. A sequence of numbers a_1, a_2, a_3, ..., a_n, ..., is called an
ARITHMETIC SEQUENCE if there is constant d, called the COMMON
DIFFERENCE, such that
$$a_n - a_{n-1} = d,$$
that is,
$$a_n = a_{n-1} + d$$
for all $n > 1$.

2. A sequence of numbers a_1, a_2, a_3, ..., a_n, ..., is called a GEOMETRIC SEQUENCE if there exists a nonzero constant r, called the COMMON RATIO, such that

$$\frac{a_n}{a_{n-1}} = r,$$

that is,

$$a_n = ra_{n-1}$$

for all $n > 1$.

3. nTH TERM OF AN ARITHMETIC SEQUENCE

If $\{a_n\}$ is an arithmetic sequence with common difference d, then

$$a_n = a_1 + (n - 1)d$$

for all $n > 1$.

4. nTH TERM OF A GEOMETRIC SEQUENCE

If $\{a_n\}$ is a geometric sequence with common ratio r, then

$$a_n = a_1 r^{n-1}$$

for all $n > 1$.

5. SUM FORMULAS FOR FINITE ARITHMETIC SERIES

The sum S_n of the first n terms of an arithmetic series $a_1 + a_2 + a_3 + ... + a_n$ with common difference d, is given by

(a) $S_n = \dfrac{n}{2}[2a_1 + (n - 1)d]$ \qquad (First Form)

or by

(b) $S_n = \dfrac{n}{2}(a_1 + a_n)$. \qquad (Second Form)

6. SUM FORMULAS FOR FINITE GEOMETRIC SERIES

The sum S_n of the first n terms of a geometric series $a_1 + a_2 + a_3 + a_n$ with common ratio r, is given by:

$$S_n = \frac{a_1(r^n - 1)}{r - 1}, \quad r \neq 1, \qquad \text{(First Form)}$$

or by

$$S_n = \frac{ra_n - a_1}{r - 1}, \quad r \neq 1. \qquad \text{(Second Form)}$$

SUM OF AN INFINITE GEOMETRIC SERIES

If $a_1 + a_2 + a_3 + \ldots + a_n + \ldots,$ is an infinite geometric series with common ratio r having the property $-1 < r < 1$, then the sum S_∞ is defined to be:

$$S_\infty = \frac{a_1}{1 - r}.$$

---

1. (A) $-11, -16, -21, \ldots$
This is an arithmetic sequence with common difference $d = -5$; $a_4 = -26$, $a_5 = -31$.

(B) $2, -4, 8, \ldots$
This is a geometric sequence with common ratio $r = -2$; $a_4 = -16$, $a_5 = 32$.

(C) $1, 4, 9, \ldots$
This is neither an arithmetic sequence $(4 - 1 \neq 9 - 4)$ nor a geometric sequence $\left(\dfrac{4}{1} \neq \dfrac{9}{4}\right)$.

(D) $\dfrac{1}{2}, \dfrac{1}{6}, \dfrac{1}{18}, \ldots$

This is a geometric sequence with common ratio $r = \dfrac{1}{3}$;

$a_4 = \dfrac{1}{54}$, $a_5 = \dfrac{1}{162}$.

3. $\displaystyle\sum_{k=1}^{101} (-1)^{k+1} = 1 - 1 + 1 - 1 + \ldots + 1$
This is a geometric series with $a_1 = 1$ and common ratio $r = -1$.

$$S_{101} = \frac{1[\,(-1)^{101} - 1\,]}{-1 - 1} = \frac{-2}{-2} = 1$$

5. This series is neither arithmetic nor geometric.

7. $5 + 4.9 + 4.8 + \ldots + 0.1$ is an arithmetic series with $a_1 = 5$, $a_{50} = 0.1$ and common difference $d = -0.1$:

$$S_{50} = \frac{50}{2}[5 + 0.1] = 25(5.1) = 127.5$$

9. $a_2 = a_1 + d = 7 + 4 = 11$
$a_3 = a_2 + d = 11 + 4 = 15$ (using $\underline{1}$)

11. $a_{21} = a_1 + (21 - 1)d = 2 + 20 \cdot 4 = 82$ (using $\underline{2}$)

$$S_{31} = \frac{31}{2}[2a_1 + (31 - 1)d] = \frac{31}{2}[2 \cdot 2 + 30 \cdot 4] = \frac{31}{2} \cdot 124 = 1922$$

[using $\underline{3}$(a)]

13. Using $\underline{3}$(b), $S_{20} = \dfrac{20}{2}(a_1 + a_{20}) = 10(18 + 75) = 930$

15. $a_2 = a_1 r = 3(-2) = -6$

$a_3 = a_2 r = -6(-2) = 12$

$a_4 = a_3 r = 12(-2) = -24$ (using $\underline{4}$)

17. Using $\underline{6}$, $S_7 = \dfrac{-3 \cdot 729 - 1}{-3 - 1} = \dfrac{-2188}{-4} = 547.$

19. Using $\underline{5}$, $a_{10} = 100(1.08)^9 = 199.90.$

21. Using $\underline{5}$, $200 = 100r^8$. Thus, $r^8 = 2$ and $r = \sqrt[8]{2} \approx 1.09.$

23. Using $\underline{6}$, $S_{10} = \dfrac{500[(0.6)^{10} - 1]}{0.6 - 1} \approx 1242,$

$S_\infty = \dfrac{500}{1 - 0.6} = 1250.$

25. $S_{41} = \sum\limits_{k=1}^{41} 3k + 3$. The sequence of terms is an arithmetic sequence.

Therefore,

$S_{41} = \dfrac{41}{2}(a_1 + a_{41}) = \dfrac{41}{2}(6 + 126) = \dfrac{41}{2}(132)$

$= 41(66)$

$= 2{,}706$

27. $S_8 = \sum\limits_{k=1}^{8} (-2)^{k-1}$. The sequence of terms is a geometric sequence with

common ratio $r = -2$ and $a_1 = (-2)^0 = 1.$

$S_8 = \dfrac{1[(-2)^8 - 1]}{-2 - 1} = \dfrac{256 - 1}{-3} = -85$

29. Let $a_1 = 13$, $d = 2$. Then, using $\underline{2}$, we can find n:

$67 = 13 + (n - 1)2$ or $2(n - 1) = 54$

$n - 1 = 27$

$n = 28$

Therefore, using $\underline{3}$(b), $S_{28} = \dfrac{28}{2}[13 + 67] = 14 \cdot 80 = 1120.$

31. (A) $2 + 4 + 8 + \cdots$. Since $r = \dfrac{4}{2} = \dfrac{8}{4} = \cdots = 2$ and $|2| = 2 > 1$, the sum

does not exist.

(B) $2, -\dfrac{1}{2}, \dfrac{1}{8}, \cdots$. In this case, $r = \dfrac{-1/2}{2} = \dfrac{1/8}{-1/2} = \cdots = -\dfrac{1}{4}.$

Since $|r| < 1$,

$S_\infty = \dfrac{2}{1 - (-1/4)} = \dfrac{2}{5/4} = \dfrac{8}{5} = 1.6.$

33. $f(1) = -1$, $f(2) = 1$, $f(3) = 3$, … . This is an arithmetic progression with $a_1 = -1$, $d = 2$. Thus, using $\underline{3}$(a),

$$f(1) + f(2) + f(3) + \cdots + f(50) = \frac{50}{2}[2(-1) + 49\cdot 2] = 25\cdot 96 = 2400$$

35. $f(1) = \frac{1}{2}$, $f(2) = \left(\frac{1}{2}\right)^2 = \frac{1}{4}$, $f(3) = \left(\frac{1}{2}\right)^3 = \frac{1}{8}$, … . This is a geometric progression with $a_1 = \frac{1}{2}$ and $r = \frac{1}{2}$. Thus, using $\underline{6}$:

$$f(1) + f(2) + \cdots + f(10) = S_{10} = \frac{\frac{1}{2}\left[\left(\frac{1}{2}\right)^{10} - 1\right]}{\frac{1}{2} - 1} \approx 0.999$$

37. Consider the arithmetic progression with $a_1 = 1$, $d = 2$. This progression is the sequence of odd positive integers. Now, using $\underline{3}$(a), the sum of the first n odd positive integers is:

$$S_n = \frac{n}{2}[2\cdot 1 + (n - 1)2] = \frac{n}{2}(2 + 2n - 2) = \frac{n}{2}\cdot 2n = n^2$$

39. $S_n = a_1 + a_1 r + \cdots + a_1 r^{n-1}$. If $r = 1$, then $S_n = na_1$.

41. No: $\frac{n}{2}(1 + 1.1) = 100$ implies $(2.1)n = 200$ and this equation does not have an integer solution.

43. Yes: Solve the equation $6 = \frac{10}{1 - r}$ for r. This yields $r = -\frac{2}{3}$. The infinite geometric series: $10 - 10\left(\frac{2}{3}\right) + 10\left(\frac{2}{3}\right)^2 - 10\left(\frac{2}{3}\right)^3 + \cdots$ has sum $S_\infty = 6$.

45. Consider the time line:

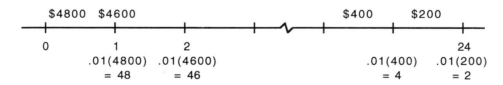

The total cost of the loan is $2 + 4 + 6 + \cdots + 46 + 48$. The terms form an arithmetic progression with $n = 24$, $a_1 = 2$, and $a_{24} = 48$. Thus, using $\underline{3}$(b):

$$S_{24} = \frac{24}{2}(2 + 48) = 24\cdot 25 = \$600$$

47. This is a geometric progression with $a_1 = 3,500,000$ and $r = 0.7$. Thus, using $\underline{7}$:

$$S_\infty = \frac{3,500,000}{1 - 0.7} \approx \$11,670,000$$

49.

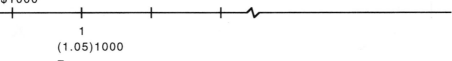

In general, after n years, the amount A_n in the account is:

$$A_n = 1000(1.05)^n$$

Thus, $A_{10} = 1000(1.05)^{10} \approx \$1628.89$

and $A_{20} = 1000(1.05)^{20} \approx \$2653.30$

EXERCISE B-3

Things to remember:

<u>1</u>. If n is a positive integer, then n FACTORIAL, denoted $n!$, is the product of the integers from 1 to n; that is,

$$n! = n \cdot (n - 1) \cdot \ldots \cdot 3 \cdot 2 \cdot 1 = n(n - 1)!$$

Also, $1! = 1$ and $0! = 1$.

<u>2</u>. If n and r are nonnegative integers and $r \leq n$, then:

$$C_{n,r} = \frac{n!}{r!(n - r)!}$$

<u>3</u>. BINOMIAL THEOREM

For all natural numbers n:

$$(a + b)^n = C_{n,0}a^n + C_{n,1}a^{n-1}b + C_{n,2}a^{n-2}b^2$$
$$+ \cdots + C_{n,n-1}ab^{n-1} + C_{n,n}b^n.$$

1. $6! = 6 \cdot 5 \cdot 4 \cdot 3 \cdot 2 \cdot 1 = 720$

3. $\dfrac{10!}{9!} = \dfrac{10 \cdot 9!}{9!} = 10$

5. $\dfrac{12!}{9!} = \dfrac{12 \cdot 11 \cdot 10 \cdot 9!}{9!} = 1320$

7. $\dfrac{5!}{2!\,3!} = \dfrac{5 \cdot 4 \cdot 3!}{2 \cdot 1 \cdot 3!} = 10$

9. $\dfrac{6!}{5!(6 - 5)!} = \dfrac{6 \cdot 5!}{5!\,1!} = 6$

11. $\dfrac{20!}{3!\,17!} = \dfrac{20 \cdot 19 \cdot 18 \cdot 17!}{3!\,17!}$

$= \dfrac{20 \cdot 19 \cdot 18}{3 \cdot 2 \cdot 1} = 1140$

13. $C_{5,3} = \dfrac{5!}{3!\,(5-3)!} = \dfrac{5!}{3!\,2!} = 10$ (see Problem 7)

15. $C_{6,5} = \dfrac{6!}{5!\,(6-5)!} = 6$ (see Problem 9)

17. $C_{5,0} = \dfrac{5!}{0!\,(5-0)!} = \dfrac{5!}{1 \cdot 5!} = 1$

19. $C_{18,15} = \dfrac{18!}{15!\,(18-15)!} = \dfrac{18 \cdot 17 \cdot 16 \cdot 15!}{15!\,3!} = \dfrac{18 \cdot 17 \cdot 16}{3 \cdot 2 \cdot 1} = 816$

21. Using $\underline{3}$,
$$\begin{aligned}
(a+b)^4 &= C_{4,0}a^4 + C_{4,1}a^3b + C_{4,2}a^2b^2 + C_{4,3}ab^3 + C_{4,4}b^4 \\
&= a^4 + 4a^3b + 6a^2b^2 + 4ab^3 + b^4
\end{aligned}$$

23. Using $\underline{3}$,
$$\begin{aligned}
(x-1)^6 &= [x + (-1)]^6 \\
&= C_{6,0}x^6 + C_{6,1}x^5(-1) + C_{6,2}x^4(-1)^2 + C_{6,3}x^3(-1)^3 \\
&\quad + C_{6,4}x^2(-1)^4 + C_{6,5}x(-1)^5 + C_{6,6}(-1)^6 \\
&= x^6 - 6x^5 + 15x^4 - 20x^3 + 15x^2 - 6x + 1
\end{aligned}$$

25.
$$\begin{aligned}
(2a-b)^5 &= [2a + (-b)]^5 \\
&= C_{5,0}(2a)^5 + C_{5,1}(2a)^4(-b) + C_{5,2}(2a)^3(-b)^2 + C_{5,3}(2a)^2(-b)^3 \\
&\quad + C_{5,4}(2a)(-b)^4 + C_{5,5}(-b)^5 \\
&= 32a^5 - 80a^4b + 80a^3b^2 - 40a^2b^3 + 10ab^4 - b^5
\end{aligned}$$

27. The fifth term in the expansion of $(x-1)^{18}$ is:
$$C_{18,4}x^{14}(-1)^4 = \dfrac{18 \cdot 17 \cdot 16 \cdot 15}{4 \cdot 3 \cdot 2 \cdot 1}x^{14} = 3060x^{14}$$

29. The seventh term in the expansion of $(p+q)^{15}$ is:
$$C_{15,6}\,p^9q^6 = \dfrac{15 \cdot 14 \cdot 13 \cdot 12 \cdot 11 \cdot 10}{6 \cdot 5 \cdot 4 \cdot 3 \cdot 2 \cdot 1}p^9q^6 = 5005p^9q^6$$

31. The eleventh term in the expansion of $(2x+y)^{12}$ is:
$$C_{12,10}(2x)^2y^{10} = \dfrac{12 \cdot 11}{2 \cdot 1}4x^2y^{10} = 264x^2y^{10}$$

33. $C_{n,0} = \dfrac{n!}{0!\,(n-0)!} = \dfrac{n!}{1 \cdot n!} = 1 \qquad C_{n,n} = \dfrac{n!}{n!\,(n-n)!} = \dfrac{n!}{n!\,0!} = 1$

35. The next two rows are:

1 5 10 10 5 1   and   1 6 15 20 15 6 1,

respectively. These are the coefficients in the binomial expansions of $(a + b)^5$ and $(a + b)^6$.

37. The nth row of Pascal's triangle gives the coefficients of $(a + b)^k$. If we let $a = 1$ and $b = -1$, we get

$$0 = (1 - 1)^n = C_{n,0}1^n + C_{n,1}(1)^{n-1}(-1) + C_{n,2}1^{n-2}(-1)^2 + \ldots + C_{n,n}(-1)^n$$

$$= C_{n,0} - C_{n,1} + C_{n,2} - C_{n,3} + \ldots + (-1)^n C_{n,n}.$$

39.
$$C_{n,r-1} + C_{n,r} = \frac{n!}{(r-1)!(n-[r-1])!} + \frac{n!}{r!(n-r)!}$$

$$= \frac{n!}{(r-1)!(n-r+1)!} + \frac{n!}{r!(n-r)!}$$

$$= \frac{r \cdot n! + (n-r+1)n!}{r!(n-r+1)!}$$

$$= \frac{(n+1)n!}{r!(n-r+1)!} = \frac{(n+1)!}{r!(n+1+r)!}$$

$$= C_{n+1,r}$$